Statistical Mechanics
Thermodynamics
and Kinetics

A Series of Books in Chemistry
Linus Pauling, Editor

Statistical Mechanics
Thermodynamics
and Kinetics

Oscar Knefler Rice

The University of North Carolina

W. H. Freeman and Company

San Francisco and London

Library of Congress Catalog Card Number 66-16379

PREFACE

Statistical mechanics has developed out of the application of the theory of probability to the analysis of the motion of large assemblages of molecules, and has led to a better understanding of the foundations of thermodynamics. But it is possible to begin the study of statistical mechanics the other way round—with the general principles of thermodynamics, which are firmly grounded on experiment. This procedure was foreshadowed in an early paper by Giauque, but as far as I know has not heretofore been developed systematically and carried to its logical conclusions. Chemistry students, although their mathematical sophistication has increased in recent years, are generally less familiar with probability theory than with thermodynamics, which gives this point of view a pedagogical advantage, at least for them. It also provides a logical basis for the statistical definition of entropy, and makes the formal analogies between the properties of the ensembles and the laws of thermodynamics almost self-evident. However, in the attempt to close the circle and gain the understanding of thermodynamics which statistical methods can give, I have not appealed to these analogies, nor have I made much use of ergodic theory. Instead, using a more intuitive approach, I have assumed that it is possible to define an entropy function (in terms of energy-level densities) that is a maximum under stated constraints at any condition of equilibrium. This is perhaps not the most elegant procedure, but the basic assumption is a statistically grounded equivalent of the second law of thermodynamics, and permits derivation of the body of thermodynamic relationships. The relation of real systems to the statistical idealizations is not what I should like to call topologically simple, but consists rather of many interlocking parts. It is only after the whole structure of ideas has been studied that one can gain a true understanding of the significance of thermodynamic equilibrium. In the course of this study, the student should increase his skill in the handling of thermodynamic equations and gain some insight into their interpretation on the molecular level.

I have slanted the applications of the theory toward the needs of the chemistry student, though I hope that a student of physics will not find them uninteresting. In particular, stress is laid on chemical equilibrium, and three chapters are devoted to chemical kinetics. Since chemists are interested in solutions, order-disorder phenomena are presented as they occur in mixtures, but the translation to magnetic phenomena is indicated. As is natural, a number of the applications discussed arise out of my own interests. I have presented my own ideas on liquid helium, which differ somewhat from those generally current, but which lead to pictorial concepts that I believe are consistent with fundamental principles. I have extended and refined these ideas, and included some new applications which indicate the extent to which they can correlate thermodynamic properties of helium 4 and both thermodynamic and magnetic properties of helium 3.

Applications to the calculation of such properties as viscosity, diffusion, and heat conduction are not included, but I have given a brief discussion of the approach to equilibrium, based on quantum transitions, which leads to a development of irreversible thermodynamics. Some applications not included in the text are presented in the form of problems; for example, certain aspects of electric and magnetic phenomena and of surface adsorption. No attempt has been made to discuss all of the sophisticated mathematical techniques that have been applied to statistical mechanical problems in recent years. The material presented should, however, provide the necessary background for the student who later wishes to acquire mastery of the advanced techniques, while giving him a feeling for the fundamental physical problems, unobscured by excessive mathematical detail.

One point of notation should be mentioned. I have chosen to follow Rushbrooke, who, in his _Introduction to Statistical Mechanics_, used special symbols, which might perhaps be better described as abbreviations, for the various partition functions. Although this practice is somewhat unusual, the partition functions occupy such a special place in the calculations that it seems to me that the adoption of this suggestive nomenclature makes for easier reading. Otherwise, I have tried to use standard nomenclature, with the definition of a symbol, repeated if need be, reasonably close to the pages in which it is used. Where it seems desirable, symbols are entered in the index and references to their definitions given.

Between the time this book was about half finished and the present, it seems that most of my friends and colleagues (being much faster than I am) have written texts on statistical mechanics. I feel, however, that my point of view and method of presentation, and to some degree the material presented, are distinctive enough to make this book a contribution to the exposition of the subject. I am, of course, much in debt to the previous literature, and this is only in part indicated by the references. These were selected, first, to suggest further reading or source material for the reader, and second, to indicate literature to which I had made direct reference in the writing of this book. Since some of the writing was done without such reference, the bibliographies are by no means adequate as a historical survey of the subject.

Most of the chapters of the book, in mimeographed form, have been used in my classes for several years, and I am indebted to many of my students for corrections, questions, and comments. In particular, Walter C. Worsham and Do-Ren Chang have called attention to many typographical errors and a few of a more serious character. I also wish to express my appreciation to Professors Benjamin Widom and Wendell Forst for reading parts of the text and making a number of helpful comments.

The early parts of the manuscript were typed by my mother, Mrs. Thekla K. Rice, and the later parts by Mrs. Evelyn Nichols and Mrs. Eloise Walker. I am grateful to all of them for their expert and careful work.

Finally I wish to thank The Journal of Physical Chemistry, The Physical Review, The Journal of the Elisha Mitchell Scientific Society, the Princeton University Press, and the Plenum Press for permission to use previously published material, as acknowledged in appropriate places in the text, and the Scientific Committee of the Institut International de Chimie in Brussels for the invitation to present, at the Twelfth Solvay Congress on Chemistry, a report that formed the basis of parts of Chapters 19 and 20.

O. K. Rice

Chapel Hill, N. C.
October, 1966.

CONTENTS

Chapter Four
**The Third Law of Thermodynamics
and the Statistical Definition of Entropy**

Chapter Five
**The Statistical Basis
of Thermodynamics**

Chapter Six
**Statistical Calculation of the
Thermodynamic Functions for an Ideal Gas**

Chapter Seven
Chemical Equilibrium

Chapter Eleven
Cluster Expansions for Imperfect Gases

Chapter Twelve
Mixtures: Order-Disorder Phenomena

Chapter Thirteen
The Liquid State

Chapter Eighteen
Equilibrium Theory of Chemical Reaction Rates

Chapter Nineteen
Recombination of Atoms and Dissociation of Diatomic Molecules

Chapter Twenty
Unimolecular Reactions

Introduction

1-1. *Thermodynamics*

Thermodynamics is a deductive science that is based upon three general laws, namely: (1) the first law, or the law of conservation of energy; (2) the second law, which deals with entropy changes in the system and which is for our purposes best expressed as a relation between the change dS of entropy in a reversible process and the heat dQ_{rev} absorbed in such a process,

$$dS = \frac{dQ_{rev}}{T} \tag{1.1}$$

where T is the temperature; and (3) the third law, which deals with the absolute value of the entropy. These laws being taken as axioms, it is possible to derive many relations among thermodynamic variables such as pressure, temperature, density, concentrations, energy, entropy, and free energy. It is never possible, from thermodynamics, to obtain a theoretical value for any one of these quantities, but the relations which exist between them have been consistently verified whenever the experimental data are adequate for the purpose. These laws and the relations deduced from them command as much confidence as any in the whole realm of science.

We assume in this book that the reader is familiar with basic thermodynamics, in particular with the definitions of the thermodynamic functions. [1–3]†

---

† Bold-face numbers in brackets indicate references cited at the end of the chapter.

1-2. *Scope and Applications of Statistical Mechanics*

The science of statistical mechanics supplements and extends the science of thermodynamics in two distinct ways. By itself, thermodynamics cannot determine the values of the thermodynamic properties characterizing any particular system. These properties depend upon the properties of the individual molecules that make up the system, on the way in which the molecules interact, and on the way in which they move. The molecules are present in such enormous numbers that one may apply the laws of probability to their configurations and motions. This is the province of statistical mechanics, and in a number of simple cases it is possible in this way to explain the bulk properties of a system in terms of its molecular properties, while in other cases progress has been made in that direction.

The second application of statistical mechanics goes deeper than this. The study by probabilistic methods, of systems containing large numbers of molecules throws much light on the nature of the fundamental laws of thermodynamics themselves. Indeed, it is in a certain sense possible to obtain a derivation of the second and third laws of thermodynamics on this basis.

The procedure thus outlined does not move along a one-way street. It is also possible, by means of a suitable and natural hypothesis, to go from thermodynamics to statistical mechanics. We shall examine the methods by which one may proceed in either direction, but, assuming the laws and methods of thermodynamics to be familiar to the reader, we move first from thermodynamics to statistical mechanics, and this will be the main topic of Chaps. 2 and 3.

Finally, we may mention the theory of rate processes. Thermodynamics deals with equilibrium states, and the applications of statistical mechanics referred to in the preceding paragraphs, are applications to equilibrium states. We also are interested in the approach to equilibrium, and the chemist is particularly interested in certain processes, such as diffusion and chemical reactions, whereby this approach occurs. The laws and procedures of statistical mechanics are highly important in the study of these processes, and a limited number of these applications will be discussed in this volume.

1-3. *Phase Space*

Since one of the principal aims of statistical mechanics is to correlate the properties of matter in bulk with the properties of individual atoms and molecules, it is seen that a knowledge of the latter properties is a prerequisite. This is essentially a matter of quantum mechanics, with which we assume the reader is sufficiently familiar for the purposes of this book [4–8]. Nevertheless, the concepts of quantum mechanics and those of statistical mechanics are so closely interrelated that a brief review of some of the salient ideas is advisable.

We start with the classical mechanical consideration of a point particle in three-dimensional space [8, Chap. 2; 9]. In classical mechanics, the position of such a particle is determined by three coordinates, for example, the three Cartesian coordinates, x, y, and z, referred to a particular set of axes. Such a particle is said to have three degrees of freedom. Its state of motion, according to classical mechanics, is given by the velocity components $\dot{x}$, $\dot{y}$, and $\dot{z}$ (the dot indicates differentiation with respect to time). For many purposes, it is more convenient to use the corresponding momenta p_x, p_y, and p_z (for $m\dot{x}$, $m\dot{y}$, and $m\dot{z}$, where m is the mass of the particle). To describe both the position and the state of motion of the particle, it is customary to set up a six-dimensional space, called the phase space, in which the six coordinates x, y, z, p_x, p_y, p_z, are marked out along six mutually perpendicular axes. A point in this space then describes both the position and the motion of the particle at some particular instant. The values of $\dot{x}$, $\dot{y}$, and $\dot{z}$ are of course given at this instant, while the values of p_x, p_y, and p_z will also be known if the force acting upon the particle is known as a function of position, i.e., as a function of x, y, and z. Thus we know not only the position of the point in the six-dimensional phase space, but also the rate at which this position is changing; hence the new position after an arbitrarily small period of time. These considerations may then be repeated. Therefore, if the position of a phase point is known at any instant of time, its entire trajectory is known.

It is not necessary to start with Cartesian coordinates. Polar or cylindrical coordinates—indeed, any suitably defined set of coordinates—would do as well. In general, the kinetic energy of the system ϵ_k, can be expressed as a function of the coordinates, say q_1, q_2, and q_3, and the corresponding velocities or time derivatives $\dot{q}_1$, $\dot{q}_2$, and $\dot{q}_3$. Furthermore, the kinetic energy will always remain quadratic in the $\dot{q}_i$. For if we consider the q_i to be functions of x, y, and z, writing

$$q_i = q_i(x, y, z), \tag{3.1}$$

we see that

$$\dot{q}_i = \frac{\partial q_i}{\partial x}\dot{x} + \frac{\partial q_i}{\partial y}\dot{y} + \frac{\partial q_i}{\partial z}\dot{z}, \tag{3.2}$$

where the partial derivatives are all functions of x, y, and z, or, by inversion of Eq. (3.1), of q_1, q_2, and q_3. Equation (3.2) may be solved for $\dot{x}$, $\dot{y}$, and $\dot{z}$ in terms of $\dot{q}_1$, $\dot{q}_2$, and $\dot{q}_3$; the $\dot{x}$, $\dot{y}$, $\dot{z}$ will be found as linear functions of the $\dot{q}_i$, the coefficients being functions either of x, y, and z or of q_1, q_2, and q_3. The original kinetic energy had the form

$$\epsilon_k = \tfrac{1}{2}m(\dot{x}^2 + \dot{y}^2 + \dot{z}^2). \tag{3.3}$$

Introduction of the newly found expressions for $\dot{x}$, $\dot{y}$, and $\dot{z}$ will clearly give a form quadratic in $\dot{q}_1$, $\dot{q}_2$, $\dot{q}_3$ (but containing cross terms such as $\dot{q}_1\dot{q}_2$) with coefficients that are functions of q_1, q_2, and q_3. It is readily verified that

$$\epsilon_k = \frac{1}{2}\sum_{i=1}^{3}\dot{q}_i\left(\frac{\partial \epsilon_k}{\partial \dot{q}_i}\right), \tag{3.4}$$

where, in any partial differentiation, all the q_i (here only q_1, q_2, and q_3) and all the other $\dot{q}_i$ are held constant. With the summation extended over all the quadratically appearing variables, a relation like Eq. (3.4) is indeed a general property of any quadratic form. It is customary to write the generalized momentum in the form

$$p_i = \frac{\partial \epsilon_k}{\partial \dot{q}_i}, \tag{3.5}$$

so that

$$\epsilon_k = \frac{1}{2}\sum_{i=1}^{3}p_i\dot{q}_i, \tag{3.6}$$

a general form which holds also for the original Cartesian coordinates.

The procedure is now to set up a phase space using the q_i and the p_i as *rectangular* coordinates. It will be observed that from Eq. (3.6) we may conclude that a six-dimensional volume (or hypervolume) in this space has the dimensions of (energy × time)[3]. These dimensions hold, regardless of the coordinates used. Furthermore, it may be shown (see

Secs. 1-8 and 1-10) that on change of variable any given hypervolume goes over to a hypervolume of equal size in the new phase space. A trajectory representing the motion of a given particle in one phase space goes over, on change of variable, to a definite corresponding trajectory in the new phase space.

A molecule which contains n atoms requires $3n$ coordinates to fix its position and is said to have $3n$ degrees of freedom. Its motion is determined by $3n$ velocities or momenta. There are forces acting between the atoms. These forces will be determined if the positions of all the atoms are known; then we may set up a $6n$-dimensional phase space, using $3n$ coordinates and $3n$ momenta as rectangular coordinates of the phase space. A point in phase space determines the position and motions of all atoms, and since the forces are known, once again the future motions will be determined, so that a single point in phase space determines a trajectory. All that we have said about transformations of coordinates of a single particle holds for many atoms, and Eq. (3.5) can be used to determine the generalized momentum. The new coordinates q_i may depend upon the coordinates of all the atoms; thus in general

$$q_i = q_i(x_1, y_1, z_1, \cdots, x_n, y_n, z_n).$$

The idea of the phase space can be further extended to include a whole assembly of molecules. If such an assembly contains N_1 molecules with n_1 atoms, N_2 molecules with n_2 atoms, etc., the total number of rectangular coordinates in the phase space will be $6N_1 n_1 + 6N_2 n_2 + \cdots$. The phase space for a single molecule has sometimes been called the μ space; that for the assembly of molecules (the entire gas, if it is a gas) has been called the γ space.

1-4. *Quantization*

In the foregoing discussion we have seen that the motion of a particle or a system of particles can be described in classical mechanics by a trajectory in the phase space, and that the possible trajectories are arbitrarily densely spaced. One effect of quantization may be approximately described by the statement that only certain trajectories are possible, so that they are in actuality not densely spaced. According to quantum mechanics, there are certain allowed energy levels; these correspond to the possible trajectories. If the phase space has f space coordinates and f momentum coordinates, it will be observed that the dimensionality is (energy $\times$ time)^f, and the density of the trajectories is such that each trajectory has for itself a hypervolume equal to h^f, where h is Planck's constant. Sometimes this is all the information needed, but sometimes the energies corresponding to the several trajectories must be known exactly.

The above statements do not constitute a full account of the effect of quantization. According to the uncertainty principle, it is not possible simultaneously to determine precisely both the position and the momentum of a particle or a system. Thus we cannot follow the motion of a system by means of a trajectory in phase space, for this implies that both position and momentum are known, and we cannot have this much information. Indeed, if δq is the uncertainty about our knowledge of a certain coordinate and δp is the uncertainty in the corresponding momentum, the uncertainty principle says that

$$\delta q \delta p \gtrsim \frac{h}{2\pi}. \tag{4.1}$$

It is still possible to assign to each quantum state a region in phase space equal to h^f, this region being large enough to provide the necessary uncertainty. For one degree of freedom, the quantum region is equal to h. Therefore if the range of the coordinate is Δq and the average difference between the momenta of two adjacent quantum states is Δp, we have †

$$\Delta q \Delta p \approx h. \tag{4.2}$$

As we have stated, each quantum state of the system has a definite energy. The uncertainty principle also states that energy and time cannot both be determined precisely and, similarly to (4.1), we write,

$$\delta \epsilon \delta t \gtrsim \frac{h}{2\pi}. \tag{4.3}$$

This relation implies that if a system is disturbed after a short time, its energy cannot be definitely known; the energy level is said to be broadened.

There is a relation for the energy similar to (4.2), which is simply expressed for one degree of freedom as

$$\Delta \epsilon \Delta t \approx h, \tag{4.4}$$

† In the usual periodic motion, Δq is the total distance traveled along the coordinate axis in both directions during the complete period.

where Δt is the "range of time" in the motion, the time required for the particle to complete a cycle in its motion (assuming it to be bound in a force field), i.e., its period, and $\Delta \epsilon$ is the energy between adjacent energy levels. The frequency $\nu = 1/\Delta t$, so

$$\Delta \epsilon \approx h\nu, \tag{4.5}$$

in which is seen the relation to Planck's original ideas on quantum theory. Equation (4.4) or (4.5) expresses part of Bohr's principle of correspondence.

There is sometimes more than one characteristic time involved in the motion of a system. For example, a particle can oscillate with a certain frequency in a certain "state" from which it may make a transition to another "state" (characterized, perhaps, by being at a different position in space) that has the same energy. This happens, for example, in quantum-mechanical "tunneling" through energy barriers. Classically, a system with constant energy cannot go from one state to another with the same energy if it has to pass through a condition in which the potential energy is higher than the total energy—for to do so would make the *kinetic* energy negative. This *can* happen in quantum mechanics. Situations of this sort are considerably more complicated than those visualized in setting up Eq. (4.5). The spacing of the energy levels in such a case may appear superficially to be quite irregular. There will be energy differences between successive levels of varying magnitudes, corresponding to the various characteristic times involved.

The δt in (4.3) is often much larger than Δt of (4.4), which is the reason that energies can be well defined. For gas molecules undergoing occasional collisions, the time between collisions will, if the gas is not too dense, be long enough that the energy level will not be appreciably broadened. We can then consider the molecules to be in definite energy levels, which change only at collision, and we can neglect the effect of the collisions in broadening the energy levels.

In systems in which the molecules interact appreciably, we must consider energy levels of the whole system.

1-5. *Energy Levels of Molecules*

Although formulas for the energy levels of molecules are derived in standard texts on quantum mechanics and in books on molecular spectroscopy [5, Chap. 10; 10, 11], some general remarks may be useful here, and some of the useful formulas will be summarized.

The motion of the electrons is so fast compared with the motion of the nuclei that in considering electronic energy states, nuclear motion can be ignored. The energy of the electrons depends upon the positions of the nuclei, and to this electronic energy must be added the mutual potential energy of the nuclei to obtain the familiar potential energy curves or surfaces. In addition, there is kinetic energy of the nuclei. The total energy, then, is conveniently separated into the kinetic energy of the nuclei and the rest of the energy, which therefore is "potential" energy with respect to the motion of the nuclei. Both the motions of the nuclei, and the motions of the electrons, are quantized. The translational energy of the molecule as a whole can always be considered (and quantized) separately from the internal motions of the molecule. Not only is the total internal energy quantized, but also the angular momentum.† If the motions of the atoms are so restricted that they do not move far from their equilibrium positions, the internal energy may be divided into parts that are quantized separately to a first approximation. These parts are the rotation and the vibrations of the various normal modes of vibration.

A diatomic molecule has six degrees of freedom of nuclear motion. Classically its position in space could be completely described by giving the three coordinates of its center of gravity, the two polar angles θ and ϕ, which determine the direction of the line joining the two atoms, and the distance r between the two atoms. The motion is given classically by the corresponding momenta. Thus we can say that there are three translational degrees of freedom, involving motion of the center of gravity, two rotational degrees of freedom involving changes in θ and ϕ, and one vibrational degree of freedom involving r. In good approximation these can all be quantized separately.

A polyatomic molecule with n atoms has $3n$ degrees of freedom. Three of these are translational, as with a diatomic molecule. Unless all the atoms lie in a straight line, an extra angle is required to fix completely the orientation of the molecule in space; thus there are normally three rotational degrees of freedom. All the other degrees of freedom are vibrational and are best described in terms of normal vibrations, in which the atoms are all displaced from their equilibrium positions in phase and all pass through their equilibrium positions simultaneously. The displacement from equilibrium occurring in such a normal vibration can be described in terms of a corresponding normal coordinate. There are $3n - 6$ (or in a linear molecule $3n - 5$) of these

† A good account of angular momentum, referring principally to angular momentum of electrons but applicable to molecules, is given by Kauzmann [12].

normal coordinates, and they may be expressed as linear combinations of the displacements of individual atoms. If the vibrations were truly harmonic, as they would be if the force necessary to displace any single atom from its equilibrium position were strictly proportional to the displacement (Hooke's law), a molecule set vibrating in a normal mode of vibration would continue to vibrate thus indefinitely, and any possible vibrational motion of the molecule could be considered to be a superposition of normal vibrations. As the vibrations become large, deviations from harmonicity become great, and the concept of normal modes of vibration breaks down. For vibrations of moderate amplitude, however, they are an extremely useful approximation. In quantum theory, if the vibrations are harmonic, each normal mode of vibration is quantized separately, and again if the vibrations are not too large, this is a good approximation.

Quantization of the internal states (rotational and vibrational) of a diatomic molecule can be handled with some precision. Consider a molecule in an electronic state that gives rise to a typical attractive potential energy. In such a diatomic molecule the relative motion of one of the atoms about the other can be shown to be the same as if one of the atoms had an infinite mass, and hence acted as a center for the other, which had a mass $\mu = m_1 m_2 / (m_1 + m_2)$, where m_1 and m_2 are the true separate masses of the atoms, μ being the reduced mass. The total energy of the system is a sum of the potential and kinetic energies (the potential energy ϵ_p including the electronic energy) and is given in classical mechanics by

$$\epsilon = \epsilon_k + \epsilon_p = \tfrac{1}{2}\mu v^2 + \epsilon_p, \tag{5.1}$$

where v is the relative velocity. When polar coordinates are used, v is conveniently resolved at any given instant into three mutually perpendicular components. One of these, the radial component, is along the line joining the two atoms and is equal to $\dot{r}$; the second is along a circle of longitude in a sphere whose center is at the origin and is equal to $r\dot{\theta}$, where θ is the polar angle; and the third is along a circle of latitude and is equal to $r\dot{\phi} \sin \theta$, where ϕ is the longitudinal angle, $r \sin \theta$ being the radius of the circle of latitude. Thus

$$\epsilon = \tfrac{1}{2}\mu \dot{r}^2 + \tfrac{1}{2}\mu r^2 \dot{\theta}^2 + \tfrac{1}{2}\mu r^2 \dot{\phi}^2 \sin^2 \theta + \epsilon_p, \tag{5.2}$$

Equation (3.5) may be applied to obtain the momenta, and it is seen that

$$p_r = \mu \dot{r}, \tag{5.3}$$

$$b_\theta = \mu r^2 \dot\theta, \tag{5.4}$$

$$p_\phi = \mu r^2 \dot\phi \, \sin^2 \theta, \tag{5.5}$$

and therefore,

$$\epsilon = \frac{p_r^2}{2\mu} + \frac{p_{\dot\theta}^2}{2\mu r^2} + \frac{p_\phi^2}{2\mu r^2 \sin^2\theta} + \epsilon_p. \tag{5.6}$$

In general ϵ_p depends only on r. This being the case, the motion occurs in a fixed plane determined by the line joining the two atoms and the velocity vector at any instant. We can consider the velocity to be first resolved into two components in this plane, one, $\dot r$, along the line joining the atoms, and the other perpendicular thereto, equal to $r\dot\chi$, where χ is an angle in the plane measured from an arbitrary position of the line of centers. By further resolving the latter component, we obtain the components previously found, and by the Pythagorean theorem

$$r^2\dot\chi^2 = r^2\dot\theta^2 + r^2\dot\phi^2 \sin^2 \theta. \tag{5.7}$$

We have, of course,

$$\begin{aligned}
\epsilon &= \tfrac{1}{2}\mu\dot r^2 + \tfrac{1}{2}\mu r^2\dot\chi^2 + \epsilon_p \\
&= \frac{p_r^2}{2\mu} + \frac{p_\chi^2}{2\mu r^2} + \epsilon_p,
\end{aligned} \tag{5.8}$$

where

$$p_\chi = \mu r^2 \dot\chi \tag{5.9}$$

is by definition the angular momentum.

The angular momentum is quantized, and we know that[†]

$$p_\chi^2 = j(j + 1)\frac{h^2}{4\pi^2}, \tag{5.10}$$

where j can take the integral values $0, 1, 2, 3, \cdots$, giving

$$\epsilon = \frac{p_r^2}{2\mu} + \frac{j(j + 1)h^2}{8\pi^2\mu r^2} + \epsilon_p. \tag{5.11}$$

With respect to the radial motion, involving changes in r, the second

---

† Since the *total* angular momentum is quantized, a slight complication occurs when the electronic state possesses an angular momentum of its own. For our purposes this may be ignored.

term in Eq. (5.11) acts like an addition to the potential energy and is known as the rotational or centrifugal potential. The potential curve then is altered into an effective potential energy, as shown in Fig. 1-1.

The lower vibrational energy levels measured from the minimum are about the same for an effective potential energy curve with moderate j as for the one with $j = 0$. The latter curve can be approximately represented near the minimum by

$$\epsilon_p = \epsilon_{p,e} + \frac{(r - r_e)^2}{2a^2}, \tag{5.12}$$

where $\epsilon_{p,e}$ is the value of ϵ_p at the minimum or equilibrium position, r_e is the corresponding value of r, and a is a constant. For the lower vibrational states, the vibrational energy is given by

$$\epsilon_v = \epsilon - \epsilon_{p,e} = h\nu_0(v + \tfrac{1}{2}), \tag{5.13}$$

where $v = 0, 1, 2, \cdots$, and ν_0, the frequency of vibration, is given by

$$\nu_0 = \frac{1}{2\pi a\mu^{1/2}}. \tag{5.14}$$

Equation (5.13) is the harmonic approximation for the vibrational energy and is adequate for many purposes. It is consistent with Eq. (4.5), but less general. In a real molecule the higher energy levels tend to get closer and closer, and Eq. (4.5) continues to hold, but Eq. (5.13) involv-

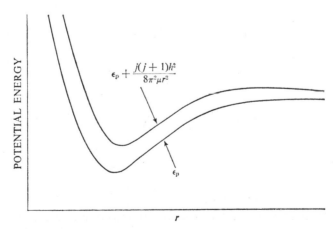

Figure 1-1. Molecular potential-energy curves, showing the effect of the rotational potential.

ing the specific, constant, harmonic-oscillator frequency ν_0 does not. The harmonic approximation holds only if the maximum displacement of r from its equilibrium value r_e is relatively small; under these circumstances we may replace r by r_e in the rotational-potential term in Eq. (5.11). This then represents the amount by which the effective potential-energy curve is raised in the neighborhood of its minimum. The total energy of the quantum state is raised by this amount:

$$\epsilon_r = \frac{j(j+1)h^2}{8\pi^2 \mu r_e^2} = \frac{j(j+1)h^2}{8\pi^2 I}, \tag{5.15}$$

where $I = \mu r_e^2$ is the moment of inertia. There is another rotational quantum number, m_j, which determines the component of the angular momentum (actually p_ϕ) on the polar axis but does not affect the energy. With fixed j, the quantum number m_j can have integral values ranging from $-j$ to j, including 0. Thus there are actually $2j + 1$ levels with rotational quantum number j and the energy given by Eq. (5.15).

Usually we have to deal with only the lowest electronic state, since the higher ones are virtually never excited, but if necessary we can always take the electronic energy [e.g., $\epsilon_{p,e}$ in Eq. (5.12)] into account. This means that we take the energy of the minimum of the potential energy as the electronic energy and consider the rest of the internal energy as being added to it. Of interest is the fact that electronic states can sometimes have a multiplicity greater than 1 (i.e., several quantum levels can have the same energy) because of spin or angular-momentum degeneracy.

Thus a molecule has electronic, rotational and vibrational energy, and also the translational energy of the center of gravity. The latter is also quantized, but the energy levels are very close together. Often it is convenient to consider the molecule to be in a rectangular "box." Here the term box is used in an idealized sense; it means that within the box the potential energy due to external fields' acting on the molecule is constant (it may be set equal to zero) and becomes suddenly infinite at the boundaries of the box. In such a case the translational energy is conveniently expressed as

$$\epsilon_t = \epsilon_x + \epsilon_y + \epsilon_z, \tag{5.16}$$

where ϵ_x, ϵ_y, and ϵ_z are the kinetic energies of the motions in the x, y, and z directions, respectively. In a rectangular box aligned parallel to the coordinate axes, these are quantized separately [**4**, Chap. 4]:

$$\epsilon_x = \frac{n_x^2 h^2}{8Ma^2},$$

$$\epsilon_y = \frac{n_y^2 h^2}{8Mb^2}, \qquad (5.17)$$

$$\epsilon_z = \frac{n_z^2 h^2}{8Mc^2},$$

where M is the total mass of the molecule, n_x, n_y, and n_z are the respective quantum numbers, and a, b, and c are the extensions of the box in the x, y, and z directions. These quantum numbers can have values 1, 2, 3, $\cdots$, but not zero. When n_x, n_y, and n_z are large, ϵ_t may be taken as a quasi-continuous function of them. Constant energy occurs on a surface in a space formed by marking off n_x, n_y, and n_z along the three axes, and the equation of the surface is

$$\epsilon_t = \frac{h^2}{8M} \left(\frac{n_x^2}{a^2} + \frac{n_y^2}{b^2} + \frac{n_z^2}{c^2} \right).$$

This is the equation of an ellipsoid whose volume in the n_x, n_y, n_z space is

$$\frac{\frac{4}{3}\pi (8M\epsilon_t)^{3/2} V}{h^3},$$

where $V = abc$ is the volume of the box. The volume in the n_x, n_y, n_z space is equal to the number of combinations of integral values included in the volume, since this will be the number of unit cubes therein. Thus the number of energy levels below ϵ_t will be the volume of the part of the ellipsoid where n_x, n_y, and n_z are all positive or

$$\frac{\frac{1}{8} \cdot \frac{4}{3}\pi (8M\epsilon_t)^{3/2} V}{h^3} = \frac{\frac{4}{3}\pi (2M\epsilon_t)^{3/2} V}{h^3}, \qquad (5.18)$$

and the number of levels between ϵ_t and $\epsilon_t + d\epsilon_t$ will be

$$n_\epsilon d\epsilon_t = \frac{2\pi (2M)^{3/2} \epsilon_t^{1/2} V}{h^3} \, d\epsilon_t. \qquad (5.19)$$

Quantization of the translational energy for a polyatomic molecule is carried out exactly as before. *Each* vibrational mode is quantized, in first approximation, as indicated by Eq. (5.13), by using its particular frequency, but there is no simple reduced mass. The quantization of rotation, if the atoms are not all in a straight line, involves the three principal moments of inertia of the molecule (moments about the principal axes). The principal axes of the molecule are three mutually perpendicular lines passing through the center of gravity, and it may be shown that if once a body is set rotating about one of these axes it will continue to rotate about it indefinitely unless disturbed by an external force (in general, if it is rotating about any other axis, the instantaneous axis of rotation changes from moment to moment). There are three rotational quantum numbers, two of which are directly involved in determining the energy.

1-6. *Wave Functions*

As noted above, it is not possible in quantum mechanics to describe the trajectory of a particle, or a system of particles, precisely. It is possible, however, to find the *probability* of any particular position. Such a probability may depend upon the position and the time. However, we shall usually be interested in stationary states with definite energy. In this case we can define a probability *amplitude* ψ, which depends only upon the positions of the particles involved. This amplitude has the properties of a standing wave; there is a different one for each energy level. It may be positive, negative, or complex. The probability of any configuration is then given by $\psi^*\psi \, d\tau$, where ψ^* is the conjugate complex and $d\tau$ is the product of the volume elements of all the particles involved; i.e., $d\tau = dx_1 dy_1 dz_1 dx_2 \cdots dz_n$ if there are n particles involved. More precisely, $\psi^*\psi \, d\tau$ is the probability that the coordinates of the particles lie in the range included in $d\tau$.

When certain types of motion are mutually independent, corresponding parts can be factored in the wave function. Thus for a diatomic molecule we may write approximately,

$$\psi = \psi_{e,n} R_{n,v}(r) \Theta_{n,j}(\theta) \Phi_{m_j}(\phi). \tag{6.1}$$

Here ψ_e is the electronic part of the wave function and depends on the coordinates of the electrons, and R, Θ, and Φ depend upon the variables indicated. The quantum number n designates the electronic states; the other quantum numbers, v, j, and m, indicate which parts of the wave function or energy corresponding thereto are determined by particular quantum numbers.

The wave function of a single particle is closely connected with its dynamical properties. We mention here the de Broglie relation

$$\lambda = \frac{h}{p}, \tag{6.2}$$

which connects the wavelength λ with the momentum p of a freely moving particle or photon, and which can be used as an approximation even if the particle is acted on by forces. This relation also has a more general application than that to a single particle. It holds for a wave which describes the collective motion of many particles (e.g., a sound wave).

In this book we will not usually require the details of the wave theory of matter except in Chap. 16 and in Sec. 17-6, where a more profound knowledge of wave mechanics is assumed, and to a small extent in certain parts of Chap. 15.

1-7. *Spin, Exchange, and Symmetry*

The wave function given in Eq. (6.1) is not complete, for electrons and nuclei are not completely described as point particles. They have, in addition to the angular momentum arising from their bodily motion, an intrinsic angular momentum, called the spin angular momentum [12, p. 305ff; 13]. The spin state of the system can be described by multiplying the wave function in Eq. (6.1) by two more factors, one the electron-spin wave function, the other the spin function for the nuclei. A single electron can have either one of two spin states, in which the component of angular momentum along some particular direction (usually determined by some field of force) is oriented in one sense (positive) or the other (negative). Corresponding to this angular momentum there is a spin coordinate whose presence we may sometimes need to recall, but whose exact nature we will not require.

In a molecule composed of light atoms, a system of interacting electrons may have a total spin angular momentum p_S, given by†

$$p_S^2 = S(S + 1) \left(\frac{h}{2\pi}\right)^2, \tag{7.1}$$

where S is an integer if there is an even number of electrons, and half an odd integer if there is an odd number of electrons. The total number

† In heavy atoms there is an appreciable interaction between spin and orbital motion, resulting in exchange between the corresponding angular momenta. In this case, the spin angular momentum cannot be separately quantized; only the total electronic angular momentum can be.

of spin states (orientations) is $2S + 1$. If there is one electron, $S = \frac{1}{2}$ and $2S + 1 = 2$. A nucleus is a complicated collection of protons and neutrons, and its total spin angular momentum will be related to a nuclear spin quantum number by an equation like (7.1).

The spin is very closely connected with an important property of an assembly of particles, its exchange symmetry. If two identical particles, or two identical systems of particles, such as two like atoms or two like molecules, are exchanged, so that the first one goes into the state of the second and *vice versa*, the final state of the entire assembly of particles, atoms, or molecules cannot be distinguished from the initial state by any known experimental means. The quantum state of the whole assembly, then, must be considered identical in the initial and final cases, and, indeed, there is only one quantum state. Since each molecule has a set of coordinates and momenta (including, in general, spin coordinates and momenta), and each of these furnishes a coordinate in the phase space for the assembly of molecules (γ space), exchange of a pair of molecules corresponds to a shift of the point representing the assembly in the phase space. A phase volume of h^f will go over to another phase volume of the same magnitude upon exchange of a pair of molecules, and each quantum state will be counted more than once if one adds over the entire phase space. If there are N molecules which can be exchanged, each quantum state of the whole assembly will be counted $N!$ times, assuming that no two molecules are in precisely the same state (including internal quantum state, translational state, and spin state). A particular state of the whole assembly means that the states of individual molecules are assigned; there are N molecules, each in its particular state. But it will be possible to choose one among N molecules to put in one of the states (which we will arbitrarily call the first state), then one among $N - 1$ molecules to put in the second state, then one among $N - 2$ molecules for the third state, $\cdots$, and finally, 1 molecule for the Nth state. So there will be $N(N - 1)(N - 2) \cdots 2 \cdot 1 = N!$ ways of setting up the state of the assembly of molecules, which will all correspond to the same quantum state. Whenever one integrates over phase space in such a way as to duplicate possible states of the system, one must divide by the number of duplications, in this case by $N!$, to avoid counting parts of the phase space which in physical fact are not distinct. This rule may be considered empirically verified, since this and only this procedure, gives results that have been experimentally confirmed.

The identity of two states that differ only in the exchange of a pair of particles or molecules must be reflected in the wave function.

The wave function must be the same before and after the exchange, except possibly for a change in sign (which would not be related to anything that could be detected physically). If the wave function is unchanged, it is said to be symmetric with respect to the exchange of the particles; if the sign changes, it is said to be antisymmetric. A wave function is always antisymmetric with respect to exchange of a pair of *elementary* material particles (electrons, protons, or neutrons). However, a molecule is a complex entity, and exchange of a pair of molecules is equivalent to the exchange of a number of elementary pairs. If an even number is exchanged, the wave function is symmetric with respect to exchange of a pair of molecules; if the number is odd, the wave function is antisymmetric.

Spin and orbital motions of electrons are but weakly coupled, at least if the atoms involved are light. Thus the energies of the spin system and of the orbital motions are approximately independent. Then two particles or two molecules or two systems of electrons may exchange states with respect either to spin only or to orbital motion only, and the spin wave function and the orbital wave function will be separately symmetric or antisymmetric. Suppose a system of electrons has a total spin quantum number S, there being thus $2S + 1$ spin states, whose corresponding spin wave functions we designate as α, β, γ, $\cdots$. A system of electrons may be in any one of these states. If system 1 is in the same state as system 2, say α, then the spin state of the combination of these two systems is $\alpha(1)\alpha(2)$ which is symmetric with respect to interchange of the two systems: $\alpha(1)\alpha(2) = \alpha(2)\alpha(1)$. However, if they are in different states, say α and β, the combined spin state $\alpha(1)\beta(2)$ is neither symmetric nor antisymmetric. After exchange, the spin wave function would be $\alpha(2)\beta(1)$. These wave functions are clearly not satisfactory. By linear combination (which according to wave mechanics is legitimate, since both of these spin states have the same energy) we can arrive at the combination

$$\alpha(1)\beta(2) + \alpha(2)\beta(1),$$

which is symmetric, and the combination

$$\alpha(1)\beta(2) - \alpha(2)\beta(1),$$

which is antisymmetric. These expressions describe possible states of the pair of systems. They do not exhaust the possibilities, of course, if different spin orientations are allowed; the wave function $\alpha(1)\alpha(2)$, already mentioned, describes another possibility, $\alpha(1)\gamma(2) \pm \alpha(2)\gamma(1)$ still other possibilities, and so on. A spin wave function must be combined with an orbital wave function of the proper symmetry to give the particular symmetry of the system. Thus with a pair of identical systems, each containing an odd number of electrons, an antisymmetric spin function must always be combined with a symmetric orbital function, and *vice versa;* while with an even number of electrons, symmetric or antisymmetric spin and orbital functions go together.

Behavior like a pair of systems of electrons will also be found for a pair of nuclei if we include only the motion of the nuclei as a whole in the orbital motion, and include all other angular momentum in the "spin." A nucleus is a system of nucleons; it will be, in general, in the lowest energy state, but this state may have an angular momentum (arising from either spin or orbital motion of the individual particles) which will be oriented like a spin and which is usually called the angular momentum of nuclear spin. The internal state of a nucleus is, indeed, very weakly coupled with the relative motion of the nuclei, so the conditions are correct for applying our remarks about a system of electrons to the nuclei.

1-8. *Transformations of the Phase Space*

As noted above, a quantum state "occupies" a region equal to h^f in the phase space. Also, transformations of coordinates are possible, and a phase space can be set up using any suitable set of coordinates with the corresponding momenta. In a new phase space a quantum state will still occupy a region equal to h^f. Indeed, any element of hypervolume in a phase space based on one set of coordinates will go over into an equal element of hypervolume in a phase space based on another set of coordinates. This theorem is essential to the development of our subject.

The proof is based upon a well-known mathematical proposition concerning the transformation of volume elements in multiple integrals when the variables are changed. Suppose we have a set of coordinates, $x_1, x_2, \cdots, x_n$, and suppose that these are transformed into another set $\xi_1, \xi_2, \cdots, \xi_n$ in such a way that each ξ is a function of all the x's, that all the ξ's are independent of each other, that the ξ's are continuous, single-valued functions of the x's and *vice versa* over the range of values considered, and that there are no singularities in the range. Then any function of the x's can just as well be considered to be a function of the ξ's. Corresponding to a particular hypervolume element $d\xi_1 d\xi_2 \cdots d\xi_n$

in the ξ space (the ξ's being taken as rectangular coordinates), there will be one in the x space whose hypervolume will be

$$\left| \frac{\partial(x_1, x_2, \cdots, x_n)}{\partial(\xi_1, \xi_2, \cdots, \xi_n)} \right| d\xi_1 \, d\xi_2 \cdots d\xi_n$$

where the symbol between the absolute-value bars stands for the determinant

$$\begin{vmatrix} \dfrac{\partial x_1}{\partial \xi_1} & \dfrac{\partial x_1}{\partial \xi_2} & \cdots & \dfrac{\partial x_1}{\partial \xi_n} \\[2mm] \dfrac{\partial x_2}{\partial \xi_1} & \dfrac{\partial x_2}{\partial \xi_2} & \cdots & \dfrac{\partial x_2}{\partial \xi_n} \\[2mm] \cdots\cdots\cdots\cdots\cdots \\ \cdots\cdots\cdots\cdots\cdots \\ \dfrac{\partial x_n}{\partial \xi_1} & \dfrac{\partial x_n}{\partial \xi_2} & \cdots & \dfrac{\partial x_n}{\partial \xi_n} \end{vmatrix}$$

which is known as the Jacobian of the transformation. The absolute value of this determinant is taken in the transformation of the hypervolume element, so that the transformed hypervolume will always be positive. We thus see that integrals over a fixed hypervolume in one of the spaces and the corresponding hypervolume in the other will bear the relationship

$$\int f(x_1, x_2, \cdots, x_n) dx_1 \, dx_2 \cdots dx_n$$

$$= \int f(\xi_1, \xi_2, \cdots, \xi_n) \left| \frac{\partial(x_1, x_2, \cdots, x_n)}{\partial(\xi_1, \xi_2, \cdots, \xi_n)} \right| d\xi_1 d\xi_2 \cdots d\xi_n, \tag{8.1}$$

where $f(\xi_1, \xi_2, \cdots, \xi_n)$ is the same function as $f(x_1, x_2, \cdots, x_n)$ expressed in terms of the other coordinates.

To make the meaning of this relationship plain, we shall consider the two-dimensional case in some detail. Suppose that a space with coordinates x, y is transformed into one with coordinates ξ, η. Consider a surface element $d\xi \, d\eta$, which may as well be placed at the origin, as shown in Fig. 1-2. When ξ goes from 0 to $d\xi$, the corresponding point in the x, y space goes from O to A (Fig. 1-3), and we have a change in x and y given by

$$dx_1 = \overline{\mathrm{OA'}} = \frac{\partial x}{\partial \xi} \, d\xi,$$

$$dy_1 = \overline{\mathrm{A'A}} = \frac{\partial y}{\partial \xi} \, d\xi.$$

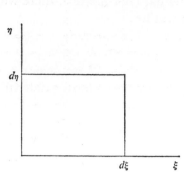

Figure 1-2.

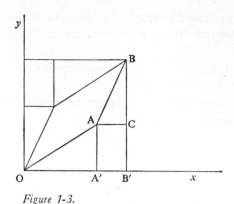

Figure 1-3.

After ξ has gone from O to $d\xi$, allow η to go from O to $d\eta$; the point on Fig. 1-3 will go from A to B, and x and y will change as follows:

$$dx_2 = \overline{\text{A}'\text{B}'} = \frac{\partial x}{\partial \eta}\, d\eta,$$

$$dy_2 = \text{CB} = \frac{\partial y}{\partial \eta}\, d\eta.$$

It is now seen that the area of the surface element (parallelogram) in the x, y space is given by

$$2\left[\tfrac{1}{2}(dx_1 + dx_2)(dy_1 + dy_2) - \tfrac{1}{2}dx_1 dy_1 - \tfrac{1}{2}dx_2 dy_2 - dx_2 dy_1\right]$$
$$= dx_1 dy_2 - dx_2 dy_1$$
$$= \left(\frac{\partial x}{\partial \xi}\frac{\partial y}{\partial \eta} - \frac{\partial x}{\partial \eta}\frac{\partial y}{\partial \xi}\right) d\xi d\eta$$
$$= \left|\frac{\partial(x, y)}{\partial(\xi, \eta)}\right| d\xi d\eta.$$

The calculation becomes much more difficult in a larger number of dimensions, but it can be carried out by a type of mathematical induction, as given in treatises on advanced calculus [**14**].

We may note that the Jacobians have the property

$$\frac{\partial(x_1, x_2, \cdots, x_n)}{\partial(x_1', x_2', \cdots, x_n')}\frac{\partial(x_1', x_2', \cdots, x_n')}{\partial(\xi_1, \xi_2, \cdots, \xi_n)} = \frac{\partial(x_1, x_2, \cdots, x_n)}{\partial(\xi_1, \xi_2, \cdots, \xi_n)}, \tag{8.2}$$

where $x_1', x_2', \cdots, x_n'$ represent another transformation of the set of coordinates. This result is fairly obvious when one considers that the effect of transforming from $x_1, x_2, \cdots, x_n$ to $x_1', x_2', \cdots, x_n'$, followed by the transformation $x_1', x_2', \cdots, x_n'$ to $\xi_1, \xi_2, \cdots, \xi_n$ must have the same result as transforming $x_1, x_2, \cdots, x_n$ at once to $\xi_1, \xi_2, \cdots, \xi_n$. It also follows directly from multiplication of the determinants.

Now we return to the principal problem of this section: the transformation of hypervolume elements in phase space. Phase space has two types of coordinates, the ordinary space coordinates and the momenta. These do not transform independently of each other—an essential fact for the proof of the theorem mentioned at the beginning of this section.

If we let $x_1, x_2, \cdots, x_f$ be the complete set of Cartesian coordinates for the various particles represented by a representative point in the phase space, we have for the kinetic energy of the system of particles

$$E_k = \sum_i \tfrac{1}{2} m_i \dot{x}_i^2. \tag{8.3}$$

The m_i will have to occur in groups of at least three, all of which are equal, but this makes no difference.

Now consider a set of transformed coordinates, $\xi_1, \xi_2, \cdots, \xi_f$. Each one is a function of all the x_i. We can write†

$$\dot{\xi}_i = \sum_j \frac{\partial \xi_i}{\partial x_j} \dot{x}_j. \tag{8.4}$$

Also, considering the x_i as functions of the ξ_i, we have

$$\dot{x}_i = \sum_j \frac{\partial x_i}{\partial \xi_j} \dot{\xi}_j \tag{8.5}$$

(all the other ξ's are constant in a partial derivative) and, therefore,

$$E_k = \frac{1}{2} \sum_i \left[m_i \left(\sum_j \frac{\partial x_i}{\partial \xi_j} \dot{\xi}_j \right)^2 \right], \tag{8.6}$$

from which we find

$$p_{\xi_l} = \frac{\partial E_k}{\partial \dot{\xi}_l}$$
$$= \sum_i \left(m_i \frac{\partial x_i}{\partial \xi_l} \sum_j \frac{\partial x_i}{\partial \xi_j} \dot{\xi}_j \right). \tag{8.7}$$

In obtaining this result, we note that although E_k may be a function of the ξ_i (since $\partial x_i / \partial \xi_j$ is in general such a function) as well as of the $\dot{\xi}_i$,

---

† In handling sets of coordinates and momenta it will be necessary to use various subscripts, e.g., i, j, k, l, for members of the same set. In any equation one such symbol may be replaced throughout by another not used in that equation.

all the ξ_i and all the $\dot{\xi}_i$ except $\dot{\xi}_l$ are held constant in the partial differentiation defining p_{ξ_l}. From Eqs. (8.5) and (8.7), remembering that
$p_{x_i} = m_i \dot{x}_i$, we have

$$p_{\xi_l} = \sum_i \frac{\partial x_i}{\partial \xi_l} p_{x_i}. \tag{8.8}$$

Since $\partial x_i / \partial \xi_l$ is a function of the ξ_i or the x_i and does not depend on
the $\dot{x}_i$ or the p_{x_i}, we see that

$$\frac{\partial p_{\xi_l}}{\partial p_{x_i}} = \frac{\partial x_i}{\partial \xi_l}, \tag{8.9}$$

where the independent sets of variables are taken as the x_i and the p_{x_i},
or the ξ_i and the p_{ξ_i}, all other members of the particular independent
set being held constant in a partial differentiation.

We can now set up the Jacobian

$$\frac{\partial(\xi_1, \xi_2, \cdots, \xi_f; p_{\xi_1}, p_{\xi_2}, \cdots, p_{\xi_f})}{\partial(x_1, x_2, \cdots, x_f; p_{x_1}, p_{x_2}, \cdots, p_{x_f})}$$

for the transformation of the $x - p_x$ phase space into the $\xi - p_\xi$ phase
space. Since $\partial \xi_i / \partial p_{x_i} = 0$ for any i and j, on making use of Eq. (8.9),
the Jacobian becomes

$$\begin{vmatrix}
\dfrac{\partial \xi_1}{\partial x_1} & \dfrac{\partial \xi_1}{\partial x_2} & \cdots & \dfrac{\partial \xi_1}{\partial x_f} & 0 & 0 & \cdots & 0 \\[2mm]
\dfrac{\partial \xi_2}{\partial x_1} & \dfrac{\partial \xi_2}{\partial x_2} & \cdots & \dfrac{\partial \xi_2}{\partial x_f} & 0 & 0 & \cdots & 0 \\[2mm]
\multicolumn{8}{c}{\cdots\cdots\cdots\cdots\cdots\cdots\cdots\cdots\cdots} \\[1mm]
\dfrac{\partial \xi_f}{\partial x_1} & \dfrac{\partial \xi_f}{\partial x_2} & \cdots & \dfrac{\partial \xi_f}{\partial x_f} & 0 & 0 & \cdots & 0 \\[2mm]
\dfrac{\partial p_{\xi_1}}{\partial x_1} & \dfrac{\partial p_{\xi_1}}{\partial x_2} & \cdots & \dfrac{\partial p_{\xi_1}}{\partial x_f} & \dfrac{\partial x_1}{\partial \xi_1} & \dfrac{\partial x_2}{\partial \xi_1} & \cdots & \dfrac{\partial x_f}{\partial \xi_1} \\[2mm]
\multicolumn{8}{c}{\cdots\cdots\cdots\cdots\cdots\cdots\cdots\cdots\cdots} \\[1mm]
\dfrac{\partial p_{\xi_f}}{\partial x_1} & \dfrac{\partial p_{\xi_f}}{\partial x_2} & \cdots & \dfrac{\partial p_{\xi_f}}{\partial x_f} & \dfrac{\partial x_1}{\partial \xi_f} & \dfrac{\partial x_2}{\partial \xi_f} & \cdots & \dfrac{\partial x_f}{\partial \xi_f}
\end{vmatrix}.$$

In expanding this determinant, we note that any term which
contains as a factor one of the terms in the lower left-hand quadrant,
such as $\partial p_{\xi_i} / \partial x_j$, will also contain a zero as a factor. Hence the Jacobian
will reduce to

$$\frac{\partial(\xi_1, \xi_2, \cdots, \xi_f)}{\partial(x_1, x_2, \cdots, x_f)} \frac{\partial(x_1, x_2, \cdots, x_f)}{\partial(\xi_1, \xi_2, \cdots, \partial \xi_f)}.$$

The first factor is the Jacobian for the change of x coordinate or configuration space to the ξ coordinate space, whereas the second factor is the Jacobian for the reverse transformation. The product must therefore be equal to unity, so we have proved that a transformation of coordinates changes an element of hypervolume in the original phase state to an equal element of hypervolume in the new phase space.

1-9. *Hamilton's Equations*

Although we base our development of statistical mechanics upon the properties of quantum states and their density in the phase space, classical mechanics can be used in numerous limiting cases. Usually the necessary equations can be derived by considering them directly as limiting cases. Occasionally, however, it is desirable to apply classical mechanics directly, and the final sections of this chapter will be devoted to some theorems which are useful in this connection [**8**, Chap. 2; **15**, **16**] and to a generalization of the result of Sec. 1-8.

We may express the energy as a function H (called the Hamiltonian) of the coordinates and the momenta (rather than as a function of the coordinates and the velocity). In particular, we may express it as a function of the transformed coordinates ξ_i and p_{ξ_i} used in Sec. 1-8. If we do this, we may show that

$$\dot{\xi}_i = \frac{\partial H}{\partial p_{\xi_i}}, \tag{9.1}$$

and

$$\dot{p}_{\xi_i} = -\frac{\partial H}{\partial \xi_i}, \tag{9.2}$$

where all the coordinates and momenta except the one indicated are held constant in the partial differentiation. These are Hamilton's equations.

First we note that in the original rectangular coordinates

$$H = \tfrac{1}{2}\sum_i \frac{p_{x_i}^2}{m_i} + E_\mathrm{p}, \tag{9.3}$$

where E_p is a function of the x_i only. Since

$$\frac{\partial H}{\partial x_i} = \frac{\partial E_\mathrm{p}}{\partial x_i} = -m\ddot{x}_i = -\dot{p}_{x_i} \tag{9.4}$$

and

$$\frac{\partial H}{\partial p_{x_i}} = \frac{p_{x_i}}{m_i} = \dot{x}_i,$$ (9.5)

we see at once that in this special case Eqs. (9.1) and (9.2) do hold.

To get the generalized equations we start with Eqs (8.4) and (8.8). In order to use Eq. (8.4), we need to evaluate the partial derivatives. Since the x's depend only on the ξ's and *vice versa*, we can write

$$dx_i = \sum_l \frac{\partial x_i}{\partial \xi_l} d\xi_l.$$ (9.6)

In order to find $\partial \xi_j / \partial x_k$ let us set all $dx_i = 0$ except dx_k and solve this set of linear equations for $d\xi_j$. We find, using Cramer's rule, $d\xi_j = dx_k \Delta_{kj} / \Delta$, where Δ is the Jacobian

$$\frac{\partial(x_1, x_2, \ldots)}{\partial(\xi_1, \xi_2, \ldots)},$$

and Δ_{kj} is a similar determinant except that the jth column and the kth row are missing and it is multiplied by $(-1)^{j+k}$. Thus

$$\frac{\partial \xi_j}{\partial x_k} = \frac{\Delta_{kj}}{\Delta}.$$ (9.7)

Let us now consider a certain set of dp_{ξ_i} and a corresponding set of dp_{x_i} with all $d\xi_i$ and all dx_i equal to zero. Under these conditions, from Eq. (8.8),

$$dp_{\xi_l} = \sum_i \frac{\partial x_i}{\partial \xi_l} dp_{x_i}.$$

Then consider the special case in which, additionally, all the dp_{ξ_i} are zero except dp_{ξ_i} and let us solve for dp_{x_k}. We get

$$dp_{x_k} = dp_{\xi_i} \frac{\Delta'_{jk}}{\Delta'},$$

where Δ' is the same as Δ except that rows and columns are interchanged, and it is therefore equal to Δ. Also Δ'_{jk} is Δ' with the jth row and kth column missing and multiplied by $(-1)^{j+k}$, and it is therefore equal to Δ_{kj}. Thus we see that

$$\frac{\partial p_{x_k}}{\partial p_{\xi_i}} = \frac{\partial \xi_j}{\partial x_k},$$ (9.8)

and using this relationship in Eq. (8.4), we have

$$\dot{\xi}_i = \sum_j \frac{\partial p_{x_i}}{\partial p_{\xi_i}} \dot{x}_j$$

$$= \sum_j \frac{\partial p_{x_i}}{\partial p_{\xi_i}} \frac{\partial H}{\partial p_{x_i}}$$

$$(9.9)$$

from Eq. (9.5). We now have to compare this with

$$\frac{\partial H}{\partial p_{\xi_i}} = \sum_j \frac{\partial H}{\partial x_j} \frac{\partial x_j}{\partial p_{\xi_i}} + \sum_j \frac{\partial H}{\partial p_{x_i}} \frac{\partial p_{x_i}}{\partial p_{\xi_i}}. \qquad (9.10)$$

The second sum in Eq. (9.10) is of course identical to the right-hand side of Eq. (9.9). Since the x's depend only on the ξ's, the partial derivatives $\partial x_j / \partial p_{\xi_i}$ in the first sum vanish. Thus Eq. (9.1) is established.

In order to prove Eq. (9.2) we note first that

$$\dot{p}_{\xi_i} = \sum_j \frac{\partial p_{\xi_i}}{\partial x_j} \dot{x}_j + \sum_j \frac{\partial p_{\xi_i}}{\partial p_{x_i}} \dot{p}_{x_i}$$

$$= \sum_j \frac{\partial p_{\xi_i}}{\partial x_j} \frac{\partial H}{\partial p_{x_i}} - \sum_j \frac{\partial x_j}{\partial \xi_i} \frac{\partial H}{\partial x_j}, \qquad (9.11)$$

by Eqs. (8.9), (9.4), and (9.5). At the same time

$$\frac{\partial H}{\partial \xi_i} = \sum_j \frac{\partial H}{\partial p_{x_i}} \frac{\partial p_{x_i}}{\partial \xi_i} + \sum_j \frac{\partial H}{\partial x_j} \frac{\partial x_j}{\partial \xi_i}. \qquad (9.12)$$

In order to prove Eq. (9.2) it will be sufficient to show that

$$\frac{\partial p_{\xi_i}}{\partial x_j} = - \frac{\partial p_{x_i}}{\partial \xi_i}. \qquad (9.13)$$

Taking note of Eq. (8.8), we see that†

$$\frac{\partial p_{\xi_i}}{\partial x_j} = \sum_l p_{x_l} \frac{\partial}{\partial x_j} \left(\frac{\partial x_l}{\partial \xi_i} \right).$$

Since the p_{ξ_i} are linear functions of the p_{x_i}, the latter are also linear functions of the former, and indeed, by Eq. (9.8),

† In the differentiation with respect to ξ_i all other ξ's are held constant; in the second differentiation with respect to x_j all other x's are held constant. In a partial differentiation with respect to any variable, all other variables *of the same set* are held constant.

$$p_{x_l} = \sum_m \frac{\partial \xi_m}{\partial x_l} p_{\xi_m}, \tag{9.14}$$

so

$$\frac{\partial p_{\xi_i}}{\partial x_j} = \sum_m \sum_l \left[\frac{\partial}{\partial x_j} \left(\frac{\partial x_l}{\partial \xi_i} \right) \right] \frac{\partial \xi_m}{\partial x_l} p_{\xi_m}. \tag{9.15}$$

On the other hand, by Eq. (9.14),

$$\frac{\partial p_{x_i}}{\partial \xi_i} = \sum_m \frac{\partial}{\partial \xi_i} \left(\frac{\partial \xi_m}{\partial x_j} \right) p_{\xi_m}. \tag{9.16}$$

We note now that

$$\sum_l \frac{\partial \xi_m}{\partial x_l} \frac{\partial x_l}{\partial \xi_i} = \frac{\partial \xi_m}{\partial \xi_i} = 0 \text{ or } 1.$$

Therefore the derivative of this sum with respect to x_j is zero:

$$\sum_l \left(\frac{\partial x_l}{\partial \xi_i} \right) \frac{\partial}{\partial x_j} \left(\frac{\partial \xi_m}{\partial x_l} \right) + \sum_l \left(\frac{\partial \xi_m}{\partial x_l} \right) \frac{\partial}{\partial x_j} \left(\frac{\partial x_l}{\partial \xi_i} \right) = 0. \tag{9.17}$$

The coefficient of p_{ξ_m} in Eq. (9.15) is equal to the second term, hence to the negative of the first term in Eq. (9.17), which is in turn equal to

$$-\sum_l \left(\frac{\partial x_l}{\partial \xi_i} \right) \frac{\partial}{\partial x_l} \left(\frac{\partial \xi_m}{\partial x_j} \right) = -\frac{\partial}{\partial \xi_i} \frac{\partial \xi_m}{\partial x_j}.$$

which is the negative of the coefficient of p_{ξ_m} in Eq. (9.16). Therefore Eq. (9.13) is correct and Eq. (9.2) follows.

1-10. *Canonical Transformations*

The transformations discussed in the two preceding sections, in which one set of coordinates is transformed into another set, the transformation of the momenta then following, are called point transformations. There is a more general type of transformation, in which a set of coordinates and momenta, $q_1, q_2, \cdots, q_f; p_1, p_2, \cdots, p_f$, is transformed to another set, $Q_1, Q_2, \cdots, Q_f; P_1, P_2, \cdots, P_f$, in such a way that $Q_1, Q_2, \cdots, Q_f$ as well as $P_1, P_2, \cdots, P_f$ are functions of *both* $q_1, q_2, \cdots, q_f$ and $p_1, p_2, \cdots, p_f$. Thus the distinction between momenta and coordinates as types of dynamical quantities becomes blurred.

If Hamilton's equations, which take the form

$$\dot{q}_i = \frac{\partial H}{\partial p_i}, \qquad \dot{p}_i = -\frac{\partial H}{\partial q_i}, \tag{10.1}$$

are valid for the first set of coordinates and also for the second set, where they take the form

$$\dot{Q}_i = \frac{\partial H}{\partial P_i}, \qquad \dot{P}_i = -\frac{\partial H}{\partial Q_i}, \tag{10.2}$$

the transformation is said to be canonical. If Eqs. (10.1) and (10.2) hold, then

$$\sum_i P_i dQ_i - \sum_i p_i dq_i = dW, \tag{10.3}$$

where dW is an exact differential.

We can prove this statement by considering two adjacent trajectories in the $2f$ dimensional phase space $q_1, q_2, \cdots, q_f; p_1, p_2, \cdots, p_f$ (Fig. 1-4). A trajectory is, of course, as always, the path over which the representative point of a system of particles moves in the phase space when the particles move under the action of the dynamical forces to which they are subjected. These trajectories determine a two-dimensional subspace. Take a normal A to the trajectories, assume that the representative particles are on A at time $t = 0$, and assume that they have advanced to some locus B at time $t = \delta t$. Define a path variable α, with $\alpha = 0$ designating the path a to b on the original trajectory and with $\alpha = \delta\alpha$ designating the path c to d on the adjacent trajectory. We shall show that the increment of Eq. (10.3) from a to b is the same as that from a to c to d to b to the second order of small quantities; thus demonstrating that dW is an exact differential.

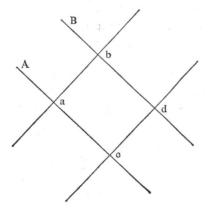

Figure 1-4.

We set $p_i dq_i = dw_i$, and indicate a particular path in the subspace of Fig. 1-4 by subscripts. The difference over the paths cd and ab is

$$dw_{i,cd} - dw_{i,ab} = \frac{\partial}{\partial \alpha}\left(p_i \frac{\partial q_i}{\partial t}\,\delta t\right)\delta\alpha$$

$$= \frac{\partial p_i}{\partial \alpha}\frac{\partial q_i}{\partial t}\,\delta t\delta\alpha + p_i \frac{\partial^2 q_i}{\partial\alpha\partial t}\,\delta t\delta\alpha.$$

The increments $dw_{i,ac} + dw_{i,db}$ are given by

$$dw_{i,ac} + dw_{i,db} = dw_{i,ac} - dw_{i,bd} = -\frac{\partial}{\partial t}\left(p_i \frac{\partial q_i}{\partial \alpha}\,\delta\alpha\right)\delta t$$

$$= -\frac{\partial p_i}{\partial t}\frac{\partial q_i}{\partial \alpha}\,\delta\alpha\delta t - p_i \frac{\partial^2 q_i}{\partial t\partial\alpha}\,\delta\alpha\delta t.$$

Since $\partial^2 q_i/\partial t\partial\alpha = \partial^2 q_i/\partial\alpha\partial t$, we see that

$$dw_{i,ac} + dw_{i,db} + dw_{i,cd} - dw_{i,ab} = \left(\frac{\partial q_i}{\partial t}\frac{\partial p_i}{\partial \alpha} - \frac{\partial p_i}{\partial t}\frac{\partial q_i}{\partial \alpha}\right)\delta\alpha\delta t$$

$$= \left(\frac{\partial H}{\partial p_i}\frac{\partial p_i}{\partial \alpha} + \frac{\partial H}{\partial q_i}\frac{\partial q_i}{\partial \alpha}\right)\delta\alpha\delta t. \qquad (10.4)$$

A similar result will be obtained for every dw_i and for every dW_i (referring to the dQ_i terms). So we see, by setting $dW_{ac} = \sum_i dW_{i,ac} - \sum_i dw_{i,ac}, \cdots$,

$$dW = dW_{ac} + dW_{db} + dW_{cd} - dW_{ab} = \left(\frac{\partial H}{\partial \alpha} - \frac{\partial H}{\partial \alpha}\right)\delta\alpha\delta t = 0, \qquad (10.5)$$

which proves the proposition.

We may also prove the converse of this proposition, namely, if Eqs. (10.1) hold and if dW is an exact differential, then Eqs. (10.2) hold. To show this write in place of (10.5) [applying the first right-hand line of Eq. (10.4) and the analogous line for the capital letters]

$$dW_{ac} + dW_{db} + dW_{cd} - dW_{ab}$$

$$= \sum_i \left(\dot{Q}_i \frac{\partial P_i}{\partial \alpha} - \dot{P}_i \frac{\partial Q_i}{\partial \alpha}\right)\delta\alpha\delta t - \sum_i \left(\dot{q}_i \frac{\partial p_i}{\partial \alpha} - \dot{p}_i \frac{\partial q_i}{\partial \alpha}\right)\delta\alpha\delta t,$$

which gives

$$\sum_i \left(\dot{Q}_i \frac{\partial P_i}{\partial \alpha} - \dot{P}_i \frac{\partial Q_i}{\partial \alpha}\right) - \frac{\partial H}{\partial \alpha} = 0, \qquad (10.5a)$$

applying the second right-hand line of Eq. (10.4) to the small letters, and setting the whole equal to zero since dW is an exact differential. There are $2f$ independent variables, one of which can be the time along the trajectory. This leaves $2f - 1$ directions in which to go to an adjacent trajectory; in other words, there are $2f - 1$ variables of the type α and $2f - 1$ equations like (10.5a). These are not quite enough to determine the $2f$ functions $\dot{Q}_i, \dot{P}_i$. However, we have another equation

$$\frac{dH}{dt} = 0 = \sum_i \left[\frac{\partial H}{\partial Q_i} \dot{Q}_i + \frac{\partial H}{\partial P_i} \dot{P}_i \right], \tag{10.6}$$

so that the $\dot{Q}_i, \dot{P}_i$ are determined, and it is seen that these equations are satisfied by Eqs. (10.2).

It may be noted that the point transformations considered in Sec. 1-9 are also canonical transformations, and the proof that dW is an exact differential holds unchanged for them. In fact, since we may now write $dQ_j = \sum_i (\partial Q_j/\partial q_i)\, dq_i$, it may be easily shown, using Eq. (9.14) that $dW = 0$; hence W is a constant.

We may use an arbitrary function of $q_1, q_2, \cdots, q_n; Q_1, Q_2, \cdots, Q_n$, called $W_1(q, Q)$ as a generating function to set up a canonical transformation, defining

$$p_i = -\frac{\partial W_1}{\partial q_i}, \qquad P_i = \frac{\partial W_1}{\partial Q_i}. \tag{10.7}$$

The first f equations of (10.7) can in principle be solved for the Q_i as functions of the p_i and the q_i; then the P_i can be found as functions of the p_i and the q_i. Thus the transformation is determined.

If, however, we are dealing with a point transformation, then, as might be expected, this program is frustrated. Even if there are fewer relations between the q_i and the Q_i than the number of variables, so that they are not completely independent of each other (a "partial" point transformation), this procedure cannot be carried out. However, there are other possibilities. The differential expressions

$$dW_2 = \sum_i P_i dQ_i + \sum_i q_i dp_i, \tag{10.8}$$

$$dW_3 = \sum_i Q_i dP_i + \sum_i p_i dq_i, \tag{10.9}$$

$$dW_4 = \sum_i Q_i dP_i - \sum_i q_i dp_i, \tag{10.10}$$

similarly can all be shown to be exact differentials for a canonical transformation. This gives us three more generating functions, $W_2(Q, p)$,

$W_3(P, q)$, $W_4(P, p)$. In these cases we expect to have f independent variables.

There are sets of equations similar to (10.7), namely,

$$P_i = \frac{\partial W_2}{\partial Q_i}, \qquad q_i = \frac{\partial W_2}{\partial p_i}, \tag{10.11}$$

$$Q_i = \frac{\partial W_3}{\partial P_i}, \qquad p_i = \frac{\partial W_3}{\partial q_i}, \tag{10.12}$$

$$Q_i = \frac{\partial W_4}{\partial P_i}, \qquad q_i = -\frac{\partial W_4}{\partial p_i}, \tag{10.13}$$

The generating functions W_1, W_2, W_3, and W_4 are not, of course, mutually independent if they generate the same transformation.

The generating functions can be used to prove certain relations between differential coefficients which make it possible to show that for any canonical transformation it is still true that the Jacobian is equal to 1. If there is no partial point transformation, there are four sets of relations, one being derivable directly from each of the generating functions. We shall quote these relations and derive one of them. They are as follows:

$$\frac{\partial q_i}{\partial Q_j} = \frac{\partial P_j}{\partial p_i}, \tag{10.14}$$

$$\frac{\partial q_i}{\partial P_j} = -\frac{\partial Q_j}{\partial p_i}, \tag{10.15}$$

$$\frac{\partial p_i}{\partial Q_j} = -\frac{\partial P_j}{\partial q_i}, \tag{10.16}$$

$$\frac{\partial p_i}{\partial P_j} = \frac{\partial Q_j}{\partial q_i}. \tag{10.17}$$

On the left-hand side of all these equations, the independent variables are the Q_j and the P_j, and on the right-hand side they are the q_i and p_i. It is, of course, the other variables of the same independent set which are held constant in the partial derivatives.

We shall prove Eq. (10.16) to illustrate how these relations are obtained. Equation (10.16) is obtained from W_1, and it must be remembered that the independent variables in W_1 are different from those on either side of Eq. (10.16). Thus in a partial derivation of W_1 different variables are held constant than those in the differentiation of p_i. From Eqs. (10.7) we see that

$$-\frac{\partial p_i}{\partial Q_j} = -\frac{\partial^2 W_1}{\partial Q_j \partial q_i} - \sum_k \frac{\partial^2 W_1}{\partial q_k \partial q_i} \frac{\partial q_k}{\partial Q_j}, \tag{10.18}$$

and

$$\frac{\partial P_j}{\partial q_i} = \frac{\partial^2 W_1}{\partial q_i \partial Q_j} + \sum_k \frac{\partial^2 W_1}{\partial Q_k \partial Q_j} \frac{\partial Q_k}{\partial q_i}. \tag{10.19}$$

Since $\partial^2 W_1 / \partial Q_j \partial q_i = \partial^2 W_1 / \partial q_i \partial Q_j$ (independent variables in W_1 are the q_i and the Q_j) we see that the sums in Eqs. (10.18) and (10.19), respectively, must be shown to be equal in order to prove Eq. (10.16).

Taking the q_i and p_i as independent variables, we may write (remembering that the independent variables in W_1 are the q_i and the Q_i)

$$-\frac{\partial p_k}{\partial q_i} = \frac{\partial^2 W_1}{\partial q_k \partial q_i} + \sum_l \frac{\partial^2 W_1}{\partial Q_l \partial q_k} \frac{\partial Q_l}{\partial q_i} = 0, \tag{10.20}$$

and taking the Q_i and the P_i as independent variables,

$$\frac{\partial P_k}{\partial Q_j} = \frac{\partial^2 W_1}{\partial Q_k \partial Q_j} + \sum_l \frac{\partial^2 W_1}{\partial q_l \partial Q_k} \frac{\partial q_l}{\partial Q_j} = 0. \tag{10.21}$$

From Eq. (10.20) we have

$$\sum_k \frac{\partial^2 W_1}{\partial q_k \partial q_i} \frac{\partial q_k}{\partial Q_j} = -\sum_l \sum_k \frac{\partial^2 W_1}{\partial Q_l \partial q_k} \frac{\partial Q_l}{\partial q_i} \frac{\partial q_k}{\partial Q_j}, \tag{10.22}$$

and from Eq. (10.21),

$$\sum_k \frac{\partial^2 W_1}{\partial Q_k \partial Q_j} \frac{\partial Q_k}{\partial q_i} = -\sum_l \sum_k \frac{\partial^2 W_1}{\partial q_l \partial Q_k} \frac{\partial Q_k}{\partial q_i} \frac{\partial q_l}{\partial Q_j}. \tag{10.23}$$

The right-hand sides of Eqs. (10.22) and (10.23) being obviously equal (by interchange of suffixes k and l in one of them), Eq. (10.16) follows from comparison of (10.18) and (10.19).

It may be remarked that Eqs. (10.14) to (10.17) hold also for the point transformation of Secs. 1-8 and 1-9. Equations (8.9) and (9.8) are special cases of Eqs. (10.14) and (10.17), respectively. Equation (9.13) is a special case of Eq. (10.16) and Eq. (10.15) also holds in a point transformation, both sides being equal to zero. Equations (10.14) to (10.17) make possible an alternative proof of Hamilton's equations for the transformed coordinates, assuming that they hold for the original ones. This proof resembles the proof given in Sec. 9 for a point transformation; so if Eqs. (10.14) to (10.17) hold, the transformation is a canonical one.

We now consider the Jacobian for a canonical transformation. It will look much like the Jacobian for the point transformation displayed in Sec. 1-8, except for the quadrant of zeros. Using (as before) Eq. (10.14) to convert $\partial P_j/\partial p_i$ to $\partial q_i/\partial Q_j$, and now also Eq. (10.15) to convert $\partial Q_i/\partial p_i$ to $-\partial q_i/\partial P_j$ it becomes, in outline,

$$\begin{vmatrix} \dfrac{\partial Q_j}{\partial q_i} & -\dfrac{\partial q_i}{\partial P_j} \\[2ex] \dfrac{\partial P_j}{\partial q_i} & \dfrac{\partial q_i}{\partial Q_j} \end{vmatrix}. \tag{10.24}$$

(Each symbol represents a group of terms, forming a quadrant of the determinant, i and j taking on all values from 1 to f and j having a constant value along a row while i has a constant value along a column.) Using the same convention for the lettering of rows and columns, and using Eqs. (10.17) and (10.16) to effect the desired transformations (this time we transform the lower left instead of the upper right quadrant) it can be seen that the Jacobian for the inverse transformation is

$$\begin{vmatrix} \dfrac{\partial q_j}{\partial Q_i} & \dfrac{\partial q_j}{\partial P_i} \\[2ex] -\dfrac{\partial P_i}{\partial q_j} & \dfrac{\partial Q_i}{\partial q_j} \end{vmatrix}. \tag{10.25}$$

If we exchange rows and columns (now designating the *new* rows by j and the *new* columns by i, expression (10.25) takes the form

$$\begin{vmatrix} \dfrac{\partial q_i}{\partial Q_j} & -\dfrac{\partial P_j}{\partial q_i} \\[2ex] \dfrac{\partial q_i}{\partial P_j} & \dfrac{\partial Q_j}{\partial q_i} \end{vmatrix} = \begin{vmatrix} -\dfrac{\partial P_j}{\partial q_i} & \dfrac{\partial q_i}{\partial Q_j} \\[2ex] \dfrac{\partial Q_j}{\partial q_i} & \dfrac{\partial q_i}{\partial P_j} \end{vmatrix} = \begin{vmatrix} \dfrac{\partial Q_j}{\partial q_i} & \dfrac{\partial q_i}{\partial P_j} \\[2ex] -\dfrac{\partial P_j}{\partial q_i} & \dfrac{\partial q_i}{\partial Q_j} \end{vmatrix} = \begin{vmatrix} \dfrac{\partial Q_j}{\partial q_i} & -\dfrac{\partial q_i}{\partial P_j} \\[2ex] \dfrac{\partial P_j}{\partial q_i} & \dfrac{\partial q_i}{\partial Q_j} \end{vmatrix}. \tag{10.26}$$

The first of the changes in (10.26) (giving the second form of the determinant) involves an exchange of certain columns, the second (giving the third form) an exchange of certain rows. These could at most produce a change of sign, but since there is an even number of operations involved even this will not occur. The third operation involves changing the sign of the lower half of the rows and then of the right-hand half of the columns. There being again an even number of operations, the determinant remains unchanged. The determinants for the direct and reverse transformations are now seen to be equal, and since their product must be unity, the Jacobians themselves are equal to 1. Thus any canonical transformation will leave an element of phase space unaltered, and so will be a satisfactory transformation.

1-11. *Liouville's Theorem*

We can now prove an important theorem which tells us about the rate of change of phase-point density in a classical system [8]. We suppose that the phase space is defined by the usual rectangular coordinates x_i, and the corresponding momenta p_{x_i}, which we will here call p_i. Any phase point will move a certain distance in a time δt. Let us now make a transformation to a new space, *not* a phase space, such that

$$\xi_i = x_i + \dot{x}_i \delta t = x_i + \frac{\partial H}{\partial p_i} \delta t,$$

$$p_{\xi_i} = p_i + \dot{p}_i \delta t = p_i - \frac{\partial H}{\partial x_i} \delta t.$$

(11.1)

In the new space each point has been transformed to the position it would have a time δt later. An element of phase volume is transformed to a new volume having the same volume as that containing the same phase points after time δt. Now,

$$\frac{\partial \xi_i}{\partial x_j} = \delta_{ij} + \frac{\partial^2 H}{\partial p_i \partial x_j} \delta t = \delta_{ij}$$

$$\frac{\partial \xi_i}{\partial p_j} = \frac{\partial^2 H}{\partial p_i \partial p_j} \delta t = \frac{\delta_{ij}}{m_i} \delta t$$

$$\frac{\partial p_{\xi_i}}{\partial p_j} = \delta_{ij} - \frac{\partial^2 H}{\partial p_j \partial x_i} \delta t = \delta_{ij}$$

$$\frac{\partial p_{\xi_i}}{\partial x_j} = - \frac{\partial^2 H}{\partial x_i \partial x_j} \delta t = h_{ij} \delta t.$$

(11.2)

In these equations

$$\delta_{ij} = \begin{cases} 0 & \text{if } i \neq j \\ 1 & \text{if } i = j \end{cases}$$

and mixed derivatives like $\partial^2 H / \partial p_i \partial x_j$ vanish because the parts of H

containing coordinates and momenta are completely separate in this system of coordinates.

The Jacobian for the transformation takes the form

$$
\begin{vmatrix}
1 & 0 & \cdots & 0 & \delta t/m_1 & 0 & \cdots & 0 \\
0 & 1 & \cdots & \cdots & 0 & \delta t/m_2 & \cdots & \cdots \\
\cdots & \cdots & \cdots & 0 & 0 & \cdots & \cdots & 0 \\
0 & \cdots & 0 & 1 & 0 & \cdots & 0 & \delta t/m_f \\
h_{11}\delta t & h_{12}\delta t & \cdots & h_{1j}\delta t & 1 & 0 & \cdots & 0 \\
h_{21}\delta t & h_{22}\delta t & \cdots & \cdots & 0 & 1 & \cdots & \cdots \\
\cdots & \cdots & \cdots & \cdots & \cdots & \cdots & \cdots & \cdots \\
h_{f1}\delta t & \cdots & \cdots & h_{fj}\delta t & 0 & \cdots & \cdots & 1
\end{vmatrix},
$$

and it is equal to 1 plus terms of at least the second power in δt, since all the terms, except the one which is a product of all the diagonals (1) must contain at least two fewer diagonal terms. In other words, $d(d\tau)/dt$, the instantaneous rate of change of the volume element containing a certain fixed number of phase points, is zero, and this is true at any time. Thus the density of phase points does not change. If this is true in one phase space it will be true in any other. Indeed, this could be seen directly, for in the general case the only difference would be that the mixed derivatives did not vanish, and although the determinant would be more complicated, it would still not contain δt to the first power. Any term containing δt to the first power, arising from the product of the diagonal terms, would cancel, because, although we would have

$$
\frac{\partial \xi_i}{\partial x_i} = 1 + \frac{\partial^2 H}{\partial p_i \partial x_i} \delta t,
$$

we would have the opposite sign in

$$
\frac{\partial p_{\xi_i}}{\partial p_i} = 1 - \frac{\partial^2 H}{\partial p_i \partial x_i} \delta t.
$$

REFERENCES

1. F. T. Wall, *Chemical Thermodynamics*, 2d ed., San Francisco, Freeman, 1965.
2. G. N. Lewis and M. Randall, *Thermodynamics* (revised by Pitzer and Brewer), New York, McGraw-Hill, 1961.
3. F. H. MacDougall, *Thermodynamics and Chemistry*, 3d ed., New York, Wiley, 1939.

4. O. K. Rice, *Electronic Structure and Chemical Binding*, New York, McGraw-Hill, 1940, Chaps. 3–9. [Available from University Microfilms, Ann Arbor, Mich.]

5. L. Pauling and E. B. Wilson, Jr., *Introduction to Quantum Mechanics*, New York, McGraw-Hill, 1935, Chaps. 1–5, 8 and 10.

6. N. F. Mott, *Elements of Wave Mechanics*, Cambridge, Eng., Cambridge Univ. Press, 1959.

7. W. Heitler, *Elementary Wave Mechanics*, 2d ed., Oxford, Eng., Clarendon Press, 1956.

8. R. C. Tolman, *The Principles of Statistical Mechanics*, Oxford, Eng., Clarendon Press, 1938.

9. W. E. Byerly, *An Introduction to the Use of Generalized Coordinates in Mechanics and Physics*, New York, Dover (reprint of 1916 ed.).

10. G. M. Barrow, *Introduction to Molecular Spectroscopy*, New York, McGraw-Hill, 1962.

11. G. Herzberg, *Molecular Spectra and Molecular Structure, I. Spectra of Diatomic Molecules*, 2d ed., Princeton, N.J., Van Nostrand, 1950.

12. W. Kauzmann, *Quantum Chemistry*, New York, Academic, 1957, Chap. 8.

13. H. Margenau and G. M. Murphy, *The Mathematics of Physics and Chemistry*, 2d ed., Princeton, N.J., Van Nostrand, 1956, p. 402ff.

14. L. P. Smith, *Mathematical Methods for Scientists and Engineers*, New York, Prentice-Hall, 1953, Secs. 61 and 68.

15. E. T. Whittaker, *Analytical Dynamics*, 3d ed., Cambridge, Eng., Cambridge Univ. Press, 1927, esp. Chaps. 11 and 12.

16. H. Goldstein, *Classical Mechanics*, Reading, Mass., Addison-Wesley, 1953, esp. Chaps. 7, 8, and 9.

PROBLEMS

1.1. In the transformation from rectangular to polar coordinates we have

$$x = r \sin \theta \cos \phi, \qquad y = r \sin \theta \sin \phi, \qquad z = r \cos \theta,$$

and in polar coordinates

$$E_k = \tfrac{1}{2}m\dot{r}^2 + \tfrac{1}{2}mr^2\dot{\theta}^2 + \tfrac{1}{2}mr^2\dot{\phi}^2 \sin^2 \theta.$$

Calculate p_ϕ by differentiation with respect to $\dot{\phi}$, and by use of Eq. (8.8). Show that the expressions coincide.

1.2. Show that the Jacobian for the transformation of the volume element in the coordinate space, $dxdydz \longrightarrow drd\theta d\phi$, is equal to $r^2 \sin \theta$. (See Prob. 1.1.)

1.3. Consider the successive transformations

$$x = r' \cos \phi', \qquad y = r' \sin \phi', \qquad z = z',$$

and

$$z' = r \cos \theta, \qquad r' = r \sin \theta, \qquad \phi' = \phi.$$

Discuss the geometrical significance of these transformations and show that the product of the Jacobians is (and should be) equal to the Jacobian for the transformation of Problem 1.2.

1.4. Suppose, in the discussion deriving Eq. (8.1), dy_1 were negative instead of positive as shown in Fig. 1-3. Draw the figure which would replace Fig. 1-3 and show that the area of the surface element in the x, y space is given, as before, by $dx_1\,dy_2 - dx_2\,dy_1$.

1.5. The Hamiltonian for a single particle moving in a potential-energy field E_p is, in polar coordinates,

$$H = \frac{p_r^2}{2m} + \frac{p_\theta^2}{2mr^2} + \frac{p_\phi^2}{2mr^2\sin^2\theta} + E_p,$$

this being essentially Eq. (5.6), with slight changes in notation. Suppose that E_p is a function of r only. Show that p_ϕ is constant. Find an expression for $\dot{p}_r$, using Hamilton's equations. Using the relation between p_x, p_θ, and p_ϕ implied by Eqs. (5.6) and (5.8), find $\dot{p}_r$ in terms of $\dot{p}_x$. Show that the same result follows directly by differentiation of Eq. (5.8).

1.6. Derive Eq. (10.15).

1.7. Assuming that Hamilton's equations hold for q_i and p_i, derive Hamilton's equations for Q_i and P_i, using Eqs. (10.14) to (10.17).

Chapter 2

The Thermodynamic Approach to Statistical Mechanics. I

2-1. *The Ideal Gas: Internal Distribution Law*

It is possible to approach statistical mechanics by a development of the ideas of thermodynamics, using an extra hypothesis to bridge the tap [1]. We will proceed from the well-known law for the equilibrium constant K, which can be developed on thermodynamic grounds,

$$\Delta G^0 = -RT \ln K, \qquad (1.1)$$

in which R is the gas constant, and T the absolute temperature. The change ΔG^0 in the standard Gibbs free energy (i.e., the free energy in the standard state) is given by

$$\begin{aligned}\Delta G^0 &= \Delta H^0 - T\Delta S^0 \\ &= \Delta E^0 + \Delta(pV)^0 - T\Delta S^0, \end{aligned} \qquad (1.2)$$

where ΔH^0 is the standard change of enthalpy, ΔS^0 the standard change in entropy, ΔE^0 the standard change in energy, and $\Delta(pV)^0$ the change in the pressure-volume product which occurs when the reactants in the standard states go over to the products in their standard states. In an ideal gas mixture there is no interaction between the molecules, so that ΔH and ΔE do not depend upon the concentration and the superscript indicating the standard state can be omitted from these symbols.

When Eq. (1.1) is applied to a mixture of ideal gases, it is usual to express the equilibrium constant in terms of pressures and to take as the standard state the condition at unit pressure, commonly one atmosphere. For the present purposes, however, it is more convenient to express the equilibrium constant in terms of concentrations. Equa-

tion (1.1) then holds unchanged, provided we take as the standard
state the condition in which the concentration is unity. For the present
our units of concentration will be moles per cubic centimeter. Equation
(1.1) is applicable to any kind of equilibrium; in particular it may be
applied to an equilibrium between two isomers. The two species of
molecules involved in such an equilibrium may be as closely related
as we wish, and the equation will apply equally well if the two species
are molecules of the same chemical kind but in different internal
quantum states, either rotational, vibrational, or electronic. A molecule
in a particular internal quantum state we call a quantum species. If
the concentration of the ith quantum species is c_i and that of the jth
quantum species is c_j, we may write for the equilibrium between them,
using the exponential rather than the logarithmic form:

$$
K_{ij} = \frac{c_j}{c_i} = \exp\left\{\frac{-\Delta G^0_{ij}}{RT}\right\}
$$

$$
= \exp\left\{\frac{-\Delta H_{ij}}{RT}\right\} \exp\left\{\frac{\Delta S^0_{ij}}{R}\right\}, \tag{1.3}
$$

where ΔG_{ij}, ΔH_{ij}, and ΔS_{ij} are respectively differences in total molal
free energy, enthalpy, and entropy (quantity for species j minus that
for species i). The superscript zero indicates, as usual, reference to the
standard state.

If we assume that the average translational energy of the molecules in any quantum state is the same as that for those in any other
quantum state (as we may if we are dealing with a perfect gas and
accept the elementary kinetic theory), then the pressure–volume product of one quantum species will equal that of any other quantum
species, and we may set the enthalpy change equal to the energy
change, writing

$$
\Delta H_{ij} = \Delta E_{ij}. \tag{1.4}
$$

Furthermore, we may assume that $\Delta E_{ij} = E_j - E_i$, where E_j and E_i
are *internal* energies, since the average translational energies will cancel
in the difference.

We now introduce the fundamental hypothesis from which we
ultimately obtain the equations of statistical mechanics from thermodynamics. We assume that, *under standard conditions, the entropy per mole
is the same for all quantum species*. This assumption is equivalent to saying
that the *a priori* probability of any quantum state is the same as that
of any other. The probability of finding a molecule in any particular

quantum state under any special set of conditions then depends upon the energy—the only discernible way in which the quantum states differ. We shall later find a close relation between entropy and probability.

On the basis of our fundamental hypothesis,

$$\Delta S_{ij}^0 = 0,\tag{1.5}$$

Eqs. (1.3), (1.4), and (1.5) yield

$$K_{ij} = \frac{c_j}{c_i} = \exp\left\{\frac{-\Delta E_{ij}}{RT}\right\}$$

$$= \exp\left\{\frac{-(E_j - E_i)}{RT}\right\}.\tag{1.6}$$

Since this equation will hold for *any* pair of quantum states, it is seen that the concentration for any quantum species, say the ith, will be proportional to the corresponding so-called Boltzmann factor $\exp\{-E_i/RT\}$. The sum of the concentrations of several quantum species, $\sum_i' c_i$ (where the prime indicates that only special designated states are to be included in the sum), will be proportional to $\sum_i' \exp\{-E_i/RT\}$. If we let a prime indicate summation over a particular set of states and a double prime indicate summation over another set of states (which may or may not overlap the first set) we may write

$$\frac{\sum_i'' c_i}{\sum_i' c_i} = \frac{\sum_i'' \exp\{-E_i/RT\}}{\sum_i' \exp\{-E_i/RT\}}.\tag{1.7}$$

Now $\sum_i'' c_i / \sum_i' c_i$ is itself an equilibrium constant, describing the equilibrium between two sets of states. We let G'^0 and G''^0 be the respective standard molal free energies of the two sets of states. It is understood, of course, that not only are the two sets of states or two sets of quantum species in equilibrium with each other, but also they are in equilibrium within themselves. Free energies are in general defined only for systems in internal equilibrium. We may set, by Eq. (1.1),

$$\frac{\sum_i'' c_i}{\sum_i' c_i} = \exp\left\{\frac{-(G''^0 - G'^0)}{RT}\right\}$$

$$= \frac{\exp\{-G''^0/RT\}}{\exp\{-G'^0/RT\}}.\tag{1.8}$$

Equation (1.8) suggests a close relationship between the standard free energy G'^0 and the sum $\sum_i' \exp\{-E_i/RT\}$, which is called the partition function (p.f.)', for the particular set of states considered. Here $G''^0 - G'^0$ is actually equal to the difference in the Helmholtz free energies, $A''^0 - A'^0$, and we shall see that the simplest relation is between the partition function and the Helmholtz free energy. We stress at the present juncture that the total concentration of molecules in any given set of quantum states is proportional to the corresponding partition function. In particular, if we set $c = \sum_i c_i$, where the unprimed sum is taken over all quantum states and hence represents the total concentration, we may write

$$\frac{c_i}{c} = \frac{\exp\{-E_i/RT\}}{\sum_i \exp\{-E_i/RT\}}, \tag{1.9}$$

or

$$c_i = c\,\frac{\exp\{-E_i/RT\}}{(\text{p.f.})_0}, \tag{1.10}$$

where $(\text{p.f.})_0 = \sum_i \exp\{-E_i/RT\}$ is the partition function of internal energy states for the entire system.

2-2. *Thermodynamic Functions of the Ideal Gas*

We shall now proceed to an investigation of the thermodynamic functions of the system. First, we can find the average value $\overline{f(E_i)}$ of any quantity $f(E_i)$ which depends on the internal energy levels. We can rewrite Eq. (1.10) as

$$n_i = N\,\frac{\exp\{-E_i/RT\}}{(\text{p.f.})_0}, \tag{2.1}$$

where n_i is the number of molecules in the ith state and N the total number of molecules (may be taken as the number in 1 mole). The desired average value is given, according to the usual definition of an average, by

$$\overline{f(E_i)} = \frac{\sum_i n_i f(E_i)}{N}$$

$$= \frac{\sum_i f(E_i)\exp\{-E_i/RT\}}{(\text{p.f.})_0}. \tag{2.2}$$

If we apply this formula to the energy itself, we see that the average internal molal energy of the whole system, $\overline{E}_i$ (which, however, we prefer to designate as E_0), is given by

$$E_0 = \frac{\sum_i n_i E_i}{N} = \frac{\sum_i E_i \exp\{-E_i/RT\}}{(\text{p.f.})_0}$$

$$= \frac{RT^2 \, \partial(\text{p.f.})_0/\partial T}{(\text{p.f.})_0}$$

$$= RT^2 \frac{\partial \ln (\text{p.f.})_0}{\partial T}. \tag{2.3}$$

We may now consider the determination of other thermodynamic quantities. Although from the remarks made above, we should expect to find a close connection between the partition function and the free energy, it is often easier to work with entropy, since in Eq. (1.5) we have one of the fundamental properties of the entropy. We shall, therefore, attempt to calculate the entropy of a mixture of molecules in different quantum states, that is, the entropy of the whole gas. The molal entropy of a single quantum species at any concentration c_i is given by the usual equation for a perfect gas:

$$S_i = S_t^0 - R \ln c_i. \tag{2.4}$$

On the right-hand side of this equation we have replaced the subscript i on S^0 with a constant subscript t, since the standard entropy is the same for all quantum species. The significance of the designation t will appear shortly.

If we have a system composed of N molecules (1 mole) with n_i molecules in the ith quantum state, we can apply the Gibbs law of mixing, which states that the entropy of the whole system is the sum of the entropies of the separate gases contained in a common volume, each one calculated as if the particular gas were present alone. This is equivalent to saying that the molal entropy of one species is not affected by the presence of another species in the same volume. Thus we can apply Eq. (2.2) to get the molal entropy $S (= \overline{S}_i)$ of the entire assembly. It is expedient, however, to use at first only the first relationship of Eq. (2.2), followed by the use of Eq. (2.4). We have

$$S = \sum_i \frac{n_i S_i}{N}$$

$$= S_t^0 \sum_i \left(\frac{n_i}{N}\right) - \sum_i \left(\frac{n_i}{N}\right) R \ln c_i$$

$$= S_t^0 - \sum_i \left(\frac{n_i}{N}\right) R \ln c_i. \tag{2.5}$$

In the last line of Eq. (2.5) we note that $\sum_i n_i = N$, so that $\sum_i (n_i/N) = 1$. From Eq. (1.10) we see that $\ln c_i = -E_i/RT + \ln c - \ln$ (p.f.)$_0$. This we can substitute into Eq. (2.5). The terms $\ln c$ and $\ln$ (p.f.)$_0$ are constant with respect to i, so where they are involved we can again apply the relation $\sum_i (n_i/N) = 1$. Thus Eq. (2.5) reduces to

$$S = S_t^0 + \frac{E_0}{T} - R \ln c + R \ln \text{(p.f.)}_0. \tag{2.6}$$

If there were only one internal quantum state, as is true for practical purposes in monatomic molecules, the molal energy E_0 would be equal to the energy of the one-quantum state, and (p.f.)$_0$ would be equal to $\exp \{-E_0/RT\}$. Equation (2.6) then would reduce to $S = S_t^0 - R \ln c$. This is essentially the same as Eq. (2.4), which is not surprising, since Eq. (2.4) gives the entropy for a group of molecules all in the same internal quantum state. The terms $E_0/T + R \ln$ (p.f.)$_0$ arise because in a real gas we have a mixture of molecules in a large number of internal quantum states. We can thus divide the entropy of Eq. (2.6) into an internal and an external or translational part, writing for the latter

$$S_t = S_t^0 - R \ln c, \tag{2.7}$$

and for the former

$$S_0 = \frac{E_0}{T} + R \ln \text{(p.f.)}_0. \tag{2.8}$$

Since we have the general relation for the Helmholtz free energy, $A = E - TS$, we may write $A_0 = E_0 - TS_0$, from which it is seen that

$$A_0 = -RT \ln \text{(p.f.)}_0. \tag{2.9}$$

Equations (2.3), (2.8), and (2.9) are extremely important, for they give connections between the thermodynamic quantities E_0, S_0, and A_0, and the partition function (p.f.)$_0$, which depends solely on the energy levels of the molecules. From these any other thermodynamic function can be obtained, although we have so far derived connections only between quantities which depend only on the internal states of the molecule.

Certain properties of Eqs. (2.8) and (2.9) warrant a brief discussion. All energies are arbitrary in the sense that the zero of energy must be selected arbitrarily. If the zero of energy is lowered by an amount W, then every energy level is raised by W, and the average molal energy E_0 is raised the same amount. This means that every term in the sum $\sum_i \exp\{-E_i/RT\}$ is multiplied by $\exp\{-W/RT\}$ and the partition function itself is multiplied by this same quantity. If W is added to E_0 and the partition function is multiplied by $\exp\{-W/RT\}$, Eq. (2.8) becomes

$$S_0 = \frac{E_0}{T} + \frac{W}{T} + R\ln(\text{p.f.})_0 + R\left(-\frac{W}{RT}\right)$$

$$= \frac{E_0}{T} + R\ln(\text{p.f.})_0. \tag{2.10}$$

That is, S_0 remains unchanged. *The entropy is an absolute quantity, which does not depend upon the arbitrary zero of energy.* On the other hand, as may readily be seen either by writing $A_0 = E_0 - TS_0$ or from Eq. (2.9), A_0 is increased by the amount W.

Since the entropy has an absolute value, we may inquire about the conditions under which it is zero. When T is very small, the partition function $\sum_i \exp\{-E_i/RT\}$ will approach its first term, $\exp\{-E_1/RT\}$ say (i.e., the term for which E_i is lowest) assuming there is only one level with this energy. All other terms are negligible, comparatively speaking. Under these circumstances, $E_0 = E_1$, and Eq. (2.8) becomes

$$S_0 = \frac{E_1}{T} + R\ln\left(\exp\left\{\frac{-E_1}{RT}\right\}\right) = 0. \tag{2.11}$$

Thus we have already an indication of the origin and meaning of the third law of thermodynamics, although we must remember that so far we have dealt only with the internal states of the molecules. It must, indeed, be recognized that this result is intimately bound up with the procedure by which we divided the entropy into the two parts given by Eqs. (2.7) and (2.8). It is not at all surprising that S_0 vanishes when T is low enough that there is essentially only one internal quantum state excited, for S_0 is just that part of the entropy which arose from the mixing of molecules in many different internal quantum states.

2-3. *Evaluation of the Internal Partition Function for Diatomic Molecules*

Before considering the translational states, we discuss the evaluation of $(\text{p.f.})_0$. As noted (Sec. 1-5), the internal energy of any molecule may be considered to be divided in electronic, vibrational, and rotational energy, and in good approximation we can write for any internal energy state

$$\epsilon_0 = \epsilon_{p,e} + \epsilon_v + \epsilon_r, \tag{3.1}$$

where, as in Sec. 1-5, $\epsilon_{p,e}$ is the value of the potential energy (including electronic energy) at the minimum of the potential-energy curve. It will be convenient to replace the subscripts in these symbols by quantum numbers specifying the state, writing

$$\epsilon_i = \epsilon_n + \epsilon_{n,v} + \epsilon_{n,j}, \tag{3.2}$$

where i is a sort of composite quantum number specifying the complete state of the molecule, n is a quantum number fixing the electronic state, and v and j are the vibrational and rotational quantum numbers, respectively. We write $\epsilon_{n,v}$ and $\epsilon_{n,j}$ to indicate that the vibrational and rotational energies depend upon the electronic state (because the frequency and moment of inertia depend on the electronic state), as well as on their own peculiar quantum numbers. The vibrational and rotational energies will be, in first approximation, independent of each other.

Noting that ϵ_n, $\epsilon_{n,v}$ and $\epsilon_{n,j}$ are energies per molecule, so that we should use the Boltzmann constant k instead of the molal gas constant, we can write

$$(\text{p.f.})_0 = \sum_n \sum_v \sum_j \exp\left\{-\frac{(\epsilon_n + \epsilon_{n,v} + \epsilon_{n,j})}{kT}\right\}. \tag{3.3}$$

In interpreting the summation over j we must recall that (Sec. 1-5) there is another quantum number m_j which does not affect the energy,[†] but which results in there being $2j + 1$ states with rotational quantum number j. Each of these states must be included in the sum, and it will be understood that the summation over j includes the appropriate contribution from each of them.

The exponential in Eq. (3.3) can be broken up into a product, and we can hold n constant, sum over v and j, and then sum over n; this gives

$$(\text{p.f.})_0 = \sum_n \left(\exp\left\{\frac{-\epsilon_n}{kT}\right\} \sum_v \sum_j \exp\left\{\frac{-\epsilon_{n,v}}{kT}\right\} \exp\left\{\frac{-\epsilon_{n,j}}{kT}\right\}\right). \tag{3.4}$$

[†] The statement is for diatomic molecules. Polyatomic molecules whose atoms are not in a straight line require a third quantum number, two of which are necessary to determine the energy. In a polyatomic molecule, v is a composite quantum number indicating the vibrational state of the whole molecule.

Since to a good approximation the vibrational and rotational states are independent of each other, we may write, in this approximation,

$$(\text{p.f.})_0 = \sum_n \left(\exp\left\{ \frac{-\epsilon_n}{kT} \right\} \sum_v \exp\left\{ \frac{-\epsilon_{n,v}}{kT} \right\} \sum_j \exp\left\{ \frac{-\epsilon_{n,j}}{kT} \right\} \right). \qquad (3.5)$$

Finally, we note that usually the potential-energy curves of a saturated molecule are far enough apart that at ordinary temperatures only states of the lowest one are appreciably populated; that is, all the other $\exp\{-\epsilon_n/kT\}$ are negligible compared with the first one. We then take the lowest value of ϵ_n as zero, neglect all higher terms, and drop the subscript n in $\epsilon_{n,v}$ and $\epsilon_{n,j}$. Thus Eq. (3.5) becomes

$$\begin{aligned} (\text{p.f.})_0 &= \sum_v \exp\left\{ \frac{-\epsilon_v}{kT} \right\} \sum_j \exp\left\{ \frac{-\epsilon_j}{kT} \right\} \\ &= (\text{p.f.})_{\text{vib}}(\text{p.f.})_{\text{rot}}. \end{aligned} \qquad (3.6)$$

This procedure of decomposing a sum of products into a product of sums, when the two factors are independent of each other, is often used and easily generalized. For example, in a polyatomic molecule the vibrational partition function $(\text{p.f.})_{\text{vib}}$ may itself (assuming harmonic vibrations) be expressed as a product of partition functions for the individual normal modes of vibration, since the total vibrational energy may be considered to be the sum of the energies contained in the various modes of vibration. Since the relationship between the partition function and the thermodynamic functions is logarithmic, the latter functions may be considered sums of individual parts.

Let us now evaluate $(\text{p.f.})_{\text{vib}}$ for a diatomic molecule. If the vibrational energy of the molecule does not become too high (essentially, if the temperature is not too high), we may consider that, to a good approximation, the vibrations of the molecule are harmonic. The allowed vibrational energy levels then are given by Eq. (5.13) of Chap. 1

$$\epsilon_v = (v + \tfrac{1}{2})h\nu, \qquad (3.7)$$

where v can take the values 0, 1, 2, 3, $\cdots$ and ν is the frequency of the oscillator. We then have

$$\begin{aligned} (\text{p.f.})_{\text{vib}} &= \sum_{v=0}^{\infty} \exp\left\{ \frac{-(v + \tfrac{1}{2})h\nu}{kT} \right\} \\ &= \exp\left\{ \frac{-\tfrac{1}{2}h\nu}{kT} \right\} \sum_{v=0}^{\infty} \exp\left\{ \frac{-vh\nu}{kT} \right\} \end{aligned} \qquad (3.8)$$

The last sum is a geometric series and is equal to $(1 - \exp\{-h\nu/kT\})^{-1}$ $= \exp\{h\nu/kT\}/(\exp\{h\nu/kT\} - 1)$. Hence we have

$$(\text{p.f.})_{\text{vib}} = \frac{\exp\{-\tfrac{1}{2}h\nu/kT\}\,\exp\{h\nu/kT\}}{\exp\{h\nu/kT\} - 1}. \tag{3.9}$$

From this the thermodynamic functions are readily found. The reader may easily verify the following relations for the molal energy, specific heat, and entropy (N is Avogadro's number) from the equations of Sec. 2-2:

$$E_{\text{vib}} = \frac{Nh\nu}{2} + \frac{Nh\nu}{\exp\{h\nu/kT\} - 1} \tag{3.10}$$

$$C_{\text{vib}} = R\left(\frac{h\nu}{kT}\right)^2 \frac{\exp\{h\nu/kT\}}{(\exp\{h\nu/kT\} - 1)^2} \tag{3.11}$$

$$S_{\text{vib}} = R\left(\frac{h\nu}{kT}\right)\left(\exp\left\{\frac{h\nu}{kT}\right\} - 1\right)^{-1} - R\ln\left(1 - \exp\left\{\frac{-h\nu}{kT}\right\}\right). \tag{3.12}$$

The quantity $h\nu/k$ which appears frequently in these equations is often designated as Θ and is called the characteristic temperature of the oscillator. In the expressions for C_{vib} and S_{vib} the quantities ν and T appear only in the combination $h\nu/kT = \Theta/T$.

It is of interest to consider the values of the quantities $(\text{p.f.})_{\text{vib}}$, E_{vib}, C_{vib}, and S_{vib} for $T = 0$, $T = \Theta$, and $T \gg \Theta$. These values are shown in Table 2-1, and may be readily verified by the reader. The thermodynamic quantities are also plotted as functions of T/Θ in Fig. 2-1. Tables of the thermodynamic functions (Planck-Einstein functions) are available [2, 3].

We now evaluate the rotational partition function. For the time being we consider molecules composed of two *different* atoms. The rota-

TABLE 2-1

Thermodynamic Quantities for the Oscillator

Quantity	$T = 0$	$T = \Theta$	$T \gg \Theta$
$(\text{p.f.})_{\text{vib}}$	$\exp\{-\tfrac{1}{2}h\nu/kT\}$	0.959	$kT/h\nu$
E_{vib}	$Nh\nu/2$	$1.082RT$	RT
C_{vib}	0	$0.921R$	R
S_{vib}	0	$1.040R$	$R\ln(ekT/h\nu)$

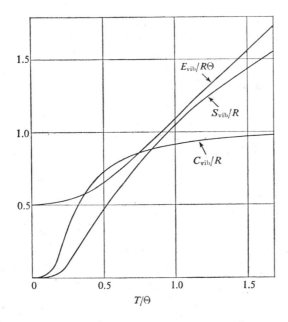

Figure 2-1. Thermodynamic functions of the harmonic oscillator.

tional energy levels of a diatomic molecule are given approximately by Eq. (5.15) of Chap. 1:

$$\epsilon_j = \frac{j(j+1)\hbar^2}{8\pi^2 I}, \qquad (3.13)$$

where j is the rotational quantum number and $I = \mu r_e^2$ is the moment of inertia. We recall again that there are actually $2j + 1$ energy levels, all of which have the energy ϵ_j. In setting up the partition function, this multiplicity or degeneracy of the rotational levels must be taken into account explicitly. Thus

$$(\text{p.f.})_{\text{rot}} = \sum_{j=0}^{\infty} (2j+1) \exp\left\{\frac{-j(j+1)\hbar^2}{8\pi^2 I k T}\right\}. \qquad (3.14)$$

In almost all cases the difference between rotational energies is small compared with kT, even at quite low temperatures. Therefore we can change the summation to an integral:

$$(\text{p.f.})_{\text{rot}} = \int_0^\infty (2j+1) \exp\left\{\frac{-j(j+1)\hbar^2}{8\pi^2 I k T}\right\} dj. \qquad (3.15)$$

If the integrand does not change much over the range from j to $j + 1$, where j is any integer, then

$$\int_{j}^{j+1} (2j + 1) \exp\left\{\frac{-j(j + 1)h^2}{8\pi^2 I k T}\right\} dj \approx (2j + 1) \exp\left\{\frac{-j(j + 1)h^2}{8\pi^2 I k T}\right\},$$

and therefore approximates one of the terms in the sum of (3.14). Hence the complete integral approximates the complete sum.

Since $(2j + 1)\, dj = d[j(j + 1)]$, the integration is readily performed, and we get

$$(\text{p.f.})_{\text{rot}} = \frac{8\pi^2 I k T}{h^2}. \tag{3.16}$$

The possibility of converting the partition function to an integral arises in what may be called the classical limit (in general, the limit of high temperature, i.e., kT large compared with the energy between energy levels). Then the exact mode of quantization is not important, although the presence of the quantum states lurks in the final formula, in the form of the h^2 in the denominator. There is another way of handling the situation in the classical limit, which we will illustrate for $(\text{p.f.})_{\text{rot}}$. As shown in Sec. 1-4, quantum levels are packed into phase space with a density such that each quantum level requires a region of size h^f where f is the number of degrees of freedom. If an element of phase space $d\tau$ is so small that the energy levels contained within it do not differ greatly in energy, and yet it is large enough to contain many energy levels, the exact part of $d\tau$ to be assigned to any particular level is not important; all that matters is that each element of phase space contains $d\tau/h^f$ quantum states. The energy ϵ is a function of the coordinates of the phase space. The contribution to the partition function of the $d\tau/h^f$ quantum levels contained in $d\tau$ is $h^{-f} \exp\{-\epsilon/kT\}\, d\tau$, where ϵ is the energy characteristic of this particular element $d\tau$. The partition function is then found by adding all terms of this sort. If, for all regions of the phase space which contribute appreciably to the partition function, it is possible to find $d\tau$'s small enough not to extend over too great an energy range (i.e., a range much less than kT) and yet large enough to contain many energy levels, we may replace the sum by the so-called phase integral, writing

$$\text{p.f.} = h^{-f} \int \exp\left\{\frac{-\epsilon}{kT}\right\} d\tau, \tag{3.17}$$

where the integration is to be taken over all allowed regions of the phase space. In essence this is not different from the reasoning used in obtaining Eq. (3.15), but it does lead to a somewhat different formulation of the problem of finding $(\text{p.f.})_{\text{rot}}$.

There are two degrees of freedom of rotation in a diatomic molecule, having to do with the polar angles θ and ϕ, that give the orientation of the line joining the nuclei. Equation (5.6) of Chap. 1 is a general expression for the energy of a diatomic molecule; the second and third terms on the right-hand side of this equation give the rotational part of the energy. If the vibration is not too highly excited, so that r does not change too greatly from r_e, we may substitute r_e for r in these terms. Then, using the definition of the moment of inertia, $I = \mu r_e^2$, we obtain the following expression for the rotational energy:

$$\epsilon_{\text{rot}} = \frac{p_\theta^2}{2I} + \frac{p_\phi^2}{2I \sin^2 \theta}. \tag{3.18}$$

This may now be substituted into Eq. (3.17), and we note that in this case $f = 2$ and $d\tau = dp_\theta dp_\phi d\theta d\phi$. Hence

$$(\text{p.f.})_{\text{rot}} = h^{-2} \int_{\phi=0}^{2\pi} \int_{\theta=0}^{\pi} \int_{p_\phi=-\infty}^{\infty} \int_{p_\theta=-\infty}^{\infty}$$

$$\exp\left\{ -\frac{p_\theta^2}{2IkT} - \frac{p_\phi^2}{2I(\sin^2 \theta)kT} \right\} dp_\theta dp_\phi d\theta d\phi. \tag{3.19}$$

We may integrate immediately with respect to ϕ, p_θ, and p_ϕ (see Appendix, Sec. 2-6), obtaining

$$(\text{p.f.})_{\text{rot}} = 2\pi h^{-2}(2\pi IkT)^{1/2} \int_0^\pi [2\pi I(\sin^2 \theta)kT]^{1/2} \, d\theta$$

$$= \frac{8\pi^2 IkT}{h^2}, \tag{3.20}$$

in agreement with Eq. (3.16).

If the two atoms in a diatomic molecule are alike, rotating the molecule through an angle of π (taking as an axis a perpendicular bisector of the line of centers) will carry it into a state indistinguishable from the initial state. Such a rotation amounts to changing ϕ to $\phi + \pi$ and θ to $\pi - \theta$, and we note that in the integral, Eq. (3.19), we have covered both positions. Actually, therefore, every state has been covered twice, and, as noted in the similar case discussed in Sec. 1-7, we must compensate for this duplication by an appropriate division. In general we may write

$$(\text{p.f.})_{\text{rot}} = \frac{8\pi^2 IkT}{h^2 \sigma}, \tag{3.21}$$

where the symmetry factor or number $\sigma = 2$ if the two atoms are alike and $\sigma = 1$ if the two atoms are different.

The thermodynamic functions associated with rotation are readily calculated from Eq. (3.21). They are given, per mole, by

$$E_{\mathrm{rot}} = RT, \tag{3.22}$$

$$C_{\mathrm{rot}} = R, \tag{3.23}$$

$$S_{\mathrm{rot}} = R \ln \left(\frac{8\pi^2 eIkT}{h^2\sigma} \right). \tag{3.24}$$

From elementary kinetic theory (or as we may anticipate from results to be obtained later) the translational energy and the translational specific heat at constant volume are given by

$$E_{\mathrm{trans}} = \tfrac{3}{2} RT, \tag{3.25}$$

$$C_{v,\mathrm{trans}} = \tfrac{3}{2} R. \tag{3.26}$$

The total energy and total specific heat are found by adding together the vibrational, rotational, and translational contributions.

Equations (3.22), (3.23), and (3.24) are valid for all diatomic molecules at sufficiently high temperatures (room temperature is always high enough). On the other hand, C_{vib} is practically zero at room temperature for many molecules with light atoms and stiff binding, such as H_2, N_2 and O_2. Thus for such molecules C_v is approximately equal to $\tfrac{5}{2} R$. It will increase above this value if the temperature is raised sufficiently. For a molecule like I_2, C_{vib} is virtually completely excited at room temperature, and $C_v \approx \tfrac{7}{2} R$. There are many intermediate cases.

There is one possibility which is still neglected—the existence of various nuclear spin states. If the nuclei have spins, various possible orientations of these spins are possible, giving rise to a multiplicity of energy levels. To an extremely close approximation, however, the energy is not affected by the nuclear spin. This simply means that all the terms in the partition function should come in not only once, but a certain small, integral number of times. Hence the partition function is multiplied by a small integer, which is independent of the temperature and all other factors. If this integer, the spin multiplicity, is equal to η, then the molal entropy will be increased by a term $R \ln \eta$. Actually this increase will not be important, since it is unchanged under all possible conditions. Even when the two atoms are separated or undergo chemical reaction, the same nuclear-spin possibilities exist, so the extra term cannot affect changes in thermodynamic quantities; in general it can simply be neglected.

The symmetry of the nuclear spin states, however, is closely connected with the symmetry number [4]. A simple example is provided by the oxygen molecule $^{16}O^{16}O$. The oxygen atom ^{16}O has zero nuclear spin, hence has only one spin state. Since the two nuclei must thus be in the same spin state, the nuclear spin function must be symmetric. Since the ^{16}O atom has an even number of elementary particles, its over-all wave function must be symmetric; thus, in view of the symmetric nuclear spin function, the nuclear orbital function must be symmetric also (see Sec. 1-7).

The nuclear wave function consists of translational, vibrational, rotational, and spin parts. The translational part involves only the motion of the center of gravity and does not depend on exchange of nuclei—hence it is always symmetric. Similarly the vibrational part, depending only on the distance between the nuclei and not otherwise on their relative positions, is always symmetric. The rotational wave functions, however, involve directly the angles θ and ϕ. Changing θ to $\pi - \theta$ and ϕ to $\phi + \pi$, as we have seen, causes the nuclei to interchange their positions. The electrons are, of course, moving in precisely the same field in either case, and so the wave function of the electrons will be unchanged. But the rotational wave function for the nuclei can be either symmetric or antisymmetric with respect to exchange of the nuclei. The forms of these functions are well known; if j is even, the rotational wave functions are symmetric. If j is odd, they are antisymmetric; thus the odd j values cannot occur. Every other rotational state in $^{16}O^{16}O$ is missing, as shown by spectroscopic investigations. Since half the terms in the sum for the rotational partition function are missing, the rotational partition function can be only half as great as it would otherwise be, at least in the high-temperature range where the sum can be changed into an integral. Thus the symmetry number comes in automatically.

For $^{16}O^{17}O$ and $^{16}O^{18}O$, since the isotopes are not identical, all the rotational states are present [5] and $\sigma = 1$. Here interchanging the two nuclei produces a new, distinguishable configuration; no duplication occurs on rotation; no states are cut out.

2-4. *Ortho- and Parahydrogen*

Although the effects of nuclear spin can usually be neglected, aside from its relation to the symmetry number, certain complications do arise when the two atoms are the same. These are not observed at room temperature, but appear when the temperature is lowered sufficiently so that the sum in Eq. (3.14) can no longer be approximated by an integral. Since the product IT appears in the terms of Eq. (3.14), the lower the value of I the higher the T at which the approximation will break down. Since hydrogen is very light, the temperature at which the breakdown occurs in this case is relatively high, in the neighborhood of 100°K. This gives rise to some phenomena of considerable interest, which we shall consider in some detail.†

The hydrogen nucleus (proton) has a spin of $\frac{1}{2}$ and thus two possible spin states. This situation is quite analogous to that of an electron, so, following Sec. 1-7, we call these nuclear spin states α and β. The spin states for the molecule (two protons), then, will have the following forms:

$$\alpha(1)\alpha(2),$$
$$\beta(1)\beta(2),$$
$$\alpha(1)\beta(2) + \beta(1)\alpha(2),$$
$$\alpha(1)\beta(2) - \beta(1)\alpha(2).$$

There are thus three possible symmetric spin functions and one antisymmetric.

The proton is an elementary particle, so the complete wave function for the nuclear motion of the hydrogen molecule must be antisymmetric. Recalling the symmetry properties of the various rotational states of the molecule as described in Sec. 2-3, we see that in this case the wave functions with even values of j will be combined with the antisymmetric spin function, while those for which j is odd will be combined with one of the symmetric spin functions. Taking account of the multiplicity of the spin state, we have

$$(\text{p.f.})_{\text{rot}} = \sum_{j=0,2,4,\cdots} (2j + 1) \exp\left\{\frac{-j(j + 1)h^2}{8\pi^2 IkT}\right\}$$
$$+3 \sum_{j=1,3,5,\cdots} (2j + 1) \exp\left\{\frac{-j(j + 1)h^2}{8\pi^2 IkT}\right\}. \tag{4.1}$$

At high temperatures it is a good approximation to average the factors 1 and 3, which multiply successive terms, thus

$$(\text{p.f.})_{\text{rot}} \approx 2 \sum_{j=0}^{\infty} (2j + 1) \exp\left\{\frac{-j(j + 1)h^2}{8\pi^2 IkT}\right\}$$
$$= 2 \times \frac{8\pi^2 IkT}{h^2} = \frac{8\pi^2 \eta IkT}{h^2 \sigma}, \tag{4.2}$$

† For a more detailed account and description of experiments see [6].

the spin multiplicity η (total number of states, symmetric or antisymmetric) being equal to 4, and the symmetry number σ being equal to 2. Again we see that the symmetry number is an expression of the fact that symmetrical spin functions and antisymmetrical spin functions can combine with only half of the rotational wave functions. Of course, as explained in Sec. 2-3, it is usual to omit the factor η.

At high temperatures Eq. (4.2) would yield the usual values of the specific heat. At low temperatures one expects to find the energy by retaining $(p.f.)_{rot}$ in the series form, and then get C_{rot} by differentiation, which will, of course, involve term-by-term differentiation of the series. However, this does not give results in agreement with experiment. It has been found that it is not easy to get equilibrium between the states with antisymmetrical spin functions (parahydrogen) and those with symmetrical spin functions (orthohydrogen). At high temperatures there is three times as much ortho- as parahydrogen, as might be expected from Eq. (4.1). This, of course, is the equilibrium expectation; ordinary hydrogen at high temperatures has usually existed in this state long enough for equilibrium to be established even though this occurs slowly. However, if hydrogen is cooled to very low temperatures, it does not all go into the state $j = 0$, as would be expected if equilibrium were established. Rather it goes into the states $j = 0$ and $j = 1$, and there are still three times as many molecules with $j = 1$ as with $j = 0$. If we treat the hydrogen as though it were a mixture of two independent gases, parahydrogen, with rotational partition function

$$(p.f.)_{rot,para} = \sum_{j=0,2,4,\cdots} (2j + 1) \exp\left\{\frac{-j(j + 1)h^2}{8\pi^2 I k T}\right\} \qquad (4.3)$$

and orthohydrogen with

$$(p.f.)_{rot,ortho} = \sum_{j=1,3,5,\cdots} (2j + 1) \exp\left\{\frac{-j(j + 1)h^2}{8\pi^2 I k T}\right\}, \qquad (4.4)$$

with three times as much ortho- as parahydrogen present, we get a value for the specific heat which is confirmed experimentally. Of course, the experimental specific heat contains the contribution $\frac{3}{2}R$ from the translational motion, but this may be allowed for.

If the hydrogen is in contact with a catalyst such as active carbon, equilibrium is established between ortho- and parahydrogen;

then at low temperatures it is possible to get pure parahydrogen. If the catalyst is now removed and the hydrogen heated, only the states with even j are excited, and the specific heat of pure parahydrogen can be measured. That of orthohydrogen can then be obtained by difference.

Deuterium is also interesting. The spin quantum number of the deuterium atom is 1, which means that there are three possible orienta-

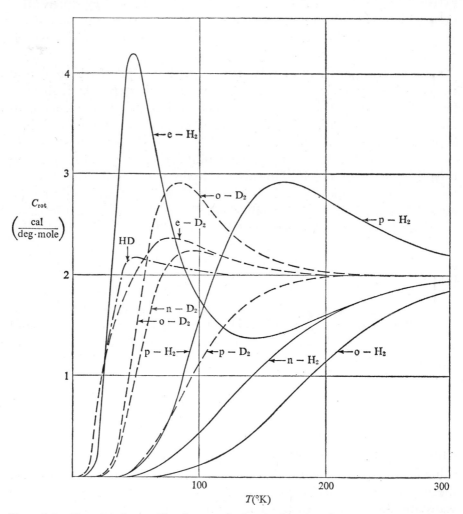

Figure 2-2. Rotational specific heats of the hydrogens (o = ortho; p = para; e = equilibrium mixture; n = normal mixture, with which the ordinary specific heats agree).

tions of the nucleus, or three possible nuclear spin states, say α, β, and γ. The possible spin states for the D_2 molecule, then, are

$$\alpha(1)\alpha(2),$$
$$\beta(1)\beta(2),$$
$$\gamma(1)\gamma(2),$$

$$\alpha(1)\beta(2) + \beta(1)\alpha(2), \quad \alpha(1)\beta(2) - \beta(1)\alpha(2),$$
$$\alpha(1)\gamma(2) + \gamma(1)\alpha(2), \quad \alpha(1)\gamma(2) - \gamma(1)\alpha(2),$$
$$\beta(1)\gamma(2) + \gamma(1)\beta(2), \quad \beta(1)\gamma(2) - \gamma(1)\beta(2).$$

There are thus six symmetrical and three antisymmetrical states. The deuterium nucleus contains two nucleons, a proton and a neutron, so that the nuclear wave function is symmetrical; therefore the symmetrical spin function will be combined with the states $j = 0, 2, 4, \cdots$, and the antisymmetrical function with the states $j = 1, 3, 5, \cdots$. The former is called orthodeuterium, the latter paradeuterium.

In the absence of a catalyst, these act like separate gases as in the hydrogen case. On this basis the thermodynamic properties of deuterium can be readily calculated, the calculated specific heat agreeing with the experimental values. In the molecule HD the question of symmetry does not enter, and all rotational states have the same weight.

In Fig. 2-2, we have plotted the specific heats for the various cases considered above. In some the specific heat rises to a maximum, then drops to the high-temperature value. These maxima are most marked when the first excited energy level has a substantial multiplicity. When there are so many states of the same energy, which will naturally all be excited in the same temperature range, there will be, over the range in which they are being excited, a relatively large increase in the average energy of the system; this energy shows up in the large value of the specific heat (compare Prob. 2.3).

2-5. *Polyatomic Molecules*

As noted in Sec. 1-5, a nonlinear polyatomic molecule with n atoms has 3 degrees of freedom of translation of the center of gravity, 3 of rotation, and $3n - 6$ of vibration. The vibrational degrees of freedom may in first approximation be described as normal modes of vibration. These normal modes are quantized in the same way as is the vibration

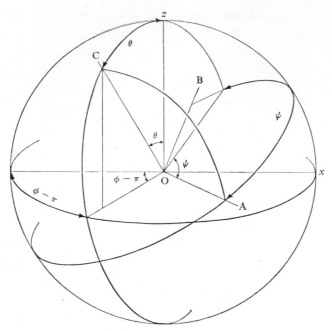

Figure 2-3. Euler angles. θ is measured in the plane COz; π is measured in the equatorial plane; ψ is the dihedral angle between planes COA, and COz, is measured in the plane AOB, perpendicular to line OC.

of a diatomic molecule and will contribute to the partition function $3n - 6$ factors like the one on the right-hand side of Eq. (3.9), with the proper frequencies inserted.

Determination of the partition function for rotation of a nonlinear polyatomic molecule is more complicated;[†] we will do this by a method which is perhaps not quite rigorous but which provides good physical insight. Let us suppose that in such a molecule the moments of inertia about the three principal axes of rotation (Sec. 1-5) are A, B, and C respectively. The orientation of such a molecule will be completely determined by three angles. Two of these may be the angles θ and ϕ made by one of the principal axes with a polar axis, say the C axis (i.e., the one with moment of inertia C). The third one, ψ, can be chosen as the dihedral angle made by the plane determined by the A and C axes with the plane determined by the C axis and the polar axis. (Fig. 2-3). These are the so-called Euler angles. A small

---

[†] For an account of the dynamics of rotation of a polyatomic molecule (a rigid body) see [**7, 8,** and **9**].

rotation is determined by the small changes $\delta\theta$, $\delta\phi$, $\delta\psi$ in the Euler angles. Such a small rotation can also be determined by three other independent variables; for example, it can be described as compounded of rotations through a small angle $\delta\alpha$ about the A axis, an angle $\delta\beta$ about the B axis, and an angle $\delta\gamma$ about the C axis, considering these axes as momentarily fixed in space, although determined by the position of the body. These angles are useful, because a classical mechanical theorem states that the kinetic energy of rotation is given by

$$\epsilon_{\text{rot}} = \tfrac{1}{2}A\dot{\alpha}^2 + \tfrac{1}{2}B\dot{\beta}^2 + \tfrac{1}{2}C\dot{\gamma}^2, \tag{5.1}$$

being composed of parts contributed by the rotation about each of the three axes. Here $\dot{\alpha}$, $\dot{\beta}$, and $\dot{\gamma}$ are of course the corresponding angular velocities ($\dot{\alpha} = \delta\alpha/\delta t$, etc.). The instantaneous axis of rotation continually changes and so do $\dot{\alpha}$, $\dot{\beta}$, and $\dot{\gamma}$. However, we can define instantaneous momenta by

$$\xi = \frac{\partial \epsilon_{\text{rot}}}{\partial \dot{\alpha}} = A\dot{\alpha}$$

$$\eta = \frac{\partial \epsilon_{\text{rot}}}{\partial \dot{\beta}} = B\dot{\beta} \tag{5.2}$$

$$\zeta = \frac{\partial \epsilon_{\text{rot}}}{\partial \dot{\gamma}} = C\dot{\gamma}$$

and write

$$\epsilon_{\text{rot}} = \frac{\xi^2}{2A} + \frac{\eta^2}{2B} + \frac{\zeta^2}{2C}. \tag{5.3}$$

Using the general method by which we derived Eq. (3.20), assuming classical mechanics, we can write

$$(\text{p.f.})_{\text{rot}} = \frac{1}{h^3} \int_{\psi=0}^{2\pi} \int_{\phi=0}^{2\pi} \int_{\theta=0}^{\pi} \int_{p_\psi=-\infty}^{\infty} \int_{p_\phi=-\infty}^{\infty} \int_{p_\theta=-\infty}^{\infty}$$

$$\exp\left\{-\frac{\xi^2}{2AkT} - \frac{\eta^2}{2BkT} - \frac{\zeta^2}{2CkT}\right\} dp_\theta dp_\phi dp_\psi d\theta d\phi d\psi, \tag{5.4}$$

where p_θ, p_ϕ, and p_ψ are respectively the momenta conjugate to θ, ϕ, and ψ.

At some fixed initial value of θ, ϕ, and ψ, a set of small angular displacements $\delta\alpha$, $\delta\beta$, and $\delta\gamma$ will correspond to changes $\delta\theta$, $\delta\phi$, and $\delta\psi$. We may then write

$$\delta\alpha = \left(\frac{\partial\alpha}{\partial\theta}\right)\delta\theta + \left(\frac{\partial\alpha}{\partial\phi}\right)\delta\phi + \left(\frac{\partial\alpha}{\partial\psi}\right)\delta\psi,$$

$$\delta\beta = \left(\frac{\partial\beta}{\partial\theta}\right)\delta\theta + \left(\frac{\partial\beta}{\partial\phi}\right)\delta\phi + \left(\frac{\partial\beta}{\partial\psi}\right)\delta\psi, \tag{5.5}$$

$$\delta\gamma = \left(\frac{\partial\gamma}{\partial\theta}\right)\delta\theta + \left(\frac{\partial\gamma}{\partial\phi}\right)\delta\phi + \left(\frac{\partial\gamma}{\partial\psi}\right)\delta\psi.$$

The coefficients in these equations are perhaps somewhat inaccurately written as partial derivatives, since α, β, and γ are not (except when $\delta\alpha$, $\delta\beta$, and $\delta\gamma$ are very small) functions of θ, ϕ, and ψ of the usual kind; however it is clear that for small displacements the quantities written as partial derivatives will be functions of θ, ϕ, and ψ. If we divide Eqs. (5.5) by the time δt in which the displacements took place, we get

$$\dot{\alpha} = \left(\frac{\partial\alpha}{\partial\theta}\right)\dot{\theta} + \left(\frac{\partial\alpha}{\partial\phi}\right)\dot{\phi} + \left(\frac{\partial\alpha}{\partial\psi}\right)\dot{\psi},$$

$$\dot{\beta} = \left(\frac{\partial\beta}{\partial\theta}\right)\dot{\theta} + \left(\frac{\partial\beta}{\partial\phi}\right)\dot{\phi} + \left(\frac{\partial\beta}{\partial\psi}\right)\dot{\psi}, \tag{5.6}$$

$$\dot{\gamma} = \left(\frac{\partial\gamma}{\partial\theta}\right)\dot{\theta} + \left(\frac{\partial\gamma}{\partial\phi}\right)\dot{\phi} + \left(\frac{\partial\gamma}{\partial\psi}\right)\dot{\psi}.$$

From Eqs. (5.2) and (5.6) we see that ξ, η, and ζ are linear functions of $\dot{\theta}$, $\dot{\phi}$, and $\dot{\psi}$, the coefficients being functions of θ, ϕ, and ψ. As always, $\epsilon_{\rm rot}$ is a quadratic function of $\dot{\theta}$, $\dot{\phi}$, and $\dot{\psi}$; thus

$$p_\theta = \frac{\partial\epsilon_{\rm rot}}{\partial\dot{\theta}}, \qquad p_\phi = \frac{\partial\epsilon_{\rm rot}}{\partial\dot{\phi}}, \qquad p_\psi = \frac{\partial\epsilon_{\rm rot}}{\partial\dot{\psi}}$$

are linear functions of $\dot{\theta}$, $\dot{\phi}$, and $\dot{\psi}$ and hence of ξ, η, and ψ. The volume element $dp_\theta dp_\phi dp_\psi$ may be transformed by means of a Jacobian (Sec. 1-8) to $d\xi d\eta d\zeta$, which will give

$$({\rm p.f.})_{\rm rot} = \frac{1}{h^3}\int_{\psi=0}^{2\pi}\int_{\phi=0}^{2\pi}\int_{\theta=0}^{\pi}\int_{\zeta=-\infty}^{\infty}\int_{\eta=-\infty}^{\infty}\int_{\xi=-\infty}^{\infty}$$

$$\exp\left\{-\frac{\xi^2}{2AkT} - \frac{\eta^2}{2BkT} - \frac{\zeta^2}{2CkT}\right\} J\, d\xi d\eta d\zeta d\theta d\phi d\psi. \tag{5.7}$$

Here J is the Jacobian in question. It depends upon the coefficients for the transformation of p_θ, p_ϕ, and p_ψ to ξ, η, and ζ, and hence is a function of θ, ϕ, and ψ. Equation (5.7) can be integrated at once with respect to ξ, η, and ζ; the result will be equal to $(ABC)^{1/2}(2\pi kT)^{3/2}$.

The integration with respect to θ, ϕ, and ψ will give some constant, which we will call a. This constant could be determined by working out the linear transformations [10] which were discussed in obtaining Eq. (5.7). However, we need know only that it does not depend upon A, B, or C; this follows because the transformation from p_θ, p_ϕ, and p_ψ to ξ, η, and ζ does not depend on A, B, or C, as may be seen in the following way. We may write, for example, $p_\theta = \partial \epsilon_{\text{rot}}/\partial \dot{\theta}$, and by using Eq. (5.1) obtain

$$p_\theta = A\dot{\alpha}\,\frac{\partial \dot{\alpha}}{\partial \dot{\theta}} + B\dot{\beta}\,\frac{\partial \dot{\beta}}{\partial \dot{\theta}} + C\dot{\gamma}\,\frac{\partial \dot{\gamma}}{\partial \dot{\theta}}$$

$$= \xi\,\frac{\partial \alpha}{\partial \theta} + \eta\,\frac{\partial \beta}{\partial \theta} + \zeta\,\frac{\partial \gamma}{\partial \theta}$$

by Eqs. (5.2) and (5.6). The relation $\partial \dot{\alpha}/\partial \dot{\theta} = \partial \alpha/\partial \theta$, for example, follows from Eq. (5.6), because θ, ϕ, and ψ are held constant in the partial differentiation, and the differential coefficients in Eq. (5.6) depend only on these variables. Since the relation between $\delta \alpha$, $\delta \beta$, $\delta \gamma$ and $\delta \theta$, $\delta \phi$, $\delta \psi$ is purely geometrical, the coefficients will not involve A, B, and C; hence the latter will not be involved in the relation between p_θ (or p_ϕ or p_ψ) and ξ, η, and ζ. Thus J and a will not involve A, B, and C.

Leaving a for the moment undetermined, we write

$$(\text{p.f.})_{\text{rot}} = ah^{-3}(ABC)^{1/2}(2\pi kT)^{3/2}. \tag{5.8}$$

We can find a otherwise, by a limiting case. Suppose that $A = B \gg C$. In this case the situation reduces to that of a heavy diatomic molecule, moving relatively slowly, with a spin around the axis joining the two atoms—on the average, a relatively rapid spin, since the moment of inertia involved is small. Since the energy rises as the square of the angular velocity, and the angular momentum rises only as the first power, the angular momentum associated with C at average energy is small. Thus the motion of the "diatomic" molecule will not be greatly affected by the rapid rotation, and the "diatomic" molecule will contribute a factor to the partition function, which, if we forget the symmetry factor, is given by Eq. (3.20):

$$\frac{8\pi^2 AkT}{h^2} = \frac{8\pi^2 (AB)^{1/2} kT}{h^2}. \tag{5.9}$$

As far as the fast rotation is concerned, being rapid it will proceed as though its axis were fixed in space. Its energy levels are given [11], according to quantum mechanics, by the condition that the momentum (which may be identified with ζ) is given by

$$\zeta = \frac{lh}{2\pi},$$ (5.10)

where l can be any positive or negative integer or zero. The corresponding energy is, therefore

$$\frac{\zeta^2}{2C} = \frac{l^2h^2}{8\pi^2C},$$ (5.11)

and the partition function is

$$(\text{p.f.})_\zeta = \sum_{l=-\infty}^{\infty} \exp\left\{\frac{-l^2h^2}{8\pi^2CkT}\right\}.$$ (5.12)

This may be evaluated by changing it to an integral. Alternatively one may set up a phase integral, analogous to Eq. (3.19), but involving only one coordinate and momentum. In either case one obtains

$$(\text{p.f.})_\zeta = \pi^{1/2}\left\{\frac{8\pi^2CkT}{h^2}\right\}^{1/2}.$$ (5.13)

If we combine Eq. (5.13) with Eq. (5.9), we see that we have evaluated the constant in Eq. (5.8), and the latter becomes

$$(\text{p.f.})_{\text{rot}} = \frac{\pi^{1/2}(8\pi^2kT/h^2)^{3/2}(ABC)^{1/2}}{\sigma}.$$ (5.14)

In Eq. (5.14) we have included a symmetry factor σ. This is necessary, because Eq. (5.14) includes contributions from all possible rotational positions of the molecule. If these rotations result in duplication of indistinguishable configurations, these must be divided out as usual.

To illustrate the evaluation of σ we may consider some examples. The molecule BF_3 has three fluorine atoms at the corners of an equilateral triangle, with the boron atom in the same plane at the center. If we supposed that the three fluorines were distinguishable we could place them in $3! = 6$ different arrangements which would be indistinguishable if the fluorines were alike. Any one of these arrangements could be reached by rotation, either by rotation about an axis through the boron perpendicular to the plane of the fluorines or by such a rotation combined with one about an axis through the boron and in the plane of the fluorines. Therefore $\sigma = 6$.

Ethane (C_2H_6) has six symmetrically placed hydrogen atoms, and one might suppose that σ would be $6! = 720$. However, the position obtained, for example, by interchanging any single pair of hydrogens can never be reached by rotation only, and actually σ is only 6. As in BF_3, three positions can be reached by rotation about an axis through the carbons, and three more by such a rotation combined with one about an axis perpendicular thereto. We assume no free rotation of the separate methyls about the C—C bond.

A molecule like NH_3, which is pyramidal rather than plane triangular, has a symmetry number of 3 rather than 6. Of special interest is the case where the pyramid is quite flat, so that the molecule is almost planar. One may ask at just what point the symmetry changes. As a matter of fact, the NH_3 molecule is itself rather flat, and may perhaps be considered an intermediate case. If the axis perpendicular to the plane of the hydrogens is held fixed in position, the molecule will be capable of two different equilibrium configurations, as shown in Fig. 2-4. If we take the perpendicular distance x between the nitrogen and the plane of the hydrogens as a coordinate, we can plot a potential-energy curve such as is shown in Fig. 2-5. This assumes that the N–H distance remains fixed, or, perhaps better, that for any value of x, the N–H distance takes that value for which the potential energy is as low as possible. It is known that the NH_3 molecule can flip from one of the equilibrium configurations to the other. If the energy level is very low compared with the height of the maximum

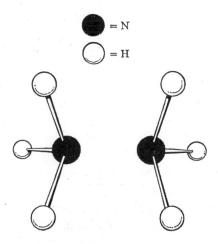

Figure 2-4. Inversion of the ammonia molecule.

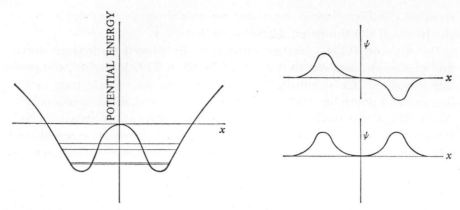

Figure 2-5. (Left). Schematic potential-energy curves and lower energy levels for the inversion of a pyramidal molecule such as ammonia.

Figure 2-6. (Right). Wave functions for the two lowest levels of Fig. 2-5.

of the potential-energy curve, the molecule will oscillate (parasol-fashion) about one of its equilibrium positions and will flip but rarely. Each of these configurations can be considered to give rise to a separate state of the system; however, a stationary state must involve both configurations, and the stationary wave functions (functions of x, assuming this coordinate separable) for the lowest energy levels are shown schematically in Fig. 2-6. One may describe the situation by saying that each energy level is split into two. The nearer the energy level is to the maximum of the potential-energy curve, the greater the interaction between the two configurations, the more rapid the rate of flipping, and the greater the separation between the two energy levels. Appreciable splitting may occur at the lowest energy level, or several of the energy-level pairs may be very close together, depending on the relation between them and the potential energy, and also on the mass of the particles involved.

Consider now the case where the rate of flipping is low. We think then of the normal (or nearly normal) mode of vibration about one of the equilibrium positions, and the one set of energy levels that go with it. Rotation of the molecule about an axis perpendicular to the x axis is capable of taking it into the other equilibrium position, with its set of energy levels, which we had not previously taken into account. This being the case, we will not introduce a symmetry number for this rotation, for this would in effect be cutting out energy levels which were actually distinct and needed to be included.

On the other hand, consider the case where the rate of flipping is rapid. In this case we must perforce take into account *both* levels of any pair simultaneously. Now rotation of 180 deg about the axis perpendicular to the *x* axis will introduce nothing new, and the result should not be counted as a new configuration. Hence the symmetry number must be introduced.

An interesting situation arises at low temperatures. Even if the rate of flipping is quite low, a temperature will be reached at which the lower level of the lowest pair of levels will be preferred over the other level. Thus, in effect, since now only one level of the pair is occupied, the symmetry number appears at low temperatures.

2-6. *Appendix: Integrals*

The integral repeatedly used in evaluating Eq. (3.19) occurs frequently in the equations of statistical mechanics; it is the well-known form

$$\int_{-\infty}^{\infty} \exp\{-ax^2\}\, dx = a^{-1/2} \int_{-\infty}^{\infty} \exp\{-x^2\}\, dx = \left(\frac{\pi}{a}\right)^{1/2}. \qquad (6.1)$$

The evaluation of $\int_{-\infty}^{\infty} \exp\{-x^2\}\, dx$ is of some interest. We have

$$\left(\int_{-\infty}^{\infty} \exp\{-x^2\}\, dx\right)^2 = \int_{-\infty}^{\infty} \exp\{-x^2\}\, dx \int_{-\infty}^{\infty} \exp\{-y^2\}\, dy$$

$$= \int_{-\infty}^{\infty} \int_{-\infty}^{\infty} \exp\{-x^2 - y^2\}\, dx\, dy$$

$$= \int_{0}^{2\pi} \int_{0}^{\infty} \exp\{-r^2\}\, r\, dr\, d\phi = \pi.$$

The change of variables is effected by setting $x = r \cos\phi$ and $y = r \sin\phi$, the Jacobian of the transformation being r.

An integral like $\int_{-\infty}^{\infty} x^{2n} \exp\{-ax^2\}\, dx$, with n an integer, can be readily found by differentiating $\int_{-\infty}^{\infty} \exp\{-ax^2\}\, dx$ repeatedly with respect to a:

$$\int_{-\infty}^{\infty} x^{2n} \exp\{-ax^2\}\, dx = \frac{1 \cdot 3 \cdot 5 \cdots (2n-1)}{2^{n+1}a^n} \left(\frac{\pi}{a}\right)^{1/2}. \qquad (6.2)$$

REFERENCES

1. W. F. Giauque, *J. Am. Chem. Soc.*, **52**, 4808 (1930).
2. Landolt-Börnstein, *Zahlenwerte und Funktionen*, Aufl. 6, Band II, Teil 4, Berlin, Springer, 1961, pp. 736ff.

3. Jahnke-Emde-Lösch, *Tables of Higher Functions*, 6th ed., Stuttgart, Tuebner (or New York, McGraw-Hill), 1960, pp. 290–92.
4. G. E. Gibson and W. Heitler, *Z. Physik*, **49**, 465 (1928).
5. W. F. Giauque and H. L. Johnston, *J. Am. Chem. Soc.*, **51**, 1436, 3528 (1929).
6. A. Farkas, *Orthohydrogen, Parahydrogen and Heavy Hydrogen*, Cambridge, Eng., Cambridge Univ. Press, 1935.
7. J. G. Coffin, *Vector Analysis*, 2d ed., New York, Wiley, 1911, Chap. 7.
8. E. T. Whittaker, *Analytical Dynamics*, 3d ed., Cambridge, Eng., Cambridge Univ. Press, 1927, Chap. 6.
9. H. Goldstein, *Classical Mechanics*, Reading, Mass., Addison-Wesley, 1953, Chaps. 4 and 5.
10. G. S. Rushbrooke, *Introduction to Statistical Mechanics*, Oxford, Eng., Clarendon Press, 1949, pp. 130–33.
11. O. K. Rice, *Electronic Structure and Chemical Binding*, New York, McGraw-Hill, 1940, pp. 45–48. [Obtainable from University Microfilms, Ann Arbor, Mich.]

PROBLEMS

2.1. Verify the low- and high-temperature forms given in Table 2-1.

2.2. Find $(p.f.)_0$, E_0, and C_0 (internal specific heat) for a molecule in which there are only two energy levels, one at $\epsilon = 0$ and one at $\epsilon = \epsilon_1$. Find the maximum value of C_0 and sketch the curve roughly. Contrast the behavior of C_0 in this case with that for a harmonic oscillator, which has an infinite number of uniformly spaced energy levels.

2.3. Find $(p.f.)_0$, E_0, and C_0 for a molecule which has one energy level at $\epsilon = 0$ and *three* at $\epsilon = \epsilon_1$. Again find the maximum value of C_0 and make a rough sketch. Contrast the behavior of C_0 with that found in Problem 2.2.

2.4. Using the formula for the vibrational energy of a harmonic oscillator, vibrating about an equilibrium position at $r = 0$,

$$\epsilon_{\text{vib}} = \frac{p_r^2}{2\mu} + \frac{br^2}{2},$$

set up the phase integral for the oscillator and find the classical limit for $(p.f.)_{\text{vib}}$. Recalling that the frequency $\nu = (2\pi)^{-1}(b/\mu)^{1/2}$, show that this expression agrees with the high-temperature limit for Eq. (3.9).

2.5. What is the probability, in the limiting classical case, that the oscillator of Prob. 2.4 should have energy between ϵ_{vib} and $\epsilon_{\text{vib}} + d\epsilon_{\text{vib}}$?

2.6. What is the probability, in the limiting classical case, that the oscillator of Prob. 2.4 should have r greater than some arbitrary value r_0?

2.7. What is the maximum displacement from its equilibrium value of the coordinate r of the oscillator of Prob. 2.4, when its energy is ϵ_{vib}? What is the *average* maximum displacement from the equilibrium value of r in an assembly of oscillators at temperature T, in the limiting classical case?

2.8. Using the partition function for a harmonic oscillator of frequency v, set up an expression for $\overline{\epsilon_{\text{vib}}^2}$. Show that

$$\overline{\epsilon_{\text{vib}}^2} = \frac{kT^2 \dfrac{d}{dT}\left[kT^2 \dfrac{d(\text{p.f.})_{\text{vib}}}{dT}\right]}{(\text{p.f.})_{\text{vib}}}$$

and that the specific heat per oscillator

$$c_{\text{vib}} = (kT^2)^{-1}(\overline{\epsilon_{\text{vib}}^2} - \overline{\epsilon_{\text{vib}}}^2)$$

2.9. A diatomic molecule has an electric moment μ. If it is placed in an electric field F, the potential energy of the molecule will depend on its orientation, namely

$$\epsilon_p = -\mu F \cos \theta$$

where θ is the angle between μ and F. Set up the rotational partition function (phase integral) for the gas in the electric field, and obtain an integral expression for the average value $\overline{\mu}_z$ of the component of μ in the direction of the field. Calculate $\overline{\mu}_z$ for the case F very small. (In order to do this, it will be necessary to expand exponentials to the third power of the variable.) Calculate the change of entropy when the field is turned on at constant temperature.

2.10. A gas consists of atoms which have spin $\frac{1}{2}$. If we enumerate the energy levels, neglecting spin, the internal partition function would be given by

$$(\text{p.f.})_0 = \sum_i \exp\left\{\frac{-\epsilon_i}{kT}\right\}.$$

The spin doubles all the levels; if we take this into account, we have

$$(\text{p.f.})_0 = 2\sum_i \exp\left\{\frac{-\epsilon_i}{kT}\right\}.$$

However, if the gas is placed in a magnetic field H the atoms will have components of magnetic moment, μ_z or $-\mu_z$, in the direction of the field, the energy level being lowered (in the first case) or raised by $\mu_z H$.

a. Write out an expression for the internal partition function $(\text{p.f.})_{0,H}$ in the magnetic field, and express it in terms of $(\text{p.f.})_0$.

b. Find an expression for the average value μ_z of the magnetic moment in the direction of the field, and reduce it to simplest terms for the case of H very small. Express this in terms of the intrinsic magnetic moment μ, remembering that, if $\mu_z = \pm\frac{1}{2}\gamma h/2\pi$ (where γ is the ratio of magnetic moment to angular momentum), $\overline{\mu} = \sqrt{\frac{1}{2}(\frac{1}{2}+1)}\,\gamma h/2\pi$.

c. Find expressions for the energy and the entropy of the system in the field. How much does the entropy differ from what it would be if there were no field?

2.11. Evaluate the classical limit of (p.f.)$_{\mathrm{r}}$ by means of Eq. (5.12), and by use of the phase integral.

2.12. In changing Eq. (5.12) to an integral it is assumed that, although C is small, CkT is still large compared with $h^2/8\pi^2$. What is the limiting value at small C of (p.f.)$_{\mathrm{rot}}$ according to Eq. (5.14)? Why is this incorrect? Find the correct limiting value of (p.f.)$_{\mathrm{r}}$ in the case that $CkT \ll h^2/8\pi^2$. What, then, will be the correct limiting value of (p.f.)$_{\mathrm{rot}}$, assuming that AkT and BkT are still large compared to $h^2/8\pi^2$? What application does this have to diatomic molecules?

2.13. If we set up Euler angles with respect to *any* set of three mutually perpendicular axes fixed in the rotating body, these will also give a satisfactory phase space. Why? Suggest why this knowledge might be useful in considering orientation of a polyatomic molecule in an electric field, when the molecule has a dipole moment not directed along one of the principal axes. Will the results of Prob. 2.9 hold?

2.14. What is the symmetry number for methane?

Chapter 3

The Thermodynamic Approach
to Statistical Mechanics. II

3-1. *Translational Partition Functions*

In the preceding chapter we showed how to express the portions of the thermodynamic functions arising from the internal motions of molecules in terms of the corresponding partition functions. Our next task is to do the same thing for the translational motion of the molecule as a whole.

As far as the translational motion is concerned, a molecule may be considered to act like a particle in a box whose energy levels are given (if it is a rectangular box, which is not an important restriction) by Eqs. (5.17) of Chap. 1. It now suggests itself that we treat the equilibrium between molecules in the various translational levels just as we treated the equilibrium between molecules in the various internal levels, and set up a partition function for the translational motion. With certain precautions, this will, indeed, give the correct result. However, such a procedure no longer bears such a close relation to the methods of thermodynamics. The equilibrium between molecules in internal levels is strictly analogous to the equilibrium between tautomers, but in thermodynamics we never deal with anything analogous to translational energy levels. Especially is this true when we consider that there are normally many more translational levels than molecules, so that only occasionally is a level occupied, and then almost invariably by only one molecule. We would have difficulty in finding a rationale for calculating the entropy of such a system. We will, therefore, proceed in a somewhat different way, which will also have the advantage of introducing certain concepts of the utmost importance to us, and which

can also be used where (unlike an ideal gas) there is appreciable interaction between the molecules.

Starting with this more general case, suppose that we have an
assembly of molecules of any kind, solid, liquid, or gaseous. We consider that we have a multitude of exact replicas of this assembly, all
with the same fixed volume and same number of molecules, forming
what is called an *ensemble* of assemblies. We suppose these assemblies
to be in thermal contact, so that they are all in equilibrium; under
these circumstances we speak of a canonical ensemble. The total energy
of an assembly is just like the internal energy of an enormous molecule.
In fact we can, if we wish, suppose that each assembly is a supermolecule, and that together they form a supergas. The translational energy
of the whole supermolecule involves only three degrees of freedom, as
compared with the enormous number of "internal" degrees of freedom,
and therefore can be neglected.

The entire energy of such an assembly, or supermolecule, is quantized, although the quantum levels are very close together. Let us designate the energy of such a quantum level as E_L, the running subscript L
indicating the Lth quantum level. Equilibrium will be established between the quantum levels of the supermolecules in the same way that
equilibrium was established between the internal levels of ordinary
molecules. So the probability that the assembly will be in one particular
quantum level will be

$$W_L = \frac{\exp\{-E_L/kT\}}{\sum\limits_{L}\exp\{-E_L/kT\}}. \tag{1.1}$$

The Boltzman constant k (rather than the gas constant R) appears in
this expression because E_L is the energy of a single supermolecule. The
partition function, which we refer to as the assembly partition function,
or the canonical partition function, we designate as (P.F.):

$$(\text{P.F.}) = \sum\limits_{L} \exp\left\{\frac{-E_L}{kT}\right\}. \tag{1.2}$$

The energy E_L includes all the energy of the assembly. If the assembly
is a perfect gas, with little interaction between the individual molecules,
it can be broken up into a sum of energies of the latter:

$$E_L = \sum\limits_{\alpha} \epsilon_{\alpha}. \tag{1.3}$$

Here ϵ_{α} is the energy of an individual molecule, and the sum is to be
taken over all molecules (α designates the molecule). If the assembly is

in a particular quantum state L, this means that the particular molecule will be in a special individual quantum state $l_{\alpha,L}$. We replace the notation ϵ_α by $\epsilon_{l_{\alpha,L}}$ in order to specify the state more completely, so that Eq. (1.3) becomes

$$E_L = \sum_\alpha \epsilon_{l_{\alpha,L}}. \tag{1.4}$$

Using this in Eq. (1.2), we have

$$(\text{P.F.}) = \sum_L \exp\left\{-\sum_\alpha \frac{\epsilon_{l_{\alpha,L}}}{kT}\right\}$$

$$= \sum_L \prod_\alpha \exp\left\{\frac{-\epsilon_{l_{\alpha,L}}}{kT}\right\}, \tag{1.5}$$

the last expression arising from the property of the exponential, that a sum in the exponent is equivalent to a product of exponentials. Each term in the summation over L is the product of N factors, where N is the total number of molecules. In the sum taken over all states L, the quantum number l (designated as $l_{\alpha,L}$) for a particular molecule α will take on every possible value.† This will be true of each of the N factors, corresponding to each of the N molecules. Further, in one term or another of the sum, every possible combination of values of l will occur. If we write out $\prod_\alpha \sum_{l_\alpha} \exp\{-\epsilon_{l_\alpha}/kT\}$, interchanging the summation and product signs, this also yields every possible combination of N factors. Hence

$$(\text{P.F.}) = \prod_\alpha \sum_{l_\alpha} \exp\left\{\frac{-\epsilon_{l_\alpha}}{kT}\right\}$$

$$= \left(\sum_l \exp\left\{\frac{-\epsilon_l}{kT}\right\}\right)^N = (\text{p.f.})^N. \tag{1.6}$$

It is possible to substitute the Nth power for the product over all molecules because the l's are the same for all α's; i.e., the allowed energies are the same for all the molecules if they are all of the same species.

The p.f. of Eq. (1.6) is slightly different from any we have written down so far, because it contains all energy levels, including those which differ only in the translational part, in the sum.

On the basis of the discussion of Sec. 1-7, Eq. (1.6) still needs to be corrected by dividing it by $N!$, since we are dealing with N identical

---

† This is true if the number of molecules occupying the energy levels in any given energy range is small compared with the number of energy levels. If this condition is not met, other considerations are necessary. This case is treated in Chap. 14.

molecules which can roam freely over a box and hence be exchanged, the exchanged positions being included. Our final form for (P.F.) is, thus,

$$\text{(P.F.)} = (N!)^{-1}\left(\sum_i \exp\left\{\frac{-\epsilon_i}{kT}\right\}\right)^N = (N!)^{-1}(\text{p.f.})^N. \tag{1.7}$$

The partition function (p.f.) may be broken up into products in the usual manner. Since the energies of the translational levels are strictly independent of the internal levels, we may write rigorously in this case

$$\text{(p.f.)} = \text{(p.f.)}_{\text{trans}}\text{(p.f.)}_0, \tag{1.8}$$

(p.f.)$_0$ being the internal partition function discussed in the last chapter.

The thermodynamic functions of an assembly are just the same things as the thermodynamic functions, per molecule, of the supergas. Therefore we may take over Eqs. (2.3), (2.8) and (2.9) of Chap. 2 if we substitute the total thermodynamic functions E, S, and A for the internal ones E_0, S_0, and A_0, the appropriate partition function (P.F.) for (p.f.)$_0$, and (since we deal with one *molecule* of supergas) k for R. Thus we have (for arbitrary N, not necessarily one mole)

$$E = kT^2 \frac{\partial \ln \text{(P.F.)}}{\partial T} \tag{1.9}$$

(a partial derivative since only T, not the volume, for example, is changed),

$$S = \frac{E}{T} + k \ln \text{(P.F.)}, \tag{1.10}$$

and

$$A = -kT \ln \text{(P.F.)} \tag{1.11}$$

Equations (1.9), (1.10), and (1.11) are perfectly general and hold for any assembly. If the assembly is an ideal gas, then in view of Eqs. (1.7) and (1.8), we have for the translational contributions to these functions

$$E_{\text{trans}} = NkT^2 \frac{\partial \ln \text{(p.f.)}_{\text{trans}}}{\partial T}, \tag{1.12}$$

$$S_{\text{trans}} = \frac{E_{\text{trans}}}{T} + kN \ln \text{(p.f.)}_{\text{trans}} - k \ln N!, \tag{1.13}$$

and

$$A_{\text{trans}} = -NkT \ln \text{(p.f.)}_{\text{trans}} + kT \ln N!. \tag{1.14}$$

In the partial differentiation with respect to T, the volume V is held constant [(p.f.)$_{\text{trans}}$ is also a function of V].

Since the pressure $P = -(\partial A/\partial V)_T$, an equation for the Gibbs free energy, $G = A + PV$, can be derived from Eq. (1.11), or, for an ideal gas, from Eq. (1.14). In the latter case, of course, $PV = NkT$; when this is added to Eq. (1.14), and $\ln N!$ is set equal to $N \ln N - N$ by the Stirling approximation† we obtain

$$G_{\text{trans}} = -NkT \ln \left(\frac{(\text{p.f.})_{\text{trans}}}{N} \right). \tag{1.15}$$

We now need to evaluate (p.f.)$_{\text{trans}}$ to have a complete account of the thermodynamic functions of a perfect gas, noting of course that

$$
\begin{aligned}
E &= E_{\text{trans}} + E_0, & S &= S_{\text{trans}} + S_0, \\
A &= A_{\text{trans}} + A_0, & G &= G_{\text{trans}} + A_0.
\end{aligned}
\tag{1.16}
$$

3-2. *Evaluation of the Translational Functions for an Ideal Gas*

Since the translational energy levels are very close together, we may for all ordinary conditions use the classical form of the partition function. We may replace a sum by an integral, or set up a phase integral. We shall do the latter. The translational energy of a molecule is $(1/2m)(p_x^2 + p_y^2 + p_z^2)$ where p_x, p_y, and p_z are the three components of momentum and m is the total mass. The element of phase space is $dp_x dp_y dp_z dx dy dz$, which will contain $h^{-3}(dp_x dp_y dp_z dx dy dz)$ energy levels; for the partition function we have, then,

---

† In statistical mechanics we are interested in the Stirling approximation for $N!$ as it is applied to the logarithm. Clearly we may write

$$\ln N! = \sum_{n=1}^{N} \ln n,$$

and if N is very large, we may suppose it to be virtually continuous and define a "derivative" with respect to N by

$$d \ln N!/dN = \tfrac{1}{2}[\ln (N + 1)! - \ln (N - 1)!] = \tfrac{1}{2}[\ln (N + 1) + \ln N].$$

Integrating both sides of the equation as if N were continuous we obtain

$$\ln N! = \tfrac{1}{2}[N \ln N - N + (N + 1) \ln (N + 1) - (N + 1)],$$

the constant of integration being found to be approximately zero. The logarithm is correct to within about 0.25% when $N = 100$; for larger N it is quite legitimate to approximate

$$\ln N! = N \ln N - N.$$

For a more precise form see [1].

$$(\text{p.f.})_{\text{trans}} = h^{-3} \int\!\!\int\!\!\int\!\!\int\!\!\int\!\!\int \exp\left\{\frac{-(p_x^2 + p_y^2 + p_z^2)}{2mkT}\right\} dp_x dp_y dp_z dx dy dz.$$

(2.1)

The integration is from $-\infty$ to ∞ for p_x, p_y, and p_z and over the volume V of the container for x, y, and z. Integrating with respect to the latter first, we get a factor V. The integrations with respect to p_x, p_y, and p_z may be performed independently, and each gives the same result (Sec. 2-6). Thus

$$(\text{p.f.})_{\text{trans}} = \left(\frac{V}{h^3}\right)\left(\int_{-\infty}^{\infty} \exp\left\{\frac{-p_x^2}{2mkT}\right\} dp_x\right)^3$$

$$= V\left(\frac{2\pi mkT}{h^2}\right)^{3/2}.$$

(2.2)

From this we readily see that $E_{\text{trans}} = \frac{3}{2}NkT = \frac{3}{2}RT$ if N is Avogadro's number, and substitution into Eq. (1.13) gives

$$S_{\text{trans}} = \frac{3}{2}Nk + Nk\ln\left[V\left(\frac{2\pi mkT}{h^2}\right)^{3/2}\right] - k\ln N!.$$

(2.3)

The Stirling approximation, $\ln N! = N\ln N - N$, gives

$$S_{\text{trans}} = \frac{5}{2}Nk + Nk\ln\left[\frac{V}{N}\left(\frac{2\pi mkT}{h^2}\right)^{3/2}\right].$$

(2.4)

This is the famous Sackur-Tetrode equation. If N is Avogadro's number, S_{trans} is the molal translational entropy:

$$S_{\text{trans,molal}} = \frac{5}{2}R + R\ln\left[\frac{V}{N}\left(\frac{2\pi mkT}{h^2}\right)^{3/2}\right].$$

(2.5)

We purposely refrained from fixing the value of N up to this point, so that we could point out an important property of Eq. (2.4). If V/N is constant, which means constant pressure, S_{trans} is proportional to N. Thus doubling the amount of gas, at a fixed pressure, doubles the entropy, as is to be expected. This would not occur without the term $-k\ln N!$, which arises from the indistinguishability of the molecules.

Equation (2.5) can of course be applied directly to monatomic molecules, and the entropy thus calculated may be compared with that obtained experimentally, through measurement of specific heats and heats of transition, with the aid of the third law of thermodynamics. The theoretical and experimental results invariably agree within the limits of the experimental error [2].

For polyatomic molecules, one must add to S_{trans} the entropy arising from the vibrational and rotational motions. Here again the agreement between theoretical and experimental results, insofar as a comparison is possible, is good, although, as we shall see in a later chapter, some care must be exercised in the interpretation of the third law of thermodynamics.

3-3. *Application to Mixtures*

It is interesting to see what happens if we have a system consisting of N_A molecules of type A and N_B molecules of type B in a volume V. Instead of Eq. (1.7) we have

$$(\text{P.F.}) = \frac{(\text{p.f.})_A^{N_A}(\text{p.f.})_B^{N_B}}{N_A!N_B!}. \tag{3.1}$$

From Eq. (1.9) we get

$$E = N_A k T^2 \frac{\partial \ln (\text{p.f.})_A}{\partial T} + N_B k T^2 \frac{\partial \ln (\text{p.f.})_B}{\partial T}$$

$$= E_A + E_B = N_A \bar{\epsilon}_A + N_B \bar{\epsilon}_B, \tag{3.2}$$

where $\bar{\epsilon}_A$ and $\bar{\epsilon}_B$ are the average molecular energies of species A and B. In place of Eq. (1.13), we obtain

$$S = \frac{E_A}{T} + \frac{E_B}{T} + N_A k \ln (\text{p.f.})_A + N_B k \ln (\text{p.f.})_B$$

$$- k \ln N_A! - k \ln N_B!, \tag{3.3}$$

which is just the sum of the entropies which the separate species A and B would have if they were separately present in a pair of different vessels, each one of which had the same volume. This is an expression of the Gibbs law of mixing. Thus the entropies of two *separate* gases are additive if they are combined in the same *volume;* the entropies of two *portions* of the *same* gas are additive if they are combined at the same *pressure.* If the molecules A and B were indistinguishable, then of course $(\text{p.f.})_A$ and $(\text{p.f.})_B$ would be indistinguishable, whereas $E_A + E_B$ would be equal to the total energy, and $N_A + N_B$ would be equal to the total number of molecules. So the first four terms of the right-hand side of Eq. (3.3) could be used unaltered. However, $-k \ln N_A! - k \ln N_B! = -k \ln (N_A!N_B!)$ would be replaced by $-k \ln (N_A + N_B)!$. The difference $-k \ln (N_A!N_B!) + k \ln (N_A + N_B)!$, a positive quantity, is called the entropy of mixing. If some of the $N = N_A + N_B$ molecules are distinguishable, we have a great many distinguishable configurations of the system, which leads to a greater entropy. Of course this could have been predicted, since the fact of indistinguishability led to a negative term in the entropy.

But suppose the two species A and B were isomers in equilibrium. We expect them to obey Eq. (3.3), since our original calculations assumed that such entropies were additive for states in equilibrium, yet the entropy should also be given by

$$S = \frac{E_A + E_B}{T} + (N_A + N_B)k \ln \left[(\text{p.f.})_A + (\text{p.f.})_B\right] - k \ln (N_A + N_B)!,$$

$$(3.4)$$

since the partition function for *all* energy levels must be $(\text{p.f.})_A + (\text{p.f.})_B$. If the molecules A and B are but tautomeric forms, the energy levels of A and B really are only one set, so

$$(\text{p.f.}) = \sum_i \exp\left\{\frac{-\epsilon_{A,i}}{kT}\right\} + \sum_j \exp\left\{\frac{-\epsilon_{B,j}}{kT}\right\} = (\text{p.f.})_A + (\text{p.f.})_B.$$

So the condition of equilibrium must be equivalence of Eqs. (3.3) and (3.4). Using the Stirling approximation and canceling equal terms, this means

$$N_A \ln (\text{p.f.})_A + N_B \ln (\text{p.f.})_B - N_A \ln N_A - N_B \ln N_B$$
$$= (N_A + N_B) \ln \left[(\text{p.f.})_A + (\text{p.f.})_B\right] - (N_A + N_B) \ln (N_A + N_B)$$

$$(3.5)$$

or

$$\ln \frac{N_A^{N_A} N_B^{N_B}}{(N_A + N_B)^{N_A + N_B}} = \ln \frac{(\text{p.f.})_A^{N_A}(\text{p.f.})_B^{N_B}}{\left[(\text{p.f.})_A + (\text{p.f.})_B\right]^{N_A + N_B}}$$

$$(3.6)$$

It is clear that one solution of this equation is

$$\frac{N_A}{N_B} = \frac{(\text{p.f.})_A}{(\text{p.f.})_B}.$$

$$(3.7)$$

This is equivalent to Eq. (1.7) of Chap. 2, except that those energies did not contain the translational part. The right-hand side of Eq. (3.7) gives a value for the equilibrium constant of the tautomers.

Equation (3.7) is the *only* solution of Eq. (3.6). Let $N_A + N_B = N$, which is constant. Then Eq. (3.6) becomes

$$N_A \ln N_A + (N - N_A) \ln (N - N_A) - N \ln N$$
$$= N_A \ln (\text{p.f.})_A + (N - N_A) \ln (\text{p.f.})_B - N \ln [(\text{p.f.})_A + (\text{p.f.})_B].$$

$$(3.8)$$

The (p.f.)'s are also constant. Differentiating the left-hand side (l.h.s.) with respect to N_A,

$$\frac{d(\text{l.h.s.})}{dN_A} = \ln \left[\frac{N_A}{(N - N_A)} \right] \qquad (3.9)$$

and the right-hand side (r.h.s.),

$$\frac{d(\text{r.h.s.})}{dN_A} = \ln \left[\frac{(\text{p.f.})_A}{(\text{p.f.})_B} \right]. \qquad (3.10)$$

Again, Eqs. (3.9) and (3.10) are equal when Eq. (3.7) is fulfilled. Thus the curves for the two sides of Eq. (3.8), taken as functions of N_A, are tangent at this point. But $d^2(\text{r.h.s.})/dN_A^2$ is always zero whereas $d^2(\text{l.h.s.})/dN_A^2$ is always positive. Therefore, this will have to be their only point of contact.

The meaning of the procedure used in this section to establish the condition for equilibrium will become clear after the discussions in Chaps. 4 and 5, and succeeding chapters, if we consider that, when N_A and N_B are held arbitrarily at some fixed values different from their equilibrium values, many possible states of the assembly are excluded; indeed, *most* of them are excluded, for many more correspond to a state of equilibrium than to any other state. Further, as far as the thermodynamic functions are concerned, the states of the assembly other than equilibrium states may be neglected if the system is allowed to proceed to equilibrium. On the other hand, use of a *complete* partition function for the *entire* system, such as $(\text{p.f.})_A + (\text{p.f.})_B$, implies that we are considering a condition of equilibrium throughout all the states. The statements of the last two sentences imply that N_A and N_B must conform to Eq. (3.5).

3-4. *Alternate Method for the Classical Molecule*

We now consider an alternate method of obtaining the (p.f.) for a molecule which is classical in every degree of freedom. If a molecule obeys the classical laws of motion, its energy may be written as

$$\epsilon = \frac{1}{2m_1}(p_{x_1}^2 + p_{y_1}^2 + p_{z_1}^2) + \frac{1}{2m_2}(p_{x_2}^2 + p_{y_2}^2 + p_{z_2}^2) + \cdots + \epsilon_p, \quad (4.1)$$

where the subscripts $1, 2, \cdots$ refer to the individual atoms in the molecule and where the potential energy ϵ_p is a function of the coordinates $x_1, y_1, z_1, x_2, y_2, z_2, \cdots$. We may then write the partition function in the form of a general phase integral:

$$(\text{p.f.}) = h^{-3n} \iint \cdots \int \exp\left\{\frac{-\epsilon}{kT}\right\} dx_1 dy_1 \cdots dp_{z_n}, \quad (4.2)$$

where n is the number of atoms in the molecule. The integration with respect to every p goes from $-\infty$ to ∞, and since any p occurs in only one factor in the integral, the integration may be readily carried out. We obtain

$$(\text{p.f.}) = \left(\frac{2\pi m_1 kT}{h^2}\right)^{3/2} \left(\frac{2\pi m_2 kT}{h^2}\right)^{3/2} \cdots \iint \cdots \int \exp\left\{\frac{-\epsilon_p}{kT}\right\} dx_1 dy_1 \cdots dz_n. \quad (4.3)$$

Let us now consider the case of a diatomic molecule, $n = 2$. Setting $m = m_1 + m_2$, and letting $\mu = m_1 m_2 / m$ be the reduced mass,

$$(\text{p.f.}) = h^{-6}(2\pi m_1 kT)^{3/2} (2\pi m_2 kT)^{3/2} \iiint\!\!\iiint \exp\left\{\frac{-\epsilon_p}{kT}\right\} dx_1 dy_1 dz_1 dx_2 dy_2 dz_2$$

$$= \left(\frac{2\pi mkT}{h^2}\right)^{3/2} \left(\frac{2\pi \mu kT}{h^2}\right)^{3/2} \iiint\!\!\iiint \exp\left\{\frac{-\epsilon_p}{kT}\right\} dx_1 dy_1 dz_1 dx_2 dy_2 dz_2, \quad (4.4)$$

We introduce the coordinates of the center of gravity, defined by

$$X = \frac{m_1 x_1 + m_2 x_2}{m}, \qquad Y = \frac{m_1 y_1 + m_2 y_2}{m},$$

$$Z = \frac{m_1 z_1 + m_2 z_2}{m}, \qquad (4.5)$$

and the relative coordinates, which give the positions of the atoms with respect to each other, are

$$x = x_2 - x_1, \qquad y = y_2 - y_1, \qquad z = z_2 - z_1. \quad (4.6)$$

According to Eq. (8.1), Chap. 1, we can replace the volume element in Eq. (4.4) by

$$\left|\frac{\partial(x_1, y_1, z_1, x_2, y_2, z_2)}{\partial(X, Y, Z, x, y, z)}\right| dXdYdZdxdydz, \tag{4.7}$$

and if we set $\xi_1 = x_1$, $\xi_2 = x_2$, $\cdots$, $\xi_n = x_n$ in Eq. (8.2) of Chap. 1 we readily see that

$$\left|\frac{\partial(x_1, y_1, z_1, x_2, y_2, z_2)}{\partial(X, Y, Z, x, y, z)}\right| = \left|\frac{\partial(X, Y, Z, x, y, z)}{\partial(x_1, y_1, z_1, x_2, y_2, z_2)}\right|^{-1}. \tag{4.8}$$

From Eqs. (4.5) and (4.6) we have

$$\left|\frac{\partial(X, Y, Z, x, y, z)}{\partial(x_1, y_1, z_1, x_2, y_2, z_2)}\right| = \begin{vmatrix} \dfrac{m_1}{m} & 0 & 0 & \dfrac{m_2}{m} & 0 & 0 \\ 0 & \dfrac{m_1}{m} & 0 & 0 & \dfrac{m_2}{m} & 0 \\ 0 & 0 & \dfrac{m_1}{m} & 0 & 0 & \dfrac{m_2}{m} \\ -1 & 0 & 0 & 1 & 0 & 0 \\ 0 & -1 & 0 & 0 & 1 & 0 \\ 0 & 0 & -1 & 0 & 0 & 1 \end{vmatrix} = 1, \tag{4.9}$$

as may be seen as a result of standard operations upon the determinant. Thus we can write

$$(\text{p.f.}) = \left(\frac{2\pi mkT}{h^2}\right)^{3/2} \left(\frac{2\pi \mu kT}{h^2}\right)^{3/2} \int\!\!\int\!\!\int\!\!\int\!\!\int\!\!\int \exp\left\{\frac{-\epsilon_p}{kT}\right\} dXdYdZdxdydz. \tag{4.10}$$

The integration with respect to X, Y, and Z will yield V, the volume of the container. We also can express $dxdydz$ in terms of the corresponding polar coordinates r, θ, ϕ, where r is the distance between the two atoms, and θ and ϕ are the polar angles for the line joining them. We have the well-known relation (which could also be obtained through the Jacobian relationship (see Prob. 1.2):

$$dxdydz = r^2 \sin\theta \, drd\theta d\phi.$$

Therefore

$$(\text{p.f.}) = \left(\frac{2\pi mkT}{h^2}\right)^{3/2} V \left(\frac{2\pi \mu kT}{h^2}\right)^{3/2} \int_0^{2\pi} \int_0^{\pi} \int_0^{\infty} \exp\left\{\frac{-\epsilon_p}{kT}\right\} r^2 \sin\theta \, drd\theta d\phi. \tag{4.11}$$

Now let us assume that $\epsilon_p = (r - r_e)^2/2a^2$ where a is a constant. This is the potential-energy function for a harmonic oscillator, as in Eq. (5.12) of Chap. 1 (with $\epsilon_{p,e}$ set equal to zero). In this case the integrations with respect to θ and ϕ can be performed immediately. Since (if a is of the order of magnitude characteristic of a molecule) the exponential will be appreciably different from zero over only a relatively small range of r near r_e, we may take r^2 outside the integral and set it equal to r_e^2. Also we can change the variable from r to $r - r_e$, and integrate the latter from $-\infty$ to ∞. Thus in good approximation,

$$(\text{p.f.}) = \left(\frac{2\pi mkT}{h^2}\right)^{3/2} V \left(\frac{2\pi\mu kT}{h^2}\right)^{3/2} (4\pi r_e^2) \int_{-\infty}^{\infty} \exp\left\{\frac{-(r - r_e)^2}{2a^2 kT}\right\} d(r - r_e)$$

$$= \left(\frac{2\pi mkT}{h^2}\right)^{3/2} V \left(\frac{2\pi\mu kT}{h^2}\right)^{3/2} 4\pi r_e^2 (2\pi a^2 kT)^{1/2}. \qquad (4.12)$$

The frequency ν_0 of an harmonic oscillator is, as noted in Eq. (5.14) of Chap. 1, equal to $(2\pi a\mu^{1/2})^{-1}$. Thus $a^2 = (4\pi^2 \nu_0^2 \mu)^{-1}$, and we can write Eq. (4.12) in the form

$$(\text{p.f.}) = \left(\frac{2\pi mkT}{h^2}\right)^{3/2} V \left(\frac{8\pi^2\mu r_e^2 kT}{h^2}\right) \frac{kT}{h\nu_0}$$

$$= (\text{p.f.})_{\text{trans}}(\text{p.f.})_{\text{rot}}(\text{p.f.})_{\text{vib}}, \qquad (4.13)$$

as was, of course, to be expected.

3-5. *Free Lengths and Free Volumes*

The partition function of a diatomic molecule is equal to an effective volume in the phase space divided by h^6, hence to an effective number of energy levels. Each factor like $(2\pi m_1 kT)^{1/2}$ has the dimensions of a momentum, and the last part of Eq. (4.12) consists of the product of two volumes, one, V, being the volume of the container. The factor $4\pi r_e^2$ is the area of a spherical shell, while $(2\pi a^2 kT)^{1/2}$ is a length, which represents the average free length of relative radial motion for the two atoms in the molecule. Thus $4\pi r_e^2 (2\pi a^2 kT)^{1/2}$ represents a free volume, which has the form of a spherical shell.

The last factor in Eq. (4.12) can be written more generally as $\int_{-\infty}^{\infty} \exp\{-\epsilon_p/kT\} d(r - r_e)$ where ϵ_p is a potential-energy function which has the same general form as a molecular potential-energy curve, namely, it has a minimum, and ϵ_p is taken as zero at the minimum. This integral of course has the dimensions of length, and we can show quite generally that, in a certain well-defined sense, it is the average free length for the motion in the r direction. It is of course to be recalled that the integration limits are an approximation. An ordinary molecular potential energy reaches an asymptote for large values of r, and so then would $\exp\{-\epsilon_p/kT\}$, which would cause the integral to become infinite. The asymptotic value of $\exp\{-\epsilon_p/kT\}$ is, however, very small, and this part of the integral, which actually refers to a dissociated molecule, is of no interest to us. We may, therefore, suppose the true potential-energy curve to be replaced, where $\exp\{-\epsilon_p/kT\}$ is very small, by one which cuts off the asymptotic contribution. Although ϵ_p is a single-valued function of $r - r_e$, we note that $r - r_e$ is a two-valued function of ϵ_p, so we write

$$\int_{-\infty}^{\infty} \exp\left\{\frac{-\epsilon_p}{kT}\right\} d(r - r_e)$$

$$= \int_{-\infty}^{0} \exp\left\{\frac{-\epsilon_p}{kT}\right\} d(r - r_e) + \int_{0}^{\infty} \exp\left\{\frac{-\epsilon_p}{kT}\right\} d(r - r_e),$$

where in each separate portion $r - r_e$ is a single-valued function of ϵ_p. We may now integrate by parts, writing, for example,

$$\int_{0}^{\infty} \exp\left\{\frac{-\epsilon_p}{kT}\right\} d(r - r_e)$$

$$= (r - r_e) \exp\left\{\frac{-\epsilon_p}{kT}\right\}\Big|_{0}^{\infty} + \frac{1}{kT} \int_{0}^{\infty} r'' \exp\left\{\frac{-\epsilon_p}{kT}\right\} d\epsilon_p,$$

where r'' is the positive value of $r - r_e$ corresponding to a given value of ϵ_p. Under our approximations the integrated part vanishes. Hence

$$\int_{0}^{\infty} \exp\left\{\frac{-\epsilon_p}{kT}\right\} d(r - r_e) = \frac{1}{kT} \int_{0}^{\infty} r'' \exp\left\{\frac{-\epsilon_p}{kT}\right\} d\epsilon_p$$

and, similarly,

$$\int_{-\infty}^{0} \exp\left\{\frac{-\epsilon_p}{kT}\right\} d(r - r_e) = -\frac{1}{kT} \int_{0}^{\infty} r' \exp\left\{\frac{-\epsilon_p}{kT}\right\} d\epsilon_p,$$

where $-r' = r - r_e$ when r is less than r_e (and is, therefore, a negative quantity). Hence

$$\int_{-\infty}^{\infty} \exp\left\{\frac{-\epsilon_p}{kT}\right\} d(r - r_e) = \frac{1}{kT} \int_{0}^{\infty} (r'' - r') \exp\left\{\frac{-\epsilon_p}{kT}\right\} d\epsilon_p$$

$$= \frac{\int_{0}^{\infty} (r'' - r') \exp\{-\epsilon_p/kT\} d\epsilon_p}{\int_{0}^{\infty} \exp\{-\epsilon_p/kT\} d\epsilon_p}.$$

In a classical calculation we always assume that energy levels are so close together that we may integrate over the quantum number instead of summing. Letting v be the vibrational quantum number, we may write $d\epsilon_{\mathrm{p}} = (d\epsilon_v/dv)dv$, where ϵ_v is the energy of the vth quantum level. This is legitimate because the potential energy is equal to the total energy when $r - r_e$ is equal to r'' or $-r'$, and the latter quantities are the same functions of ϵ_v as of ϵ_{p}. Thus ϵ_{p} may be replaced by ϵ_v as the variable of integration. Further, by Eq. (4.5) of Chap. 1, $d\epsilon_v/dv$ is equal to $h\nu$. Thus our integral becomes

$$\int_{-\infty}^{\infty} \exp\left\{\frac{-\epsilon_{\mathrm{p}}}{kT}\right\} d(r - r_e) = \frac{\int_0^{\infty} (r'' - r') \exp\left\{-\epsilon_v/kT\right\} \nu \, dv}{\int_0^{\infty} \exp\left\{-\epsilon_v/kT\right\} \nu \, dv},$$

and we see that it is equal to the average value of the free displacement $r'' - r'$ from one side of the potential-energy curve to the other, weighted according to the Boltzmann factor, as usual, but also according to the frequency, that is, the number of times these extreme positions are reached. Thus $\int_{-\infty}^{\infty} \exp\left\{-\epsilon_{\mathrm{p}}/kT\right\} d(r - r_e)$ is appropriately called an average free length or simply a free length.

Sometimes we encounter three-dimensional oscillators, in which a particle is oscillating in three dimensions about a position of equilibrium. By means of such a picture, we can give an approximate description of a particle in the field of force arising from its neighbors in a crystal or a liquid. If the forces in the x, y, and z directions are independent of each other, so that the potential energy can be separated into three independent parts, then each of these parts can be shown in the manner just indicated to give rise to a free length, since the configuration integral (that part of the phase integral which depends on the coordinates but not the momenta, i.e., $\iiint \exp\left\{-\epsilon_{\mathrm{p}}/kT\right\} dx dy dz$) can be separated into the product of three integrals, and the entire configuration integral will itself be a free volume. If the integral cannot be separated, the situation is not so easily visualized, but it is a natural generalization to consider the phase integral as a free volume.

3-6. *The Probability of Translational States and the Law of Equipartition of Energy*

The probability that the entire assembly should be in some particular energy level is proportional to $\exp\left\{-E_L/kT\right\}$. If E_L is composed of a number of additive parts, as in the case of an ideal gas, we may hold all these parts but one, say the translational energy $\epsilon_{t,1}$ of a particular molecule, No. 1, constant. Then the relative probability of this molecule being in any particular translational state is proportional to $\exp\{-\epsilon_{t,1}/kT\}$. However, the factor $\exp\{-\epsilon_{t,1}/kT\}$ is independent of the rest of the energy; thus, we may simply say that the probability of any particular molecule being in a particular translational state is proportional to $\exp\{-\epsilon_{t,1}/kT\}$ without qualification, and the Boltzmann factor has the same interpretation for translational energy as for internal energy.

Similar reasoning can be applied in the classical limit. The probability of finding an assembly in the state determined by its being in a particular volume element of the phase space of the entire assembly is proportional to the volume element times the Boltzmann factor, and hence is given (where, here, N is the total number of *atoms*, not molecules) by

$$\frac{\exp\{-E/kT\}\,dx_1 dy_1 \cdots dp_{zN}}{\iint \cdots \int \exp\{-E/kT\}\,dx_1 dy_1 \cdots dp_{zN}}.$$

If we wish the probability that any given molecule is in a given state, or if we wish the probability that any given coordinate or momentum lies within a given range, we must integrate the numerator with respect to all coordinates and momenta other than the one or ones singled out. This statement is true even if the assembly is not an ideal gas, or if the coordinates are not rectangular coordinates. However, an especially simple relationship exists with the momenta if the coordinates are ordinary rectangular coordinates, for then we can write E as equal to H of Eq. (9.3) of Chap. 1. The integral over all coordinates will then cancel between numerator and denominator, as will the integral over any one of the momenta. The probability that p_{x_1}, for example, lies between p_{x_1} and $p_{x_1} + dp_{x_1}$ thus becomes

$$\frac{\exp\{-p_{x_1}^2/2m_1 kT\}\,dp_{x_1}}{\int_{-\infty}^{\infty}\exp\{-p_{x_1}^2/2m_1 kT\}\,dp_{x_1}} = \frac{\exp\{-p_{x_1}^2/2m_1 kT\}\,dp_{x_1}}{(2\pi m_1 kT)^{1/2}}.$$

From this it is readily shown that the average of $p_{x_1}^2/2m_1$ (i.e., of the kinetic energy associated with the coordinate x_1) is $\frac{1}{2}kT$. This, of course, is true of any rectangular coordinate, and it shows that in any classical case the kinetic energy is equal to $\frac{1}{2}kT$ times the number of degrees of freedom. This result is known as the law of equipartition of energy, and is exemplified by the cases we have already considered. The last statement is obviously true for translational motion in an ideal gas, and to the extent that rotation and vibration are independent of each other, it is true for each of them separately. It will be noted that the average energy of each classical vibrational degree of freedom is kT, but half of this is potential energy and the average kinetic energy is indeed $\frac{1}{2}kT$.

REFERENCES

1. H. Margenau and G. M. Murphy, *The Mathematics of Physics and Chemistry*, 2d ed., Princeton, N.J., Van Nostrand, 1956, p. 97.
2. G. N. Lewis and M. Randall, *Thermodynamics* (revised by Pitzer and Brewer), New York, McGraw-Hill, 1961, Chap. 27.

PROBLEMS

3.1. Verify the interchange of summation and product signs between Eq. (1.5) and Eq. (1.6) for a miniature case where there are three (distinguishable) molecules distributed among five quantum levels.

3.2. It is sometimes true in an imperfect gas or liquid, or sometimes even in a molecular solid, that the individual internal quantum levels of the molecules are at least approximately unaffected by the state of the assembly. In this case show that (P.F.) can be written in the form $(P.F.)_t(p.f.)_0^N$, where $(p.f.)_0 = \sum_i \exp\{-\epsilon_i/kT\}$, the sum being taken over the internal levels.

3.3. Using Eqs. (5.17) of Chap. 1, write down the translational partition function in the form of a sum. Evaluate the partition function by converting the sum to an integral.

3.4. The kinetic energy of N atoms of mass m is $E_k = \sum_{i=1}^{3N} p_i^2/2m$ where p_1, p_2, p_3 are the components of the momentum of the first molecule, and so on. The volume of an n-dimensional sphere of radius r is given (if n is even) by the expression

$$V_n(r) = \pi^{n/2}r^n/(n/2)!$$

From this and the energy expression find the number of energy levels between E_k and $E_k + dE_k$. Find (P.F.) for an ideal monatomic gas directly without using (p.f.).

3.5. Show how Eq. (3.1) follows from the considerations of Sec. 3-1.

3.6. From $P = -(\partial A/\partial V)_T$ and Eq. (3.1), using the properties of the partition functions, find P for a mixture and express it in terms of what the pressures of A and B would be without the other being present.

3.7. The following statement has been made: The entropies of two separate gases are additive if they are combined in the same volume; the entropies of two portions of the same gas are additive if they are combined at the same pressure. Deduce and make the corresponding statement for the two free energies, A and G.

3.8. Set up the phase integral for the translational motion of an ideal gas in a box, subject to a gravitational field, which means that the potential energy of each particle will be mgz, where z is the distance above the bottom of the box. Calculate the average height of the molecules above the bottom of the box, assuming that the height of the box is h_0.

3.9. The value of a determinant is not altered if one row or column is added to another row or column. By repeated application of this theorem show that the determinant of Eq. (4.9) is properly evaluated.

3.10. Find the average value of $|v_x|$, the absolute value of the x-component of velocity, for a freely moving particle.

3.11. Find the average value of the absolute value of the velocity for a freely moving particle.

3.12. Find an expression for the number of molecules having energy greater than a fixed value ϵ_0 in a perfect monatomic gas.

Chapter 4

The Third Law of Thermodynamics and the Statistical Definition of Entropy

4-1. *The Third Law of Thermodynamics*

We now know how to calculate the partition function for a perfect gas, and from it, the thermodynamic quantities. The perfect gas is, of course, a special case, for which the calculations are easy. Another special case—that of arbitrarily low temperature—can also be handled easily. Of course, no substance is a gas at sufficiently low temperatures, and one must take into account the interaction between the molecules. However, usually we can suppose that there is one lowest energy level for an assembly. If this is the case, then, if the assembly comes to equilibrium, it will certainly be in this energy level at absolute zero. Let the energy of this energy level be E_1. Then the canonical partition function for the assembly reduces at a low enough temperature to $\exp\{-E_1/kT\}$, since all the higher terms will be negligible compared with the first one. Applying Eq. (1.10) of Chap. 3, which, as noted, is perfectly general, we have for the entropy

$$S = \frac{E_1}{T} + k \ln \exp\left\{\frac{-E_1}{kT}\right\} = 0. \tag{1.1}$$

Thus we have generalized the previous conclusion that $S_0 = 0$ at sufficiently low temperatures [Chap. 2, Eq. (2.11)].

Since Eq. (1.1) here, and Eqs. (2.4) and (2.5) of Chap. 3 are all based on Eq. (1.10) of Chap. 3, they are quite consistent with each other, as is implied by the discussion at the end of Sec. 3-2. Starting with the assumption that $S = 0$ at $T = 0$, one can obtain the entropy of an essentially perfect gas by integrating C/T, where C is the specific heat, from $T = 0$ to the temperature in question and adding in terms of the form $\Delta H/T$ (ΔH being the change in enthalpy) for all phase transitions, such as changes in structure of the solid, melting, and evaporation. Sometimes a further correction is needed for gas imperfections. The experimental entropy can then be compared with that calculated from Eq. (2.5) of Chap. 3, together with the contributions from the internal states. Very good agreement is obtained.

But these ideas penetrate more deeply than would be indicated merely by the above paragraph. For Eq. (1.1) holds for nearly all substances and places the entropy on a common absolute basis. Thus, sup· pose that two gaseous molecules A and B combine to give a third gas of the formula AB. The change in entropy of the reaction

$$A + B \longrightarrow AB$$

may be found by threefold use of Eq. (2.5) of Chap. 3, calculating separately the molal entropies of A, B, and AB and subtracting the sum of the first two from the third.

Occasionally the lowest energy level is not single. Instead there may be many quantum states of the assembly with the same lowest energy, or at least the system becomes frozen into a condition, which persists to absolute zero, in which it may be in any one of many energy levels. This has the same effect on the entropy as if the quantum states had exactly the same energy. A situation of this sort arises in the case of carbon monoxide. The CO molecules form a crystal in which each molecule has a certain position, with its long axis in a definite direction. However, the oxygen may be randomly placed at either end, without reference to the orientation of the neighboring molecules. The energy of a CO molecule is probably not absolutely independent of the position of the oxygen atom, irrespective of the orientation of the neighbors. At the temperature at which the crystal is formed, however, the difference in energy between the two positions (separated by 180°) is small compared with kT, so the molecules are oriented randomly. As the temperature is lowered, it becomes more and more difficult for the molecules to change their orientation in the lattice, and the ability to change direction is lost before kT becomes comparable to the difference in energy between the two possible orientations. Thus the random arrangement becomes "frozen in." In a crystal at absolute zero, each molecule may be oriented in one of two ways, and N molecules may be oriented in any one of 2^N ways.

If there were actually 2^N energy levels with the lowest energy, E_1, then the partition function would become $2^N \exp\{-E_1/kT\}$, and instead of Eq. (1.1) we would obtain

$$S = \frac{E_1}{T} + k \ln \left(2^N \exp\left\{\frac{-E_1}{kT}\right\}\right) = Nk \ln 2. \tag{1.2}$$

Since we have derived Eq. (1.10) of Chap. 3 on the basis of complete thermal equilibrium between the assemblies in an ensemble and since this includes equilibrium *within* an assembly, it is not strictly correct to apply Eq. (1.2) to a situation like that of CO, in which the random orientation of the molecules is frozen in, without true equilibrium. However, if a certain excited state becomes frozen in, obviously the heat that would have been lost in the transition to the lower energy state will not be lost. Thus the corresponding contribution to the specific heat, C, will *not* be made, and hence the corresponding entropy loss on cooling, arising from $\int (C/T)\,dT$, will not occur. But we wish to get a value for the molal entropy of the gas at room temperature that agrees with Eq. (2.5) of Chap. 3 (after taking into account the contribution from rotation and vibration by calculation from experimentally determined values for $\int (C/T)\,dT$ and $\Delta H/T$. To do this we must assume that the molal entropy of CO at $0°K$ is $R \ln 2$ [1].

Actually, of course, the 2^N states which result from the different orientations of the CO molecules must exhibit a range of energies. The crystal could be accidentally frozen into one of low energy, perhaps even the one with all the molecules oriented, although for this there would be only one chance in 2^N. In such a case, the crystal would have lost the corresponding energy on its approach to absolute zero. As the crystal warms up, this energy would have to be reabsorbed, and there would be a contribution to the specific heat; however, it would still appear not to contribute to the entropy. The entropy change in a small range of temperature is given by $(C/T)\,dT$ only if equilibrium is at all times established. If the heat is absorbed at a temperature which is much higher than the equilibrium temperature, then C/T will be much less than it is supposed to be. Thus C/T will not indicate an entropy change comparable to that indicated if the change of energy state takes place in the range of temperatures at which the energy levels would be in equilibrium.

4-2. *Entropy and Probability: The Classical Case*

The above discussion suggests that the entropy is closely related to the number of energy levels in which an assembly might be found under given conditions. Indeed, the general formula, Eq. (1.10) of Chap. 3 (which was, of course, derived only for equilibrium) agrees with this conception. We may write this equation in the form

$$S = k \ln \left(\sum_L \exp \left\{ \frac{-(E_L - E)}{kT} \right\} \right) = k \ln (\text{P.F.})_E, \tag{2.1}$$

where $(\text{P.F.})_E$ is defined by the equation. We note that the sum in Eq. (2.1) is just the assembly partition function if all the energies are referred to the average energy of all the assemblies in the ensemble as the zero of energy. That is why we refer to it as $(\text{P.F.})_E$.

The terms in $(\text{P.F.})_E$ for which $E_L - E \gg kT$ are very small. On the other hand, terms for which $E - E_L \ll kT$ are very large, but there are very few of them. We may show that only terms for which the absolute value $E_L - E$ is very small compared with NkT make an appreciable contribution to S, and that indeed we may write

$$S = k \ln \Omega, \tag{2.2}$$

where Ω is the number of terms that contribute appreciably. This is essentially the conclusion we reached in Sec. 4-1 for the limiting case of extremely low temperatures. We now attempt to use Eq. (2.2) for high temperatures, where classical concepts may be used. Then in Sec. 4-3 we shall give a more general treatment, including intermediate temperatures where we are not approaching absolute zero but where quantum effects are of importance.

Our approach to the problem will be through the fluctuations in energy in the ensemble. We want to learn how far, on the average, energies of assemblies in the ensemble differ from the average energy. Thus we might attempt to evaluate $\overline{|E_L - E|}$, the average value of $|E_L - E|$; the energy, E, is of course already an average energy. However, it is much easier to evaluate the average of $(E_L - E)^2$, which is always positive, making designation of an absolute value unnecessary. If we then take the square root, $(\overline{(E_L - E)^2})^{1/2}$ we will get essentially the same information as we would get from $\overline{|E_L - E|}$.

We may write

$$\overline{(E_L - E)^2} = \overline{E_L^2 - 2E_L E + E^2} = \overline{E_L^2} - E^2, \tag{2.3}$$

since $\overline{E_L} = E$, which in a further averaging will be taken as a constant. We now return to Eq. (1.4) of Chap. 3:

$$E_L = \sum_\alpha \epsilon_{l_\alpha, L}.$$

This equation, as a matter of fact, we can use for any system, even if it is not a perfect gas, writing simply

$$E_L = \sum_\alpha \epsilon_{\alpha, L}, \tag{2.4}$$

where $\epsilon_{\alpha, L}$ is the energy of the molecule α at some particular instant,† when the quantum number for the whole assembly is L. If the molecules have mutual potential energy, we need only have some system for dividing this energy between them; this system must be symmetrical with respect to all the molecules (assuming all the molecules are of the same kind). If the mutual potential energy of any pair of molecules is independent of the presence of other molecules this is simple: we merely divide the mutual potential energy of any pair equally between the molecules. We may then write

$$\overline{E_L^2} = E^2 = \left(\overline{\sum_\alpha \epsilon_{\alpha, L}}\right)^2 = \left(\sum_\alpha \overline{\epsilon_{\alpha, L}}\right)^2 \tag{2.5}$$

(the sum of an average is the average of a sum), and

$$\overline{E_L^2} = \overline{\left(\sum_\alpha \epsilon_{\alpha, L}\right)^2}. \tag{2.6}$$

If we are to find an average energy for a particular molecule over all the assemblies in an ensemble, we must be able to identify the designated molecule in each of the assemblies. This identification is to some extent arbitrary, since exchange of like molecules does not change the state of the system. The most reasonable procedure is to assign the same value of α to molecules which are in roughly corresponding positions in the various assemblies. This cannot, of course, be entirely unequivocal, since the arrangement of the molecules will differ from assembly to assembly, but it is definite enough to enable us to make a reasonable assignment of correspondence. We can then make the as-

---

† This procedure is not strictly in accord with the uncertainty principle, since the energy cannot be exactly defined in a very short time. See Sec. 4-3 of this chapter.

sumption of uniformity, supposing that the surroundings of any molecule (with a given α) are on the average the same as those of any other (with any other α) and that the average energy of any of the molecules (except the relatively few near the wall) is the same as that of any other. Thus $\overline{\epsilon_{\alpha,L}}$ will be the same for any α, and we have $\sum_{\alpha}\overline{\epsilon_{\alpha,L}} = N\bar{\epsilon}$, or

$$E^2 = N^2\bar{\epsilon}^2. \tag{2.7}$$

To get a simpler expression for Eq. (2.6), we note that in $(\sum_{\alpha}\epsilon_{\alpha,L})^2$ we will have N terms of the type $\epsilon_{\alpha,L}^2$ all of which will have the same average $\overline{\epsilon^2}$, and $N(N-1)/2$ cross terms of the form $2\epsilon_{\alpha,L}\epsilon_{\beta,L}$, where β is simply another value of α. If the energies of any two molecules are independent of each other, the average value of $\epsilon_{\alpha,L}\epsilon_{\beta,L}$ will be $\bar{\epsilon}\bar{\epsilon} = \bar{\epsilon}^2$ (to get the average we may take any value of α and get the average for $\epsilon_{\beta,L}$, then average over $\epsilon_{\alpha,L}$). We thus have

$$\overline{E_L^2} = N\overline{\epsilon^2} + N(N-1)\bar{\epsilon}^2. \tag{2.8}$$

The energies of two molecules may not be independent if they are close together. However, the energies of molecules which are not close together may certainly be considered independent. Only a relatively few pairs will be composed of close neighbors; their number will be proportional to N rather than to $N(N-1)$. To take care of this we may write, instead of Eq. (2.8),

$$\overline{E_L^2} = N\overline{\epsilon'^2} + N(N-1)\bar{\epsilon}^2 \tag{2.9}$$

where $\overline{\epsilon'^2}$ is different from, but certainly of the same order of magnitude as $\overline{\epsilon^2}$ (except possibly very near a critical point—see Sec. 4-3). From Eqs. (2.3), (2.7) and (2.9), we obtain

$$\overline{(E_L - E)^2} = N(\overline{\epsilon'^2} - \bar{\epsilon}^2). \tag{2.10}$$

Now $\overline{\epsilon'^2} - \bar{\epsilon}^2$ will be expected to be of the same order of magnitude as (not much larger than) the square of the fluctuation in ϵ. Since there is rapid exchange between kinetic and potential energy, we may expect the fluctuation to be of the order of magnitude of the square of the average kinetic energy. If the assembly consists of molecules with f degrees of freedom, the average kinetic energy (see Sec. 3-6) will be in the classical case $fkT/2$. Therefore

$$\overline{(E_L - E)^2} \approx N\left(\frac{fkT}{2}\right)^2. \tag{2.11}$$

Thus $((\overline{E_L - E)^2})^{1/2}$, which gives roughly the range of energies contributing effectively to (P.F.), will be approximately $(fkT/2)N^{1/2}$. If N is of the order of Avogadro's number, and f is a reasonably small integer, this range will be absolutely negligible compared with RT.

The principal contributions to (P.F.) or $(P.F.)_E$ must come from a range of energies about as large as the probable fluctuations of energy. Suppose we let $n_{E_L} dE_L$ be the number of energy levels in the range between E_L and $E_L + dE_L$. The energy levels being so very close together, we can replace sums by integrals, writing

$$(P.F.)_E = \int_0^\infty n_{E_L} \exp\left\{\frac{-(E_L - E)}{kT}\right\} dE_L \qquad (2.12)$$

The integrand of this expression will have an appearance something like that shown in Fig. 4-1, in which we plot it against E_L. It has a very strong maximum at E; as a matter of fact, we cannot in any manageable graph do justice to this maximum—it is very much narrower than can actually be shown. The peak has, roughly, a width equal to $(fkT/2)N^{1/2} = (NfkT/2)/N^{1/2}$. Since at the peak E_L is equal, or very nearly equal, to E, so that $\exp\left\{-(E_L - E)/kT\right\} = 1$, the height of the peak is equal to n_E. We can thus write

$$(P.F.)_E \approx \frac{n_E(NfkT/2)}{N^{1/2}} \approx \Omega, \qquad (2.13)$$

where Ω here may be very roughly defined as the number of energy levels likely to be actually occupied, or "available" to the system under the given circumstances. From Eq. (2.13), Eq. (2.2) follows. Inasmuch

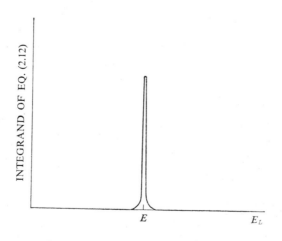

Figure 4-1.

as n_E is the density of energy levels at the peak, and the factor multiplying it is the important range of energies, Ω is approximately the number of levels in this range.

It may be seen that Ω can be evaluated very roughly. If we miss it even by a factor of N this would not matter, for it would introduce into the entropy only a term $k \ln N$, which is completely negligible compared with kN, if N is a very large number. Thus we can determine the important range of energies very roughly, with one precaution— we must not extend too far the range of energies over which we count levels. Should this range become of the order of magnitude of NkT, we would get into trouble, because even the logarithm of the density of levels varies appreciably over such a range. A certain amount of empiricism enters our considerations, for we rely on experience to know just what range of energies is a negligible one.

Since we know that the entropy is proportional to N for a system at a fixed pressure, under this condition Ω and hence n_E must be at least roughly proportional to some quantity raised to the Nth power. We will evaluate Ω directly in some special cases later, but this particular property shows up in the examples discussed in this chapter (in Sec. 4-1 and in the following pages).

We now begin to understand the statement that entropy is a measure of probability. S is equal to $k \ln \Omega$, where Ω, the number of different energy levels available to the system under certain conditions of restraint, is a measure of the probability of the state of the system. If some of the restraints are removed and Ω thereby increased, the system will tend to occupy the newly available energy levels. It will proceed irreversibly to a state of higher entropy. It would be very improbable that the system would remain in its original state once the constraints are removed. If Ω_2 levels are available after the restraint is removed and Ω_1 were available before (assuming that the system has the same amount of energy—within fluctuations—in the two conditions), then the probability of its later being found in the original state is Ω_1/Ω_2.

Let us illustrate by a very simple case. We imagine that we have a box of length $2a$, width b, and height c, subdivided by a partition into two compartments of length a. In one of these compartments there is confined a gas with N molecules. The energy ϵ of a molecule is given by an expression such as

$$\epsilon = \frac{n^2 h^2}{8ma^2} + \frac{k^2 h^2}{8mb^2} + \frac{l^2 h^2}{8mc^2},$$

where n, k, and l are quantum numbers determining the motion in the three respective directions of space. A quantum level is determined if all three quantum numbers are given. We remove the partition and the energy levels become

$$\epsilon = \frac{n^2 h^2}{8m(2a)^2} + \frac{k^2 h^2}{8mb^2} + \frac{l^2 h^2}{8mc^2}$$

A given value of ϵ will remain the same as it was before if n is doubled. Thus for any given range of energies there will be twice as many values of n, since n takes on all integral values. The density of energy levels is doubled. We arrive at the conclusion that the probability of finding the molecule somewhere in the box of length $2a$ is twice as great as the probability of finding it in *one* of the partitions of length a, a conclusion which we would have reached by common-sense considerations. It is clear that for the gas of N molecules, $\Omega_2/\Omega_1 = 2^N$, and we can write

$$S_2 - S_1 = k \ln \Omega_2 - k \ln \Omega_1 = Nk \ln 2,$$

a well-known result for the change of entropy when an ideal gas doubles its volume without change of temperature.

Of course, if we had a liquid in one of the compartments, it would not tend to immediately spread out into the other compartment until both were uniformly filled, for this would require energy, and the relation between energy levels in the systems of length a and of length $2a$ would be very much more complicated.

4-3. *Entropy and Probability: A Generalization*

In contrast to the situation very close to the absolute zero or at high temperatures, where classical methods may be used, there is a region of intermediate low temperatures where classical methods are no longer valid. Here Eq. (2.4) may be called into some question, because of the uncertainty principle which says that the energy of any particle or molecule cannot be measured with an accuracy greater than about $h/2\pi\delta t$ when it remains undisturbed for a time δt. In a dense gas or in a condensed phase, one might question whether a single molecule can ever be thought of as undisturbed.

We shall, therefore, develop a more general and, indeed, more accurate expression for the fluctuation of the energy. If we differentiate the expression for the average energy of the ensemble,

$$E = \frac{\sum_L E_L \exp\{-E_L/kT\}}{\sum_L \exp\{-E_L/kT\}}$$

with respect to T, we obtain an expression for the specific heat at constant volume:

$$C_v = \frac{1}{kT^2} \left\{ \frac{\sum_L E_L^2 \exp\{-E_L/kT\}}{\sum_L \exp\{-E_L/kT\}} - \frac{\left(\sum_L E_L \exp\{-E_L/kT\}\right)^2}{\left(\sum_L \exp\{-E_L/kT\}\right)^2} \right\}$$

$$= \frac{1}{kT^2}\,(\overline{E_L^2} - E^2) = \frac{1}{kT^2}\,\overline{(E_L - E)^2} \tag{3.1}$$

This gives us a new expression for the average square of the fluctuation in energy:

$$\overline{(E_L - E)^2} = C_v k T^2. \tag{3.2}$$

The more general expression for Ω is

$$\Omega = n_E(C_v k T^2)^{1/2} = n_E N^{1/2}(c_v k T^2)^{1/2} \tag{3.3}$$

where c_v is the specific heat per molecule. As before, Ω is proportional to $N^{1/2}$. Since we usually expect c_v to be of the order of fk we see that Eq. (2.13) overestimates Ω by an unimportant factor of about $f^{1/2}$. At low temperatures c_v may become small, as noted in the discussion of the oscillator in Chap. 2. In any case, the maximum of Fig. 4-1 will remain very narrow, and we will still be able to use Eq. (2.2), taking Ω as the number of "available" levels, that is, the number included within the bounds of this maximum.

In Chap. 12 it will be seen that under certain unusual circumstances (in the immediate neighborhood of critical points) the specific heat may actually approach infinity. The regions within which the specific heat could possibly be large enough to cause any difficulty are very small indeed and for present purposes can be ignored. (See Prob. 4.8.)

4-4. *Mixtures and Polyphase Systems*

We have so far assumed that the assemblies of interest are essentially homogeneous and contain only one kind of molecule. However, the same general ideas may be applied with only slight changes to mixtures.

To fix these ideas, suppose that we have an assembly with N_A molecules of kind A and N_B of kind B. It is then easy enough to show that Eq. (2.10) will be replaced by

$$(E_L - E)^2 = N_A(\overline{\epsilon_A'^2} - \bar{\epsilon}_A^2) + N_B(\overline{\epsilon_B'^2} - \bar{\epsilon}_B^2). \qquad (4.1)$$

In attempting to estimate the size of the energy fluctuations of an individual molecule, we must now recognize that the energy may also be affected by a change in environment of a particular molecule. However, a change in environment large enough to change the energy by an amount much greater than kT will not occur often enough greatly to affect the average energy. Thus the average fluctuation in the energy of molecules A will be about $f_A kT/2$ (f_A is not to be interpreted as exactly the number of degrees of freedom of molecule A, but still it will not be much different). Similarly, for molecules B we will have $f_B kT/2$. We may then write an equation exactly like Eq. (2.11), with f an average value for the two kinds of molecules, and which can be handled in exactly the same way. The generalization of Sec. 4-3 will not be more difficult for mixtures than for a pure substance.

Polyphase systems can also be treated under the same general scheme. Suppose, for example, we have two phases, and let the number of attainable energy levels be Ω_1 and Ω_2, respectively. An energy level for the whole system is a combination of energy levels for the respective phases; we can thus write for the whole system $\Omega = \Omega_1\Omega_2$ which gives

$$S = k \ln \Omega = k \ln \Omega_1 + k \ln \Omega_2, \qquad (4.2)$$

so that the entropy of the two phases together is the sum of the entropies of the separate phases. There will, to be sure, be some transfer of material from one phase to another; if so, there will be a separate set of energy levels for each distribution, and the number of available levels will be essentially the same for each distribution of molecules between the phases, at least if the phases are in equilibrium.† If they are not in equilibrium, the number will be the same for all distributions which conform to a certain specification of the state of the system. The total number of energy levels for all the distributions together will be of the order of $\Delta N \Omega_1 \Omega_2$, where ΔN is the number of different distributions possible. ΔN will be less than N, where N is of the order of

---

† In anticipation of later conclusions, it may be remarked that the equilibrium is determined by making $\Omega = \Omega_1\Omega_2$ a maximum, so this quantity has an essentially fixed value at equilibrium.

Avogadro's number, so it cannot affect the entropy. This conclusion will be examined in more detail in some special cases later.

4-5. *An Alternative Expression for the Entropy*

In conclusion, we shall derive an alternative equation for the entropy. The probability that an assembly, which is part of an ensemble at temperature T, should be in the energy state E_L is given by

$$W_L = \frac{\exp \{-E_L/kT\}}{(\text{P.F.})} = \frac{\exp \{-(E_L - E)/kT\}}{(\text{P.F.})_E}. \tag{5.1}$$

It is possible to show that the entropy is given by

$$S = -k \sum_L W_L \ln W_L. \tag{5.2}$$

This follows directly on inserting the second expression of Eq. (5.1) into Eq. (5.2), and comparing the result with Eq. (2.1). We obtain

$$S = k \sum_L \frac{\exp \{-(E_L - E)/kT\}}{(\text{P.F.})_E} \left[\frac{E_L - E}{kT} + \ln (\text{P.F.})_E \right]; \tag{5.3}$$

E/kT and $\ln (\text{P.F.})_E$ are constants in the summation and we note that

$$\sum_L \exp \left\{ \frac{-(E_L - E)}{kT} \right\} = (\text{P.F.})_E,$$

and that

$$\sum_L \frac{E_L \exp \{-(E_L - E)/kT\}}{(\text{P.F.})_E} = E.$$

Then we see that Eq. (5.3) is equivalent to Eq. (2.1).

In much the same way we can show that if

$$w_{0,i} = \frac{\exp \{-\epsilon_i/kT\}}{(\text{p.f.})_0} = \frac{\exp \{-(\epsilon_i - \epsilon_0)/kT\}}{(\text{p.f.})_{\epsilon_0}} \tag{5.4}$$

is the probability that a molecule is in the internal state i, then the internal entropy is given by

$$S_0 = -Nk \sum_i w_{0,i} \ln w_{0,i}. \tag{5.5}$$

On the same basis, one could write

$$S = -k \ln N! - Nk \sum_i w_i \ln w_i, \tag{5.6}$$

where w_i is the probability of state i, including the translational states.

Equation (5.2), though different in form, has an interpretation similar to that of Eq. (2.2). We can write Eq. (5.2) in the form

$$S = -k \overline{\ln W_L}, \tag{5.7}$$

since the right-hand side of Eq. (5.2) gives the average indicated in Eq. (5.7), by the usual definition of an average. If the values of W_L which contribute most to the sum are nearly all alike, then $\overline{\ln W_L} = \ln \overline{W_L}$, and since the sum of all the probabilities must be unity, $\overline{W_L}\Omega \approx 1$. It is, of course, not true that almost all the probabilities are the same, but in view of the inaccuracy with which Ω may be determined, the approximation is good enough.

It appears from the above discussion that Eq. (5.2) will be a legitimate expression for the entropy even if the distribution in energy set up under any particular set of constraints is different from that of a canonical ensemble, provided Eq. (2.2) holds. But in view of the insensitivity of the entropy function, and since the edges of the distribution among energy levels are never important, it seems reasonable to assume that for Eq. (2.2) to hold the distribution in energy need only have a strong maximum.

The definition of entropy given in this section has the advantage that it can be extended to cases where equilibrium between the various energy levels is not established (this generalization will be used in Chap. 17). Here we have started with Eq. (5.1), which defines W_L in terms of the equilibrium set up in a canonical ensemble, but the probability of finding an assembly in a given state is a perfectly definite quantity in any ensemble. Similarly, the probability of finding a molecule in a given energy level is a definite quantity in any gas, even though the gas is not in internal equilibrium.

REFERENCE

1. J. O. Clayton and W. F. Giauque, *J. Am. Chem. Soc.*, **54,** 2610 (1932).

PROBLEMS

4.1. Nitric oxide, NO, forms a dimer N_2O_2 which is stable in the solid phase. This dimer has two possible orientations, which have almost the same energy in the crystal. Assuming the molecule gets frozen in at a relatively high temperature, what will the apparent entropy be at 0°K?

4.2. Assume that the 2^N energy levels, which arise from the two possible orientations of each of N molecules of CO, are spread over a certain small range of energies about the energy E and that their distribution may be approximated by a Gaussian distribution law, there being, according to such a law, $A \exp \{-(E_L - E)^2/(\Delta E)^2\} \, dE_L$ energy levels in the range of energies between E_L and $E_L + dE_L$. Both A and ΔE are constants, ΔE being equal to about half the width of the distribution. We determine A by adding the numbers of all the energy levels:

$$\int_{-\infty}^{\infty} A \exp \left\{ \frac{-(E_L - E)^2}{(\Delta E)^2} \right\} d(E_L - E) = 2^N.$$

Set up an integral expression for $(\text{P.F.})_E$, evaluate the integral, and show that the corresponding entropy is equal to $Nk \ln 2$, provided $\Delta E \ll N^{1/2}kT$, which is consistent with the condition mentioned in Sec. 4-1 for the temperature at which the orientations must be frozen in in order for an entropy of $Nk \ln 2$ to persist at 0°K. (See Problem 4.3.)

4.3. Let the average difference in energy of the two ends of a CO molecule in the crystal be $\delta\epsilon$. Show that ΔE, as defined in Problem 4.2, is of the order of magnitude of $N^{1/2}\delta\epsilon$.

4.4. Suppose that n_{E_L} is proportional to E_L^N, where N is the number of molecules. Find the temperature at which the integrand of Eq. (2.12) has a maximum at $E_L = E$. Find the "half-width" of this maximum, i.e., roughly the change in E_L necessary to make the integrand fall to one-half its maximum value. Express this in terms of kT and N.

4.5. Calculate the probability that all the molecules of a mole of gas in a total volume V will find themselves in a volume V', where $V' = V(1 - 10^{-10})$.

4.6. A box containing 2×10^{20} molecules is divided into two equal compartments, the molecules being able to pass freely from one to the other. What will be the ratio of the probability that one of the compartments will contain 1.00010×10^{20} molecules to the probability that it will contain 1.00000×10^{20}? Give a rough numerical evaluation.

4.7. In a box containing 100 divisions or cells 10^{24} molecules are freely distributed. Calculate the probability of having any one cell half empty with the excess molecules placed in any other one cell. Calculate the change of entropy.

4.8. For an assembly in a canonical ensemble containing one mole, make a rough estimate of the value of C_v/R that would be necessary to cause extremely large average energy fluctuations of the assembly, say of the order of magnitude of the average energy itself.

4.9. Show without using Eq. (5.1) or (5.3) that Eq. (5.2) is consistent with the Gibbs law of mixing for two gases consisting of different species of molecules.

4.10. Show that, for a perfect gas with N molecules, it follows directly from Eq. (5.2), without using Eq. (5.1) or (5.3), that

$$S = -Nk \sum_i w_i \ln w_i - k \ln N!,$$

where $w_i = \exp\{\epsilon_i/kT\}/(\text{p.f.})$ is the probability of a single molecule's being in the ith quantum level.

Hint: Consider the relation between the w_i and W_L and note that $\sum_L$ is the same as $\sum_{i_1,i_2,\ldots}$, where i_1, i_2, $\cdots$ denote quantum states of the individual molecules. The sum $\sum_L$ will break up into a large number of separate sums. Choose the order of summation in $\sum_{i_1,i_2,\cdots}$ correctly for each of these partial sums. Treat the molecules first as distinguishable and introduce the $N!$ term later.

4.11. If there are $n_\epsilon d\epsilon$ energy levels for a molecule of ideal gas, in the range ϵ to $\epsilon + d\epsilon$, and if w_ϵ is the probability that a level of energy ϵ is occupied, show how to convert Eq. (5.6) to an integral for the classical limit. If the volume in which the gas is contained is doubled, how are n_ϵ and w_ϵ affected? Calculate the change in entropy from the integral expression.

Chapter 5

The Statistical Basis of Thermodynamics

5-1. *Fundamental Assumptions*

The discussion of the preceding pages suggests that we *start* with the expression,

$$S = k \ln \Omega, \tag{1.1}$$

which we obtained on the basis of thermodynamics, as our *definition* of entropy. We will, however, extend our concepts somewhat beyond those of the preceding chapter. There we considered a canonical ensemble and defined Ω in a way which could be described roughly as saying that it was the number of energy levels available to the system (of given volume, composition, etc.) at a given temperature. To make this definition more general, Ω will be taken as the number of energy levels actually used by an assembly under some particular set of constraints. In view of the insensitivity of the logarithmic function, we do not need to determine Ω with any great degree of precision. Since it turned out that Ω was the number of energy levels in a small, but not very precisely defined, range of energies, the extended definition of Ω should be satisfactory, and should, indeed, involve nothing essentially new. It is necessary to make sure that our constraints are not so rigid as to prevent the system from reaching the energy levels which should properly be available. This will not happen ordinarily if we stick to reasonable physical models and do not imagine restraints not conceivably attainable by a physical process.

To have a real statistical definition of entropy we must make sure that the system is described in terms of fundamental variables. This means that we

1. Designate the number of molecules of various kinds,
2. Define the volume in which the system is confined,
3. Indicate what forces are acting upon the assembly,
4. Specify the energy of the assembly plus some auxiliary equipment.

However, we must not specify the energy of the assembly itself too precisely, otherwise we would unduly limit Ω. Such quantities as temperature and the pressure of the assembly itself (we may specify an applied pressure as part of the forces acting on the assembly) are derived quantities, and must be defined in terms of the more fundamental quantities.

The hypothesis embodied in Eq. (1.1), understood in the light of the foregoing discussion, we shall designate as *Assumption I*.

We shall of course assume the first law of thermodynamics; our aim will be to show that, from the statistical ideas, we can derive the second law of thermodynamics as expressed by Eq. (1.1) of Chap. 1. To do this, however, we will need another assumption:

Assumption II. An assembly tends actually to occupy (move in and out of) the energy levels available all weighted equally. Thus Ω and S will tend to reach the maximum value possible under the given conditions of constraint. Then we can already see that one of the principles of thermodynamics, that the entropy of an isolated system tends to a maximum, follows, and that this principle is now based on statistical concepts. It is also seen that Ω and therefore the entropy will depend only on the specifications and the constraints placed upon the system; therefore it may be said to be a function only of the variables of state. However, these properties alone, without the connections with other thermodynamic properties, mean very little. To the finding of these connections, we shall now address ourselves, and we shall show that all the general equations of thermodynamics follow. Thus we shall have completed the circle, having shown on the one hand that Assumption I and hence Assumption II follow from thermodynamics, and being prepared to show on the other that thermodynamics follows from Assumption I and Assumption II.

5-2. *Pressure and Temperature: The Thermodynamic Equations*

Let us consider an assembly of definite numbers of various species of molecules, contained in a vessel closed by a weighted piston (Fig. 5-1). The energy of this system is the sum of the internal energy E of the assembly of molecules plus PV, where P is the force per unit area of

Figure 5-1. Cylinder with weighted piston.

the piston, exerted by the force of gravity acting on the weight, and V is the volume of the assembly. Let us suppose this system to be isolated so that $E + PV$ is constant.† Note that P is also constant, since it is the pressure due to the force of gravity on the piston, not to the pressure of the substance in the cylinder, except at equilibrium. If the piston moves so that V changes, E will also change, since some energy is transferred to the piston. Some of this may be, temporarily, kinetic energy of the piston and of the assembly, but because of frictional forces within the assembly, kinetic energy will eventually be changed to internal energy (heat energy). The system will have a tendency to acquire that volume for which the value of Ω or S is a maximum under the constraint $dE = -PdV$.

In this system the actual constitution of the cylinder and piston play no decisive role. Their mass can always be made negligible with respect to the mass of material contained in the assembly. Thus their effect as heat reservoirs may be neglected. Of course, a large mass would be required to produce a large force in a gravitational field, but most of such a mass could be effectively insulated thermally, or another kind of force field could be used. However, one could never prevent some exchange of energy with the "apparatus."

This exchange can serve a useful purpose, by preventing the energy of the assembly from being too well defined. If V and $PV + E$ (hence E) were fixed *exactly*, there would be only one possible quantum

---

† We can if we wish consider our assembly to be an example of those in an ensemble of assemblies all having the same energy. An ensemble in which all the assemblies have essentially the same energy, or in which the total energy range is very small, is called a microcanonical ensemble.

state; Ω would be just 1 and S would be zero. But, even if the cylinder and piston were considered structureless, the piston would always be exchanging kinetic energy with the assembly, and would have an energy of the order of kT. Since factors in Ω of the order of magnitude of N, the number of molecules in the assembly, are unimportant, it will be seen by comparison with the energy ranges considered in Secs. 4-2 and 4-3 that an energy range of kT is ample to make the value of Ω effectively the same as it would be for a canonical ensemble having assemblies with the same value of V and same average value of E. On the other hand, energy exchange with a relatively small number of molecules constituting the cylinder and piston would not affect the energy too much. If Eq. (2.11) of Chap. 4 had a factor of N^2 instead of N, so that the (P.F.) contained a factor of N instead of $N^{1/2}$, the extra factor $N^{1/2}$ itself could produce no significant change in Ω, but the total energy range would begin to be appreciable. Since Ω is a function of energy, it would be affected in this way. This, of course, is not the kind of energy fluctuation we intend to include when calculating Ω, but it is clear that the piston cannot produce a fluctuation of this magnitude.

The preceding discussion is, in a sense, premature. It can only show us that if we can derive the laws of thermodynamics on a statistical basis we will run into no inconsistency, since the preceding chapter already assumed thermodynamics as a basis. So far, from the statistical viewpoint of this chapter, we do not yet know what temperature is, and so, strictly, we can only *assume* that the uncertainties in E are such as to assure the full development of Ω.

Finally, we might suppose that we should consider the whole system, cylinder, piston, and assembly of molecules. If this system is truly isolated, it must be in a state of definite total energy, no matter what the position of the piston. It might be supposed that the piston would not tend to take an equilibrium position, because this would result in no change in Ω. This problem has been extensively discussed in classical statistical mechanics in terms of the so-called ergodic theorem [1–3]. In general, the system would tend to go to an equilibrium configuration because, even with energy fixed, the equilibrium configurations occupy an overwhelmingly large fraction of the reachable phase space. From the quantum mechanical viewpoint, states in which the energy is divided in different specific ways between the piston and the assembly (the latter in some quantum state of its own) could be considered unperturbed quantum states, which under the perturbation of the interaction between piston and assembly combine in linear combinations to give the stationary states of the whole system. In these linear combinations we would find, in general, that the unperturbed states with the properties of the equilibrium state of the system would be heavily represented, because of their overwhelming numbers, and a system in almost any one of these stationary states of the whole system, piston and cylinder plus assembly, would have essentially the equilibrium properties.

But from our point of view the proper answer is that in any statistical theory some random process must be assumed. We are not too restricted in the nature of that process, and it is sufficient to assume only a random exchange of energy between the assembly and the piston considered as a whole (a very moderate introduction of randomness).

With this explanation, then, we proceed to the problem. As stated, there is a tendency for the volume V enclosed by the piston to reach a value for which S is a maximum, with $dE = -P\,dV$. Thus at the volume at which the system is in equilibrium we have $dS = 0$, and therefore

$$P = -\left(\frac{\partial E}{\partial V}\right)_S. \tag{2.1}$$

This is the fundamental equation for the pressure of an assembly in equilibrium with its surroundings. Under the circumstances, the applied pressure P is equal to the pressure of the substance inside the cylinder.

The meaning of Eq. (2.1) may perhaps be brought out a little more precisely. The state of an assembly such as that shown in Fig. 5-1 is completely determined if V and E are given, since its energy levels depend only on V, and the distribution among the energy levels depends on E. As alternative variables we can take V and S. We have then (always assuming internal equilibrium in the assembly)

$$dE = \left(\frac{\partial E}{\partial V}\right)_S dV + \left(\frac{\partial E}{\partial S}\right)_V dS,$$

from which we see that, under the conditions of the experiment in which $E + PV$ is held constant and P is constant,

$$\left(\frac{\partial E}{\partial V}\right)_{E+PV} = -P = \left(\frac{\partial E}{\partial V}\right)_S + \left(\frac{\partial E}{\partial S}\right)_V\left(\frac{\partial S}{\partial V}\right)_{E+PV}.$$

But at equilibrium, $(\partial S/\partial V)_{E+PV} = 0$; hence for equilibrium Eq. (2.1) follows.

The general expression for the conservation of energy, when heat may be exchanged between the assembly and its surroundings and when there is always equilibrium with the surroundings, is

$$dE = dQ_{rev} - P_{rev}\, dV. \tag{2.2}$$

A process carried out so that there is equilibrium between an assembly and its surroundings is reversible, in the sense that the direction in which the process will go depends on infinitesimal displacements from the equilibrium conditions. To indicate this, we write dQ_{rev} for the heat absorbed in a reversible process and P_{rev} for the pressure given by Eq. (2.1), although the system differs from the previous one in that the assembly can exchange energy with its surroundings. This interchange can contribute to the fluctuations of energy, but we will not introduce enough extra available energy levels to affect the entropy (at least this will appear later to be a self-consistent assumption). If P_{rev} were *not* equal to the value given by Eq. (2.1), then for any fixed energy of assembly plus piston we could find a more probable state without exchanging energy with the surroundings. This would contradict our statement that we are in a state of equilibrium. (The subscript "rev" is used only in Chap. 5; equilibrium is usually implied by the context.)

Since the state of the assembly is determined by E and V and since S is assumed not to depend on the surroundings of the system (i.e., on whether or not the system is in thermal contact with the surroundings), we have

$$dS = \left(\frac{\partial S}{\partial V}\right)_E dV + \left(\frac{\partial S}{\partial E}\right)_V dE; \tag{2.3}$$

by Eq. (2.2),

$$dS = \left(\frac{\partial S}{\partial V}\right)_E dV + \left(\frac{\partial S}{\partial E}\right)_V (dQ_{rev} - P_{rev}\, dV); \tag{2.4}$$

and by Eq. (2.1)

$$dS = \left(\frac{\partial S}{\partial V}\right)_E dV + \left(\frac{\partial S}{\partial E}\right)_V \left[dQ_{rev} + \left(\frac{\partial E}{\partial V}\right)_S dV\right]. \tag{2.5}$$

For the partial derivatives of the three interdependent variables we may write

$$\left(\frac{\partial S}{\partial V}\right)_E = -\left(\frac{\partial S}{\partial E}\right)_V \left(\frac{\partial E}{\partial V}\right)_S, \tag{2.6}$$

Therefore, under conditions of equilibrium

$$dS = \left(\frac{\partial S}{\partial E}\right)_V dQ_{rev}. \tag{2.7}$$

Now, defining T, the temperature, we set

$$\left(\frac{\partial S}{\partial E}\right)_V = \frac{1}{T} \tag{2.8}$$

and obtain

$$dS = \frac{dQ_{rev}}{T}. \tag{2.9}$$

Equation (2.9), together with the fact that S is a function only of the variables of state, is the usual mathematical formulation of the second law of thermodynamics. This derivation is quite general with respect to the composition of the assembly considered; it need not be a *pure* substance.

It can be seen that $(\partial S/\partial E)_V$ does have the properties expected of the temperature. Suppose that we have two systems of any kind at constant volume and that we place them in thermal contact so that energy can pass from one to the other. If they are isolated from their surroundings, the energy dE_1 gained by the first system will be equal to the energy $-dE_2$ lost by the second one. The total change of entropy of the combined system will be

$$
\begin{aligned}
dS &= \left(\frac{\partial S_1}{\partial E_1}\right)_{V_1} dE_1 + \left(\frac{\partial S_2}{\partial E_2}\right)_{V_2} dE_2 \\
&= \left[\left(\frac{\partial S_1}{\partial E_1}\right)_{V_1} - \left(\frac{\partial S_2}{\partial E_2}\right)_{V_2}\right] dE_1.
\end{aligned}
\tag{2.10}
$$

At the equilibrium state of the combined system, $dS = 0$; hence

$$\left(\frac{\partial S_1}{\partial E_1}\right)_{V_1} = \left(\frac{\partial S_2}{\partial E_2}\right)_{V_2}, \tag{2.11}$$

which gives $T_1 = T_2$, the expected condition.

Furthermore, since the entropy must be a maximum, $(\partial^2 S/\partial E_1^2)_{V_1,V_2}$ must be negative. This will hold for any system. In particular, the two portions in thermal contact could be identical. In this case, when Eq. (2.11) holds we have $(\partial^2 S_1/\partial E_1^2)_{V_1} = (\partial^2 S_2/\partial E_2^2)_{V_2}$. Also,

$$
\begin{aligned}
\left(\frac{\partial^2 S}{\partial E_1^2}\right)_{V_1,V_2} &= \left(\frac{\partial^2 S_1}{\partial E_1^2}\right)_{V_1} + \left(\frac{\partial^2 S_2}{\partial E_1^2}\right)_{V_2} \\
&= \left(\frac{\partial^2 S_1}{\partial E_1^2}\right)_{V_1} + \left(\frac{\partial^2 S_2}{\partial E_2^2}\right)_{V_2},
\end{aligned}
$$

since $dE_2 = -dE_1$. Therefore

$$
\left(\frac{\partial^2 S}{\partial E_1^2}\right)_{V_1,V_2} = 2\left(\frac{\partial^2 S_1}{\partial E_1^2}\right)_{V_1}.
$$

Hence $(\partial^2 S_1/\partial E_1^2)_{V_1}$ must be negative; in other words $1/T_1$ decreases with E_1, as expected.

A somewhat similar result can be obtained for the pressure at a boundary. Consider an assembly of constant total volume and energy, with a movable boundary separating two parts of it. Suppose that this boundary changes its position slightly; then $dV_1 = -dV_2$, and $dE_1 = -dE_2$. We will have

$$
dS = \left(\frac{\partial S_1}{\partial E_1}\right)_{V_1} dE_1 + \left(\frac{\partial S_2}{\partial E_2}\right)_{V_2} dE_2 + \left(\frac{\partial S_1}{\partial V_1}\right)_{E_1} dV_1 + \left(\frac{\partial S_2}{\partial V_2}\right)_{E_2} dV_2.
$$

Since we have found $(\partial S_1/\partial E_1)_{V_1} = (\partial S_2/\partial E_2)_{V_2}$, and since $dS = 0$ if we have an equilibrium state, we find $(\partial S_1/\partial V_1)_{E_1} = (\partial S_2/\partial V_2)_{E_2}$. Using Eq. (2.6) with (2.11), we find

$$
\left(\frac{\partial E_1}{\partial V_1}\right)_{S_1} = \left(\frac{\partial E_2}{\partial V_2}\right)_{S_2},
$$

which says essentially that at equilibrium the first portion of the assembly exerts the same pressure on the other portion as the latter does on it.

If heat cannot be exchanged between the two parts of the assembly, then each part will come to equilibrium separately with the movable boundary, as the assembly came to equilibrium with the piston to give Eq. (2.1). Unless the forces exerted on the two sides of the boundary are equal it will move. Thus the two portions must come to the same pressure even if their temperatures are different.

From Eq. (2.9), the first law of thermodynamics, and the fact that S is a function only of the variables of state, all the equations of thermodynamics follow. These include the statistical equations derived in the preceding chapters, because if the internal quantum state of a molecule or supermolecule is fixed, Ω depends only on the density of translational energy levels, which is independent of the internal quantum state. Thus the fundamental assumptions in Secs. 2-1 and 3-1 follow and may in a sense be considered equivalent to Assumptions I and II of this chapter, giving a sort of reciprocal relation between thermodynamics and statistical mechanics.

The assumption that S is a function of the variables of state, depends upon Ω being roughly invariant no matter how the constraints are put on the system. For example, for a given assembly at energy E and volume V, we assume Ω to be sufficiently closely the same, whether or not E and V are determined by setting the total energy of the assembly and compressing it with a piston or by having the assembly, in a box of constant volume, be one of a canonical ensemble. The discussion already given indicates the self-consistency of this assumption, because with it Assumptions I and II of Sec. 5-1 lead to the results of the preceding chapters, from which one ultimately shows that Ω is invariant to the degree required.

The discussion of this section is perfectly general with respect to the type of assembly. It need not be a one-component system, nor a one-phase system. It is, however, restricted in the kind of forces exerted upon the assembly and the kind of work done on it, only pressure–volume work being considered. This restriction, however, is easily removed, as we see in the next section.

5-3. *Other Kinds of Forces*

The deduction of Sec. 5-2 can be carried out in its entirety for any other kind of work, or for combinations of various kinds of work. For example, if we had a "force" X (such as surface tension or electromotive force) and a "displacement" Y (such as surface area or charge), the system would come under constant P and X, to a condition at which S was a maximum under the constraint $E + PV - XY = $ const. Under this constraint we have

$$dE = -PdV + XdY, \tag{3.1}$$

and at equilibrium, where $dS = 0$, we would have

$$P = -\left(\frac{\partial E}{\partial V}\right)_{S,Y} \tag{3.2}$$

and

$$X = \left(\frac{\partial E}{\partial Y}\right)_{S,V}. \tag{3.3}$$

In place of the general equation for dE, Eq. (2.2), we would have

$$dE = dQ_{\text{rev}} - P_{\text{rev}}\, dV + X_{\text{rev}}\, dY, \tag{3.4}$$

and in place of Eq. (2.3),

$$dS = \left(\frac{\partial S}{\partial V}\right)_{E,Y} dV + \left(\frac{\partial S}{\partial Y}\right)_{E,V} dY + \left(\frac{\partial S}{\partial E}\right)_{V,Y} dE. \tag{3.5}$$

Exactly the same deduction would lead to Eq. (2.9) and to the relations regarding the temperature. Equation (2.8) is of course replaced by

$$\left(\frac{\partial S}{\partial E}\right)_{V,Y} = \frac{1}{T}. \tag{3.6}$$

We may illustrate the possibilities with a couple of special kinds of forces and displacements. Consider the system shown in Fig. 5-2, in which we have in the cylinder a two-phase liquid–vapor system with a bent wire upon which a film forms and which may be used to increase or decrease the total surface area. This wire is suspended from a pulley with a counterweight to balance the surface tension. If the weight is kept constant, then, neglecting buoyancy effects, X is constant. Suppose that the system contains a small amount of surface-active agent, so active that it is practically all adsorbed on the surface. Then the surface concentration of the surface-active agent will decrease with increasing surface, and the surface tension will increase. A point of balance will be reached as the weight moves down to the point where the surface force balances the weight. When there is no surface-

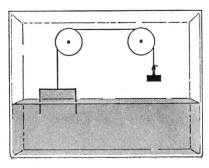

Figure 5-2. Liquid with portion of surface balanced against weight.

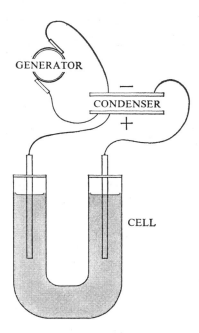

Figure 5-3. Electrolytic cell balanced against condenser and generator.

active agent, the surface tension is virtually constant, and the balance can be reached only if the weight has almost the exact compensating value. But even in this case the balance can be reached, for stretching the surface in an isolated system will lower the temperature and so increase the surface tension.

Consider now an electrolytic cell with two electrodes attached to a condenser, which is in turn connected to a frictionless generator which maintains the condenser plate at a certain potential X (Fig. 5-3). At this potential there is a certain charge on the condenser plates. If this is not the potential of the cell, current will flow, but the charge of the condenser will be kept constant by current flowing through the generator. Work will be done on the generator or it will do work, depending on the direction of the current, and this work may be made to cause a weight to rise or fall. (For example, the generator could paddle liquid up to a reservoir, from which the liquid flows at a constant rate, doing work on the generator as it goes down. At balance, as much liquid would be raised as lowered.) The whole system, including the weight, is self-contained. Since the generator is frictionless, no work is required to keep it moving except when current flows. When current flows through the cell (and hence through the generator) it changes the composition and concentration of the materials within the

cell. These changes will go on until the potential of the cell is equal
to the potential of the condenser, and a balance is reached.

5-4. *Fluctuations*

The discussion of Sec. 5-2 gives the value of the volume V at equilibrium, but no idea of the relative probabilities of finding the system at
other volumes. We shall investigate this problem when only pressure–
volume work is involved. Letting Ω_{max} be the value of Ω at the equilibrium volume, we want to find the ratio Ω/Ω_{max} (where Ω is the value
at some other volume) to get the relative probability of finding the
system in some other state than the most probable. From Eq. (1.1) we
may write

$$\frac{\Omega}{\Omega_{max}} = \exp\left\{\frac{S - S_{max}}{k}\right\}. \tag{4.1}$$

Since $(\partial S/\partial V)_{E+PV}$ is equal to zero where $S = S_{max}$, we may write

$$S - S_{max} = \frac{1}{2}\left(\frac{\partial^2 S}{\partial V^2}\right)_{E+PV,max}(V - V_{max})^2, \tag{4.2}$$

taking the second term of a Taylor expansion.

The subscript means that $E + PV$ remains constant in the differentiation; P is also a constant, since it is the constant pressure
exerted by the piston, and *not* the equilibrium pressure of the assembly
at given V and T. As before, we shall write the latter as P_{rev}.

Now in general (not necessarily at V_{max}) we may write, using
the standard transformations of partial derivatives,

$$\left(\frac{\partial S}{\partial V}\right)_{E+PV} = \left(\frac{\partial S}{\partial V}\right)_E + \left(\frac{\partial S}{\partial E}\right)_V\left(\frac{\partial E}{\partial V}\right)_{E+PV}$$

$$= -\left(\frac{\partial S}{\partial E}\right)_V\left(\frac{\partial E}{\partial V}\right)_S - \left(\frac{\partial S}{\partial E}\right)_V P$$

using $dE = -d(PV)$, with P constant. Thus

$$\left(\frac{\partial S}{\partial V}\right)_{E+PV} = T^{-1}(P_{rev} - P) \tag{4.3}$$

by Eqs. (2.1) and (2.8). [Equation (2.1) holds for the equilibrium pressure under any conditions.] Of course, when P is the equilibrium pres-

sure, $(\partial S/\partial V)_{E+PV} = 0$, which is the situation at V_{max}. From Eq. (4.3)

$$\left(\frac{\partial^2 S}{\partial V^2}\right)_{E+PV} = \left(\frac{\partial T^{-1}}{\partial V}\right)_{E+PV}(P_{rev} - P) + T^{-1}\left(\frac{\partial P_{rev}}{\partial V}\right)_{E+PV}. \qquad (4.4)$$

If this is evaluated at V_{max}, then since $P_{rev} = P$, the first term drops out, so we have

$$\left(\frac{\partial^2 S}{\partial V^2}\right)_{E+PV,max} = \frac{1}{T}\left(\frac{\partial P_{rev}}{\partial V}\right)_{E+PV,max}. \qquad (4.5)$$

Now

$$\left(\frac{\partial P_{rev}}{\partial V}\right)_{E+PV} = \left(\frac{\partial P_{rev}}{\partial V}\right)_T + \left(\frac{\partial P_{rev}}{\partial T}\right)_V\left(\frac{\partial T}{\partial V}\right)_{E+PV}$$

$$= \left(\frac{\partial P_{rev}}{\partial V}\right)_T + \left(\frac{\partial P_{rev}}{\partial T}\right)_V\left[\left(\frac{\partial T}{\partial V}\right)_S + \left(\frac{\partial T}{\partial S}\right)_V\left(\frac{\partial S}{\partial V}\right)_{E+PV}\right]. \qquad (4.6)$$

We again note that $(\partial S/\partial V)_{E+PV} = 0$ when $V = V_{max}$, and set

$$\left(\frac{\partial T}{\partial V}\right)_S = -\left(\frac{\partial T}{\partial S}\right)_V\left(\frac{\partial S}{\partial V}\right)_T = -\left(\frac{\partial T}{\partial S}\right)_V\left(\frac{\partial P_{rev}}{\partial T}\right)_V,$$

using a thermodynamic relationship, which does not at this stage introduce anything nonstatistical, since we have shown that the thermodynamic equations follow from the statistical assumptions. The expression after the last equals sign can be rewritten $-T(\partial P_{rev}/\partial T)_V/C_v$, and we have, by Eqs. (4.6) and (4.5),

$$\left(\frac{\partial^2 S}{\partial V^2}\right)_{E+PV,max} = \frac{1}{T}\left(\frac{\partial P_{rev}}{\partial V}\right)_{T,max} - \frac{1}{C_v}\left(\frac{\partial P_{rev}}{\partial T}\right)^2_{V,max}. \qquad (4.7)$$

As an example, which will give the order of magnitude, let us evaluate Eq. (4.7) for one mole of a perfect monatomic gas, for which $P_{rev} = RT/V$ and $C_v = \frac{3}{2}R$. We find

$$\left(\frac{\partial^2 S}{\partial V^2}\right)_{E+PV,max} = -\frac{5}{3}\frac{R}{V^2_{max}}, \qquad (4.8)$$

and from Eqs. (4.2) and (4.1),

$$\frac{\Omega}{\Omega_{max}} = \exp\left\{-\frac{5}{6}\frac{R}{k}\frac{(V - V_{max})^2}{V^2_{max}}\right\}. \qquad (4.9)$$

Inasmuch as R/k is equal to Avogadro's number and hence is very large, it is clear that even very small deviations of V from $V_{\max}$ will be highly improbable. While this calculation strictly holds only for an ideal gas, in general the thermodynamic quantities will not differ widely from those of an ideal gas, and the general conclusions will hold in almost any case.

5-5. *Entropy of Fluctuation*

If in some special case $(\partial^2 S/\partial V^2)_{E+PV,\max}$ should be very small (essentially equal to zero) there would be appreciable fluctuations over a much greater range of volumes than in the case just considered. Over this larger range Ω would be essentially equal to $\Omega_{\max}$, and so over the same range the entropy would not change appreciably. But will the fluctuations themselves contribute to the entropy? The total entropy should of course be given by $k \ln \Omega_{\mathrm{tot}}$, where Ω_{tot} is the total number of energy levels consistent with the fluctuations. The problem, then, is to compare Ω_{tot} with $\Omega_{\max}$. Obviously Ω_{tot} will be much greater than $\Omega_{\max}$; the question is whether the ratio will be large enough to affect the entropy.

We shall consider three closely adjacent states of the system: an original state, a final state reached by changing the volume by δV with $E + PV$ held constant, where P is the external pressure applied by the piston, and an intermediate state reached by holding E constant (see Table 5.1). We wish to know how many new energy levels

TABLE 5.1

State	Volume	Energy	Temperature	$E + PV$	Ω
Original	V	E	T	$E + PV$	Ω_0
Intermediate	$V + \delta V$	E	T_i	$E + PV + P\delta V$	Ω_i
Final	$V + \delta V$	$E + \delta E$	$T + \delta T$	$E + PV$	Ω_f

can be made available to the assembly by a given volume change. If δV is very small, the levels contained in Ω_f will overlap those of Ω_0, but by how much? In other words, how many new levels are contributed to Ω_{tot}, or, how large does δV need to be in order to avoid duplication between Ω_0 and Ω_f? This we investigate by considering the relation of Ω_0 to Ω_i to Ω_f.

To fix the ideas, let us suppose δV is negative, so that $V + \delta V$ is associated with contraction from V. All the energy levels of Ω_i then will be contained in Ω_0, but Ω_i would contain some of the levels in Ω_f only if the energy $E + \delta E$ does not differ from the energy E associated with the original volume V by more than $N^{1/2}(c_v k)^{1/2} T$ (approximately) according to Eqs. (3.2) and (3.3) of Chap. 4 (since the latter is a good enough approximation for Ω). Let us then set

$$\delta E \approx N^{1/2}(c_v k)^{1/2} T, \tag{5.1}$$

with, of course,

$$\delta E = -P \delta V. \tag{5.2}$$

We see from Eqs. (5.1) and (5.2) that the change of volume just necessary to prevent duplication between the intermediate and the final states and hence between the initial and final states is given by

$$-P \delta V \approx N^{1/2}(c_v k)^{1/2} T. \tag{5.3}$$

If Ω retains its maximum value over a range of volumes ΔV, that is, if the contributions to Ω_{tot} come from fluctuations over a volume range ΔV, then, roughly, we may say that

$$\frac{\Omega_{\text{tot}}}{\Omega_{\text{max}}} \approx \frac{\Delta V}{\delta V} \approx \frac{P \Delta V}{N^{1/2}(c_v k)^{1/2} T}. \tag{5.4}$$

If ΔV is unusually large, we might expect $P \Delta V$ to approach RT, which will make

$$\frac{\Omega_{\text{tot}}}{\Omega_{\text{max}}} \approx N^{1/2}, \tag{5.5}$$

where $N \approx$ Avogadro's number. Even if it is much larger than this, fluctuations in volume under adiabatic conditions will not, in themselves, affect the entropy appreciably.

5-6. *Pressure in a Canonical Ensemble*

We now discuss briefly an alternative expression for the pressure. We go back to the equation

$$S = \frac{E}{T} + k \ln \sum_L \exp \left\{ \frac{-E_L}{kT} \right\}, \tag{6.1}$$

which, as shown earlier, is equivalent for all practical purposes to Eq. (1.1). Note that the energy levels E_L will in general depend upon the volume of the system, but not on the temperature. We see then, that

$$dS = \frac{dE}{T} - \frac{E}{T^2} dT - \frac{\sum_L (dE_L/dV) \exp \{-E_L/kT\}}{T \sum_L \exp \{-E_L/kT\}} dV$$
$$+ \frac{1}{T^2} \frac{\sum_L E_L \exp \{-E_L/kT\}}{\sum_L \exp \{-E_L/kT\}} dT.$$

Of course N is held fixed. Since

$$E = \frac{\sum_L E_L \exp \{-E_L/kT\}}{\sum_L \exp \{-E_L/kT\}},$$

the equation for dS reduces to

$$dS = \frac{dE}{T} - \frac{\sum_L (dE_L/dV) \exp \{-E_L/kT\}}{T \sum_L \exp \{-E_L/kT\}} dV. \tag{6.2}$$

Incidentally we see that this is consistent with our definition of T by Eq. (2.8). We also see from Eq. (6.2) that if we solve to get dE in terms of dS and dV,

$$P_{\text{rev}} = -\left(\frac{\partial E}{\partial V}\right)_S = -\frac{\sum_L (dE_L/dV) \exp \{-E_L/kT\}}{\sum_L \exp \{-E_L/kT\}}. \tag{6.3}$$

Now dE_L/dV is the work done by the assembly per unit increase of volume if it is in and remains in the particular quantum state designated by L. Therefore $-dE_L/dV$ may be called the pressure P_L of an assembly in quantum state L. By Eq. (6.3) it is seen that the thermodynamic pressure is the average of the pressure of all the assemblies in a canonical ensemble.

According to the adiabatic hypothesis of the quantum theory [4], if any parameter, such as the volume, is changed very slowly, a system in a given quantum state will remain in that quantum state. But a process will be reversible only if it is carried out very slowly.

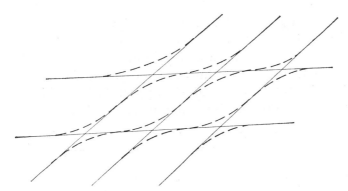

Figure 5-4. Crossing of energy levels.

Therefore, in just such a process the pressure of any given assembly should be P_L, and the conception that the thermodynamic pressure is the average of such P_L's is a very satisfying one.

We should naturally expect the P_L's for the various levels which contribute appreciably to the average in Eq. (6.3) to be very nearly alike. The derivation of Eq. (2.1) from Eq. (1.1) implied that all levels contributing to Ω were accessible levels. If there were a certain level in the energy range which could never be reached, it could not contribute to Ω. It must be possible to shift freely from one contributing level to another. This means that the various levels E_L will not cross each other as the volume is changed. The fact that it is possible to shift from one energy level to another, means that the corresponding wave functions are not truly stationary wave functions. Expressed in quantum mechanical language, there will be a perturbation which will push the energy levels apart, and in a slow adiabatic process the tendency will be to follow the broken rather than the solid lines in Fig. 5-4. Since the closely spaced energy levels do not cross, they must all go in the same general direction. Thus dE_L/dV will not vary rapidly or randomly with E_L.

There may, however, be inaccessible energy levels, and if these become accessible they can change the state of equilibrium completely. Consider the case of a mixture of O_2 and H_2. There are many energy levels corresponding to the presence of molecules of H_2O, which are ordinarily inaccessible. If one compresses a mixture of O_2, H_2, and H_2O, one will have to compress it very slowly, indeed, to go adiabatically from one state of chemical equilibrium to another. For all practical purposes, these states are, in a slow compression process, mutually nonintraconvertible. Thus there are many different sets of states, corresponding to the same E and V, for which the value of dE_L/dV will be quite different. Each of these sets of states can give rise to a condition of metastable equilibrium. True equilibrium will correspond to the situation in which Ω has an absolute maximum, but if these states are not accessible, the metastable state will appear to be stable, and the system will take on the properties of the metastable state.

5-7. *An Assembly in Contact with a Reservoir*

An assembly in a canonical ensemble is of course in thermal contact with all the other assemblies of the ensemble, and these act as a heat reservoir for the assembly which is singled out. It is sometimes desired to consider an assembly in contact with a reservoir of unspecified type. The general characteristics of such a reservoir are that it be very large (have a very large heat capacity) compared with the assembly, and it be in thermal contact with the assembly. The total energy of interaction with the assembly must be small compared with the energy of the assembly; indeed, it must be small compared with the normal fluctuations (as in a canonical ensemble) of the assembly. This low interaction energy can still be sufficient to develop fully the equilibrium distribution of the reservoir, for it may still be large compared with kT, which we have seen would be adequate.†

The reservoir being so large, it will in effect hold the assembly at a fixed temperature, if the energy of reservoir plus assembly is fixed at E within the limits noted. There will be exchanges of energy between the assembly and the reservoir. If the assembly is in some particular energy level with energy E, the reservoir will, neglecting the perturbations due to the interaction with the assembly, have an energy very close to $E_{r,1} = E - E_1$. Because of these perturbations the reservoir may be in any one of many energy levels and will have the entropy characteristic of this energy, which we will call S_1. The probability of this state will be proportional to $\Omega_1 = \exp\{S_1/k\}$. The probability that the assembly will be in a level with energy E_2 will, in similar fashion, be proportional to $\Omega_2 = \exp\{S_2/k\}$, and the ratio of the probabilities will be

$$\frac{W_2}{W_1} = \frac{\Omega_2}{\Omega_1} = \exp\left\{\frac{S_2 - S_1}{k}\right\}. \qquad (7.1)$$

† A minor exception may occur at very low temperatures, where $c_v \ll k$.

The reservoir being so large, the temperature may be considered essentially constant, and we may, integrating Eq. (2.8), write

$$S_2 - S_1 = \frac{E_{r,2} - E_{r,1}}{T}$$

$$= \frac{E_1 - E_2}{T}. \tag{7.2}$$

Thus the ratio of the probabilities of the two states of the assembly will be

$$\frac{W_2}{W_1} = \exp\left\{\frac{-(E_2 - E_1)}{kT}\right\}, \tag{7.3}$$

and the assembly will behave just like a member of a canonical ensemble. More precisely, in a microcanonical ensemble of assemblies plus reservoirs, the assemblies will be distributed among their energy levels as in a canonical ensemble.

It is interesting to see how the large reservoir, which because of its size has a much greater density of energy levels than the assembly, controls the situation through its energy-level density (its entropy) and forces upon the assembly the canonical distribution. This occurs because the reservoir with its large size and increasing density of levels with increasing energy tends to take energy from the assembly.

REFERENCES

1. T. L. Hill, *Statistical Mechanics*, New York, McGraw-Hill, 1956, Chap. 1.
2. R. C. Tolman, *The Principles of Statistical Mechanics*, Oxford, Eng., Clarendon Press, 1938, Sec. 25.
3. A. I. Khinchin, *Mathematical Foundations of Statistical Mechanics*, New York, Dover, 1949.
4. H. A. Kramers, *Quantum Mechanics* (trl. by D. ter Haar), New York, Interscience, 1957, Sec. 54.

PROBLEMS

5.1. Assume that there are two assemblies, with thermal contact, one of which (No. 1) is at constant volume and the other of which (No. 2) is at constant pressure maintained by a weighted piston. Show that at equilibrium

$$\left(\frac{\partial S_1}{\partial E_1}\right)_{V_1} = \left(\frac{\partial S_2}{\partial H_2}\right)_{P_2},$$

where $H_2 = E_2 + P_2 V_2$ is the enthalpy; hence that $(\partial S/\partial H)_P$ is also equal to $1/T$.

5.2. Using Eq. (2.8), prove that $(\partial E/\partial V)_S$ is equal to $(\partial A/\partial V)_T$, and using Eq. (3.6) prove that $(\partial E/\partial Y)_{S,V,\ldots}$ is equal to $(\partial A/\partial Y)_{T,V,\ldots}$.

5.3. In the system described in Prob. 2.10, the magnetic field, if held constant, may be considered as a parameter rather than a thermodynamic variable. Using the first result of Problem 5.2 and the results of part c of Prob. 2.10, show that the pressure of the system in the magnetic field is the same as if no magnetic field were present.

5.4. Repeat the argument by which Eq. (2.9) was obtained for the case illustrated by Fig. 5-2, assuming V constant but letting the surface area be a variable.

5.5. The total energy of an isotropic, constant-volume, paramagnetic body with induced magnetic moment M in the direction of an applied field H is $E_H = E - MH$, where E is the nonmagnetic part of the energy. This total energy E_H is analogous to enthalpy in Prob. 5.1. The induced moment M may depend on T as well as on H, and E may depend on M. Suppose that such a system has thermal contact with system No. 1 of Prob. 5.1. Show that

$$\left(\frac{\partial S_1}{\partial E_1}\right)_{V_1} = \left(\frac{\partial S}{\partial E_H}\right)_{H,V}$$

where S is the entropy of the paramagnetic body, and H is analogous to P_2 in Prob. 5.1.

5.6. The body described in Prob. 5.5 is placed in a constant magnetic field H, and no heat is transferred to or from it. Its magnetic moment M will come to some equilibrium value. Show that, when this state of equilibrium is reached, $H = (\partial E/\partial M)_S$. From this show (considering now a process in which H is no longer constant) that $M_{\text{rev}} = -(\partial E_H/\partial H)_S$, where M_{rev} is the equilibrium value of M. Here $E_H = E - M_{\text{rev}}H$.

5.7. From the results of Prob. 5.6 show that at equilibrium $(\partial E_H/\partial S)_H = (\partial E/\partial S)_M$, hence that the latter differential coefficient may also be set equal to T.

5.8a. The body described in Probs. 5.5 and 5.6 is placed in a magnetic field parallel to the z direction, which varies with z. The force exerted by the magnetic field on the body is then $M\, dH/dz$. Show that if the body is in thermal equilibrium with its surroundings and M has its equilibrium value M_{rev}, then

$$dE_H = dQ_{\text{rev}} - M_{\text{rev}}\, dH$$

when the body is moved reversibly in the field by an external machine.

b. Using the results of Probs. 5.5 and 5.6, show that for the process described in part a, $dS = dQ_{\text{rev}}/T$.

5.9. Consider a body in a pressure field, produced, for example, by immersing it in a liquid which is under the influence of gravity. It is assumed that the body is in mechanical contact with the liquid, but it may or may not be in thermal contact. Formulate a problem analogous to Prob. 5.8 (including the analogies of such parts of Probs. 5.5 and 5.6 as may be necessary).

5.10. In the case of an ideal magnetic substance with elementary magnetic moment μ, $M_{rev} = N\mu^2 H/3kT$, where N is the total number of elementary magnets and M is the total induced magnetic moment. This is analogous to the ideal gas law, except that in the latter case V is inversely proportional to P, whereas M_{rev} is directly proportional to H (i.e., M_{rev} is analogous to density rather than volume). Work out the equation for the magnetic case analogous to Eqs. (4.8) and (4.9), using necessary results from preceding problems, and thermodynamic relations (which may be inferred by analogy if need be), and discuss the fluctuations.

5.11. Although, in the magnetic case, the total magnetic moment M takes the place of V (or more precisely, V^{-1}) and H of P in the thermodynamic equations, the energy of a given quantum level depends on V in the one case and on H in the other. The value of M depends on the total angular momentum of the body which is quantized. Therefore M is fixed for a given quantum level and may be written M_L. Considering, therefore, H as a primary variable, derive and interpret the equation which takes the place of Eq. (6.3) for the magnetic case, using the result of Prob. 5.6.

5.12. Let us suppose that we have an ensemble of identical assemblies in thermal contact, each one being equipped with a piston which maintains a pressure P, as described in Sec. 5-2. The total energy of the assembly plus the piston, in a particular quantum state, is $H_L = E_L + PV$. A partition function for this system may be set up in the form (P.F.) = $\sum_L \exp\{-H_L/kT\}$. Find expressions for average value of H, for the entropy, and for G, the Gibbs free energy in terms of the new partition function. Assuming that large fluctuations in V are improbable, show from the expression for S, that the entropy is the same as if V were fixed. (Here H is enthalpy, not magnetic field.)

Chapter 6

Statistical Calculation of the Thermodynamic Functions for an Ideal Gas

6-1. *Maximization of Probability*

Although we have already found the entropy and other thermodynamic functions for an ideal gas, and though the results of Chap. 5 may be considered to be a statistical justification for this procedure, it will nevertheless be of interest to find the maximum value of Ω under fixed conditions by direct calculation. We may then use this maximum value in the expression

$$S = k \ln \Omega, \tag{1.1}$$

to get the equilibrium value of the entropy. We shall obtain, incidentally, an expression for the probability that a molecule have any given energy.

Suppose that we have N identical molecules, each with f atoms, in a box of volume V. Then the phase space of the molecules is a $6f$-dimensional space whose rectilinear coordinates are the $3f$ coordinates $q_1, q_2, \cdots, q_{3f}$ of the molecule and the corresponding momenta $p_1, p_2, \cdots, p_{3f}$. Naturally, for three of the q's we shall choose the coordinates of the center of gravity of the molecule. Their range will, of course, be restricted by the size of the box. According to classical mechanics, as noted in Chap. 1, a point in the phase space completely determines the position and the condition of motion of a molecule. Such a point is called a representative point. We will now find out how the representative points of the N molecules may be expected to be distributed in the phase space. According to the quantum theory, with its uncertainty principle, a representative point specifies the state of a molecule more completely than is actually permissible, and the best we can do is to confine the molecule to a region which is of the order of magnitude of h^{3f}. This will not bother us here because we will be dealing with regions much larger than h^{3f}.

In order to determine Ω, we need to find out how many different ways we can distribute the representative points in the phase space when the entire system has a certain energy. Each distribution of representative points represents a quantum state of the entire assembly. However, we do not wish to define the energy too exactly. We have seen that we may take Ω as equal to the number of energy levels in a range of energy which is of the order of magnitude (with a wide range of latitude) of the fluctuations of energy in a canonical ensemble.

Let us divide up the phase space into cells, each of which contains a large number, C, of energy levels, and yet is small enough so that the energy range of these energy levels is very much less than kT. This restricts us to high temperatures, but not to *very* high temperatures, since the translational energy levels are extremely close together. Let us number these cells serially, and suppose that the number of molecules in the respective cells is n_1, n_2, n_3, $\cdots$. We shall also choose the cells large enough so that at least for relatively low energies the n's are large numbers. This should be relatively easy, since the number of molecules is very large. We will restrict ourselves, however, to pressures low enough so that the n's are all very small compared with C. Ordinarily this condition is fulfilled with a gas, for the translational energies are very close together, and in a range of energies equal to kT there are many energy levels per molecule. When the condition is not fulfilled, quantum effects become important, and the situation needs special consideration.

Let us consider the situation within a given cell. If the molecules were distinguishable, each molecule would have the possibility of being in any one of C quantum levels (provided the molecules did not interfere with each other), and the number of ways the n_1 molecules could be placed in cell 1, for instance, would be C^{n_1}. However, interchanging molecules would not change the state of the system. The number of interchanges is the number of ways in which they can be placed in linear order, or $n_1!$. Hence the number of distinct states of the n_1 molecules in cell 1 is $C^{n_1}/n_1!$. At least this is true if no two molecules are in the same energy state, and such a coincidence is very unlikely, in any case, since there are so many more energy levels than molecules. If two of them were in the same energy level, they could not be interchanged, since they would be in the same place.

The total number of ways of distributing the molecules in their respective cells will be the product of the numbers in the individual cells, or

$$\frac{C^{n_1} C^{n_2} C^{n_3} \cdots}{n_1! n_2! n_3! \cdots} = \frac{C^N}{n_1! n_2! n_3! \cdots}, \tag{1.2}$$

the last transformation following because

$$n_1 + n_2 + n_3 + \cdots = \sum_i n_i = N. \tag{1.3}$$

To each cell we may assign a certain energy, say ϵ_i for the ith cell. Of course this is not an exact energy, for each cell represents a range of energies, but the total energy E will be given approximately by

$$E = \sum_i n_i \epsilon_i. \tag{1.4}$$

If E is taken as a fixed constant, this with V and N should fix the state of the system. We have an additional condition, Eq. (1.4) on the number n_i of molecules whose representative point lies in any cell. However, because the cell does not have any absolutely definite energy there is some leeway in the total energy. As earlier discussions have made clear, this freedom is actually quite necessary in order to get a "full development" of Ω. It will turn out that the results we obtain will be independent of C so long as it fulfills the moderate conditions placed upon it.

The number of states that fulfill the conditions (1.3) and (1.4) within the limits indicated will be given by

$$\Omega = \sum_{(n_i)} \frac{C^N}{n_1! n_2! n_3! \cdots} = \sum_{(n_i)} \frac{C^N}{\prod_i n_i!}, \tag{1.5}$$

where $\sum_{(n_i)}$ means a sum of all possible terms of the type shown where the n_i take on all possible values consistent with Eqs. (1.3) and (1.4).

It is not necessary to evaluate the sum which appears in the expression for Ω. Since the logarithm of Ω is to be taken and is so insensitive, we need take only the largest term of the sum, discarding all others. The fact that we will get the previously derived expression for the entropy in this manner is one point in favor of this procedure, but we shall examine it more closely later.

To find the largest term in the sum, we need the values of the n_i which make the term a maximum. We may just as well make the logarithm of the term a maximum, the condition for which is

$$\delta \ln \frac{C^N}{n_1! n_2! n_3! \cdots} = -\delta \ln n_1! - \delta \ln n_2! - \delta \ln n_3! - \cdots + \delta N \ln C = 0,$$

$$(1.6)$$

where δ indicates a small variation. For the term $C^N/n_1! n_2! n_3! \cdots$ to be a maximum, its variation with respect to all the n_i in any possible way must be zero. This is indicated in Eq. (1.6). If n is a large number it can be treated as a continuous variable, and by Stirling's theorem $\delta(\ln n!) = \delta n \ln n$.† Therefore Eq. (1.6) may be written

$$\delta n_1 (\ln n_1 - \ln C) + \delta n_2 (\ln n_2 - \ln C) + \delta n_3 (\ln n_3 - \ln C) + \cdots = 0.$$

$$(1.7)$$

It is clear, of course, that the term $\delta N \ln C = \sum_i \delta n_i \ln C$ need not have been written down, since $\delta N = 0$, but it turns out to be convenient to include it. The n_i cannot all be varied independently of each other because of Eqs. (1.3) and (1.4), which may be written

$$\delta N = \delta n_1 + \delta n_2 + \delta n_3 + \cdots = 0$$

$$(1.8)$$

and

$$\delta E = \epsilon_1 \delta n_1 + \epsilon_2 \delta n_2 + \epsilon_3 \delta n_3 + \cdots = 0.$$

$$(1.9)$$

All but two of the δn_i in the conditional equation (1.6) are independent, but if all but two are given, the remaining two can be determined by the conditions (1.8) and (1.9).

Let us now multiply Eq. (1.8) by a constant quantity‡ which we call $-\alpha$ and Eq. (1.9) by a constant quantity $-\beta$ and add the results to Eq. (1.7). We obtain

$$\delta n_1 (\ln n_1 - \alpha - \beta \epsilon_1 - \ln C) + \delta n_2 (\ln n_2 - \alpha - \beta \epsilon_2 - \ln C)$$
$$+ \delta n_3 (\ln n_3 - \alpha - \beta \epsilon_3 - \ln C) + \cdots = 0.$$

$$(1.10)$$

Although we do not know what n_1 and n_2 are, they evidently have definite values imposed upon them by the condition of maximum probability, together with Eqs. (1.8) and (1.9), and we shall determine α and β so that

---

† See footnote, p. 71.
‡ We will frequently use this "method of undetermined, or Lagrange, multipliers." See [1].

$$\ln n_1 - \alpha - \beta\epsilon_1 - \ln C = 0$$

and

$$\ln n_2 - \alpha - \beta\epsilon_2 - \ln C = 0.$$

Equation (1.10) then becomes

$$\delta n_3(\ln n_3 - \alpha - \beta\epsilon_3 - \ln C) + \delta n_4(\ln n_4 - \alpha - \beta\epsilon_4 - \ln C) + \cdots = 0.$$

$$(1.11)$$

Since two of the δn_i are missing from this equation, all that remain may be given arbitrary values. Suppose, for example, we set all the δn_i except δn_3 equal to zero. We then must have, clearly,

$$\ln n_3 - \alpha - \beta\epsilon_3 - \ln C = 0$$

in order for Eq. (1.11) to hold with this condition imposed. We see, in general, that

$$\ln n_i - \alpha - \beta\epsilon_i - \ln C = 0, \tag{1.12}$$

or

$$n_i = C \exp\{\alpha\} \exp\{\beta\epsilon_i\}. \tag{1.13}$$

If desired, α and β can be evaluated, at least in principle, in terms of N and E from Eqs. (1.3) and (1.4). We shall shortly show, however, that they are connected with certain thermodynamic quantities. (Indeed, for β this is already obvious from Eq. (1.13), but we prefer to base the connection on relations obtained in this chapter.)

Equation (1.13) gives the value of n_i which will determine the largest term in Ω. If we substitute this largest term for Ω in Eq. (1.1) we find

$$
\begin{aligned}
S &= k \ln \frac{C^N}{n_1! n_2! n_3! \cdots} \\
&= kN \ln C - kn_1 \ln n_1 - kn_2 \ln n_2 - kn_3 \ln n_3 - \cdots \\
&\qquad + kn_1 + kn_2 + kn_3 + \cdots \\
&= kN \ln C - k \sum_i n_i \ln n_i + kN.
\end{aligned}
\tag{1.14}
$$

In getting the middle line of Eq. (1.14), the Stirling approximation $\ln n! = n \ln n - n$ for large n was used. By using Eq. (1.13) this becomes

$$S = -k \sum_i n_i\alpha - k \sum_i n_i\beta\epsilon_i + kN; \tag{1.15}$$

$\sum_i n_i\epsilon_i$ is obviously the total energy E, so Eq. (1.15) becomes

$$S = -kN\alpha - k\beta E + kN. \tag{1.16}$$

If we substitute Eq. (1.13) into Eq. (1.3), we obtain

$$C \sum_i \exp\{\alpha\} \exp\{\beta\epsilon_i\} = N. \tag{1.17}$$

Hence we have

$$\alpha = \ln N - \ln \left(C \sum_i \exp\{\beta\epsilon_i\} \right), \tag{1.18}$$

and Eq. (1.16) becomes

$$S = kN \ln \left(C \sum_i \exp\{\beta\epsilon_i\} \right) - k\beta E - kN \ln N + kN \tag{1.19}$$

Now $\sum_i \exp\{\beta\epsilon_i\}$ is a summation over cells each containing C quantum levels of approximately the same energy. Multiplying by C converts it into a summation over energy levels instead of over cells, for now there will be (in effect) one term per energy level instead of one term per cell. The final result is obviously independent of C. With the understanding that henceforth we are summing over energy levels, we may drop the C in Eq. (1.19) and write

$$S = kN \ln \sum_i \exp\{\beta\epsilon_i\} - k\beta E - kN \ln N + kN. \tag{1.20}$$

By substituting Eq. (1.13) into Eq. (1.4) and using Eq. (1.17) we obtain

$$\sum_i^{(c)} \epsilon_i C \exp\{\alpha\} \exp\{\beta\epsilon_i\} = N \frac{\sum_i^{(c)} \epsilon_i \exp\{\beta\epsilon_i\}}{\sum_i^{(c)} \exp\{\beta\epsilon_i\}} = E. \tag{1.21}$$

The (c) indicates that the summation is with respect to cells. Multiplying numerator and denominator by C, we may convert to summation over energy levels. Thus

$$N \frac{\sum_i \epsilon_i \exp\{\beta\epsilon_i\}}{\sum_i \exp\{\beta\epsilon_i\}} = E. \tag{1.22}$$

From Eq. (1.22) we see that if the volume is held constant, so that the energy levels remain constant, β depends only on E/N. We can therefore write, holding N constant,

$$\left(\frac{\partial S}{\partial E}\right)_V = \frac{1}{T}$$

$$= kN \frac{\sum_i \epsilon_i (\partial \beta/\partial E)_V \exp\{\beta\epsilon_i\}}{\sum_i \exp\{\beta\epsilon_i\}} - k\beta - kE(\partial\beta/\partial E)_V. \qquad (1.23)$$

Since $(\partial\beta/\partial E)_V$ is a constant in the summation, the first and third terms after the last equals sign of Eq. (1.23) cancel, by Eq. (1.22), so we see that

$$\beta = -\frac{1}{kT}. \qquad (1.24)$$

We can therefore write

$$\sum_i \exp\{\beta\epsilon_i\} = \text{(p.f.)}, \qquad (1.25)$$

and Eq. (1.20) obviously reduces to the previously derived equation for the entropy.

We can now write the equation for the probability that a molecule be found in a particular quantum state. Equation (1.13) gives the most probable number of molecules in the ith cell. If we want to find the number of molecules in one of the quantum states, say the jth in this cell, we can simply divide the right-hand side by C, obtaining

$$n_j = \exp\{\alpha\} \exp\left\{\frac{-\epsilon_j}{kT}\right\}. \qquad (1.26)$$

Since the number of quantum states in a cell is much larger than the number of molecules in it, n_j is a small fraction, whereas the numbers in the original cells were always integers.

By adding over all the quantum states we have

$$\exp\{\alpha\} \sum_j \exp\left\{\frac{-\epsilon_j}{kT}\right\} = N, \qquad (1.27)$$

so that

$$\exp\{\alpha\} = \frac{N}{\text{(p.f.)}}, \qquad (1.28)$$

and the probability of finding a molecule in the jth quantum level is

$$\frac{n_j}{N} = \frac{\exp\{-\epsilon_j/kT\}}{(\text{p.f.})}, \tag{1.29}$$

an expression quite analogous to the expression for the probability of finding a molecule in a particular internal quantum state (compare Sec. 3-6). From this equation Maxwell's distribution law of velocities is readily found.

6-2. *Interpretation of* β

Let us return to β, which we have seen is equal to $-1/kT$. We can see from general considerations that β has some connection with temperature. Suppose, for example, that we had two separate portions of gas, which need not be of the same kind, in two separate boxes, but in thermal contact with each other. We can divide the phase space of each portion into numbered cells of C' and C'' quantum states respectively. If the cells of the first portion have respectively n_1', n_2', n_3', $\cdots$ representative points of molecules in them, and the cells of the second portion have n_1'', n_2'', n_3'', $\cdots$ representative points, the number of ways all the molecules can be placed in the quantum states is

$$\frac{C'^{N'}}{n_1'!n_2'!n_3'!\cdots} \cdot \frac{C''^{N''}}{n_1''!n_2''!n_3''!\cdots}. \tag{2.1}$$

To find the most probable state of the system, this expression is to be maximized. There are two conditions

$$n_1' + n_2' + n_3' + \cdots = N', \tag{2.2}$$

and

$$n_1'' + n_2'' + n_3'' + \cdots = N'', \tag{2.3}$$

but only one condition

$$\epsilon_1'n_1' + \epsilon_2'n_2' + \epsilon_3'n_3' + \cdots + \epsilon_1''n_1'' + \epsilon_2''n_2'' + \epsilon_3''n_3'' + \cdots = E, \tag{2.4}$$

where E is the total energy. Now in calculating the maximum term according to the standard procedure outlined above we will have two undetermined constants α' and α'', but only one β. Thus the two portions of gas in thermal contact, which have a common temperature, are seen in a perfectly trivial way to have a common β, which we might thus suppose, even without further evidence, to have some of the attributes of temperature.

6-3. *Interpretation of α: The Chemical Potential*

It will also be of interest to find a physical interpretation of α. To get some idea of what to look for, let us see how two systems may have α in common. Suppose that the two systems mentioned above contain the same kind of molecules and that they are open to each other so molecules can pass from one to the other. The molecules in the two boxes would perhaps have different potential energies; for example, one of them could be higher in the gravitational field than the other. In any case, an expression like (2.1) would hold for the combined system. But now we would have only one equation of the type of (2.2) and (2.3), namely,

$$n_1' + n_2' + n_3' + \cdots + n_1'' + n_2'' + n_3'' + \cdots = N, \tag{3.1}$$

where N is the total number of molecules in both containers. Thus in this case we have not only a common β but also a common α. This suggests that α is connected with the chemical potential.

Let us therefore calculate the chemical potential.[†] From Eqs. (1.20) and (1.24), for a system in a single container,

$$TS - E = -A = NkT \ln \text{(p.f.)} - NkT \ln N + NkT, \tag{3.2}$$

and we see that the chemical potential (per molecule) is given by

$$\mu = \left(\frac{\partial A}{\partial N}\right)_{T,V} = -kT \ln \text{(p.f.)} + kT \ln N. \tag{3.3}$$

Comparing this with Eq. (1.28), we see that

$$\alpha = \frac{\mu}{kT}. \tag{3.4}$$

Note that if we have an assembly of perfect gas molecules divided into two portions in thermal contact and capable of exchanging molecules, and if these two parts are in equilibrium, so that $T' = T'' = T$ and

$$- kT \ln \text{(p.f.)}' + kT \ln N' = -kT \ln \text{(p.f.)}'' + kT \ln N'' = \mu,$$

[†] For a detailed discussion of the chemical potential from the point of view of thermodynamics see [2].

where $N' + N'' = N$, then we expect from thermodynamics to have, for the whole system, if the free energies are additive, since μ has a common value,

$$S = \frac{E}{T} - \frac{N\mu}{T} + Nk. \tag{3.5}$$

We have further

$$\mu = -kT \ln\left[(\text{p.f.})' + (\text{p.f.})''\right] + kT \ln (N' + N''), \tag{3.6}$$

for if

$$\frac{(\text{p.f.})'}{N'} = \frac{(\text{p.f.})''}{N''} = \exp\left\{\frac{-\mu}{kT}\right\},$$

then

$$\frac{(\text{p.f.})' + (\text{p.f.})''}{N' + N''} = \exp\left\{\frac{-\mu}{kT}\right\}$$

also. But

$$(\text{p.f.})' + (\text{p.f.})'' = \sum_{i'} \exp\left\{\frac{-\epsilon_i'}{kT}\right\} + \sum_{i''} \exp\left\{\frac{-\epsilon_i''}{kT}\right\}$$

$$= \sum_i \exp\left\{\frac{-\epsilon_i}{kT}\right\}, \tag{3.7}$$

where the last sum goes over all energy states of the combined system, and is, therefore, the partition function of the entire assembly. Thus for the entropy of the complete assembly, regardless of whether or not it is split up among several containers, we can write, as we should expect,

$$S = \frac{E}{T} + Nk \ln (\text{p.f.}) - Nk \ln N + Nk. \tag{3.8}$$

When we define the chemical potential μ in terms of $(\text{p.f.})'$ and N', or in terms of $(\text{p.f.})''$ and N'', we assume that N' and N'' are exactly in the equilibrium ratio. This is, of course, implied, inasmuch as we assume that μ is the same whether it is defined in terms of the primed or the doubly primed quantities. However, the combined assembly certainly has many states in which the molecules are not distributed between the two containers in exactly the equilibrium ratio. In any case we always take the distribution which has the maximum probability and neglect all other possibilities. This results, as we see, in the sum of the entropies of the two parts giving an expression entirely equivalent to the expression for the entropy of the whole assembly. This result is, of course, expected, but we must examine the basis upon which it rests with more care.

6-4. *Fluctuations*

The original procedure by which we derived Eq. (1.19) rests upon the much more drastic assumption that a whole series of distribution numbers, $n_1, n_2, n_3, \cdots$, has the equilibrium values, and all other possibilities are neglected. To justify this neglect, let us return to the expression [logarithm of one of the terms in the summation (over cells) in Eq. (1.5)]

$$\ln \tau = \ln \frac{C^N}{n_1! n_2! n_3! \cdots} = N \ln C - \sum_i n_i \ln n_i + N. \qquad (4.1)$$

By its nature $\ln \tau$ has a positive value, so the two positive terms are together larger than the sum of negative terms ($n_i \ln n_i$ itself is always either positive, if $n_i > 1$, or zero if $n_i = 0$ or 1). Terms for which n_i is small will not contribute very much to the sum $\sum_i n_i \ln n_i$. For example, consider a monatomic gas and choose the size of the cells so that we have 10^6 cells with an energy less than kT. Thus (since the number of energy levels of a perfect monatomic gas goes up about as the $\frac{3}{2}$ power of the energy) there are a little over 10^8 cells with an energy less than $25\ kT$. If we had, say, 10^{23} molecules, the most strongly occupied cells would each contain roughly $10^{23}/10^6 = 10^{17}$ molecules, and the total contribution of cells with energy greater than $25\ kT$, each containing $10^{17}/e^{25} \approx 10^6$ molecules or less would be negligible. For practical purposes, then, we may assume that the n_i are large numbers and use the Stirling approximation for the factorials. We assume that τ is a continuous function of the n_i, and will attempt to expand it about the position of its maximum by means of a generalized Taylor series. At the maximum, the sum of the contributions of all first derivatives will be zero, and it is also clear from Eq. (4.1) that all mixed second derivatives of τ, such as $\partial^2 \tau / \partial n_1 \partial n_2$, will be zero. The second derivatives are as follows:

$$\frac{\partial^2 \ln \tau}{\partial n_i^2} = -\frac{\partial^2 (n_i \ln n_i)}{\partial n_i^2} = -n_i^{-1}. \qquad (4.2)$$

Hence to terms of the second order the deviation $\delta \tau$ of τ from its maximum value when $n_1, n_2, n_3, \cdots$ deviate by $\delta n_1, \delta n_2, \delta n_3, \cdots$ is given by

$$\delta \ln \tau = \ln \tau - \ln \tau_{max} = -\tfrac{1}{2} [n_1^{-1} (\delta n_1)^2 + n_2^{-1} (\delta n_2)^2 + \cdots], \qquad (4.3)$$

from which we obtain

$$\frac{\tau}{\tau_{\max}} = \exp\left\{ -\frac{1}{2}\left[\frac{(\delta n_1)^2}{n_1} + \frac{(\delta n_2)^2}{n_2} + \cdots \right] \right\}. \tag{4.4}$$

It is therefore clear that as soon as $(\delta n_i)^2$ becomes much greater than n_i for *even one* cell, the value of τ will have decreased much below its maximum value. In order to get an idea of orders of magnitude, take the situation with the monatomic gas mentioned above, which contains 10^{23} molecules and for which there are 10^6 cells in the energy range kT. Each cell in the important range of energies contains, as we have seen, about 10^{17} molecules. Then an exceedingly small fractional deviation can make $(\delta n_i)^2$ of the order of n_i, and deviations which are much greater than this will be highly improbable.

We now ask: How many possible distributions are there such that all the δn_i are small enough to be of the order of magnitude of $n_i^{1/2}$ or less? Assuming that all the δn_i are independent, which is not quite true (a factor which would, if taken into account, lessen the number of possibilities) the number of possible distributions would be roughly equal to the product $\prod_i \delta n_i = \delta n_1 \delta n_2 \delta n_3 \cdots = \prod_i n_i^{1/2}$. Then Ω might be improved by multiplying $\tau_{\max}$ by a factor of this order. The possible contribution to $S = k \ln \Omega$ due to these neglected distributions is $k \sum_i \ln n_i^{1/2} = \frac{1}{2}k \sum_i \ln n_i$. Of course, this sum should be confined to values of i for which n_i has a fairly large value, since those for which n_i is small do not contribute appreciably to the entropy. The effective number of terms in the sum $\sum_i \ln n_i$ is small compared with the total number N of molecules, and therefore it cannot give an appreciable contribution to the entropy. Perhaps the relative unimportance of the sum $\frac{1}{2}k \sum_i \ln n_i$ can be better seen by comparing it with the sum $k \sum_i n_i \ln n_i$, which occurs in the direct evaluation of $k \ln \Omega$, and which is itself very much less than $kN \ln C$. It is seen that term by term the terms of $\frac{1}{2}k \sum_i \ln n_i$ are negligible unless n_i is so small that its total contribution, $kn_i \ln n_i$, is itself negligible.

6-5. *The Chemical Potential in Mixtures*

The relation between α and μ would not be useful unless an entirely similar relation held for a mixture of perfect gas molecules. Suppose that we have two kinds of molecules, species A and species B; each type of molecule would then have a phase space of its own. Suppose that the phase space for type A is divided into cells containing C_A

quantum states, and that for type B is divided into cells containing C_B quantum states. The number of possible arrangements for a given distribution of molecules in cells would in each case be given by an expression like Eq. (1.2), and the total number of arrangements for the whole system would be given by

$$\frac{C_A^{N_A}}{n_{A1}!n_{A2}!n_{A3}!\cdots} \cdot \frac{C_B^{N_A}}{n_{B1}!n_{B2}!n_{B3}!\cdots}. \tag{5.1}$$

This must be maximized under conditions

$$n_{A1} + n_{A2} + n_{A3} + \cdots = n_A, \tag{5.2}$$

$$n_{B1} + n_{B2} + n_{B3} + \cdots = n_B, \tag{5.3}$$

and

$$\epsilon_{A1}n_{A1} + \epsilon_{A2}n_{A2} + \epsilon_{A3}n_{A3} + \cdots + \epsilon_{B1}n_{B1} + \epsilon_{B2}n_{B2} + \epsilon_{B3}n_{B3} + \cdots = E. \tag{5.4}$$

Clearly there will be two α's, which we may call α_A and α_B. The values of the n's which make (5.1) a maximum will be

$$n_{Ai} = \exp\{\alpha_A\}\exp\{\epsilon_{Ai}\beta\}, \tag{5.5}$$

and

$$n_{Bj} = \exp\{\alpha_B\}\exp\{\epsilon_{Bj}\beta\}, \tag{5.6}$$

where i and j now refer to quantum states, and, summing over all i and j,

$$N_A = \exp\{\alpha_A\}\,(\text{p.f.})_A, \tag{5.7}$$

$$N_B = \exp\{\alpha_B\}\,(\text{p.f.})_B. \tag{5.8}$$

The total entropy is equal to the sum of the entropies of the two species taken separately, so the total entropy is given by

$$S = \frac{E}{T} + kN_A\ln(\text{p.f.})_A - kN_A\ln N_A + kN_A$$
$$+ kN_B\ln(\text{p.f.})_B - kN_B\ln N_B + kN_B, \tag{5.9}$$

whence

$$A = -kTN_A\ln(\text{p.f.})_A + kTN_A\ln N_A - kTN_A$$
$$- kTN_B\ln(\text{p.f.})_B + kTN_B\ln N_B - kTN_B. \tag{5.10}$$

On differentiating partially with respect to N_A and N_B it is readily seen that

$$\mu_A = \left(\frac{\partial A}{\partial N_A}\right)_{V,T,N_B} = kT \ln N_A - kT \ln \text{(p.f.)}_A \tag{5.11}$$

$$\mu_B = \left(\frac{\partial A}{\partial N_B}\right)_{V,T,N_A} = kT \ln N_B - kT \ln \text{(p.f.)}_B, \tag{5.12}$$

whence, from Eqs. (5.7) and (5.8),

$$\alpha_A = \frac{\mu_A}{kT}, \tag{5.13}$$

$$\alpha_B = \frac{\mu_B}{kT}. \tag{5.14}$$

REFERENCES

1. H. Margenau and G. M. Murphy, *The Mathematics of Physics and Chemistry*, 2d ed., Princeton, N.J., Van Nostrand, 1956, p. 209ff.
2. F. H. MacDougall, *Thermodynamics and Chemistry*, 3d ed., New York, Wiley, 1939, pp. 136–38.

PROBLEMS

6.1. Find the probability that the velocity of a molecule should lie between v and $v + dv$.

6.2. Some atoms have three energy levels, owing to a spin magnetic moment in a magnetic field, at $\epsilon = -\epsilon_0$, $\epsilon = 0$, and $\epsilon = \epsilon_0$. If these levels are in equilibrium with each other, but relax very slowly with the rest of the degrees of freedom, we may apply Eqs. (1.3), (1.4), and (1.26) to them. Find the temperature of this system if the average energy is (a) $-\frac{1}{2}\epsilon_0$, (b) if it is 0, and (c) if it is $\frac{1}{2}\epsilon_0$. Find the spin entropy and specific heat of N atoms in each case. Suggest how a state with average energy $\frac{1}{2}\epsilon_0$ might be reached.

6.3. Show that the entropy of the system discussed in Sec. 6-3 is equal to the sum of the entropies of the primed and double-primed portions.

6.4. If there are N' molecules in one vessel and N'' in another, the total entropy

$$S = S' + S''$$

$$= \frac{E'}{T'} + N'k \ln \text{(p.f.)}' - k \ln N'!$$

$$+ \frac{E''}{T''} + N''k \ln \text{(p.f.)}'' - k \ln N''!$$

Supposing the two vessels to be in thermal and material contact but that $E' + E''$ and $N' + N''$ are constant, show, by maximizing S, that when equilibrium is established, $T' = T''$ and $\mu' = \mu''$. Note that (p.f.) is a function of T and N, but that the volume of each vessel is assumed to be constant. Treat this as a new variation problem involving all possible variables.

6.5. Suppose that we have a gas divided between two vessels which are in contact so that molecules can be exchanged from one to the other, as in Prob. 6.4. One of the vessels, with volume V'', is higher in the gravitational field than is the other, which has volume V'. The potential energy of the molecule in the double-primed vessel exceeds that of a molecule in the primed vessel by ϵ_p. Find the ratio of the number of molecules in the two vessels in a form involving V'', V', and ϵ_p. Work this problem by considering the results of maximizing the distribution among cells in the two vessels.

6.6. Find the chemical potential μ of the system described in Prob. 2.9 and find an expression for $(\partial \mu / \partial F)_{N,T}$. Suppose there is a gradient of electric field in the vessel, along the z direction. Given dF/dz find dN/dz.

6.7. What will be the probability, relative to the equilibrium or maximum probability, that the number n_{-1} in the state $\epsilon = -\epsilon_0$ in case (a) of Prob. 6.2 should differ from its most probable value by δn, while at the same time n_1 (the number in the state $\epsilon = \epsilon_0$) differs from its most probable value by $-\delta n$? Suppose that δn is allowed to take any value. Approximately how much would this contribute to the entropy over and above what it would be if only the distribution of maximum probability were allowed? Find the expression for a system containing a total of N atoms, and evaluate for $N = 10^{24}$.

6.8. In standard works on thermodynamics (e.g., in Chap. 8 [2]) a discussion is given for the conditions for thermodynamic equilibrium under various constraints. Compare these conditions with the conditions which we have used [such as making Ω a maximum or finding the largest term in (P.F.)], and show which of the latter can be brought into correspondence with which of the thermodynamic conditions.

Chemical Equilibrium

7-1. *Use of the Canonical Partition Function*

We now take up in some detail the equilibrium between two molecules A and B to form a molecule AB:

$$A + B \rightleftarrows AB,$$

all species acting as ideal gases. We start with the canonical partition function, $(P.F.) = \sum_L \exp\{-E_L/kT\}$. If there are certain numbers N_A, N_B, and N_{AB} of A, B, and AB respectively we have, analogously to Eq. (1.4), of Chap. 3,

$$E_L = \sum_\alpha \epsilon_{l_\alpha,L} + \sum_\beta \epsilon_{k_\beta,L} + \sum_\gamma \epsilon_{m_\gamma,L}, \tag{1.1}$$

where $\sum_\alpha$ sums over the N_A molecules of type A ($\epsilon_{l_\alpha,L}$ being the energy of the αth molecule in the quantum state l in which it finds itself when the state of the whole assembly is L), $\sum_\beta$ goes over the N_B molecules of the type B, and $\sum_\gamma$ goes over the N_{AB} molecules of type AB.

The same argument which resulted in Eq. (1.7) of Chap. 3 gives in this case

$$(P.F.) = \frac{(p.f.)_A^{N_A}}{N_A!} \frac{(p.f.)_B^{N_B}}{N_B!} \frac{(p.f.)_{AB}^{N_{AB}}}{N_{AB}!}. \tag{1.2}$$

This is for fixed values of N_A, N_B, and N_{AB}. Any other set of values of N_A, N_B, and N_{AB} gives a different set of energy levels E_L for the whole system. Thus the complete partition function, for all possible values of N_A, N_B, and N_{AB}, is

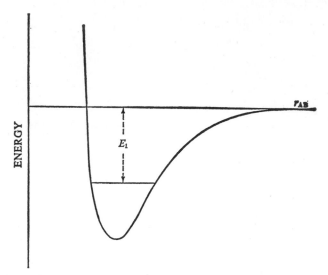

Figure 7-1.   Potential-energy curve of diatomic molecule.

$$(\text{P.F.}) = \sum_{N_A} \sum_{N_B} \sum_{N_{AB}} \frac{(\text{p.f.})_A^{N_A}}{N_A!} \frac{(\text{p.f.})_B^{N_B}}{N_B!} \frac{(\text{p.f.})_{AB}^{N_{AB}}}{N_{AB}!}, \tag{1.3}$$

$$N_A + N_{AB} = N_{A,\text{tot}} = \text{const.}, \qquad N_B + N_{AB} = N_{B,\text{tot}} = \text{const.} \tag{1.4}$$

The sums are over values of N_A, N_B, and N_{AB} consistent with Eqs. (1.4). Only the values of N_A, N_B, and N_{AB} matter, not *which* molecules are separate and which combined, for exchanging two N_A's, whether combined or uncombined, does not give distinct energy levels.

The partition functions must be referred to consistent energy levels. For example, suppose that A and B are atoms, and that the potential-energy curve for combination of A and B to form the molecule AB has the form shown in Fig. 7-1. Then if the energy of the pair A and B is supposed to be zero if they are separated and have no kinetic energy, the energy levels of molecule AB must be calculated with the asymptote as zero. Thus the value of the energy level indicated in the figure will be $-E_1$.

In the light of the discussion in Chapters 5 and 6, we will not hesitate to replace (P.F.) by the largest term in Eq. (1.3). To find the largest term, we set the variation of the logarithm of such a term (varying N_A, N_B, and N_{AB}) equal to zero:

$$\delta \ln \left\{ \frac{(\text{p.f.})_A^{N_A}}{N_A!} \frac{(\text{p.f.})_B^{N_B}}{N_B!} \frac{(\text{p.f.})_{AB}^{N_{AB}}}{N_{AB}!} \right\}$$

$$= \delta N_A \ln (\text{p.f.})_A + \delta N_B \ln (\text{p.f.})_B + \delta N_{AB} \ln (\text{p.f.})_{AB}$$

$$- \delta N_A \ln N_A - \delta N_B \ln N_B - \delta N_{AB} \ln N_{AB}$$

$$= 0. \tag{1.5}$$

Also, by Eqs. (1.4),

$$\delta N_A + \delta N_{AB} = 0, \tag{1.6a}$$

$$\delta N_B + \delta N_{AB} = 0. \tag{1.6b}$$

Multiplying Eq. (1.6a) by a constant α_A and Eq. (1.6b) by a constant α_B and adding them to Eq. (1.5), we get

$$\delta N_A[\ln (\text{p.f.})_A - \ln N_A + \alpha_A] + \delta N_B[\ln (\text{p.f.})_B - \ln N_B + \alpha_B]$$

$$+ \delta N_{AB}[\ln (\text{p.f.})_{AB} - \ln N_{AB} + \alpha_A + \alpha_B] = 0. \tag{1.7}$$

We can choose α_A and α_B to make the first two brackets in Eq. (1.7) equal to zero. Then the last one is also equal to zero. We find

$$\alpha_A = -\ln (\text{p.f.})_A + \ln N_A = \frac{\mu_A}{kT}, \tag{1.8}$$

$$\alpha_B = -\ln (\text{p.f.})_B + \ln N_B = \frac{\mu_B}{kT}, \tag{1.9}$$

$$\alpha_A + \alpha_B = -\ln (\text{p.f.})_{AB} + \ln N_{AB} = \frac{\mu_{AB}}{kT}, \tag{1.10}$$

the chemical potentials being defined in the usual way from the expression for A for a mixture of N_A molecules A, N_B molecules B, and N_{AB} molecules AB. We see that, as expected, for the maximum term, which we assume represents a state of equilibrium,

$$\mu_A + \mu_B = \mu_{AB}, \tag{1.11}$$

and also that

$$\frac{N_{AB}}{N_A N_B} = \frac{(\text{p.f.})_{AB}}{(\text{p.f.})_A (\text{p.f.})_B}. \tag{1.12}$$

The equilibrium constant is given by

$$K = \frac{N_{AB}/V}{(N_A/V)(N_B/V)} = \frac{(p.f.)^0_{AB}}{(p.f.)^0_A(p.f.)^0_B},$$

(1.13)

where $(p.f.)^0_A$, etc., are defined by equations like

$$(p.f.)^0_A = \frac{(p.f.)_A}{V}.$$

(1.14)

By comparing Eq. (1.14) with Eq. (1.15) of Chap. 3, it will be seen that

$$(p.f.)^0_A = \exp\left\{-\frac{G^0_A}{RT}\right\},$$

(1.15)

where G^0_A is the value of the molal Gibbs free energy of species A when it is at unit concentration; i.e., $N/V = 1$. Thus Eq. (1.13) is equivalent to

$$K = \exp\left\{-\frac{\Delta G^0}{RT}\right\},$$

(1.16)

where $\Delta G^0 = G^0_{AB} - G^0_A - G^0_B$, which is of course the standard form. Note that K is expressed in terms of concentration, and the standard state is therefore the condition of unit concentration. Since in general for an ideal gas

$$E = RT^2 \frac{\partial \ln (p.f.)}{\partial T} = RT^2 \frac{\partial \ln (p.f.)^0}{\partial T},$$

we see from Eq. (1.13) that

$$\frac{d \ln K}{dT} = \frac{\Delta E}{RT^2},$$

(1.17)

where $\Delta E = E_{AB} - E_A - E_B$ is the molal energy change. It is important to note that this holds only if K is expressed in terms of concentration. Were we dealing with K_p, expressed in terms of partial pressures, we would have had the usual van't Hoff equation,

$$\frac{d \ln K_p}{dT} = \frac{\Delta H}{RT^2}$$

(1.18)

where ΔH is the molal enthalpy change.

7-2. *Maximization of* Ω

The result expressed by Eq. (1.12) can also be obtained by maximizing the expression for the number of ways in which N_A molecules of A, N_B molecules of B, and N_{AB} molecules of AB, can be placed in cells containing respectively C_A, C_B, and C_{AB} quantum states per cell. This expression is

$$\frac{C_A^{N_A}}{n_{A1}! n_{A2}! n_{A3}! \cdots} \cdot \frac{C_B^{N_B}}{n_{B1}! n_{B2}! n_{B3}! \cdots} \cdot \frac{C_{AB}^{N_{AB}}}{n_{AB1}! n_{AB2}! n_{AB3}! \cdots}. \tag{2.1}$$

It can be maximized under the conditions

$$n_{A1} + n_{A2} + n_{A3} + \cdots = n_A, \tag{2.2}$$

$$n_{B1} + n_{B2} + n_{B3} + \cdots = n_B, \tag{2.3}$$

$$n_{AB1} + n_{AB2} + n_{AB3} + \cdots = n_{AB}, \tag{2.4}$$

and

$$n_{A1}\epsilon_{A1} + n_{A2}\epsilon_{A2} + n_{A3}\epsilon_{A3} + \cdots + n_{B1}\epsilon_{B1} + n_{B2}\epsilon_{B2} + n_{B3}\epsilon_{B3} + \cdots$$
$$+ n_{AB1}\epsilon_{AB1} + n_{AB2}\epsilon_{AB2} + n_{AB3}\epsilon_{AB3} + \cdots = E. \tag{2.5}$$

This process will require the use of three undetermined α's (α_A, α_B, and α_{AB}) and one β; from it we may calculate the entropy of a system with fixed N_A, N_B, and N_{AB}. The result of this process will clearly be

$$S = \frac{E}{T} + kN_A \ln (\text{p.f.})_A - kN_A \ln N_A + kN_A$$

$$+ kN_B \ln (\text{p.f.})_B - kN_B \ln N_B + kN_B$$

$$+ kN_{AB} \ln (\text{p.f.})_{AB} - kN_{AB} \ln N_{AB} + kN_{AB}. \tag{2.6}$$

We can now maximize S with varying N_A, N_B, and N_{AB}, under the conditions

$$N_A + N_{AB} = N_{A,\text{tot}} = \text{const.},$$
$$N_B + N_{AB} = N_{B,\text{tot}} = \text{const.},$$
$$E = \text{const.}$$

Variation of N_A, N_B, and N_{AB} may produce a variation in T if E is held constant. However, we note that $\delta(E/T) = -(E/T^2)\delta T$ and that

$$kN_A \frac{\partial \ln (\text{p.f.})_A}{\partial T} \delta T = \frac{E_A}{T^2} \delta T,$$

$$kN_B \frac{\partial \ln (\text{p.f.})_B}{\partial T} \delta T = \frac{E_B}{T^2} \delta T,$$

$$kN_{AB} \frac{\partial \ln (\text{p.f.})_{AB}}{\partial T} \delta T = \frac{E_{AB}}{T^2} \delta T.$$

Since $E = E_A + E_B + E_{AB}$, all the terms arising from changes in T cancel, and what remains then is exactly the same problem we have already solved. Its solution leads as before to Eqs. (1.11), (1.12), and (1.13).

The expression (2.1), may also be maximized in another way. Instead of two steps we may go directly to the maximum of Eq. (2.1) under the conditions

$$n_{A1} + n_{A2} + n_{A3} + \cdots + n_{AB1} + n_{AB2} + n_{AB3} + \cdots = N_{A,\text{tot}}, \quad (2.7)$$

$$n_{B1} + n_{B2} + n_{B3} + \cdots + n_{AB1} + n_{AB2} + n_{AB3} + \cdots = N_{B,\text{tot}}, \quad (2.8)$$

which are less restrictive than Eqs. (2.2), (2.3), and (2.4). The other condition, Eq. (2.5), is of course retained unchanged. We use two multipliers, α_A and α_B, for Eqs. (2.7) and (2.8), and setting the coefficients of δn_{Ai}, δn_{Bj}, and δn_{ABk} equal to zero in the resulting variational expression gives

$$\ln n_{Ai} - \alpha_A - \beta \epsilon_{Ai} - \ln C_A = 0, \tag{2.9}$$

$$\ln n_{Bj} - \alpha_B - \beta \epsilon_{Bj} - \ln C_B = 0, \tag{2.10}$$

$$\ln n_{ABk} - (\alpha_A + \alpha_B) - \beta \epsilon_{ABk} - \ln C_{AB} = 0, \tag{2.11}$$

or

$$n_{Ai} = C_A \exp\{\alpha_A\} \exp\{\beta \epsilon_{Ai}\}, \tag{2.12}$$

$$n_{Bj} = C_B \exp\{\alpha_B\} \exp\{\beta \epsilon_{Bj}\}, \tag{2.13}$$

$$n_{ABk} = C_{AB} \exp\{\alpha_A + \alpha_B\} \exp\{\beta \epsilon_{ABk}\}. \tag{2.14}$$

Now we see from Eqs. (2.12), (2.13), and (2.14) that

$$N_A = C_A \exp\{\alpha_A\} \sum_i \exp\{\beta \epsilon_{Ai}\}, \tag{2.15}$$

$$N_B = C_B \exp\{\alpha_B\} \sum_j \exp\{\beta \epsilon_{Bj}\}, \tag{2.16}$$

$$N_{AB} = C_{AB} \exp\{\alpha_A + \alpha_B\} \sum_k \exp\{\beta \epsilon_{ABk}\}. \tag{2.17}$$

Dividing Eq. (2.17) by (2.15) and (2.16), we get Eq. (1.12). Therefore this process also gives the same result for the equilibrium constant.

7-3. *Heuristic Discussion*

We now consider a pictorial and less formal interpretation of Eq. (1.12). If we set up the partition function of a *pair* of molecules, A and B, we need first to consider the energy levels of the pair. A typical energy level would be $\epsilon_{Ai} + \epsilon_{Bj}$, and the partition function would be

$$\sum_{i,j} \exp\left\{-\frac{\epsilon_{Ai} + \epsilon_{Bj}}{kT}\right\} = \sum_i \exp\left\{-\frac{\epsilon_{Ai}}{kT}\right\} \sum_j \exp\left\{-\frac{\epsilon_{Bj}}{kT}\right\}$$

$$= (\text{p.f.})_A(\text{p.f.})_B. \tag{3.1}$$

Following the general principles used before, but applied now to a *pair* of molecules rather than a single molecule, we state that the probability of finding this pair combined into AB as compared with the probability of its being uncombined should be equal to the ratio of the partition functions: $(\text{p.f.})_{AB}/(\text{p.f.})_A(\text{p.f.})_B$.

A molecule A is simultaneously a member of $N_{B,tot}$ pairs. The average time it is combined with one particular B molecule, compared with the average time it is free, is $(\text{p.f.})_{AB}/(\text{p.f.})_A(\text{p.f.})_B$. The time it is combined with any one of the B molecules compared with the time it is free is $N_B(\text{p.f.})_{AB}/(\text{p.f.})_A(\text{p.f.})_B$. In this expression we multiplied by N_B rather than $N_{B,tot}$, because $N_{B,tot} - N_B(= N_{AB})$ of the B molecules are not available, being already combined with other A molecules. This ratio holds good for all the A molecules and will therefore be equal to the fraction of them combined at any time, i.e., N_{AB}, divided by the number, N_A, uncombined. This gives

$$\frac{N_{AB}}{N_A} = \frac{N_B(\text{p.f.})_{AB}}{(\text{p.f.})_A(\text{p.f.})_B}, \tag{3.2}$$

which, of course, is equivalent to Eq. (1.12). This heuristic and admittedly unrigorous derivation of Eq. (1.12) may give a better insight into the meaning of that equation than the more rigorous derivations already given.

7-4. *Dissociation of a Diatomic Molecule*

We now consider how to evaluate the ratio $(\text{p.f.})_{AB}/(\text{p.f.})_A(\text{p.f.})_B$ when A and B are atoms and AB is a diatomic molecule. We first treat all the degrees of freedom as classical, even the vibrational motion of AB.

We can then treat the partition functions as phase integrals. The difference between the phase integral (p.f.)$_{AB}$ for the pair of atoms A and B and the phase integral (p.f.)$_A$(p.f.)$_B$ for the same pair of atoms depends essentially on which part of the phase space is to be included. In calculating (p.f.)$_{AB}$, we will include that part of the phase space for which r, the distance between the nuclei, is close to the minimum of the potential energy curve, whereas (p.f.)$_A$(p.f.)$_B$ involves regions of the phase space for which r is greater. In the latter case, the mutual potential energy will not, in most regions, be appreciably different from zero, and we may write for the energy of the pair

$$\epsilon = \frac{p_{Ax}^2 + p_{Ay}^2 + p_{Az}^2}{2m_A} + \frac{p_{Bx}^2 + p_{By}^2 + p_{Bz}^2}{2m_B}, \tag{4.1}$$

where m_A and m_B are the masses of the respective molecules and $p_{Ax}, \cdots, p_{Bx}, \cdots$ are components of the respective momenta.

We may then write

$$\text{(p.f.)}_A\text{(p.f.)}_B \tag{4.2}$$
$$= h^{-6}g_Ag_B \underset{\substack{\text{all regions} \\ r \text{ large}}}{\iint \cdots \int} \exp\left\{-\frac{\epsilon}{kT}\right\} dp_{Ax}\, dp_{Ay} \cdots dp_{Bz} dx_A dy_A \cdots dz_B,$$

where $x_A, y_A, \cdots, z_B$ are the Cartesian coordinates of the atoms A and B, where ϵ is to be evaluated from Eq. (4.1), and where g_A and g_B are the degeneracies of the lowest electronic energy levels of A and B We may assume that we have a mixture of ideal gases in which the molecules do not interfere with each other, if the atoms are free to move through a volume which is large compared with the volume in which there is appreciable interaction. If this is so, we may extend the integration with respect to $dx_A dy_A \cdots dz_B$ in Eq. (4.2) over all the space in the box containing the gases, while of course each p can go from $-\infty$ to ∞. The integration with respect to $dx_A dy_A \cdots dz_B$ gives V^2, where V is the volume of the vessel, and the integrals with respect to the p's are the same as those previously encountered. We then obtain

$$\text{(p.f.)}_A\text{(p.f.)}_B = g_Ag_B\left(\frac{2\pi m_A kT}{h^2}\right)^{3/2}\left(\frac{2\pi m_B kT}{h^2}\right)^{3/2}V^2. \tag{4.3}$$

We can include the regions of small r in the integral of Eq. (4.2), which should have been confined to large r, because we ignored the true course of the potential energy curve in the region of small r. On this account, the contributions to the integral from small r were negligible. In evaluating (p.f.)$_{AB}$, which includes the regions of small r, the true course of the potential energy curve in this region must be considered. Only because the potential-energy well is so deep is (p.f.)$_{AB}$ ever comparable to (p.f.)$_A$(p.f.)$_B$. As a matter of fact, only the regions near the minimum of the potential energy contribute appreciably to (p.f.)$_{AB}$. Since we take the energy of the separated atoms A and B as zero, the total energy in the neighborhood of the minimum of the potential-energy curve is given approximately by

$$\epsilon = \frac{p_{Ax}^2 + p_{Ay}^2 + p_{Az}^2}{2m_A} + \frac{p_{Bx}^2 + p_{By}^2 + p_{Bz}^2}{2m_B} - \epsilon_D + \frac{(r - r_e)^2}{2a^2}, \qquad (4.4)$$

where $-\epsilon_D$ is the potential energy of the minimum of the potential-energy curve with respect to the asymptotic portion as zero, and a is a constant. The potential-energy part of Eq. (4.4) is just the same as Eq. (5.12) of Chap. 1, with $\epsilon_{p,e}$ set equal to $-\epsilon_D$. The partition func-has been evaluated in Sec. 3-4 and is given in Eq. (4.12) of Chap. 3. We should multiply the latter equation by the factor g_{AB}, the multiplicity of the lowest state of the molecule, which was not considered in Sec. 3-4. If we divide the result by Eq. (4.3) above (noting that m_A and m_B of this chapter are respectively the same as m_1 and m_2 of Chap. 3), we obtain

$$\frac{(p.f.)_{AB}}{(p.f.)_A (p.f.)_B} = \frac{g_{AB}}{g_A g_B} \frac{4\pi r_e^2 (2\pi a^2 k T)^{1/2}}{V} \exp\left\{\frac{\epsilon_D}{kT}\right\}. \qquad (4.5)$$

It is important to note that ϵ_D times Avogadro's number is almost, but *not* exactly, equal to ΔE of Eq. (1.17).

Using Eq. (1.12), Eq. (4.5) may be written in the form

$$\frac{N_{AB}}{N_A} = N_B \frac{g_{AB}}{g_A g_B} \frac{4\pi r_e^2 (2\pi a^2 k T)^{1/2}}{V} \exp\left\{\frac{\epsilon_D}{kT}\right\}, \qquad (4.6)$$

which gives the relative numbers of A's attached to B's or free. Otherwise stated, this is the chance that a given A is attached to a B as compared with the chance that it is free. This equation may be readily interpreted [1]. On the right-hand side of Eq. (4.5) there remain, in addition to N_B (which gives the number of free B's to which attachment of an A can be made) three factors, one being a ratio of multiplicities, one a ratio of volumes, and one an energy term or Boltzmann factor. The volume factor is of special interest. The numerator of this ratio was discussed in detail in Sec. 3-5; it can be considered as a free volume for the motion of an A atom in the field of a B. The probability that an A atom should be attached to a B is proportional to this free volume divided by the free volume V of an unattached A. The volume ratio $4\pi r_e^2(2\pi a^2 kT)^{1/2}/V$ is always very small, even when multiplied by N_B, but this may be counteracted by the factor $\exp\{\epsilon_D/kT\}$.

This simple interpretation of the association needs some modification when the vibrational levels of the molecule AB are quantized. It is seen that Eq. (4.6) arises essentially from the assumption that (p.f.)$_{\text{vib}}$ for the molecule AB is classical. Equation (4.6) must, therefore, be corrected by multiplying it by the ratio of the quantum partition function to the classical one. It thus becomes

$$\frac{N_{AB}}{N_A} = N_B \frac{g_{AB}}{g_A g_B} \frac{4\pi r_e^2(2\pi a^2 kT)^{1/2}}{V} \exp\left\{\frac{\epsilon_D}{kT}\right\} \frac{(\text{p.f.})_{\text{vib}}}{kT/h\nu_0} \tag{4.7}$$

where ν_0 is the frequency of the vibration, which is of course related to a by Eq. (5.14) of Chap. 1:

$$\nu_0 = \frac{1}{2\pi a \mu^{1/2}} \tag{4.8}$$

Equation (4.7) can be written

$$\begin{aligned}
K &= \frac{g_{AB}}{g_A g_B} 4\pi r_e^2(2\pi a^2 kT)^{1/2} \exp\left\{\frac{\epsilon_D}{kT}\right\} \frac{(\text{p.f.})_{\text{vib}}}{kT/h\nu_0} \\
&= \frac{g_{AB}}{g_A g_B} 4\pi r_e^2(2\pi a^2 kT)^{1/2} \exp\left\{\frac{\epsilon_D}{kT}\right\} \frac{\exp\{-h\nu_0/2kT\} \exp\{h\nu_0/kT\}}{(\exp\{h\nu_0/kT\} - 1)kT/h\nu_0},
\end{aligned} \tag{4.9}$$

where K is the equilibrium constant for the reaction $A + B \rightleftarrows AB$. If the potential energy does not have the strictly harmonic form shown in Eq. (4.4) a further correction can be made.

7-5. *Equilibrium Involving Two Like Molecules: Effect of Symmetry*

To bring out the effect of symmetry in molecular equilibrium, we now deal with an equilibrium of the type

$$2A \rightleftarrows A_2,$$

in which the entities which combine are alike. In this case we find for fixed values of N_A and N_{A_2}

$$(\text{P.F.}) = \frac{(\text{p.f.})_A^{N_A}}{N_A!} \frac{(\text{p.f.})_{A_2}^{N_{A_2}}}{N_{A_2}!}, \tag{5.1}$$

and we maximize the right-hand side under the condition

$$N_A + 2N_{A_2} = N_{A,\text{tot}} = \text{const.} \tag{5.2}$$

This gives

$$\delta N_A \ln (\text{p.f.})_A + \delta N_{A_2} \ln (\text{p.f.})_{A_2} - \delta N_A \ln N_A - \delta N_{A_2} \ln N_{A_2} = 0, \tag{5.3}$$

with

$$\delta N_A + 2\delta N_{A_2} = 0. \tag{5.4}$$

Multiplying Eq. (5.4) by α and adding it to Eq. (5.3), we obtain

$$\delta N_A [\ln (\text{p.f.})_A - \ln N_A + \alpha] + \delta N_{A_2} (\text{p.f.})_{A_2} - \ln N_{A_2} + 2\alpha] = 0. \tag{5.5}$$

In the usual manner, we fix α to make the first bracket zero; then the second bracket is zero also, and we see that

$$2 \ln \left[\frac{(\text{p.f.})_A}{N_A} \right] = \ln \left[\frac{(\text{p.f.})_{A_2}}{N_{A_2}} \right]. \tag{5.6}$$

The usual definition of the chemical potential will yield

$$2\mu_A = \mu_{A_2}. \tag{5.7}$$

Eq. (5.6) can be rewritten

$$\frac{N_{A_2}}{N_A^2} = \frac{(\text{p.f.})_{A_2}}{(\text{p.f.})_A^2}. \tag{5.8}$$

It will be instructive to consider the heuristic derivation of Eq. (5.8). We start by finding the partition function of a pair $A + A$. The energy levels are of the form $\epsilon_{Ai} + \epsilon_{Aj}$ and we might expect the partition function for a pair to be

$$\sum_{i,j} \exp \left\{ \frac{-(\epsilon_{Ai} + \epsilon_{Aj})}{kT} \right\} = \sum_i \exp \left\{ \frac{-\epsilon_{Ai}}{kT} \right\} \sum_j \exp \left\{ \frac{-\epsilon_{Aj}}{kT} \right\} = (\text{p.f.})_A^2.$$

However, the energy level obtained by the interchange of two molecules is identical to the energy level before the exchange. Each energy level is therefore counted twice in the double sum, and the partition function is actually $(\text{p.f.})_A^2/2$. Therefore the fraction of the time that a given atom or molecule is attached to another is given by $2N_A(\text{p.f.})_{A_2}/(\text{p.f.})_A^2$. This is true for any atom. One might therefore think that the ratio N_{A_2}/N_A would be $2N_A(\text{p.f.})_{A_2}/(\text{p.f.})_A^2$. However, when two A's are combined with each other, they form only *one* pair A_2, although *each one* is held for a certain length of time, while the combination is maintained. The above expression therefore counts every pair twice, and we should write

$$\frac{N_{A_2}}{N_A} = \frac{N_A(\text{p.f.})_{A_2}}{(\text{p.f.})_A^2},$$

equivalent to Eq. (5.8). Note that $(\text{p.f.})_{A_2}$ *may* contain a symmetry factor; it certainly does if the A's are atoms. Effectively, the symmetry factor is taken care of in $(\text{p.f.})_A^2/2$. Since it remains in $(\text{p.f.})_{A_2}$, the equilibrium constant will be given, if the A's are atoms, by the right-hand side of Eq. (4.9) divided by 2.

It will be seen that the expression for the equilibrium ratio in terms of partition functions has the expected relation to the stoichiometry of the chemical reaction, and it should now be clear how to extend the statistical mechanical considerations to reactions of any degree of complexity.

7-6. *Combination of Complex Molecules*

We may now consider how to modify Eq. (4.7) when the molecules A and B which take part in the reaction $A + B \rightleftharpoons AB$ are complicated molecules. As a simple example in which the situation is fairly clear, let us take the reaction

$$2CH_3 \rightleftharpoons C_2H_6.$$

We first need to analyze the various degrees of freedom of the reactant and the product. The treatment of the translational and rotational degrees of freedom is fairly straightforward. The translational motion of the center of gravity of the pair of methyl radicals may be treated separately from the relative translation of the two methyl radicals with respect to each other.

There are two types of vibrational motion to consider, one connected with the stretching and one with the bending† of bonds. We cannot, of course, treat the stretching or the bending of particular bonds individually, since the motions are combined into normal vibrations. However, certain normal vibrations are composed of motions of the stretching type, whereas others are composed of bending motions. The *numbers* of such vibrations can be found by considering the motions of individual atoms with respect to their neighbors, assuming the latter fixed in position, for it does not matter what coordinates are counted in order to determine the number of degrees of freedom. Furthermore, certain normal modes of vibration will be particularly associated with special types of stretching and bending vibrations. In CH_3 and C_2H_6, the types are quite limited, but in a more complex organic molecule there will be, as well as C—H stretchings and bendings, a variety of stretchings and bendings of bonds involving heavy atoms. All these are associated with different frequencies [2, 3], hydrogen stretchings having the highest frequencies, hydrogen bendings next, then heavy atom stretchings, then heavy atom bendings, which can have quite low frequencies, especially if there are long chains of atoms in the molecule. Frequencies dependent on double bonds are higher than those dependent on single bonds.

Let us now take up the ethane molecule, which has altogether $8 \times 3 = 24$ degrees of freedom. There are three degrees of freedom of translation and three of rotation. There are seven stretching degrees of freedom, one primarily a C—C stretching involving the C—C bond, while the other six are C—H stretchings, one for each hydrogen. The other eleven degrees of freedom are C—H bending vibrations (including the torsional oscillation or "hindered rotation" about the C—C bond). One might expect twelve bending vibrations, since each hydrogen could bend in either one of two mutually perpendicular directions. However, if these are all in phase they will result in a rotation about the C—C axis, which has already been counted.

We summarize the situation for this reaction in Table 7-1, the assignments for CH_3 being fairly obvious. The degrees of freedom shown in boldface type are those which would occur in the recombination of two atoms. Since the methyl radicals taken as a whole do somewhat resemble two atoms, we may assume that on recombination the

---

† In the term "bending" we include various types of motion associated with relatively low frequencies, which have been called by special names, such as "rocking" (e.g., motion of an end methyl group involving bending of the C—C bond) and "twisting," or "torsional vibration" (e.g., hindered rotation of the same methyl group around the C—C bond as an axis). See [2].

degrees of freedom of the methyl radicals shown in boldface go over, speaking roughly, into the boldface degrees of freedom of C_2H_6. If these degrees were the only ones, we would have an expression exactly like Eq. (4.7), except that the right-hand side would be divided by 2, because of the symmetry number, the two methyl radicals being alike.

TABLE 7-1

	No. of degrees of freedom	
Type of motion	2 CH_3	C_2H_6
Translation of center of gravity	**3**	**3**
Relative translation	**3**	0
Rotation, large moment of inertia (axis perpendicular to C—C)	0	**2**
Rotation, small moment of inertia (about C—C axis in C_2H_6)	6	1
Vibration, C—C stretching	0	**1**
Vibration, C—H stretching	6	6
Vibration, C—H bending	6	11

Other than these six "principal" degrees of freedom, we see that the rotational degrees of freedom of CH_3 (all, of course, with small moment of inertia, since they involve only motions of the hydrogen atoms) have gone over into one rotation of C_2H_6 and five C—H bending vibrations. Whatever changes occur in the other degrees of freedom will not cause great changes in the partition functions. We can therefore write as a reasonable approximation

$$\frac{N_{C_2H_6}}{N_{CH_3}^2} = \frac{g_{C_2H_6}}{g_{CH_3}^2} \frac{4\pi r_e^2 (2\pi a^2 kT)^{1/2}}{2V} \exp\left\{\frac{\epsilon_D}{kT}\right\} \frac{h\nu_0}{kT}$$

$$\times \frac{\exp\{-h\nu_0/2kT\} \exp\{h\nu_0/kT\}}{\exp\{h\nu_0/kT - 1\}} \frac{(\text{p.f.})_{\text{rot,C—C}}^{(1)}(\text{p.f.})_{\text{C—H bend}}^{(5)}}{[(\text{p.f.})_{\text{rot,CH}_3}^{(3)}]^2}. \tag{6.1}$$

Here $g_{C_2H_6} = 1$ and, presumably, $g_{CH_3} = 2$, since there will be one unpaired electron; a is related to the force constant of the C—C vibration in ethane and ν_0 is the corresponding frequency; r_e is approximately the C—C distance in ethane. In the numerator, $(\text{p.f.})_{\text{rot,C—C}}^{(1)}$ is the partition function for the rotation about the C—C axis in ethane, and

$(p.f.)^{(5)}_{C-H \text{ bend}}$ is the vibrational partition function (or product of five partition functions) for five C—H bending degrees of freedom of ethane. In the denominator $(p.f.)^{(3)}_{rot,CH_3}$ is the rotational partition function for CH_3. (The superscript in parentheses gives the number of degrees of freedom involved.) Because the C—C axis in ethane has a three-fold symmetry, $(p.f.)^{(1)}_{rot,C-C}$ involves a symmetry number of 3, whereas $(p.f.)^{(3)}_{rot,CH_3}$ involves a symmetry number of 6, since the atoms in CH_3 are probably almost coplanar in the normal state with H—C—H angles of 120° (see the discussion at the end of Sec. 2-5).

The partition functions for vibrations are usually much smaller than the partition functions of rotations. Bending vibrations have lower frequencies than stretching vibrations, but for C—H bendings, except for the torsional oscillations of the two methyl radicals about the line joining the carbon atoms, $h\nu/kT$ is considerably greater than 1 at room temperature, so that only the lowest level of each vibration has an appreciable population. As a rough approximation, $(p.f.)^{(5)}_{C-H \text{ bend}}$ can be taken as equal to $\exp\{-\epsilon_0/kT\}$ where ϵ_0 is the sum of the zero-point energies of the five vibrations.

We use Eq. (5.13) of Chap. 2 for $(p.f.)^{(1)}_{rot,C-C}$ (including, however, the symmetry number of 3) and Eq. (5.14) of Chap. 2 for $(p.f.)^{(3)}_{rot,CH_3}$ (symmetry number 6). Thus we obtain for the ratio of the rotational partition functions

$$\frac{(p.f.)^{(1)}_{rot,C-C}}{[(p.f.)^{(3)}_{rot,CH_3}]^2} = \frac{6^2(8\pi^2 I_{C-C}kT/h^2)^{1/2}}{3\pi^{1/2}(8\pi^2 kT/h^2)^3 I_1 I_2 I_3}, \tag{6.2}$$

where I_{C-C} is the moment of inertia of the ethane about the line joining the carbon atoms, and I_1, I_2, and I_3 are the moments of inertia of the methyl radical. For numerical values we may take $I_{C-C} = 11 \times 10^{-40}$ gm cm^2, $I_1 = 6 \times 10^{-40}$ gm cm^2, and $I_2 = I_3 = 3 \times 10^{-40}$ gm cm^2, and calculate the ratio

$$\frac{(p.f.)^{(1)}_{rot,C-C}}{[(p.f.)^{(3)}_{rot,CH_3}]^2} \approx 0.0027$$

at 300°K. The necessity of "freezing-out" the rotations into vibrations will therefore cause the equilibrium constant for the reaction $2CH_3 \rightleftharpoons C_2H_6$ to be multiplied by this small factor. The ethane will be correspondingly less stable than if it consisted simply of two atoms. And of course the factor $\exp\{-\epsilon_0/kT\}$ must not be forgotten. This turns out to be of the order of $10^{-6.5}$ at room temperature, and will have a large influence on Eq. (6.1), making the ethane much less stable than it would otherwise be.

We finally consider a slightly more complicated equilibrium, that between a methyl radical and an ethyl radical to form propane:

$$CH_3 + CH_2CH_3 \rightleftharpoons CH_3CH_2CH_3.$$

We need first a brief discussion of the 27 vibrational frequencies of propane. These can be divided into two main classes: skeletal vibrations and C—H vibrations, each of these being further subdivided into stretching and bending vibrations. The skeletal vibrations are like those that would be exhibited by a kinked chain of three carbon atoms if no hydrogens were attached. Such a chain has three vibrational modes, two of which may be described as C—C stretchings. There is one of these for each bond, but of course it must not be thought that only one bond takes part in each of these stretchings, since, as usual, we have to deal with normal vibrations. The third mode is a skeletal bending vibration.

Of the other frequencies of propane eight will be C—H stretchings, leaving sixteen C—H bendings. This number of bending vibrations, twice the number of C—H bonds, is to be expected in this case, since all of the rotations will involve the carbon skeleton because the C—C—C chain is kinked. Two of these rotations will have large moments of inertia. The other rotation, about an axis roughly along the chain, will involve the heavier atoms, but not quite such large distances; it has an intermediate moment of inertia.

With these remarks, then, we can construct Table 7-2, similar to Table 7-1.

Here again, the degrees of freedom shown in boldface correspond roughly to the degrees of freedom which would be involved if we had two atoms combining to form a molecule. But this is a rougher correspondence than in the recombination of two methyl radicals. We see at once that there is an ambiguity: We do not know which one of the C—C stretching vibrations is the corresponding one. However, for a general understanding of what is involved, even a partial correspondence should be helpful. In view of the correspondence already listed it appears (and indeed it is clear enough physically since rotations of separate parts will in general be stopped when they combine with something else) that the two rotations of C_2H_5 with large moment of inertia will not correspond to the rotations of C_3H_8 with large moment. Instead, one of them will go over to the skeletal bending, while the other will go over to the rotation of intermediate moment. Also, clearly, the four rotations with small moment of inertia will go over into four

TABLE 7-2

	No. of degrees of freedom	
Type of motion	$CH_3 + C_2H_5$	C_3H_8
Translation of center of gravity	**3**	**3**
Relative translation	**3**	0
Rotation, large moment of inertia	$2(C_2H_5)$	**2**
Rotation, intermediate moment of inertia	0	1
Rotation, small moment of inertia	$4(3CH_3, 1C_2H_5)$	0
Vibration, C—C stretching	1	$2(= \mathbf{1} + 1)$
Vibration, skeletal bending	0	1
Vibration, C—H stretching	8	8
Vibration, C—H bending	12	16

C—H bending vibrations (one probably a torsional oscillation of the recombining methyl radical about the C—C bond formed). We will then get instead of Eq. (4.7), the approximation:

$$\frac{N_{C_3H_8}}{N_{CH_3}N_{C_2H_5}} = \frac{g_{C_3H_8}}{g_{CH_3}g_{C_2H_5}} \frac{4\pi r_e^2 (2\pi a^2 kT)^{1/2}}{2V} \exp\left\{\frac{\epsilon_D}{kT}\right\} \frac{h\nu_0}{kT}$$

$$\times \frac{\exp\{-h\nu_0/2kT\} \exp\{h\nu_0/kT\}}{\exp\{h\nu_0/kT - 1\}} \frac{(\text{p.f.})^{(1)}_{\text{rot, int. mom}}(\text{p.f.})^{(1)}_{\text{skel. bend}}(\text{p.f.})^{(4)}_{\text{C—H bend}}}{(\text{p.f.})^{(2)}_{\text{rot, large mom}}(\text{p.f.})^{(4)}_{\text{rot, small mom}}}.$$

$$(6.3)$$

Although r_e and a are somewhat ambiguous, we may estimate them from the rotational moments and stretching frequencies of C_3H_8; r_e will undoubtedly have an effective value appreciably greater than for the methyl radical recombination. A skeletal bending frequency may be only a half to a third that of C—H bending, so the $(\text{p.f.})^{(1)}_{\text{skel. bend}}$ will be somewhat larger than a $(\text{p.f.})_{\text{C—H bend}}$ would be. This would tend to make the last factor of Eq. (6.3) larger than the last factor of Eq. (6.1); however, the large moments of inertia in the denominator will more than outweigh this effect.

It will be noted that a symmetry number of 2 appears in Eq. (6.3)—propane has a symmetry factor of 2, the two ends being the same. It might be thought strange, since the methyl radical and ethyl radical from which the molecule is formed are not alike, and it can be seen that the propane molecule can split in two ways to form methyl and ethyl radicals. These two ways should, however, not be counted separately if the atoms are all indistinguishable, nor, indeed, are they, if we apply the standard procedure to derive Eq. (1.12) for this case, setting

$$N_{CH_3} + N_{C_2H_8} = N_{CH_3,tot} = \text{const.}$$

and

$$N_{C_2H_5} + N_{C_2H_8} = N_{C_2H_5,tot} = \text{const.},$$

for this does not allow the two possibilities to make any separate contribution to the (P.F.) in Eq. (1.2). Therefore there is no need to divide the originally calculated product of sums by 2, as there is for $(p.f.)_{C_2H_8}$. It is therefore correct that the latter should contain the factor $\frac{1}{2}$, while the partition function for the separated pair, $(p.f.)_{CH_3}(p.f.)_{C_2H_5}$, does not.

A symmetry number of 6 occurs in $(p.f.)_{rot,\,small\,mom}^{(4)}$ because of the symmetry of the methyl radical. Probably there is no symmetry in C_2H_5.

The more complicated the radicals, the less exact will an equation like (6.3) be, although it may still be useful. When a molecule decomposes into two smaller stable molecules usually some bonds are broken and others formed; then a different analysis of the "principal coordinates" becomes necessary.

In a reaction such as

$$C_2H_5 + H \rightleftharpoons C_2H_6,$$

the light H atom could hardly alter the rotational states of the C_2H_5; rather we have to think of the relative translational motion as going over into three degrees of freedom of vibration. A somewhat similar situation would hold if a monatomic gas molecule were absorbed at specific sites on a surface. Some of these cases are illustrated by problems attached to this chapter. In general, it will be necessary to make a special analysis of each case. The examples presented are intended to be illustrative only.

7-7. *The Chemical Potential and the General Chemical Equilibrium*

We originally defined the chemical potential in Sec. 6-3, and showed the connection between the chemical potential and the undetermined Lagrange multipliers which are used in determining maxima in statistical mechanics. From this relationship we have found it possible to express the criterion for equilibrium in terms of the chemical potential, e.g., Eq. (1.11). Equations of this type are of course well-known in thermodynamics. They can be put on a general basis in statistical mechanics, in terms of the canonical partition function.

The essence of the situation is that the total number of particles is constant and that some stoichiometric relation exists between the various species present. We assume that the system is maintained at constant temperature and constant total volume, and that the process can be described by a generalized equation

$$aA + bB + \cdots \rightleftharpoons pP + qQ + \cdots$$

where $a, b, \cdots, p, q, \cdots$ are stoichiometric integers. The partition function for the system, if the numbers of molecules of substances $A, B, \cdots, P, Q, \cdots$ are fixed, is $(P.F.)_{(N)}$, where (N) stands for a set of subscripts $N_A, N_B, \cdots, N_P, N_Q, \cdots$. The partition function, when the reaction is allowed to take place, is

$$(P.F.) = \sum_{(N)} (P.F.)_{(N)}, \tag{7.1}$$

the sum being over all possible values of $N_A, N_B, \cdots, N_P, N_Q, \cdots$ such that in going from one set of N's to another, we have

$$\frac{\delta N_A}{a} = \frac{\delta N_B}{b} = \cdots = \frac{-\delta N_P}{p} = \frac{-\delta N_Q}{q} \cdots. \tag{7.2}$$

As usual, we set $(P.F.)$ equal to the maximum term, which is determined by

$$\delta N_A \frac{\partial \ln (P.F.)_{(N)}}{\partial N_A} + \delta N_B \frac{\partial \ln (P.F.)_{(N)}}{\partial N_B} + \cdots$$
$$+ \delta N_P \frac{\partial \ln (P.F.)_{(N)}}{\partial N_P} + \delta N_Q \frac{\partial \ln (P.F.)_{(N)}}{\partial N_Q} + \cdots = 0. \tag{7.3}$$

Now by definition,

$$\mu_A = -kT \frac{\partial \ln (P.F.)_{(N)}}{\partial N_A}, \tag{7.4}$$

and so on (where V, T, and all other N are held constant), so we may write directly

$$\mu_A \delta N_A + \mu_B \delta N_B + \cdots + \mu_P \delta N_P + \mu_Q \delta N_Q + \cdots = 0 \qquad (7.5)$$

and, by Eq. (7.2)

$$a\mu_A + b\mu_B + \cdots = p\mu_P + q\mu_Q + \cdots. \qquad (7.6)$$

Thus we see that the usual thermodynamic condition for equilibrium [4] comes directly from the maximization of the partition function. This relation is more general than the relations obtained in the earlier sections of this chapter, for it is not confined to an ideal gas. If we define an activity by the equation

$$\lambda = \exp\left\{\frac{\mu}{kT}\right\}, \qquad (7.7)$$

then it is seen that Eq. (7.6) reduces to

$$\frac{\lambda_P^p \lambda_Q^q \cdots}{\lambda_A^a \lambda_B^b \cdots} = 1. \qquad (7.8)$$

It may be readily verified that for an ideal gas λ is proportional to the concentration. It is also true that in a very dilute solution λ is proportional to the concentration. Let us define a quantity z by the equation

$$z = \zeta\lambda, \qquad (7.9)$$

where ζ is a constant which makes z equal to the concentration when the concentration is very small. Then it is seen that

$$\frac{z_P^p z_Q^q \cdots}{z_A^a z_B^b \cdots} = \frac{\zeta_P^p \zeta_Q^q \cdots}{\zeta_A^a \zeta_B^b \cdots} = K, \qquad (7.10)$$

where K is the usual equilibrium constant.

7-8. *Phase Equilibrium*

The same general ideas can be used for phase equilibria. If we have two phases, 1 and 2, we can write the partition function as

$$(P.F.) = \sum_{(N_1, N_2)} (P.F.)_{(N_1)}(P.F.)_{(N_2)}, \qquad (8.1)$$

where $(P.F.)_{(N_1)}$ and $(P.F.)_{(N_2)}$ designate partition functions for a given phase with particular numbers of every kind (A, B, $\cdots$) of molecule, and where the sum is taken over all possible numbers consistent with conditions

$$N_{A1} + N_{A2} = N_{A,tot},$$
$$N_{B1} + N_{B2} = N_{B,tot}, \tag{8.2}$$
$$\cdots\cdots\cdots\cdots\cdots$$

Again we replace (P.F.) by its maximum term, assuming total volume V and temperature constant. Although the total volume is held constant, the volumes of the individual phases may not be. Since the total volume is constant, we will have

$$\delta V_1 = -\delta V_2 = \delta V, \tag{8.3}$$

and, from Eq. (8.2)

$$\delta N_{A1} = -\delta N_{A2} = \delta N_{A},$$
$$\delta N_{B1} = -\delta N_{B2} = \delta N_{B}, \tag{8.4}$$
$$\cdots\cdots\cdots\cdots\cdots\cdots$$

(defining δN_A, δN_B, $\cdots$). Thus to find the maximum term of (P.F.) we set

$$\delta\{\ln\,[(P.F.)_{(N_1)}(P.F.)_{(N_2)}]\} = 0,$$

or

$$\delta N_A \left[\left(\frac{\partial \ln (P.F.)_{(N_1)}}{\partial N_{A1}}\right)_{V_1,T} - \left(\frac{\partial \ln (P.F.)_{(N_2)}}{\partial N_{A2}}\right)_{V_2,T}\right]$$
$$+ \delta N_B \left[\left(\frac{\partial \ln (P.F.)_{(N_1)}}{\partial N_{B1}}\right)_{V_1,T} - \left(\frac{\partial \ln (P.F.)_{(N_2)}}{\partial N_{B2}}\right)_{V_2,T}\right]$$
$$+ \cdots + \delta V \left[\left(\frac{\partial \ln (P.F.)_{(N_1)}}{\partial V_1}\right)_{T,(N_1)} - \left(\frac{\partial \ln (P.F.)_{(N_2)}}{\partial V_2}\right)_{T,(N_2)}\right] = 0,$$

where in a partial differentiation with respect to a given constituent, numbers of all other constituents are held constant. The last equation gives

$$\delta N_A(\mu_{A1} - \mu_{A2}) + \delta N_B(\mu_{B1} - \mu_{B2}) + \cdots - \delta V(P_1 - P_2) = 0, \tag{8.5}$$

where μ_{A1} and μ_{A2} are the chemical potentials of substance A in phases 1 and 2, etc., and P_1 and P_2 are the pressures of the respective phases. We have arranged the situation so that δN_A, δN_B, $\cdots$, and δV can be freely varied. Therefore, Eq. (8.5) gives

$$\mu_{A1} = \mu_{A2}, \qquad \mu_{B1} = \mu_{B2}, \qquad \cdots\cdots\cdots, \qquad P_1 = P_2. \tag{8.6}$$

We thus have equality of the chemical potentials between the phases.

It may equally well be said that the chemical potential of any constituent in either of the two phases is equal to the chemical potential of that constituent in the whole system. The latter quantity for substance A, for example, may be defined as

$$
\begin{aligned}
\mu_A &= \left(\frac{\partial A}{\partial N_A}\right)_{T,V} \\
&= -kT\left[\frac{\partial \ln(\text{P.F.})}{\partial N_A}\right]_{T,V},
\end{aligned}
\tag{8.7}
$$

where V and N_A refer to the whole assembly (i.e., both phases together: $N_A = N_{A,\text{tot}}$). We may readily show that for an assembly at equilibrium it does not matter how an addition dN_A to the system is distributed between the two phases nor how it affects the individual volumes. We may write $(\text{P.F.}) = (\text{P.F.})_{(N_1)}(\text{P.F.})_{(N_2)}$, where, at least before the addition, $(\text{P.F.})_{(N_1)}(\text{P.F.})_{(N_2)}$ is the maximum term from Eq. (8.1). Then

$$
\begin{aligned}
\mu_A &= -kT\left\{\left(\frac{\partial \ln(\text{P.F.})_{(N_1)}}{\partial N_{A1}}\right)_{T,V_1}\frac{dN_{A1}}{dN_A} + \left(\frac{\partial \ln(\text{P.F.})_{(N_1)}}{\partial V_1}\right)_{T,(N_1)}\frac{dV_1}{dN_A}\right. \\
&\quad \left. + \left(\frac{\partial \ln(\text{P.F.})_{(N_2)}}{\partial N_{A2}}\right)_{T,V_2}\frac{dN_{A2}}{dN_A} + \left(\frac{\partial \ln(\text{P.F.})_{(N_2)}}{\partial V_2}\right)_{T,(N_2)}\frac{dV_2}{dN_A}\right\} \\
&= \mu_{A1}\frac{dN_{A1}}{dN_A} - P_1\frac{dV_1}{dN_A} + \mu_{A2}\frac{dN_{A2}}{dN_A} - P_2\frac{dV_2}{dN_A},
\end{aligned}
\tag{8.8}
$$

where dN_{A1}, dN_{A2}, dV_1, and dV_2 are the changes which happen to be associated with dN_A, these being restricted by the conditions

$$
\begin{aligned}
dV_1 + dV_2 &= 0, \\
dN_{A1} + dN_{A2} &= dN_A.
\end{aligned}
\tag{8.9}
$$

When applied to Eq. (8.8), the conditions (8.9) together with Eqs. (8.6), which hold since $(\text{P.F.})_{(N_1)}$ and $(\text{P.F.})_{(N_2)}$ start as the equilibrium quantities, give

$$\mu_A = \mu_{A1} = \mu_{A2}, \qquad \mu_B = \mu_{B1} = \mu_{B2}, \tag{8.10}$$

the latter equations being the generalization to the other constituents.

The chemical potentials are, of course, expected to be independent of the size of a phase, provided its composition, temperature, and pressure remain the same. This follows because two or more parts of a phase are in equilibrium with each other. The same treatment that led to Eqs. (8.10) will indicate that at a given temperature, chemical potentials and pressures for the parts are equal, regardless of their relative size (as long as each contains many molecules so that the partition function can be set equal to its largest term). Thus ln (P.F.) will be proportional to the total number of molecules in the assembly, provided the composition and pressure remain fixed. Indeed we may write for a change in $A[= -kT \ln (\text{P.F.})]$ in which pressure, temperature, and composition remain fixed (the N's changing, but keeping their proportions constant),

$$dA = \left(\frac{\partial A}{\partial N_A}\right)_{T,V,N_B,N_C,\cdots} dN_A + \left(\frac{\partial A}{\partial N_B}\right)_{T,V,N_A,N_C,\cdots} dN_B$$

$$+ \cdots + \left(\frac{\partial A}{\partial V}\right)_{T,N_A N_B \cdots} dV$$

$$= \mu_A dN_A + \mu_B dN_B + \cdots - P dV \tag{8.11}$$

or, integrating, keeping the ratios $N_A : N_B : \cdots : V$ constant,

$$A = -kT \ln (\text{P.F.}) = \mu_A N_A + \mu_B N_B + \cdots - PV \tag{8.12}$$

At constant temperature, pressure, and composition, V is itself proportional to the total number of molecules. Equation (8.12) can, of course, be written in the familiar form

$$G = \mu_A N_A + \mu_B N_B + \cdots. \tag{8.13}$$

We have assumed in this section that the composition is completely described by N_A, N_B, $\cdots$. If there are equilibria involved in which other species are formed, this will not affect the results if A, B, $\cdots$ are the independent components. For example, if there is an equilibrium $A + B \rightleftarrows AB$, in this section N_A really represents $N_{A,\text{tot}}$ or $N_A + N_{AB}$. It does not matter in what form a small increment of any component is added; since the assembly is close to equilibrium, any subsequent adjustment necessary to reestablish equilibrium will occur with negligible change of free energy.

7-9. *Solid–Vapor Equilibrium*

The idea of constant chemical potentials throughout a phase is more or less intuitively obvious, but one may wonder about conditions for two different phases to exist in equilibrium with each other. This can be readily understood in a one-component system (systems with more than one component will be treated later). Let us consider, as an illustration, the process of vaporization of a one-component atomic solid. Suppose that each atom in the solid has an effective free volume (v_f), in roughly the sense of Sec. 3-5, and suppose that there are N_s atoms in the solid and N_g atoms in the gas phase. The partition function for the solid will be (taking the potential energy of the gas as the zero of energy)

$$(\text{P.F.})_s = \left(\frac{2\pi mkT}{h^2}\right)^{3N_s/2} v_f^{N_s} \exp\left\{\frac{N_s \epsilon_s}{kT}\right\},$$

where ϵ_s would be the energy of sublimation per atom at absolute zero if there were no zero-point energy. It will be remarked that there are $N_s!$ different ways that the atoms in the solid can be arranged. These, however, have not been included in the expression for $(\text{P.F.})_s$, for v_f is an individual free volume, which is attached to a specific site and which is occupied by a particular atom and not shared by other atoms, in contrast to the volume available for a gas molecule. The expression we have written for (P.F.) is for one particular arrangement of atoms or sites, and since the factor $N_s!$ has not been implicitly included, it must not be divided out. [The volume of a gas would be more nearly equivalent in magnitude to $N_s v_f$, and the factor $N_s^{N_s}$ which would then occur in (P.F.) is roughly of the order of magnitude of $N_s!$, which can be approximated by $(N_s/e)^{N_s}$.]

The partition function for the system gas-plus-solid will be

$$(\text{P.F.}) = \sum_{N_s, N_g} \left(\frac{2\pi mkT}{h^2}\right)^{3N_s/2} v_f^{N_s} \exp\left\{\frac{N_s \epsilon_s}{kT}\right\}$$

$$\times \frac{1}{N_g!} \left(\frac{2\pi mkT}{h^2}\right)^{3N_g/2} (V - N_s v_s)^{N_g}, \tag{9.1}$$

where v_s is the atomic volume of the solid. We shall find the largest term under the condition

$$N_s + N_g = N = \text{const.} \tag{9.2}$$

Thus the condition for the largest term may be written

$$\delta N_s \left[\ln v_f + \frac{\epsilon_s}{kT} - \frac{N_g v_s}{V - N_s v_s} - \ln (V - N_s v_s) + \ln N_g \right] = 0. \tag{9.3}$$

If the molal volume of the solid is negligible compared with that of the gas, then the term $N_g v_s/(V - N_s v_s)$ can be neglected, and we have

$$N_{\text{g}} = \frac{V - N_{\text{s}}v_{\text{s}}}{v_{\text{f}}} \exp\left\{\frac{-\epsilon_{\text{s}}}{kT}\right\}. \tag{9.4}$$

Once more we have a volume factor and an energy factor, so the analogy to the association of a pair of atoms is evident. That the multiplicity of possible arrangements in the solid phase is cancelled because the atoms are indistinguishable is analogous to the effect of the symmetry factor in the ordinary chemical equilibrium. The equilibrium between the phases is brought about by the balance between the effect of the volume factor (which favors vaporization) and that of the energy factor (which favors condensation). The calculation is not complete, since no effort has been made to evaluate v_{f}, and quantum effects have not been taken into account (although they might have been implicitly included in assigning the value of v_{f}). It is seen that the concentration of the vapor, $N_{\text{g}}/(V - N_{\text{s}}v_{\text{s}})$ is fixed, and hence the pressure. The condition that there should be two phases present is merely that, under this pressure, Nv_{s} is less than V. If Nv_{s} becomes equal to V, all the molecules will be in the solid phase, and if the value of Nv_{s} characteristic of the vapor pressure exceeds V then v_{s} must decrease and the pressures must go up.

We may now return to Eq. (9.3) and investigate the effect of the neglected term $N_{\text{g}}v_{\text{s}}/(V - N_{\text{s}}v_{\text{s}})$. If this is included N_{g} will still be proportional to $V - N_{\text{s}}v_{\text{s}}$, since these quantities occur only in the combination $N_{\text{g}}/(V - N_{\text{s}}v_{\text{s}})$, and we must solve for this quantity in terms of quantities which depend only on the solid. If the vapor is ideal we may write $P = N_{\text{g}}kT/(V - N_{\text{s}}v_{\text{s}})$. Therefore a more exact form of Eq. (9.4) is

$$N_{\text{g}} = \frac{V - N_{\text{s}}v_{\text{s}}}{v_{\text{f}}} \exp\left\{\frac{-\epsilon_{\text{s}}}{kT}\right\} \exp\left\{\frac{Pv_{\text{s}}}{kT}\right\}. \tag{9.5}$$

Of course, this is in actuality an implicit equation for N_{g}.

7-10. *Some Relations Which Hold for a Change of Phase*

Suppose that we have a system with two phases of volume V_1 and V_2, such that $V = V_1 + V_2$, in equilibrium. Let us apply Eq. (8.12) to each phase separately. Writing

$$(\text{P.F.})_1 = \exp\left\{\frac{-(\mu_{\text{A}}N_{\text{A1}} + \mu_{\text{B}}N_{\text{B1}} + \cdots)}{kT}\right\} \exp\left\{\frac{PV_1}{kT}\right\}, \tag{10.1}$$

and

$$(\text{P.F.})_2 = \exp\left\{\frac{-(\mu_A N_{A2} + \mu_B N_{B2} + \cdots)}{kT}\right\} \exp\left\{\frac{PV_2}{kT}\right\}. \tag{10.2}$$

We see that we have

$$(\text{P.F.}) = (\text{P.F.})_1(\text{P.F.})_2$$

$$= \exp\left\{\frac{-(\mu_A N_A + \mu_B N_B + \cdots)}{kT}\right\} \exp\left\{\frac{PV}{kT}\right\}, \tag{10.3}$$

or

$$\exp\left\{\frac{PV}{kT}\right\} = (\text{P.F.}) \exp\left\{\frac{\mu_A N_A + \mu_B N_B + \cdots}{kT}\right\}. \tag{10.4}$$

In a one-component system,

$$\exp\left\{\frac{PV}{kT}\right\} = (\text{P.F.}) \exp\left\{\frac{\mu N}{kT}\right\}, \tag{10.5}$$

or, returning to the logarithmic form,

$$PV = kT \ln (\text{P.F.}) + \mu N. \tag{10.6}$$

Holding V (and also T) constant and allowing N to vary, we have

$$V\left(\frac{\partial P}{\partial N}\right)_V = kT\left[\frac{\partial \ln (\text{P.F.})}{\partial N}\right]_V + \mu + N\left(\frac{\partial \mu}{\partial N}\right)_V,$$

or, by the definition of μ,

$$V\left(\frac{\partial P}{\partial N}\right)_V = N\left(\frac{\partial \mu}{\partial N}\right)_V. \tag{10.7}$$

Since both μ and P depend on the density, and since both $\mu_1 = \mu_2$ and $P_1 = P_2$ must hold at equilibrium at constant temperature, there are two conditions on the densities of the two phases. Only by accident could these conditions hold for more than one pair of densities, or, therefore, for more than one value of μ and P. Thus, in a system with two phases in equilibrium, we may set both sides of Eq. (10.7) equal to zero. Thus, as long as the two phases are in equilibrium in a fixed volume (P.F.) exp $\{\mu N/kT\}$ will be constant with varying N.

In a many-component system, since the pressure and chemical potential of any phase are functions only of the composition at constant temperature, we can remove some of one phase and add an equal volume of the other; thus we will get a series of states involving different values of N_A, N_B, $\cdots$ for which Eq. (10.4) holds, and (P.F.) $\times$ exp $\{(\mu_A N_A + \mu_B N_B + \cdots)/kT\}$ is constant with varying N_A, N_B, $\cdots$, in a fixed volume at equilibrium.

7-11. *Stability of Phases*

Maximizing (P.F.) to find the state of equilibrium of two phases resulted in the condition described by Eq. (8.5). This is only part of the condition for (P.F.) to be a maximum—as far as Eq. (8.5) is concerned it could just as well be a minimum. If it is to be a maximum, the second variation must be negative. If we consider separately transfers of N_A, of N_B, etc., and changes of V_1 and V_2, under conditions (8.3) and (8.4), we see that we must have

$$(\delta N_A)^2 \left[\left(\frac{\partial^2 \ln (P.F.)_{(N_1)}}{\partial N_{A1}^2} \right)_{V_1, T} + \left(\frac{\partial^2 \ln (P.F.)_{(N_2)}}{\partial N_{A2}^2} \right)_{V_2, T} \right] < 0,$$

$$(\delta N_B)^2 \left[\left(\frac{\partial^2 \ln (P.F.)_{(N_1)}}{\partial N_{B1}^2} \right)_{V_1, T} + \left(\frac{\partial^2 \ln (P.F.)_{(N_2)}}{\partial N_{B2}^2} \right)_{V_2, T} \right] < 0, \qquad (11.1)$$

$$\cdot \quad \cdot \quad \cdot \quad \cdot \quad \cdot \quad \cdot \quad \cdot \quad \cdot \quad \cdot \quad \cdot \quad \cdot \quad \cdot \quad \cdot$$

$$(\delta V)^2 \left[\left(\frac{\partial^2 \ln (P.F.)_{(N_1)}}{\partial V_1^2} \right)_{T, (N_1)} + \left(\frac{\partial^2 \ln (P.F.)_{(N_2)}}{\partial V_2^2} \right)_{T, (N_2)} \right] < 0,$$

from which it follows that

$$\left(\frac{\partial \mu_{A1}}{\partial N_{A1}} \right)_{V_1, T} + \left(\frac{\partial \mu_{A2}}{\partial N_{A2}} \right)_{V_2, T} > 0,$$

$$\left(\frac{\partial \mu_{B1}}{\partial N_{B1}} \right)_{V_1, T} + \left(\frac{\partial \mu_{B2}}{\partial N_{B2}} \right)_{V_2, T} > 0, \qquad (11.2)$$

$$\cdot \quad \cdot \quad \cdot \quad \cdot \quad \cdot \quad \cdot \quad \cdot \quad \cdot \quad \cdot$$

$$\left(\frac{\partial P_1}{\partial V_1} \right)_{T, (N_1)} + \left(\frac{\partial P_2}{\partial V_2} \right)_{T, (N_2)} < 0.$$

If we now suppose that the two "phases" are identical, i.e., that we have merely divided our system into two parts, we see that this gives us as conditions of stability

$$\left(\frac{\partial \mu_A}{\partial N_A}\right)_{V,T} > 0,$$

$$\left(\frac{\partial \mu_B}{\partial N_B}\right)_{V,T} > 0, \tag{11.3}$$

$$\cdot \quad \cdot \quad \cdot \quad \cdot \quad \cdot$$

$$\left(\frac{\partial P}{\partial V}\right)_{T,(N_i)} < 0.$$

If these conditions are not fulfilled, the compositions of the "phases" will tend to change; i.e., the system will, in actual fact, tend to separate into distinct phases, if there is even a slight disturbance from the equilibrium condition. Stated in words, we may say that, for a phase to be stable, chemical potentials must increase with the concentration of the corresponding component, and that pressure must increase with density.

REFERENCES

1. J. E. Mayer and M. G. Mayer, *Statistical Mechanics*, New York, Wiley, 1940, pp. 213–17.

2. G. Herzberg, *Molecular Spectra and Molecular Structure, II. Infrared and Raman Spectra of Polyatomic Molecules*, 2d ed., Princeton, N.J., Van Nostrand, 1945.

3. L. J. Bellamy, *Infra-red Spectra of Complex Molecules*, 2d ed., New York, Wiley, 1958.

4. M. W. Zemansky, *Heat and Thermodynamics*, 4th ed., New York, McGraw-Hill, 1957, Chap. 17.

PROBLEMS

7.1. Get the expression for the Helmholtz free energy A from Eq. (1.2), and express it in terms of N_{AB}, $N_{A,tot}$, and $N_{B,tot}$ by use of Eqs. (1.4). Find μ_A by differentiating with respect to $N_{A,tot}$, holding $N_{B,tot}$ constant, but allowing N_{AB} to vary with $N_{A,tot}$ in any way (i.e., assume any arbitrary value for $dN_{AB}/dN_{A,tot}$). Show that the terms involving $dN_{AB}/dN_{A,tot}$ contribute nothing if Eq. (1.12) holds.

7.2. Using the expression for (P.F.) as a function of N_{AB}, $N_{A,tot}$, and $N_{B,tot}$ (see Prob. 7.1) show that $[\partial \ln (P.F.)/\partial N_{AB}]_{N_{A,tot}, N_{B,tot}} = 0$ at equilibrium, and that in general (equilibrium or not)

$$\left(\frac{\partial^2 \ln (P.F.)}{\partial N_{AB}^2}\right)_{N_{A,tot}, N_{B,tot}} = -\frac{1}{N_{AB}} - \frac{1}{N_A} - \frac{1}{N_B}.$$

Using an expansion about the equilibrium point find the approximate probable range of N_{AB}. Estimate the sum in Eq. (1.3). Is use of the largest term justified?

7.3. Consider the equilibrium $CH_3CH_2Cl \rightleftharpoons CH_3CH_2 + Cl$. Make an analysis of the changes which occur in the degrees of freedom when this reaction occurs, pointing out how those for the reactant are correlated, at least approximately, with those of the products. Write down an approximate expression for the equilibrium constant, based on this correlation, with a brief explanation as to how the various degrees of freedom are involved.

7.4. Complete the analysis (see end of Sec. 7-6) of the equilibrium, $C_2H_6 \rightleftharpoons C_2H_5 + H$, answering questions similar to those in Prob. 7.3, but taking due account of the differences arising from the small mass of H.

7.5. Make an analysis similar to that in Prob. 7.3 for the reaction $CH_3NNCH_3 \rightleftharpoons 2CH_3 + N_2$.

7.6. A certain solid surface contains a total number N of active centers, upon which the molecules of a gas may be adsorbed. Of these active centers, N_A are occupied by adsorbed molecules, N_S are vacant, and there are N_G unadsorbed gas molecules in a volume V. Assume the system to be classical throughout.

a. Show by the heuristic method of Sec. 7-3 that the equilibrium numbers are related as follows:

$$\frac{N_A}{N_G} = N_S \frac{(c.i.)_A}{V} \exp\left\{\frac{\epsilon_A}{kT}\right\},$$

where $(c.i.)_A$ is the configuration integral part of the partition function (free volume) of an adsorbed molecule, and ϵ_A is the potential energy of adsorption to the most stable adsorbed position for any center.

b. Find (P.F.) for this problem, assuming fixed N_A and N_G. This will require consideration of the number of possible arrangements of N_A molecules on N sites.

c. Show that maximization of (P.F.) with respect to variation in N_A and N_G ($N_A + N_G$ being constant) yields the result of (a).

7.7. Consider a surface with N fixed sites upon which one molecule can be adsorbed in different energy levels, which, however, form a similar set for each site. Define a cell as the group of similar energy levels, all having the same energy, from all the sites. Thus the levels in a cell are all alike except for their being at different sites. An adsorbed molecule is in a cell and in a site simultaneously. An "arrangement" is a set of adsorbed molecules in specified energy levels in specified sites. Changing from one level to another within a site, or changing a molecule from one site to another even though it remains in the corresponding energy level, changes the arrangement, but interchanging two molecules which are in the same cell does not. Suppose that we have an assembly in which there are altogether N_A adsorbed molecules, n_1 in cell 1, n_2 in cell 2, etc. Show that the number of arrangements consistent with this specification is

$$\frac{N!}{(n_1!n_2!n_3! \cdots)(N - N_A)!}.$$

If there are N_G molecules in the gas phase, find Ω for this system (adsorbed molecules plus gas).

7.8. Use the result of Prob. 7.7 and the methods of Chap. 6 to find an expression for N_A/P, where P is the pressure in the gas phase. Assuming that the energy to remove an adsorbed molecule from its position of lowest energy (neglecting zero-point energy) is ϵ_A, bring ϵ_A into the expression explicitly.

7.9. Work out the condition for equilibrium for two condensed phases, say solid and liquid in terms of their free volumes and energies. Show that, if the free volumes and energies (corresponding to ϵ_s in Sec. 7-9—one such energy for each phase) are functions of P and T, then at a given temperature it follows from your relation that equilibrium can occur only at some particular pressure determined by your relation.

Chapter 8

Imperfect Gases: Classical Case

8-1. *The Second Virial Coefficient as an Association Phenomenon*

The pressure of a perfect gas, containing N molecules at temperature T in a volume V, is given by the well-known equation

$$P = \frac{NkT}{V}. \tag{1.1}$$

This equation assumes no interaction between the molecules, and no quantum effects. In general, if interaction occurs, the pressure may be expressed as a series in V^{-1}, thus

$$P = \frac{NkT}{V}\left(1 + \frac{BN}{V} + \frac{CN^2}{V^2} + \cdots\right), \tag{1.2}$$

where $B, C, \cdots$ are functions of T but not of the density N/V; they are known as the second, third, etc., virial coefficients. It may be shown that B is determined by interactions involving two molecules at a time, C by interactions involving three molecules at a time, and so on.

If we assume that the gas is dilute enough so that we can neglect the chances that three or more molecules will be close together, we may apply the general methods of Chap. 7 to the discussion of pairs of molecules, and thus derive an expression for B. Although much more general methods are available, we shall introduce this subject in this manner, because of the physical insight it gives.

Let us consider the pressure exerted by molecules A, B, and AB which are in equilibrium according to the equation

$$A + B \rightleftarrows AB,$$

assuming each of the individual species acts as a perfect gas. The pressure will be given by [from Prob. 5.2 and Eq. (1.11), p. 70]

$$P = kT \left(\frac{\partial \ln (\text{P.F.})}{\partial V} \right)_T. \tag{1.3}$$

The canonical partition function (P.F.) is given by Eq. (1.2) of Chap. 7:

$$(\text{P.F.}) = \frac{(\text{p.f.})_A^{N_A}}{N_A!} \frac{(\text{p.f.})_B^{N_B}}{N_B!} \frac{(\text{p.f.})_{AB}^{N_{AB}}}{N_{AB}!}, \tag{1.4}$$

where N_A, N_B, and N_{AB} are the numbers of the respective species and $(\text{p.f.})_A$, $(\text{p.f.})_B$ and $(\text{p.f.})_{AB}$ are the partition functions of the individual molecule of type A, B, and AB. These functions are all functions of V; however, since we are at equilibrium, variation of (P.F.) with respect to N_A, N_B, and N_{AB} must vanish. Therefore, in applying Eq. (1.3) we may treat Eq. (1.4) as though N_A, N_B, and N_{AB} were constant, and we find

$$P = \frac{N_A kT}{(\text{p.f.})_A} \frac{\partial (\text{p.f.})_A}{\partial V} + \frac{N_B kT}{(\text{p.f.})_B} \frac{\partial (\text{p.f.})_B}{\partial V} + \frac{N_{AB} kT}{(\text{p.f.})_{AB}} \frac{\partial (\text{p.f.})_{AB}}{\partial V}. \tag{1.5}$$

If the reaction were $2A \rightleftarrows A_2$ the result would be

$$P = \frac{N_A kT}{(\text{p.f.})_A} \frac{\partial (\text{p.f.})_A}{\partial V} + \frac{N_{A_2} kT}{(\text{p.f.})_{A_2}} \frac{\partial (\text{p.f.})_{A_2}}{\partial V}. \tag{1.6}$$

In any case, for any particular species, if such a species behaves as a perfect gas, $\partial \ln (\text{p.f.})/\partial V$ or $(\text{p.f.})^{-1} \partial(\text{p.f.})/\partial V$ is equal to V^{-1}, and the total pressure is the sum of the pressures of the separate species acting as perfect gases.

One might suppose that one could apply these ideas directly to a dilute imperfect gas, by imagining that the gas consisted of single molecules which acted like a perfect gas, and of interacting pairs which also acted like a perfect gas. The difference between an imperfect gas and a gas in which some of the molecules react chemically is that in the former the interactions are very much smaller than in the latter. In consequence, the interacting pairs of an imperfect gas are not so stable as they generally are if there is a chemical reaction, and the deviation from the pressure expected if there were no interaction at all is much less. If this small deviation is to be calculated with any accuracy, we must be very careful about the various quantities which enter the equations. In particular, we must be sure to define $(p.f.)_A$ and $(p.f.)_{A_2}$ in Eq. (1.6), for example, in such a way that they do not overlap.

To see how this works, consider an absurdly simple case. Suppose that we have a gas of point molecules, which do not interact at all, but suppose that we arbitrarily say that two of these point molecules form a pair if their mutual distance is less than σ. Using the usual formula for the partition function of a point molecule of mass m, we write [Eq. (2.2) of Chap. 3]

$$(p.f.)_A = \left(\frac{2\pi m k T}{h^2}\right)^{3/2} V. \tag{1.7}$$

The internal partition function of A_2 will be $\frac{1}{2}(2\pi\mu k T/h^2)^{3/2} \cdot \frac{4}{3}\pi\sigma^3$. The last factor is the volume factor, since in this case there is free relative motion within a sphere whose volume is $\frac{4}{3}\pi\sigma^3$. The $\frac{1}{2}$ comes from the symmetry factor, and μ is the reduced mass of a pair. Combining this internal (p.f.) with the over-all translational partition function of the pair, recalling that the total mass of a pair is $2m$ and that $\mu = m/2$, we write

$$(p.f.)_{A_2} = \left(\frac{4\pi m k T}{h^2}\right)^{3/2} V \cdot \frac{1}{2}\left(\frac{2\pi\mu k T}{h^2}\right)^{3/2} \cdot \frac{4}{3}\pi\sigma^3$$

$$= \left(\frac{2\pi m k T}{h^2}\right)^{3} V \cdot \frac{2}{3}\pi\sigma^3. \tag{1.8}$$

Substituting these expressions in Eq. (1.6) we find

$$P = (N_A + N_{A_2})\frac{kT}{V},$$

but we know that, actually, since these point molecules do not interact,

$$P = N_{A,tot}\frac{kT}{V},$$

where $N_{A,tot} = N_A + 2N_{A_2}$ is the total number of A molecules, single or paired. The reason for the discrepancy is that the partition functions for the single molecules and the pairs overlap. This overlapping occurs because we have included in the partition function of a given single molecule those regions within a distance σ of the other single molecules. (We neglect the times a single molecule approaches a pair, these occasions being rare if the gas is dilute.) The total volume which is thus excluded for a given molecule is $N_A \cdot \frac{4}{3}\pi\sigma^3$. One might suppose, then, that V should be replaced by $V - N_A \cdot \frac{4}{3}\pi\sigma^3$ in (p.f.)$_A$. However, in (p.f.)$_{A_2}$ there is only *one* free volume of $\frac{4}{3}\pi\sigma^3$ for relative motion of a pair. Therefore, the volume excluded from (p.f.)$_A$ should be excluded only for one of the pair of molecules involved, or the excluded volume per molecule will be $\frac{2}{3}\pi\sigma^3$. So V is replaced by $V - N_A \cdot \frac{2}{3}\pi\sigma^3$ in (p.f.)$_A$, and we shall see that this is what is necessary to give us the correct result for the pressure. We have

$$(\text{p.f.})_A = \left(\frac{2\pi mkT}{h^2}\right)^{3/2} (V - N_A \cdot \tfrac{2}{3}\pi\sigma^3).$$

(1.9)

If this is used in Eq. (1.6) we obtain

$$P = N_A \frac{kT}{(V - N_A \cdot \frac{2}{3}\pi\sigma^3)} + N_{A_2}\frac{kT}{V}.$$

(1.10)

Carrying out a binomial expansion, we get

$$P = \frac{N_A kT}{V}\left(1 + \frac{N_A \cdot \frac{2}{3}\pi\sigma^3}{V}\right) + N_{A_2}\frac{kT}{V}.$$

(1.11)

By applying Eq. (5.8) of Chap. 7 we immediately get the approximate expression

$$\frac{N_{A_2}}{N_A} = N_A \cdot \frac{\frac{2}{3}\pi\sigma^3}{V}.$$

(1.12)

The ratio (second right-hand term) is, of course, simply the volume factor (in the same sense as used in Chap. 7), divided by the symmetry number. From this we see that we now have

$$P = (N_A + 2N_{A_2})\frac{kT}{V} = N_{A,\text{tot}}\frac{kT}{V},$$

(1.13)

which is the correct expression. It is true that we have made some approximations in obtaining this result, but in no case have we neglected any term of lower order than $(\sigma^3/V)^2$, so Eq. (1.13) is correct and consistent within terms of this order, which is all that we need at present.

This is, of course, a roundabout way of calculating the pressure of a perfect gas, but it leads at once to the evaluation of the second virial coefficient for a gas of hard spheres. A gas of hard spheres of diameter σ is equivalent to a gas of point particles in which the particles are constrained not to approach each other closer than σ, which now defines a true "exclusion sphere." So (p.f.)$_A$ for the single molecules can be found by eliminating the regions in which a pair is closer than σ, i.e., by Eq. (1.9) within its limits of approximaticn. On the other hand, the pairs A_2 are excluded entirely; in other words N_{A_2} is zero. Thus for the hard spheres, up to terms of the order $\frac{2}{3}\pi\sigma^3/V$, we have simply

$$P = \frac{N_A kT}{V}\left(1 + \frac{N_A \cdot \frac{2}{3}\pi\sigma^3}{V}\right), \tag{1.14}$$

and the second virial coefficient is

$$B = \tfrac{2}{3}\pi\sigma^3. \tag{1.15}$$

The pressure is, of course, increased over the perfect-gas pressure because the free volume for motion of the molecules is decreased by the exclusion spheres.

These results may be readily generalized. Indeed, if σ is now chosen large enough so that there is no appreciable physical interaction between the molecules at that distance, and (p.f.)$_A$ and (p.f.)$_{A_2}$ are defined accordingly, Eq. (1.11) is already quite general. For (p.f.)$_{A_2}$ depends on the volume only through the factor V, which comes from the over-all translational motion, and the volume-dependent part of (p.f.)$_A$ will be defined, avoiding the overlap, in the same way as before.

We wish then to compare Eq. (1.11) with Eq. (1.13), which is the expression for a perfect gas. This suggests that we write Eq. (1.11) in the form

$$P = (N_A + 2N_{A_2})\frac{kT}{V}\left[1 + \frac{2}{3}\pi\sigma^3\frac{N_A}{V} - \frac{N_{A_2}}{N_A}\right], \tag{1.16}$$

which, in view of the fact that N_{A_2}/N_A and $\frac{2}{3}\pi\sigma^3 N_A/V$ are both very much less than 1 in a dilute gas, is very approximately† equivalent. In general, N_{A_2}/N_A will not be given by Eq. (1.12), but we can write

$$\frac{N_{A_2}}{N_A} = \frac{N_A(\text{p.f.})_{A_2}}{(\text{p.f.})_A^2}, \tag{1.17}$$

and for this term it will be sufficient to write (p.f.)$_A$ in the approximate form

---

† "Approximate" means "close"; therefore, "very approximate" means "very close." In recent years "very approximate" has frequently been incorrectly used to mean "very roughly approximate," but that is not the meaning of the expression when used in this book.

$$(\text{p.f.})_A = \left(\frac{2\pi m k T}{h^2}\right)^{3/2} V(\text{p.f.})_{0,A} \tag{1.18}$$

and, instead of Eq. (1.8),

$$(\text{p.f.})_{A_2} = \left(\frac{4\pi m k T}{h^2}\right)^{3/2} V(\text{p.f.})_{0,A_2} \tag{1.19}$$

where m is the mass of A, and where $(\text{p.f.})_{0,A}$ and $(\text{p.f.})_{0,A_2}$ are the internal parts of the respective partition functions. In particular, $(\text{p.f.})_{0,A_2}$ contains the contribution of the relative motion of the two A parts, only the translational motion of the center of gravity (giving rise to the volume dependent part) being excluded from $(\text{p.f.})_{0,A_2}$. Equation (1.17) becomes

$$\frac{N_{A_2}}{N_A} = \left(\frac{\pi m k T}{h^2}\right)^{-3/2}\left[\frac{(\text{p.f.})_{0,A_2}}{(\text{p.f.})_{0,A}^2}\right]\frac{N_A}{V}, \tag{1.20}$$

and, comparing Eq. (1.16) with (1.13), we have

$$B = \frac{2}{3}\pi\sigma^3 - \left(\frac{h^2}{\pi m k T}\right)^{3/2}\left[\frac{(\text{p.f.})_{0,A_2}}{(\text{p.f.})_{0,A}^2}\right]. \tag{1.21}$$

This expression is perfectly general if quantum effects on the translation are ignored (but cf. Sec. 16-3). It holds for molecules of any complexity, provided proper account is taken of their complex interaction, depending upon the relative positions of all the atoms in the two molecules. Actually it will not be possible to evaluate the partition functions involved, except in the simplest cases.

8-2. *The Second Virial Coefficient for a Pair of Atoms*

We shall take up in some detail the case in which the entities A are atoms. In this case we may set $(\text{p.f.})_{0,A} = 1$, and, if the temperature is high enough so that the system may be considered to be classical, we may write, as in Eq. (4.11) of Chap. 3,

$$(\text{p.f.})_{0,A_2} = \frac{1}{2}\left(\frac{2\pi\mu k T}{h^2}\right)^{3/2}\int_{r=0}^{r=\sigma}\int_{\theta=0}^{\theta=\pi}\int_{\phi=0}^{\phi=2\pi}\exp\left\{\frac{-\epsilon_\text{p}}{kT}\right\}r^2\sin\theta\,d\phi d\theta dr, \tag{2.1}$$

where r, θ, and ϕ are the polar coordinates of the relative position of the two atoms, and the integration with respect to r is limited to $r = \sigma$, essentially by definition of A_2, with σ as in Eq. (1.21) large compared with the range of ϵ_p. The factor $\frac{1}{2}$ is, as usual, derived from the symmetry number. By integrating with respect to θ and ϕ, Eq. (2.1) can be reduced to

$$(\text{p.f.})_{0,A_2} = 2\pi \left(\frac{2\pi\mu kT}{h^2}\right)^{3/2} \int_0^\sigma \exp\left\{\frac{-\epsilon_p}{kT}\right\} r^2 \, dr. \tag{2.2}$$

Recalling that $\mu = m/2$, we see that

$$B = 2\pi \int_0^\sigma \left(1 - \exp\left\{\frac{-\epsilon_p}{kT}\right\}\right) r^2 \, dr.$$

Since σ is so large that ϵ_p at σ does not differ from its asymptotic value, which is taken as zero, this being consistent with the energy scale used to evaluate $(\text{p.f.})_{0,A}$, the integrand is zero at $r = \sigma$ and the upper limit may as well be taken as infinity. Thus

$$B = 2\pi \int_0^\infty \left(1 - \exp\left\{\frac{-\epsilon_p}{kT}\right\}\right) r^2 \, dr. \tag{2.3}$$

It will be observed that the arbitrary distance σ has disappeared from the equation.

8-3. *The Lennard-Jones Potential: Comparison with Experiment*

In order to evaluate Eq. (2.3) and compare it with experiment, one needs some way to estimate ϵ_p. The van der Waals potential between two rare-gas atoms (or between some symmetrical saturated molecules whose interactions behave much like those of rare-gas atoms) is often approximated by the so-called 6–12 Lennard-Jones potential:

$$\epsilon_p = \frac{c_{12}}{r^{12}} - \frac{c_6}{r^6}. \tag{3.1}$$

It is often convenient to recast the constants, writing†

$$\epsilon_p = 4\epsilon_M \left[\left(\frac{r_0}{r}\right)^{12} - \left(\frac{r_0}{r}\right)^6\right]. \tag{3.2}$$

It is seen that r_0 is one of the values of r which makes ϵ_p equal to zero

---

† A more usual terminology is to use ϵ for ϵ_M and σ for r_0, but we have already made other use of ϵ and σ.

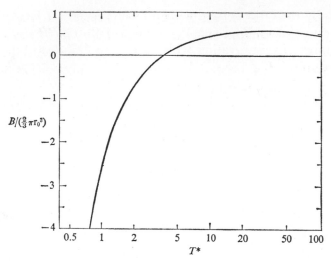

Figure 8-1.   Reduced virial coefficient as a function of reduced temperature, from the Lennard-Jones potential.(After Table I-B of Hirschfelder, Curtiss, and Bird [1].)

(the other is $r = \infty$). It is also readily verified that $-\epsilon_M$ is the value of ϵ_p at the minimum of the curve. It is convenient to set $r^* = r/r_0$ and $T^* = kT/\epsilon_M$. Then B takes the form

$$B = \tfrac{2}{3}\pi r_0^3 \int_0^\infty \left(1 - \exp\left\{\frac{-4(r^{*-12} - r^{*-6})}{T^*}\right\}\right) d(r^{*3}), \qquad (3.3)$$

and it is seen that, for any atoms or molecules for which the Lennard-Jones potential is a good approximation and for which quantum effects are not important, $B/\tfrac{2}{3}\pi r_0^3$ is a universal function of T^*. It can be evaluated by expanding the exponentials and integrating the resulting series term by term. The function is displayed in Fig. 8-1. Values of B are obtained by pressure measurements at various temperatures, but to place a substance on the diagram, values of ϵ_M and r_0 must be chosen. This is done in such a way as to get the best fit to the curve. The curve in Fig. 8-1 does, indeed, give an excellent indication of the trend of B with temperature [1].† At any low temperature B is negative, because of the predominance of the effects of the attractive forces, which causes the exponential in Eq. (3.3) to be large. At high temperature B becomes positive, but it should eventually reach a maximum and decrease, because, as the atoms move faster and hit each other harder, they

† A theoretical discussion with comparisons with experiment given by Münster [2].

penetrate each other more and the effective average "excluded volume" decreases. This maximum shows up in helium, for which measurements can be carried to large values of T^*, but for He and other light molecules the experimental points at low T^* fall to the left of the theoretical curve on account of quantum effects.

The fact that the Lennard-Jones potential gives a good description of the experimental data indicates that it gives at least a good qualitative description of the interatomic potential energy. It cannot, however, be concluded from this agreement alone that the description is a detailed quantitative one, because the second virial coefficient is quite insensitive to the exact form of the potential-energy curve.

8-4. *An Approximate Interpretation of the Virial Coefficient*

We have developed the idea that gas imperfections are an association phenomenon, but we have finally arrived at an equation, (2.3), in which this idea may not seem too obvious. However, we may note that the factor $\exp\{-\epsilon_p/kT\}r^2\,dr$ is proportional to the probability that a pair have their interatomic distance between r and $r + dr$, and the negative of the integrand is proportional to this probability, minus the probability that would exist were there no force between particles. At large distances, where ϵ_p is essentially zero, the integrand vanishes. At small distances, in the repulsive region, $\exp\{-\epsilon_p/kT\}$ rapidly approaches zero. As a rough approximation we may say that the integrand is equal to 1 for $r < r_0$, and write†

$$B = \frac{2}{3}\pi r_0^3 - 2\pi \int_{r_0}^{\infty} \left(\exp\left\{\frac{-\epsilon_p}{kT}\right\} - 1\right) r^2\,dr, \qquad (4.1)$$

where the second term on the right is the negative contribution to B due to the excess of the association over the number of pairs which would normally exist if there were no forces for $r > r_0$. We can describe $4\pi \int_{r_0}^{\infty} (\exp\{-\epsilon_p/kT\} - 1)r^2\,dr$ as the total excess probability that one particle is in the neighborhood of another when the probability of finding the particle in unit volume at a great distance from the second one has been normalized to unity. This excess probability may, therefore,

---

† B has the dimensions of volume. Note that any space around a given molecule from which other molecules are excluded contribute fully to B, any volume from which they are partially excluded contributes proportionately, while a volume with excess neighbors makes a corresponding negative contribution. In each case there is a factor $\frac{1}{2}$ (avoiding duplication between pairs of molecules).

be set equal to twice an equilibrium constant K, for the extra association. The factor of two arises because two molecules form one pair.
Therefore

$$B = \tfrac{2}{3}\pi r_0^3 - K, \tag{4.2}$$

where r_0 is approximately the kinetic theory diameter obtained from
viscosity measurements by means of Chapman's equation based upon
the Sutherland model of a hard sphere of diameter r_0 with attractive
forces [1, pp. 549–51; 3–5].

Roughly, K may be taken as the equilibrium constant for molecules trapped together by the van der Waals forces, and not having
enough energy to dissociate. This assumption is not quite correct, for
in the region of the attractive forces, the density of pairs which have
enough energy to dissociate again will not be quite as large as it would
be if there were no forces. This difference will contribute to the K which
appears in Eq. (4.2). We shall neglect this effect and will try to evaluate
the partition function for the associated pairs by classical or semi-
classical methods.

Consider first the vibration of the two A's with respect to each
other. If we suppose that the energy difference between adjacent vibra-
tional levels of some particular energy ϵ is $\delta\epsilon$, then the number of energy
levels in an energy range $d\epsilon$ will be $d\epsilon/\delta\epsilon = (\tau_\epsilon/h)\, d\epsilon$, by Eq. (4.4) of
Chap. 1, where τ_ϵ is the period of vibration at energy ϵ. The partition
function, then, will be given by

$$(\text{p.f.})_{A_2,\text{vib}} = \int_{-\epsilon_M}^{0} \frac{\tau_\epsilon}{h} \exp\left\{\frac{-\epsilon}{kT}\right\} d\epsilon, \tag{4.3}$$

the zero of energy being taken as the potential energy of a separated
pair. This is the part of the internal partition function of A_2 which has
to do with the relative vibrational motion of the two A's as wholes.

The vibrational component of the relative velocity of the two
molecules of the pair will be $[2(\epsilon - \epsilon_p)/\mu]^{1/2}$, where $\mu = m/2$ is the
reduced mass, and ϵ is the total vibrational energy, and we may write

$$\tau_\epsilon = 2 \int_{r_1}^{r_2} \left[\frac{2(\epsilon - \epsilon_p)}{\mu}\right]^{-1/2} dr, \tag{4.4}$$

where r_1 and r_2 are the values of r when $\epsilon_p = \epsilon$. For ϵ_p we may use the
Lennard-Jones expression, as given by Eq. (3.1). We note that

$$dr = \frac{r^{-5}\, dr^6}{6} \approx \frac{r_e r^{-6}\, dr^6}{6}, \tag{4.5}$$

where r_e is the value of r at the minimum of the potential-energy curve. Substituting r_e for one of the factors r in the expression will be a good approximation in the integral, since the *first* power of r will vary only relatively slowly over the important range of integration. If we now substitute $x = r^6$ in Eq. (3.1) and then use the result, and Eq. (4.5), in Eq. (4.4) we obtain

$$\tau_\epsilon \approx \frac{r_e}{6} (2\mu)^{1/2} \int_{x_1}^{x_2} (\epsilon x^2 + c_6 x - c_{12})^{-1/2} \, dx. \tag{4.6}$$

This integral is a known form [6]. If it is evaluated at the two limits, at which $\epsilon x^2 + c_6 x - c_{12}$ vanishes, τ_ϵ becomes

$$\tau_\epsilon = \frac{\pi r_e}{6} \left(\frac{-2\mu}{\epsilon} \right)^{1/2}. \tag{4.7}$$

If this be inserted into Eq. (4.3), the latter becomes

$$(\text{p.f.})_{\text{vib},A_2} = (2\mu)^{1/2} \frac{\pi r_e}{6h} \int_{-\epsilon_M}^{0} (-\epsilon)^{-1/2} \exp\left\{ \frac{-\epsilon}{kT} \right\} d\epsilon. \tag{4.8}$$

On substituting $x = -\epsilon/kT$ and $x_M = \epsilon_M/kT$, Eq. (4.8) becomes

$$(\text{p.f.})_{\text{vib},A_2} = (2\mu kT)^{1/2} \frac{\pi r_e}{6h} \int_0^{x_M} x^{-1/2} \exp\{x\} \, dx. \tag{4.9}$$

We may now evaluate K of Eq. (4.2), again applying Eqs. (1.17), (1.18), and (1.19).† We have

$$K = \left(\frac{h^2}{\pi m k T} \right)^{3/2} \frac{(\text{p.f.})_{0,A_2}}{(\text{p.f.})_{0,A}^2}. \tag{4.10}$$

If the internal partition functions of the separate A's are unaltered by the loose van der Waals coupling this reduces to

$$K = \left(\frac{h^2}{\pi m k T} \right)^{3/2} (\text{p.f.})_{\text{vib},A_2} (\text{p.f.})_{\text{rot},A_2}, \tag{4.11}$$

where both $(\text{p.f.})_{\text{vib},A_2}$ and $(\text{p.f.})_{\text{rot},A_2}$ refer to the motion of the two A's

---

† The difference between Eq. (1.21) and Eq. (4.1) or (4.2) is that the arbitrary distance σ appears in the former and r_0 appears in the latter. In Sec. 8-1 the two A's are considered to form an A_2 whenever they are within a distance σ, so *all* energy levels for relative motion, when the A's are this close, must appear in $(\text{p.f.})_{0,A_2}$. In Eq. (4.10) on the other hand, $(\text{p.f.})_{0,A_2}$ contains only energy levels in which the two A's are physically held together.

with respect to each other. Taking $(\text{p.f.})_{\text{rot},A_2} = \frac{1}{2} \cdot 8\pi^2 \mu r_e^2 kT/h^2$, we obtain

$$K = \frac{1}{3}\pi^{3/2}r_e^3 \int_0^{x_M} x^{-1/2} \exp\{x\} \, dx. \tag{4.12}$$

The integral cannot be evaluated analytically. We may, however, consider the limiting cases, $\epsilon_M \ll kT$ ($x_M \ll 1$) and $\epsilon_M \gg kT$ ($x_M \gg 1$). When x_M is very small, $\exp\{x\}$ may be set equal to 1, the integral approaches $2(\epsilon_M/kT)^{1/2}$, and Eq. (4.12) reduces to

$$\lim_{T \to \infty} K = \frac{2}{3}\pi^{3/2}r_e^3 \left(\frac{\epsilon_M}{kT}\right)^{1/2}. \tag{4.13}$$

When T is very large, the high vibrational levels become important, and for them the vibration and rotational motions are not independent of each other. Nevertheless, Eq. (4.13) should be a reasonable approximation. At high temperatures, when the levels below the dissociation limit are uniformly filled and all make the contribution 1 to the partition function, $(\text{p.f.})_{\text{vib},A_2}$, as expected, becomes independent of temperature. This may be seen by substituting $2(\epsilon_M/kT)^{1/2}$ for the integral in Eq. (4.9).

If x_M is very large, $\exp\{x\}$ becomes the predominating factor in the integrand, and we may set $x^{-1/2} = x_M^{-1/2}$, since the greatest value of $\exp\{x\}$ occurs at $x = x_M$. Thus

$$\lim_{T \to 0} K = \frac{1}{3}\pi^{3/2}r_e^3 \left(\frac{kT}{\epsilon_M}\right)^{1/2} \exp\left\{\frac{\epsilon_M}{kT}\right\}. \tag{4.14}$$

If the Lennard-Jones potential-energy curve, Eq. (3.1) or (3.2), is expanded about the position r_e of its minimum

$$\epsilon_p = -\epsilon_M + \frac{(r - r_e)^2}{2a^2} \tag{4.15}$$

it is found by comparing a^{-2} with $d^2\epsilon_p/dr^2$ (evaluated at r_e) that $a^2 = r_e^2/72\epsilon_M$. On making this substitution, Eq. (4.14) takes the form

$$\lim_{T \to 0} K = 2\pi r_e^2 \, \delta r \exp\left\{\frac{\epsilon_M}{kT}\right\}, \tag{4.16}$$

where

$$\delta r = (2\pi a^2 kT)^{1/2}. \tag{4.17}$$

This final value of K corresponds exactly to Eq. (4.6) of Chap. 7, if

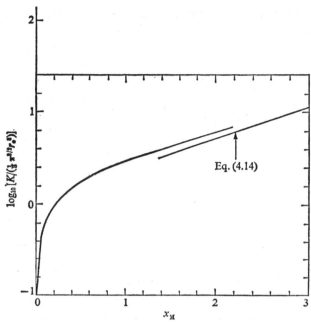

Figure 8-2. Van der Waals equilibrium constant as a function of $x_M = \epsilon_M/kT$.

we note the factor of $\frac{1}{2}$ (from symmetry) is in Eq. (4.16), if the g's of Eq. (4.6) of Chap. 7 are set equal to 1 (or g_{AB} is set equal to $g_A g_B$), and if ϵ_D is identified with ϵ_M. This result is, of course, to be expected for small T if classical mechanics can still be used.

In Fig. 8-2 we have plotted $\log_{10} [K/(\frac{1}{3}\pi^{3/2}r_e^2)]$ against x_M, using values of the integral obtained from numerical integration. As may be seen from evaluation of $d \ln K/dT$, the average heat of dissociation of the van der Waals complex changes from $\epsilon_M - \frac{1}{2}kT$ at low temperatures to $\frac{1}{2}kT$ at high.

We shall apply these ideas to some measurements on the association of benzene and iodine molecules, but we first must find the virial coefficients in mixtures of gases.

8-5. *Mixtures of Imperfect Gases*

Two different kinds of molecules, A and B, can interact to form van der Waals pairs A_2, B_2, and AB. We thus have five different types of molecular entity to consider, and an obvious generalization of Eqs. (1.5) and (1.6) gives

$$P = \frac{N_A kT}{(\text{p.f.})_A} \frac{\partial (\text{p.f.})_A}{\partial V} + \frac{N_B kT}{(\text{p.f.})_B} \frac{\partial (\text{p.f.})_B}{\partial V} + \frac{N_{A_2} kT}{(\text{p.f.})_{A_2}} \frac{\partial (\text{p.f.})_{A_2}}{\partial V}$$

$$+ \frac{N_{B_2} kT}{(\text{p.f.})_{B_2}} \frac{\partial (\text{p.f.})_{B_2}}{\partial V} + \frac{N_{AB} kT}{(\text{p.f.})_{AB}} \frac{\partial (\text{p.f.})_{AB}}{\partial V}. \tag{5.1}$$

Once again $(\text{p.f.})_A$ and $(\text{p.f.})_B$ must be corrected so that there will be no overlapping. Using arbitrary σ's as in Sec. 8-1, there will be effective volumes for A and B, as follows:

$$V_A = V - N_A \cdot \tfrac{2}{3} \pi \sigma_{A_2}^3 - N_B \cdot \tfrac{2}{3} \pi \sigma_{AB}^3, \tag{5.2}$$

and

$$V_B = V - N_B \cdot \tfrac{2}{3} \pi \sigma_{B_2}^3 - N_A \cdot \tfrac{2}{3} \pi \sigma_{AB}^3. \tag{5.3}$$

Now, in place of Eq. (1.11) we find

$$P \approx \frac{N_A kT}{V} \left(1 + \frac{N_A}{V} \cdot \frac{2}{3} \pi \sigma_{A_2}^3 + \frac{N_B}{V} \cdot \frac{2}{3} \pi \sigma_{AB}^3 \right)$$

$$+ \frac{N_B kT}{V} \left(1 + \frac{N_B}{V} \cdot \frac{2}{3} \pi \sigma_{B_2}^3 + \frac{N_A}{V} \cdot \frac{2}{3} \pi \sigma_{AB}^3 \right)$$

$$+ \frac{N_{A_2} kT}{V} + \frac{N_{B_2} kT}{V} + \frac{N_{AB} kT}{V}. \tag{5.4}$$

In analogy to Eq. (1.16) we write

$$P \approx \frac{N_{A,\text{tot}} kT}{V} \left(1 + \frac{N_A}{V} \cdot \frac{2}{3} \pi \sigma_{A_2}^3 + \frac{N_B}{V} \cdot \frac{2}{3} \pi \sigma_{AB}^3 - \frac{N_{A_2}}{N_A} - \frac{N_{AB}}{2 N_A} \right)$$

$$+ \frac{N_{B,\text{tot}} kT}{V} \left(1 + \frac{N_B}{V} \cdot \frac{2}{3} \pi \sigma_{B_2}^3 + \frac{N_A}{V} \cdot \frac{2}{3} \pi \sigma_{AB}^3 - \frac{N_{B_2}}{N_B} - \frac{N_{AB}}{2 N_B} \right), \tag{5.5}$$

where

$$N_{A,\text{tot}} = N_A + 2 N_{A_2} + N_{AB},$$

and

$$N_{B,\text{tot}} = N_B + 2 N_{B_2} + N_{AB}.$$

Finally we may write

$$P \approx \frac{NkT}{V} \left[1 + \left(\frac{2}{3} \pi \sigma_{A_2}^3 x_A^2 + \frac{4}{3} \pi \sigma_{AB}^3 x_A x_B + \frac{2}{3} \pi \sigma_{B_2}^3 x_B^2 \right) \frac{N}{V} \right.$$

$$\left. - \left(\frac{N_{A_2}}{N_A^2} x_A^2 + \frac{N_{AB}}{N_A N_B} x_A x_B + \frac{N_{B_2}}{N_B^2} x_B^2 \right) N \right], \tag{5.6}$$

where $N = N_{A,tot} + N_{B,tot}$ and x_A and x_B are mole fractions:

$$x_A = \frac{N_{A,tot}}{N} \approx \frac{N_A}{N}; \qquad x_B = \frac{N_{B,tot}}{N} \approx \frac{N_B}{N}.$$

The ratios N_{A_2}/N_A^2, N_{B_2}/N_B^2, and $N_{AB}/N_A N_B$ can be evaluated by using Eq. (1.20), the analogous equation for B, and

$$\frac{N_{AB}}{N_A N_B} = \left(\frac{h^2}{2\pi\mu_{AB}kT}\right)^{3/2} \frac{(p.f.)_{0,AB}}{(p.f.)_{0,A}(p.f.)_{0,B}V}, \tag{5.7}$$

where μ_{AB} is the reduced mass of $A + B$. Comparing Eq. (5.6) with Eq. (1.2), we see that it is natural to write in this case

$$B = x_A^2 B_A + 2x_A x_B B_{AB} + x_B^2 B_B \tag{5.8}$$

where B_A and B_B are defined by expressions analogous to Eq. (1.21), and

$$B_{AB} = \frac{2}{3}\pi\sigma_{AB}^3 - \frac{1}{2}\left(\frac{h^2}{2\pi\mu_{AB}kT}\right)^{3/2} \frac{(p.f.)_{0,AB}}{(p.f.)_{0,A}(p.f.)_{0,B}}. \tag{5.9}$$

With this definition the virial equation can be written exactly in the form of Eq. (1.2). Writing

$$P = \frac{N(x_A + x_B)kT}{V} + \frac{N^2 kT}{V^2}(x_A^2 B_A + 2x_A x_B B_{AB} + x_B^2 B_B), \tag{5.10}$$

we see that we may also set

$$P = P_A + P_B + \frac{2kT}{V^2} x_A x_B N^2 B_{AB}, \tag{5.11}$$

where P_A is the pressure which would be observed if $x_A N = N_{A,tot}$ molecules of substance A were present alone in volume V, where P_B is the pressure which would be observed if $x_B N = N_{B,tot}$ molecules of substance B were present alone in volume V, whereas P is the observed pressure with N_A molecules of A and N_B of B present in the same volume. Since these quantities can all be measured experimentally, it is possible to determine B_{AB} from Eq. (5.11).

The partition function $(p.f.)_{0,AB}$ may be evaluated by an equation exactly similar to Eq. (2.1), except that the symmetry-caused factor $\frac{1}{2}$ will be absent [although its place is taken by the $\frac{1}{2}$ before the last term in Eq. (5.9)]. Using Eq. (2.2) (setting $\mu = \mu_{AB}$), Eq. (5.7), and Eq. (5.9), and again noting that if A and B are atoms, $(p.f.)_{0,A} =$

$(\text{p.f.})_{0,\text{B}} = 1$ we see, by the same reasoning used in obtaining Eq. (2.3), that for a pair of atoms

$$B_{\text{AB}} = 2\pi \int_0^\infty \left(1 - \exp\left\{\frac{-\epsilon_{\text{p,AB}}}{kT}\right\}\right) r^2 \, dr. \tag{5.12}$$

We may also apply to B_{AB} the approximate considerations of Sec. 8-4. We have, in exact analogy to Eq. (4.2),†

$$B_{\text{AB}} = \tfrac{2}{3}\pi r_{0,\text{AB}}^3 - \tfrac{1}{2}K_{\text{AB}}, \tag{5.13}$$

where $r_{0,\text{AB}}$ may be taken as the mean of $r_{0,\text{A}}$ and $r_{0,\text{B}}$. We can also evaluate K_{AB} by the equation analogous to Eq. (4.11). Remembering that $(\text{p.f.})_{\text{rot,AB}}$ has a symmetry factor of 1, we find in this case

$$K_{\text{AB}} = \tfrac{2}{3}\pi^{3/2} r_{e,\text{AB}}^3 \int_0^{x_M} x^{-1/2} \exp\{x\} \, dx. \tag{5.14}$$

8-6. *Use of the Approximate Formula: The Interaction of Iodine and Benzene*

We shall illustrate the use of some of the equations of the preceding sections, especially Eq. (5.13), by considering the interaction between benzene and iodine molecules in the vapor phase. As noted above, the forces of interaction are probably so weak that the partition functions for the internal degrees of freedom, and for the rotations, are not changed on association. Thus, for practical purposes the molecules may be treated as spherically symmetrical and structureless.

The quantity P in Eq. (5.11) was measured by Atack and Rice [7] over a range of temperatures and pressures, whereas P_A and P_B were obtained from known empirical equations of state (i.e., from earlier measurements), by using the values of $N_{\text{A,tot}}$, or $N_{\text{B,tot}}$, T, and V involved. Thus it was possible to obtain B_{AB}. It was necessary to make very accurate pressure measurements, since small differences are involved. From viscosity measurements, $r_{0,\text{AB}}$ was estimated as 4.56Å. Thus the equilibrium constant K_{AB} can be determined from Eq. (5.13).

The values of $\log K_{\text{AB}}$ for iodine–benzene are plotted in Fig. 8-3 (with K expressed, however, in terms of pressures), together with curves for iodine and for benzene, as obtained from the earlier data, for com-

---

† In this case the equilibrium constant itself (*not* $2K$) is equal to $4\pi \int_{r_0}^\infty (\exp\{-\epsilon_p/kT\} - 1)r^2 \, dr$, because the atoms A and B are different.

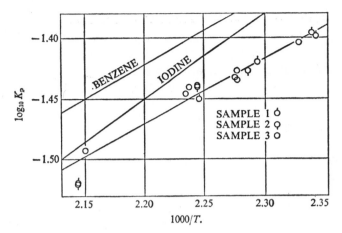

Figure 8-3. Equilibrium constant for Van der Waals interactions of benzene and iodine. In the case of pure benzene and iodine log $2K_p$ rather than log K_p is plotted, because this gives a more meaningful comparison of intermolecular forces [compare Eqs. (4.12) and (5.14)]. (From Atack and Rice [7].)

parison. The slope of the line corresponds to $\Delta E = -1.55$ kcal mole^{-1} for

$$I_2 + C_6H_6 \longrightarrow I_2 \cdot C_6H_6.$$

This value of ΔE is enough greater than RT at the mean temperature of 450°K of Atack and Rice's experiments so that we may feel justified in attempting to fit the limiting case of large x_M to the results. In this case the equation corresponding to Eq. (4.16) is

$$K_{AB} = 4\pi r^2_{e,AB}\delta r_{AB} \exp\left\{\frac{\epsilon_M}{kT}\right\}; \tag{6.1}$$

ΔE is not equal to $(R/k)\epsilon_M$ because ΔE contains thermal energy, and the mean thermal energy of the combined pair oscillating about the equilibrium position is about $\frac{1}{2}kT$ greater than that of the separated pair. Thus at 450°K,

$$\frac{R}{k}\epsilon_M \approx 1.55 + \frac{1}{2}RT = 2.0 \text{ kcal mole}^{-1}.$$

From the point of view of Eq. (6.1), the difference between ΔE and $(R/k)\epsilon_M$ simply means that the temperature coefficient of K is not determined solely by the exponential factor, but is also affected by the factor δr_{AB} which is proportional to $T^{1/2}$.

The value of K_{AB} at 450°K is 2.1×10^{-21} cc molecule^{-1}. We have estimated $r_{e,AB}$ as 5Å, slightly larger than $r_{0,AB}$. We then find $\delta r_{AB} = 0.71$Å, a very reasonable value for the free length. At 300°K the value of δr_{AB} will be 0.58Å, and from Eq. (6.1) we find $K_{AB} = 5.2 \times 10^{-21}$ cc molecule^{-1} at 300°K, a value which will be found useful in Chap. 19.

REFERENCES

1. J. O. Hirschfelder, C. F. Curtiss, and R. B. Bird, *Molecular Theory of Gases and Liquids*, New York, Wiley, 1954, p. 162ff.
2. A. Münster, Statistische Thermodynamik, Berlin, Springer, 1956, Kap. 11.
3. T. S. Wheeler, *Rec. Trav. Chim.*, **51**, 1204 (1932).
4. S. Chapman and T. G. Cowling, *The Mathematical Theory of Non-Uniform Gases*, Cambridge, Eng., Cambridge Univ. Press, 1939, pp. 182–86.
5. R. D. Present, *Kinetic Theory of Gases*, New York, McGraw-Hill, 1958, pp. 110–12.
6. B. O. Peirce, *A Short Table of Integrals*, 3d ed., Boston, Ginn, 1929, No. 161 (or No. 127).
7. D. Atack and O. K. Rice, *J. Phys. Chem.*, **58**, 1017 (1954).

PROBLEMS

8.1. Assume that for $r < r_e$ the value of ϵ_p of Eq. (2.3) is $+\infty$, and, for $r > r_e$, that $\epsilon_p = -c_6/r^6$. Equation (2.3) will then split into two parts, one for $r < r_e$, for which the integral is readily evaluated, and one for $r > r_e$. In the latter make a substitution of variables so that the new variable x will be dimensionless and will be integrated between the limits 0 and $(c_6/r^6 kT)^{1/2}$. Plot out the integrand as a function of x, and use this to get a rough evaluation of B as a function of temperature.

8.2. For a mixture of point particles A and B, find the equations analogous to Eq. (1.12), remembering that the symmetry number of AB is 1. Now derive the equation analogous to Eq. (1.13), and show that the total pressure of the mixture is the sum of the perfect-gas pressures for A and B.

8.3. Derive the equation for the pressure assuming that A and B are hard spheres of diameter σ_A and σ_B, respectively, instead of point particles as in Prob. 8.2. Compare the result with the results of Sec. 8-1.

Chapter 9

The Solid State

9-1. *The Einstein Model*

We have seen in the foregoing chapters that the thermodynamic properties of dilute gases were successfully handled by the methods of statistical mechanics. A gas is a system in which molecular chaos or disorder is complete; it is easily analyzed because the molecules are rarely close together, so that the forces between them seldom come into play. A crystalline solid, on the other hand, is a system in which the atoms or molecules are always in contact with each other, but a certain simplicity arises because the system is well ordered. The thermodynamic properties of at least the simplest of these systems, the monatomic solids, can also be successfully discussed. Much more difficult to handle are the liquids and dense gases, in which both intermolecular forces and disorder play an essential role.

In this chapter we shall discuss primarily the simple monatomic solids, paying special attention to solid argon, which illustrates the general principles involved. A monatomic solid consists of a large number of atoms in regular array, a lattice. Each atom has a position of equilibrium, its lattice point, about which it vibrates because of thermal agitation and zero-point energy. As a first approximation, following the suggestion of Einstein, we assume that the field exerted on any atom by its neighbors is the same as if the latter were all fixed in their equilibrium positions in the solid. Each atom may then be treated as if it were independent of all the other atoms, vibrating in the field of the neighbor atoms with a certain frequency. As a matter of fact, the frequency may depend on the direction of the vibration in space, but if the lattice has cubic symmetry, the frequency will be, in first approximation, independent of direction and will be the same for all atoms. Thus we may say that the force pulling the atom back to its equilibrium position will depend only on its displacement δ. If the displacement is small, we may assume that the motion is harmonic and write for the potential energy associated with a displacement δ

$$\delta\epsilon_p = \frac{\varkappa\delta^2}{2} = \frac{1}{2}\varkappa(\delta_x^2 + \delta_y^2 + \delta_z^2), \tag{1.1}$$

where $\varkappa$ is a force constant, and δ_x, δ_y, δ_z are the components of δ in the indicated directions of space. If the atom is displaced in any particular direction, say the x direction, it will vibrate with a frequency given by

$$\nu_E = \frac{1}{2\pi}\left(\frac{\varkappa}{m}\right)^{1/2} \tag{1.2}$$

where m is its mass, this being the usual formula for the frequency of a harmonic oscillator. The motions in the three directions of space are quantized separately, so that the energy levels have the form

$$\epsilon_v = h\nu_E(v_x + \tfrac{1}{2} + v_y + \tfrac{1}{2} + v_z + \tfrac{1}{2}), \tag{1.3}$$

where v_x, v_y, and v_z are the three quantum numbers (v stands for these collectively). This is the vibrational energy reckoned as an increase in energy over the energy the system would have if all the atoms were at rest in their equilibrium positions.

The total energy of an assembly of N atoms executing the vibrations described is

$$E = \sum_i \epsilon_{v_i} + E_0, \tag{1.4}$$

where v_i is the collective quantum number for the ith atom, and where E_0 is the potential energy of the whole system at rest, that is, the energy of the assembly when all the atoms are stationary in their equilibrium positions. The ith atom is here characterized by its position in the lattice. An exchange of atoms would produce an identical set of energy levels; however, we do not need to introduce such exchanges, since the motion of each atom is confined to a particular region in space. The atoms will not tend to move out of their regions, so that they do not have simultaneously the possibility, even conceptually, of occupying the same energy level. If we do not introduce such exchanges we will not need to eliminate them (compare Sec. 7-9). Thus in setting up the canonical partition function we write

$$(\text{P.F.}) = (\text{p.f.})^N, \tag{1.5}$$

which is analogous to Eq. (1.7) of Chap. 3, but, for the reasons just explained, is not divided by $N!$. It will not always be possible to find individual (p.f.)'s for the atoms in a condensed phase; however, even if this is not possible it will sometimes be convenient to use Eq. (1.5) to *define* (p.f.) for a condensed phase.

In the Einstein solid we have obviously

$$(\text{p.f.}) = (\text{p.f.})^3_{\text{vib}} \exp\left\{\frac{-E_0}{NkT}\right\}, \tag{1.6}$$

where $(\text{p.f.})_{\text{vib}}$ is the usual one-dimensional vibrational partition function for an oscillator with frequency ν_E reckoned from the bottom of its potential-energy curve. Therefore in this theory the solid has the specific heat, energy, entropy, etc., of $3N$ oscillators of frequency ν_E. Just as in the treatment in Sec. 2-3, we can introduce the characteristic temperature $\Theta_E = h\nu_E/k$. The thermodynamic quantities C_v, E_t/T (where $E_t = E - E_0$ is the thermal energy), and S are functions of Θ_E/T, the quantities Θ_E and T appearing only in this combination.

Some of the properties of monatomic solids are correctly given by the Einstein model. At high temperatures the molal heat capacity (usually measured at constant pressure, but approximately the same as that at constant volume) is approximately given by $3R$ (law of Dulong and Petit). At low temperatures, the specific heat drops off, as would be expected from the theory. However, if Θ_E is adjusted to fit the specific heat curve in the range of temperatures where C_v is only slightly less than $3R$, it is found that the further drop at lower temperatures is not so sharp as the theory would predict.

9-2. *The Debye Model*

To correct the deficiencies of the Einstein model of a solid we need a more realistic appraisal of the actual distribution of frequencies. The solid is not a collection of $3N$ *independent* oscillators; the oscillators interact, and the solid may be better considered as a giant oscillating molecule with $3N$ normal modes of vibration, each with its own frequency. Then we have

$$(\text{P.F.}) = \prod_{j=1}^{3N} \frac{\exp\left\{-\frac{1}{2}h\nu_j/kT\right\}\exp\left\{h\nu_j/kT\right\}}{\exp\left\{h\nu_j/kT\right\} - 1} \exp\left\{\frac{-E_0}{kT}\right\}, \tag{2.1}$$

that is, the canonical partition function is the product of the individual partition functions of the $3N$ modes of oscillation with frequencies ν_j where j goes from 1 to $3N$. Each mode of vibration is of course individually quantized, as was assumed in writing Eq. (2.1). Written in logarithmic form, the resulting sum can be changed to an integral, since the frequencies are many and close together. We have

$$\ln (\text{P.F.}) = \int_0^{\nu_m} \left(\ln \frac{\exp \{-\tfrac{1}{2}h\nu/kT\} \exp \{h\nu/kT\}}{\exp \{h\nu/kT\} - 1} \right) N_\nu \, d\nu - \frac{E_0}{kT}, \qquad (2.2)$$

where ν_m is the highest allowable frequency (there are $3N$ frequencies equal to or less than ν_m), and where $N_\nu \, d\nu$ is the number of frequencies in the range ν to $\nu + d\nu$. The problem now resolves itself into the evaluation of N_ν.

This problem has recently received much attention [1-4]. It is, however, a complicated mathematical one, which is not really a part of statistical mechanics. We shall be content with the approximation introduced by Debye, which is based on a consideration of N_ν at low frequencies (long wavelengths) and an extrapolation therefrom. These modes involve large numbers of atoms moving more or less in unison over considerable distances in space; thus, they are described as having wavelengths much greater than molecular dimensions. Such a mode is in fact either a sound wave, that is, a compressional wave in which the medium is displaced in the direction of the wave propagation, or a transverse elastic wave, in which the displacement is perpendicular to the direction of wave propagation.

Whether a given wave can persist, and hence be included among the normal oscillations, depends upon whether it reinforces itself upon reflection from the surfaces of the solid. At least this is a good description of the situation if the solid is of a sufficiently regular shape, which we assume, since we do not believe that the thermodynamic properties depend appreciably upon the shape. Reinforcement depends in turn on the relation between the wavelength and the dimensions of the solid, only certain wavelengths being permitted. The wave velocity u may, for long wavelengths, be taken as constant for any given type of wave, and since the wavelength λ and the frequency ν are related to u by the relation

$$u = \lambda\nu, \qquad (2.3)$$

this will determine the allowed frequencies.

We may imagine our solid to be a rectangular parallelepiped.

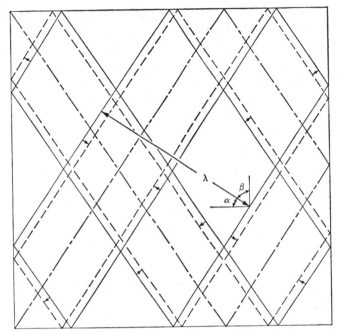

Figure 9-1. Interference of waves in a solid (two-dimensional illustration).

A sound wave or shear wave will be reflected specularly (angle of reflection equal to the angle of incidence) from a surface. Since the wave front is perpendicular to the direction of propagation, we can assume that the wave front is also reflected specularly. The character of the interference and the conditions for reinforcement may be understood by considering a two-dimensional wave, as illustrated in Fig. 9-1. This figure shows a set of reinforcing wave fronts; the solid lines show them in a special position, the broken lines show them at a slightly later time. Half of a set of parallel wave fronts is moving in one direction, half in the other direction; the wavelength, as shown on the diagram, is the distance between wave fronts moving in the same direction. In the position shown by the solid lines there is no displacement of the medium in the case of the transverse waves,† since the waves going in opposite directions are just out of phase. The maximum displacement

---

† In the case of longitudinal waves, if the displacement along a reflected wave front continued to have the same relation to the direction of propagation, the situations of reinforcement and of cancellation would be just reversed. This will also be true if (as expected) the direction of displacement with respect to the direction propagation is reversed at each reflection, since, as Fig. 9-1 shows, the adjacent (oppositely moving) wave fronts have an even number of reflections between them.

occurs when the wave fronts going in opposite directions just coincide, as indicated by the dot-dash lines. We thus have a standing wave set up. The condition for this to be possible is that the wave fronts, after a series of reflections, should come back on themselves, as shown in the figure. This coincidence involves certain integral relations between λ and the lengths of the rectangle, a and b. It may be seen, by examining the figure, that in this case we have $\lambda/\cos \alpha = 2a/3$ and $\lambda/\cos \beta = 2b/2$, where α and β are the angles (taken as less than $\pi/2$) between the direction of propagation and the sides a and b, respectively. In general, for a three-dimensional wave, with a slab of lengths a, b, and c, we have (see Fig. 9-2)

$$\frac{\lambda}{\cos \alpha} = \frac{2a}{k_x}, \qquad \frac{\lambda}{\cos \beta} = \frac{2b}{k_y}, \qquad \frac{\lambda}{\cos \gamma} = \frac{2c}{k_z}, \tag{2.4}$$

where k_x, k_y, and k_z are integers. Cosine α, cos β, and cos γ are the direction cosines of the direction of propagation in the directions of space, and we have the usual relation

$$\cos^2 \alpha + \cos^2 \beta + \cos^2 \gamma = 1,$$

which gives, with Eqs. (2.3) and (2.4),

$$\left(\frac{u}{\nu}\right)^2 \left[\left(\frac{k_x}{2a}\right)^2 + \left(\frac{k_y}{2b}\right)^2 + \left(\frac{k_z}{2c}\right)^2\right] = 1. \tag{2.5}$$

The number of frequencies in any given range of frequencies will be given by the number of integral triplets k_x, k_y, and k_z in that range. If we set up a space in which k_x, k_y, and k_z are plotted as the three rectangular coordinates, we see that in that space there is one triplet

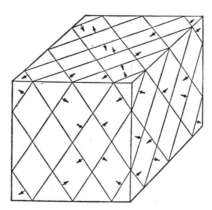

Figure 9-2. Waves in a three-dimensional solid.

k_x, k_y, k_z corresponding to each unit cube in this space. Let us characterize, for example, each cube by its greatest (algebraic) values of k_x,
k_y, k_z. If we set $\nu = $ const., Eq. (2.5) is the equation of an ellipsoid
whose volume is $\frac{4}{3}\pi \cdot 8abc \cdot (\nu^3/u^3)$ and the number of triplets k_x, k_y, k_z
between two values of ν will be $4\pi \cdot 8abc \, \nu^2/u^3 \, d\nu$. Actually, we are interested in only positive values of k_x, k_y, and k_z, since negative values have
no meaning. Thus we divide by 8, and we have then

$$N_\nu \, d\nu = 4\pi V \frac{\nu^2}{u^3} \, d\nu, \tag{2.6}$$

where $V = abc$ is the volume of the solid.

This equation was of course derived for a rectangular solid, but
since the number of frequencies in a given range is proportional to V
we suspect any solid could be considered as represented at least approximately by a collection of much smaller cubes, put together so as to
give the actual outline of the solid if not viewed too closely. In other
words, we suppose that we can integrate to get a value of $N_\nu \, d\nu$ for the
entire solid, in the same way that we integrate to find V. Thus the
assumption that we have made that the thermodynamic properties are
independent of the shape of the material is at least consistent with what
we have found.

Equation (2.6) takes into account only one kind of wave in the
solid. There are two kinds, the compressional and the transverse, which
are discussed in some detail in Sec. 9-4, and there are two independent
polarizations of the transverse waves with the displacements perpendicular to each other. Thus Eq. (2.6) will be replaced by

$$N_\nu \, d\nu = 4\pi V \nu^2 \, d\nu \, (u_l^{-3} + 2u_t^{-3}), \tag{2.7}$$

where u_l and u_t are the velocities of the longitudinal and transverse
waves, respectively. As a matter of fact, even in a solid with cubic
symmetry, the velocity of the transverse wave varies with the direction
of propagation and with the polarization. The value of u_t inserted in
Eq. (2.7) may be considered to be an average value.

Debye's assumption regarding the distribution of frequencies is
that Eq. (2.7) holds, with *constant* u_l and u_t, for all frequencies up to ν_m.
Thus the frequency distribution resembles that shown in Fig. 9-3, there
being a strong peak at ν_m and no higher frequencies. Since there are
altogether $3N$ frequencies, this approximation gives

$$\int_0^{\nu_m} N_\nu \, d\nu = 3N \tag{2.8}$$

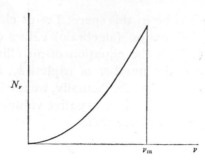

Figure 9-3. The Debye frequency distribution.

whence, by Eq. (2.7),

$$4\pi V(u_l^{-3} + 2u_t^{-3}) = \frac{9N}{v_m^3} \tag{2.9}$$

and

$$N_v \, dv = 9N \frac{v^2}{v_m^3} \, dv. \tag{2.10}$$

Substituting Eq. (2.10) into Eq. (2.2) we obtain

$$kT \ln (\text{P.F.})$$
$$= \frac{9NkT}{v_m^3} \int_0^{v_m} \left(\ln \frac{\exp\{-\frac{1}{2}hv/kT\} \exp\{hv/kT\}}{\exp\{hv/kT\} - 1} \right) v^2 \, dv - E_0, \tag{2.11}$$

an expression which can be evaluated numerically. It is convenient to change the variable of integration to $x = hv/kT$, and to set $hv_m/k = \Theta$ (the Debye temperature) writing

$$kT \ln (\text{P.F.})$$
$$= 9NkT \left(\frac{T}{\Theta}\right)^3 \int_0^{\Theta/T} \left(\ln \frac{\exp\{-x/2\} \exp\{x\}}{\exp\{x\} - 1} \right) x^2 \, dx - E_0$$
$$= 9NkT \left(\frac{T}{\Theta}\right)^3 \int_0^{\Theta/T} [-\tfrac{1}{2}x^3 - x^2 \ln (1 - \exp\{-x\})] \, dx - E_0$$
$$= -\frac{9}{8} Nk\Theta - 9NkT \left(\frac{T}{\Theta}\right)^3 \int_0^{\Theta/T} x^2 \ln (1 - \exp\{-x\}) \, dx - E_0. \tag{2.12}$$

The first term in the last expression is the contribution from the zero-point energy, and the last, $-E_0$, is a contribution from potential energy. The middle term can be reduced by integration by parts, which yields

$$kT \ln (\text{P.F.}) = -\frac{9}{8} Nk\Theta - 3NkT \ln \left(1 - \exp\left\{\frac{-\Theta}{T}\right\}\right) + NkTD\left(\frac{\Theta}{T}\right) - E_0,$$

(2.13)

where

$$D\left(\frac{\Theta}{T}\right) = 3 \left(\frac{T}{\Theta}\right)^3 \int_0^{\Theta/T} \frac{x^3}{\exp\{x\} - 1} \, dx.$$

(2.13a)

Applying the familiar formula $E = kT^2(\partial \ln (\text{P.F.})/\partial T)_V$, we can find the energy of the system. In this differentiation we assume E_0 constant, since it depends only on the mutual distance of the atoms in their equilibrium positions, and this distance will not change if the volume is constant. Likewise Θ will be constant, since its value depends only on the mutual forces between the atoms when they undergo small displacements, forces which will not change if the volume is unchanged. The change in T affects the average amplitude of the vibrations, but this will not affect the frequencies. The result is

$$E = \frac{9}{8} Nk\Theta + 3NkTD\left(\frac{\Theta}{T}\right) + E_0.$$

(2.14)

This may be written in the form

$$E = E_z + E_t + E_0,$$

(2.15)

where

$$E_z = \tfrac{9}{8}Nk\Theta$$

(2.16)

is the zero-point energy, and

$$E_t = 3NkTD\left(\frac{\Theta}{T}\right)$$

(2.17)

is the thermal energy.

The thermodynamic property of solids which is most frequently examined is the specific heat. The specific heat at constant volume, C_v, is found by differentiating Eq. (2.14), E_0 and Θ being held constant. We find

$$C_v = 3Nk\left[4D\left(\frac{\Theta}{T}\right) - \frac{3\Theta/T}{\exp\{\Theta/T\} - 1}\right].$$

(2.18)

Usually it is C_p which is measured, but it does not differ greatly from

C_v for solids, and a correction which is based on other thermodynamic data, or which is semiempirical, can be made.

We may examine the behavior of C_v at very low and very high temperatures. At high temperatures, the value of the upper limit in the integral in Eq. (2.13a) is small. When x is small, the denominator in the integrand is approximately x, so $D(\Theta/T)$ approaches 1. The fraction $(\Theta/T)/(\exp\{\Theta/T\} - 1)$ also approaches 1 in this limit, so C_v approaches $3Nk$, or $3R$ per mole, which is the Dulong-Petit value. At low temperatures, the upper limit in the integral approaches infinity, and $D(\Theta/T)$ can be shown to have a value of $(\pi^4/5)(T/\Theta)^3$. Then C_v approaches the value

$$C_v = \frac{12}{5}\,\pi^4 Nk \left(\frac{T}{\Theta}\right)^3 = \frac{16\pi^5 k^4 T^3 V}{15h^3}\left(\frac{1}{u_l^3} + \frac{2}{u_t^3}\right), \qquad (2.19)$$

the latter relation coming from application of Eq. (2.9). It is seen that C_v approaches zero as T^3 at low temperatures. The entire course of the C_v curve as calculated from the Debye theory is shown in Fig. 9-4.

The entropy can be obtained from the usual relation $S = E/T + k \ln (\text{P.F.})$. Applying Eqs. (2.13) and (2.14), we find that

$$S = 4NkD\left(\frac{\Theta}{T}\right) - 3Nk \ln\left(1 - \exp\left\{\frac{-\Theta}{T}\right\}\right). \qquad (2.20)$$

From Eqs. (2.16)–(2.20), it is seen that, for molal quantities,

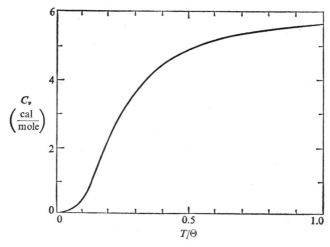

Figure 9-4.   Specific-heat curve for a Debye solid.

E_z/T, E_t/T, C_v, and S are functions of Θ/T or T/Θ, only. Tables of these quantities and of $D(\Theta/T)$ are readily available [5, 6].

Specific-heat data for many simple solids have been compared with the curve shown in Fig. 9-4, and in general the agreement is very good, showing that the Debye approximation is reasonably adequate.† In particular, the proportionality with T^3 at low temperatures is verified. Usually the value of Θ or ν_m is chosen so as to best fit the data. The values so obtained are in reasonable agreement with what might be expected from Eq. (2.9), u_l and u_t being calculated from the elastic constants of the solid. As we have noted, experiments generally yield values of C_p rather than C_v, but a correction can generally be made to convert C_p to C_v. These corrections are always negligible at very low temperatures, where the coefficient of expansion is also low (for reasons we shall presently see). At higher temperatures, the values of C_v eventually obtained are for successively greater volumes with increasing temperature, owing to the thermal expansion. Therefore, the C_v values should not be interpreted on the basis of a curve for a single Θ. However, this effect is not important for the harder solids; it is of some importance for a soft solid like argon. But disregarding this effect of expansion, it has been found both theoretically and experimentally, where the data are adequate, that the apparent value of Θ depends on the temperature.‡ This occurs because the Debye approximation is not exact; it is not correct to suppose that u_l and u_t remain constant with ν if ν increases considerably. In the next sections we will give an elementary discussion of the relation between the frequencies and the intermolecular forces, which will throw some light on the temperature dependence of Θ.

Before this, however, we will examine further the T^3 dependence of the specific heat, or, what comes to the same thing, the T^4 dependence of the energy. Let us fix our attention on one of the normal modes of vibration of the solid, say one in which the energy between adjacent energy levels is $\Delta\epsilon$ ($= h\nu$). Then the average energy of this particular oscillator over and above its zero-point energy, that is, its thermal energy, is given by the expression

---

† The general agreement with the Debye theory is well illustrated by Fowler [7, Fig. 10].

‡ In comparing the experimental value of Θ with that calculated from the elastic constant, one should use the low temperature or T^3 part of the specific-heat curve, since this is the part which depends directly upon excitations with long wavelength, and one must be sure that the extrapolation actually reaches to low enough values of T. A discussion of the experimental data in the light of the more exact theories has been given by Blackman [1].

$$\epsilon_t = \frac{\Delta\epsilon \exp\{-\Delta\epsilon/kT\} + 2\Delta\epsilon \exp\{-2\Delta\epsilon/kT\} + 3\Delta\epsilon \exp\{-3\Delta\epsilon/kT\} + \cdots}{1 + \exp\{-\Delta\epsilon/kT\} + \exp\{-2\Delta\epsilon/kT\} + \cdots}.$$

(2.21)

Equation (2.21) can be reduced to

$$\epsilon_t = \frac{\Delta\epsilon}{\exp\{\Delta\epsilon/kT\} - 1} = \frac{h\nu}{\exp\{h\nu/kT\} - 1}$$

(2.22)

in conformity with Eq. (3.10) of Chap. 2, but we prefer to use Eq. (2.21) for the present purpose, since we can more readily generalize to the case of nonuniformity of energy intervals between successive levels.

The total thermal energy of all the oscillators will be found by adding or integrating over terms given by Eq. (2.20):

$$E_t =$$

$$\int \frac{\Delta\epsilon\exp\{-\Delta\epsilon/kT\} + 2\Delta\epsilon\exp\{-2\Delta\epsilon/kT\} + 3\Delta\epsilon\exp\{-3\Delta\epsilon/kT\} + \cdots}{1 + \exp\{-\Delta\epsilon/kT\} + \exp\{-2\Delta\epsilon/kT\} + \cdots} N_{\Delta\epsilon}d\Delta\epsilon$$

(2.23)

where $N_{\Delta\epsilon}d\Delta\epsilon = hN_\nu \, d\nu$ is the number of oscillators with energy intervals between $\Delta\epsilon$ and $\Delta\epsilon + d(\Delta\epsilon)$. The limits of the integral will, according to the Debye theory, range from $\Delta\epsilon = 0$ to $\Delta\epsilon = h\nu_m$. However, if T is very low, since the high $\Delta\epsilon$'s contribute very little, the upper limit can be set at infinity. Since by Eq. (2.6) $N_{\Delta\epsilon}$ is proportional to $(\Delta\epsilon)^2$, it is readily seen from Eq. (2.23) that

$$E_t \propto T^4 \int_0^\infty \frac{x \exp\{-x\} + 2x \exp\{-2x\} + 3x \exp\{-3x\} + \cdots}{1 + \exp\{-x\} + \exp\{-2x\} + \exp\{-3x\} + \cdots} x^2 \, dx.$$

(2.24)

It is further seen that the proportionality with T^4 does not depend upon the fact that the successive energies above the zero-point energy are in the ratio 1, 2, 3, $\cdots$ (i.e., that the oscillators are harmonic). Any set of numbers will do, provided they are the same for all $\Delta\epsilon$. If this condition is met, the temperature dependence of E depends only on the dependence of $N_{\Delta\epsilon}$ on $\Delta\epsilon$. The eventual breakdown of the T^4 law for the energy occurs, of course, because the extension of the integral to infinity is not valid when T approaches Θ, or this may be expressed by saying that $N_{\Delta\epsilon} \propto (\Delta\epsilon)^2$ is not an exact law, but that $N_{\Delta\epsilon}$ becomes equal to zero when $\Delta\epsilon$ is greater than $h\nu_m$.

9-3. *Calculation of the Einstein Frequency from the Intermolecular Forces*

Although the Debye model is considerably more successful in reproducing the experimental data on the specific heat of solids than is the Einstein model, the Einstein frequency has a considerable importance, in that it is readily calculated from molecular constants [8] and has a definite relation to the Debye ν_m. In calculating the Einstein frequency for a simple monatomic solid we fix attention on a particular molecule and the effect of its displacements, assuming that its neighbors are fixed in position. Then the change in its potential energy due to its displacement will be given (in the case of cubic symmetry, to which we confine our discussion) by Eq. (1.1). The total change of potential energy is obtained by adding over all the molecules in the system

$$\delta E_p = \frac{\varkappa}{2} \sum_i (\delta_{xi}^2 + \delta_{yi}^2 + \delta_{zi}^2). \tag{3.1}$$

In this approximation the potential energy depends only on the squares of the displacements of the individual molecules, and each molecule moves independently of the others. In reality, however, the change of potential energy of a molecule depends not only on its own displacement, but also on the displacement of its neighbors.

Suppose, for example, that two neighboring molecules, labeled 1 and 2, had respective displacements in the x direction, δ_{x1} and δ_{x2}. If they were independent, the change of potential energy of the system would be proportional to $\delta_{x1}^2 + \delta_{x2}^2$. However, the actual mutual potential of this pair depends on the distance between them, that is, on $\delta_{x2} - \delta_{x1}$. We therefore expect a term in the potential energy expression which depends on $\delta_{x2} - \delta_{x1}$. We do not expect a term proportional to $\delta_{x2} - \delta_{x1}$ itself (such a term may exist but will be canceled out by the contributions from other pairs), because then it would be possible for δE_p to be negative, so that the potential energy would become less than it was at the position of equilibrium. Thus the first contributing term will be proportional to $(\delta_{x2} - \delta_{x1})^2 = \delta_{x2}^2 + \delta_{x1}^2 - 2\delta_{x2}\delta_{x1}$, the term $-2\delta_{x2}\delta_{x1}$ being previously unaccounted for. In general, the mutual interactions of the displacements of neighboring atoms will be described by cross terms of this sort. By setting up the proper linear combinations of the δ_x's, δ_y's, and δ_z's (i.e., the normal coordinates for the vibration of the solid), one can express the potential energy in terms of the new coordinates by an expression which has no cross terms. The motions of the normal coordinates are then independent of each other, and the frequency of each one can be found. There will be a spectrum of frequencies instead of a single frequency, but it can be shown that the average value of the squares of the frequencies will be unchanged [8]. The Debye spectrum of frequencies is, of course, only an approximation to the true spectrum, but to be consistent the average of the squares of the frequencies should be equal to the square of the Einstein frequency. This means that we will have

$$\frac{1}{3N}\int_0^{\nu_m} \nu^2 N_\nu \, d\nu = \nu_E^2, \tag{3.2}$$

where N_ν is given by Eq. (2.10). This gives

$$\tfrac{3}{5}\nu_m^2 = \nu_E^2 \tag{3.3}$$

or

$$\Theta = (\tfrac{5}{3})^{1/2}\Theta_E, \tag{3.4}$$

where Θ is the Debye temperature.

We will now attempt to calculate Θ_E for a cubic close-packed (face-centered) crystal, composed of monatomic molecules, such as argon. In such a crystal the atoms are arranged in planes in which each atom is surrounded by six others whose equilibrium positions form a regular hexagon, as shown in Fig. 9-5. There will be successive parallel planes, all similar. (Similar sets of parallel planes can also be passed through the atoms in other directions.) In the next plane above the one shown in Fig. 9-5 the atoms will be shifted so that an atom in the higher plane lies over a space in the plane below. There are twice as many spaces as atoms in a plane, so only half the spaces are covered. If atoms lie above spaces 1, 3, and 5, then, in the plane below the one shown,

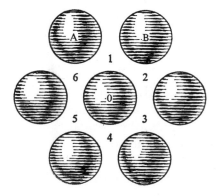

Figure 9-5. Hexagonal plane in a close-packed crystal.

atoms will be below 2, 4, and 6 in cubic close-packing. Four adjacent atoms, such as 0, A, B, and 1, form a regular tetrahedron. The distance between equilibrium positions of adjacent atoms we shall call a.

We assume that the mutual potential energy of a pair of atoms depends only on the distance between them and that these potential energies are additive and independent of the positions of other neighbors. The force between a pair of argon atoms can be approximately represented by the Lennard-Jones equation [Eq. (3.1) of Chap. 8], but, so long as we consider only nearest neighbors, we will be interested only in that part near the minimum and will expand the potential energy ϵ_p between a pair of atoms about its minimum, r_e, writing for the present purposes,

$$\epsilon_p \approx \epsilon_e + b_2(r - r_e)^2 - b_3(r - r_e)^3 + b_4(r - r_e)^4 \tag{3.5}$$

where r is the interatomic distance. If it is necessary to consider more distant atoms, we will use the form

$$\epsilon_p = -c_6 r^{-6} - c_8 r^{-8}. \tag{3.6}$$

Only the attractive part of the potential need be considered for such atoms, and the usual inverse sixth-power term may be corrected by the eighth-power term. The constants c_6 and c_8 can be estimated theoretically for the rare gases.

In order to calculate the change in potential energy, ϕ, caused by a certain displacement δ of the central atom (atom 0 in Fig. 9-5), we need to find the change δ_a caused in each of the distances of neighbors to the central atom and add up the corresponding potential energy changes, which can be represented to the second order as

$$\delta\epsilon_p = \frac{d\epsilon_p}{dr}\delta_a + \frac{1}{2}\frac{d^2\epsilon_p}{dr^2}\delta_a^2. \tag{3.7}$$

Consider two atoms initially at distance a, one of them being displaced a distance δ in a direction making an angle θ with the original direction of the line of centers (Fig. 9-6). We see from the figure, using the law of cosines, that

$$r^2 = (a + \delta_a)^2 = a^2 + \delta^2 - 2a\delta\cos\theta,$$

or

$$\delta_a^2 + 2a\delta_a - \delta^2 + 2a\delta\cos\theta = 0.$$

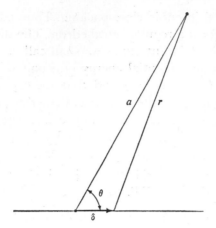

Figure 9-6.

This is a quadratic equation which may be solved for δ_a, giving the following result

$$\delta_a = -a \pm a \left[1 - 2\frac{\delta}{a}\cos\theta + \left(\frac{\delta}{a}\right)^2 \right]^{1/2}.$$

Since δ and δ_a are very small compared with a, clearly the positive sign must be used. If the bracket is expanded by the binomial theorem, we get, to the second order of small quantities, after some cancellation and using $\sin^2\theta = 1 - \cos^2\theta$,

$$\delta_a = -\delta\cos\theta + \frac{1}{2}\frac{\delta^2}{a}\sin^2\theta. \tag{3.8}$$

This may now be substituted in Eq. (3.7) and the summation made over all neighbors (each characterized by a particular value of θ) to get the value of ϕ as a function of δ. In a crystal of cubic symmetry the same result will be obtained regardless of the direction of displacement of the central atom. If this were not true, an average over all directions could be obtained by assuming the surrounding atoms to be smeared at uniform surface density over surrounding spheres at the appropriate distances, being sure that this density is taken so as to give the correct total number of atoms at each distance.

Substituting Eq. (3.8) in Eq. (3.7), we obtain, to terms in δ^2,

$$\delta\epsilon_p \approx \left[-\delta\cos\theta + \frac{1}{2}\frac{\delta^2}{a}\sin^2\theta \right]\frac{d\epsilon_p}{dr} + \frac{1}{2}\delta^2\cos^2\theta\frac{d^2\epsilon_p}{dr^2}. \tag{3.9}$$

On summing over the twelve nearest neighbors, it is seen that their contribution to ϕ will be given to the second order of small quantities by

$$12\left[-\delta\,\overline{\cos\theta}+\frac{1}{2}\frac{\delta^2}{a}\,\overline{\sin^2\theta}\right]\frac{d\epsilon_p}{dr}+6\delta^2\,\overline{\cos^2\theta}\,\frac{d^2\epsilon_p}{dr^2}$$

where the bar indicates an average over all these neighbors. If we replace this average by an average over the sphere (found by integration with respect to the solid angle ω, where $d\omega = \sin\theta\,d\theta d\phi$, and division by the total solid angle, 4π), we may consider θ to be the polar angle in a system of polar coordinates. Then $\overline{\cos\theta} = 0$, since $\cos\theta$ is as often positive (θ between 0 and $\pi/2$) as it is negative (θ between $\pi/2$ and π), $\overline{\cos^2\theta} = \frac{1}{3}$, and $\overline{\sin^2\theta} = \frac{2}{3}$. Thus the contribution to ϕ becomes

$$4\frac{\delta^2}{a}\frac{d\epsilon_p}{dr} + 2\delta^2\frac{d^2\epsilon_p}{dr^2}. \tag{3.10}$$

The derivatives may be evaluated from Eq. (3.5), inserting a for r after differentiation. To the resulting expression must be added similar terms for next nearest neighbors, etc. These will have different coefficients, the derivatives must be evaluated from Eq. (3.6), and the proper value of r for these more distant neighbors inserted. These additional contributions will be quite small and may actually be somewhat questionable, since they refer to interactions of atoms which have other atoms more or less between them. However, including them in the expression, we obtain

$$\phi = \sum_i \frac{n_i}{6}\left[2\frac{\delta^2}{a_i}\left(\frac{d\epsilon_p}{dr}\right)_{r=a_i} + \delta^2\left(\frac{d^2\epsilon_p}{dr^2}\right)_{r=a_i}\right], \tag{3.11}$$

where n_i is the number of atoms at distance a_i, the sum being taken over all distances a_i which occur in the lattice. The force constant of this potential-energy field will be given by the coefficient of $\frac{1}{2}\delta^2$ in this expression, and the frequency (the Einstein frequency) will be

$$\nu_E = \frac{1}{2\pi}\left(\frac{\sum_i [(2/a_i)(d\epsilon_p/dr)_{r=a_i} + (d^2\epsilon_p/dr^2)_{r=a_i}]n_i}{3m}\right)^{1/2} \tag{3.12}$$

where m is the mass of the atoms. The Debye Θ is given by

$$\Theta = \frac{h}{2\pi k}\left(\frac{\sum_i [(2/a_i)(d\epsilon_p/dr)_{r=a_i} + (d^2\epsilon_p/dr^2)_{r=a_i}]5n_i}{9m}\right)^{1/2}. \tag{3.13}$$

It is convenient to write Eq. (3.11) in the form

$$\phi = 4B\delta^2, \tag{3.14}$$

which gives

$$\Theta^2 = \frac{10h^2 B}{3\pi^2 mk^2}. \tag{3.15}$$

If we use Eq. (3.5) for the nearest neighbors and Eq. (3.6) for the others, then for the face-centered cubic lattice we have

$$B = b_2 - \left(3b_3 - \frac{2b_2}{a}\right)(a - r_e) + \left(6b_4 - \frac{3b_3}{a}\right)(a - r_e)^2$$
$$+ \frac{4b_4}{a}(a - r_e)^3 - \frac{1.003c_6}{a^8} - \frac{0.726c_8}{a^{10}}. \tag{3.16}$$

The last two terms come from differentiating Eq. (3.6) and summing over all atoms but the nearest neighbors, using the formula of Jones and Ingham [9].

This expression will give Θ as a function of a, or of the molecular volume of the solid, provided the constants in Eq. (3.5) are known. Its use does depend, however, upon the assumption that the vibrations are harmonic, all powers of δ above δ^2 being neglected in Eq. (3.9). If anharmonicity is important, the entire problem becomes much more difficult, since the idea of normal vibrations then breaks down. If the anharmonicity is not large, then an approximate correction can be made by assuming that the thermodynamic properties change just as they would if the Einstein model held [10–11].† Even this procedure is not easy, although it is not impossible, since some estimate can be made of the effect of the higher powers in the potential-energy curve on the energy levels of the system.

9-4. *Effective Value of Θ at Low Temperatures*

If the Debye assumption regarding the distribution of frequencies were exactly correct, the procedure outlined in the preceding section would, at least in principle, give the thermodynamic properties exactly. Actually it is found that if T/Θ is greater than about 0.25, any reasonable distribution of frequencies will give about the same results for the energy

† See also [5, pp. 750–51; 12].

and specific heat, provided that the average of the squares of the frequencies is fixed [8]. Even so crude a representation as the Einstein model gives reasonably good results. However, at lower values of T/Θ the results depend more strongly on the frequency distribution. At low T/Θ the calculations depend almost entirely on the low frequencies; it is just in the range of low frequencies that Debye's assumption that N_ν is proportional to ν^2 holds, for a low frequency means a long wavelength, and as long as the wavelength is large compared with interatomic distances, the wave velocities will remain constant. If we can calculate the velocities, we can find a value of Θ which can be used at low temperatures. However, since N_ν deviates from the ν^2 law at higher ν, this value of Θ, which we will call Θ_0, will not necessarily coincide with the value obtained by setting $\nu_m^2 = \tfrac{5}{3}\overline{\nu^2}$; i.e., it will differ from the value of Θ obtained in Sec. 9-3. We will now attempt to calculate u_l and u_t, and thus find Θ_0.

Let us take up first the transverse waves. We assume that we have a wave which is propagating in the x direction and is polarized in the z direction; that is, all displacements are in the z direction. We shall designate by Z the displacement of any atom from its equilibrium position. If the motion is harmonic, we may write for the total potential energy due to this wave

$$E_{\nu,\mathrm{p}} = \tfrac{1}{2}N\eta\overline{Z^2},\tag{4.1}$$

where $\overline{Z^2}$ is the average square of the displacement, N is the total number of atoms, and η is the force constant. In similar fashion we can write for the kinetic energy

$$E_{\nu,\mathrm{k}} = \frac{1}{2}Nm\overline{\left(\frac{dZ}{dt}\right)^2}.\tag{4.2}$$

Assuming that the wave is a sinusoidal standing wave, we may take Z as the following function of the distance x along the direction of propagation, and of the time t:

$$Z = Z_m \sin\left(\frac{2\pi x}{\lambda}\right)\sin(2\pi\nu t),\tag{4.3}$$

λ and ν being the wavelength and frequency, respectively. Also,

$$\frac{dZ}{dt} = 2\pi\nu Z_m \sin\left(\frac{2\pi x}{\lambda}\right)\cos(2\pi\nu t).\tag{4.4}$$

Using Eqs. (4.3) and (4.4) in (4.1) and (4.2) we obtain for the total
energy of the wave

$$E_\nu = E_{\nu,\mathrm{p}} + E_{\nu,\mathrm{k}} = \frac{1}{2} N\eta Z_m^2 \overline{\sin^2\left(\frac{2\pi x}{\lambda}\right)} \sin^2(2\pi\nu t)$$

$$+ \frac{1}{2} Nm(2\pi\nu)^2 Z_m^2 \overline{\sin^2\left(\frac{2\pi x}{\lambda}\right)} \cos^2(2\pi\nu t)$$

$$= \frac{1}{4} N\eta Z_m^2 \sin^2(2\pi\nu t) + \frac{1}{4} Nm(2\pi\nu)^2 Z_m^2 \cos^2(2\pi\nu t), \qquad (4.5)$$

since the average of the square of the sine is $\frac{1}{2}$. In order for E_ν to be
constant, we must have $\eta = (2\pi\nu)^2 m$, which gives the usual relationship

$$\nu = \frac{1}{2\pi}\left(\frac{\eta}{m}\right)^{1/2}. \qquad (4.6)$$

In order to relate η to the interatomic forces, we need to relate Z to
the relative displacement of neighboring atoms. We consider the relative displacement in the z direction of two atoms which are nearest
neighbors, and whose equilibrium positions are a distance a apart (see
Fig. 9-7). Let us designate by θ and ϕ the polar coordinates of the line

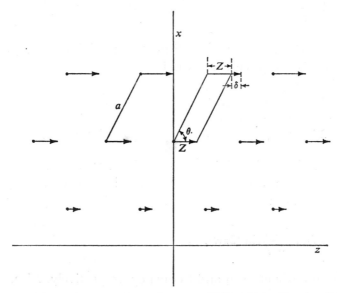

Figure 9-7. Illustrating the relation between dZ/dx and δ. (For simplicity in drawing,
it has been assumed in the illustration that the line joining the two adjacent atoms lies
in the *x–z* plane. This is not necessarily the case.)

of centers, θ being the angle made with the direction of displacement or polarization and ϕ being the usual azimuthal angle. The component of a in the direction of propagation will be the x component of a or $a \sin \theta \cos \phi$. The relative displacement of the two atoms in the direction z of polarization due to the wave motion, we will call δ, and it will be given by dZ/dx multiplied by the component of a in the x direction, or

$$\delta = \frac{dZ}{dx} a \sin \theta \cos \phi. \tag{4.7}$$

The actual change in distance δ_a of these two atoms will be given in terms of δ by Eq. (3.8) (but note that the angle between a and δ is now $\pi - \theta$, so $-\cos \theta$ replaces $\cos \theta$), and the change in potential energy of a particular pair of atoms will be given by inserting the expression for δ into (3.9). If we consider only nearest neighbors, the resulting relation must be summed over all such neighbors to obtain the change of potential energy of some central atom. The actual result will depend upon the direction of propagation and the direction of polarization. However, we may get a reasonable average by simply averaging uniformly over all directions of space, as we did in the last section, and we obtain

$$\left[\frac{dZ}{dx} a \, \overline{\cos \theta \sin \theta \cos \phi} + \frac{1}{2} \left(\frac{dZ}{dx} \right)^2 a \, \overline{\sin^4 \theta \cos^2 \phi} \right] \frac{d\epsilon_p}{dr}$$

$$+ \frac{1}{2} \left(\frac{dZ}{dx} \right)^2 a^2 \, \overline{\sin^2 \theta \cos^2 \theta \cos^2 \phi} \, \frac{d^2\epsilon_p}{dr^2}$$

$$= \frac{2}{15} \left(\frac{dZ}{dx} \right)^2 a \frac{d\epsilon_p}{dr} + \frac{1}{30} \left(\frac{dZ}{dx} \right)^2 a^2 \frac{d^2\epsilon_p}{dr^2}, \tag{4.8}$$

since the average of $\cos \theta \sin \theta \cos \phi$ obviously vanishes, while it may be readily shown that

$$\overline{\sin^4 \theta \cos^2 \phi} = \tfrac{4}{15} \qquad \text{and} \qquad \overline{\sin^2 \theta \cos^2 \theta \cos^2 \phi} = \tfrac{1}{15}.$$

Again one may include successive shells of more distant atoms simply by inserting the appropriate interatomic distance for a and adding over all these shells. Since the wavelength is assumed to be long compared with interatomic distances, dZ/dx may be given the value at the position midway between a pair of atoms. However, in obtaining the entire potential energy of the wave we must average $(dZ/dx)^2$ over all values of x. It is seen, by differentiating Eq. (4.3) and performing this averaging process, that

$$\overline{\left(\frac{dZ}{dx}\right)^2} = \left(\frac{2\pi}{\lambda}\right)^2 \overline{Z^2}.$$

(4.9)

Utilizing (4.8) and (4.9), then, we find

$$E_{\nu,p} = \frac{1}{2} N \left(\frac{2\pi}{\lambda}\right)^2 \overline{Z^2} \sum_i n_i \left[\frac{2}{15} a_i \left(\frac{d\epsilon_p}{dr}\right)_{r=a_i} + \frac{1}{30} a_i^2 \left(\frac{d^2\epsilon_p}{dr^2}\right)_{r=a_i}\right].$$

(4.10)

The factor $\frac{1}{2}$ enters because the potential energy is a sum of mutual potential energies of *pairs;* otherwise we should count the mutual potential energy of each pair twice. By comparison with Eq. (4.1) we can easily obtain the value of η, and from Eq. (4.6) the value of ν. We find

$$u_t = \nu\lambda = a \left(\frac{\sum_i \frac{1}{30}\alpha_i^2[4a_i^{-1}(d\epsilon_p/dr)_{r=a_i} + (d^2\epsilon_p/dr^2)_{r=a_i}]n_i}{m}\right)^{1/2},$$

(4.11)

where $\alpha_i = a_i/a$.

We turn now to the compressional waves, which are actually just like the transverse waves, except that the direction of propagation now coincides with the direction of displacement. The latter we continue to call z, so z replaces x in Eqs. (4.3), (4.4), and (4.5), and dZ/dz replaces dZ/dx. Since the factor $\sin\theta\cos\phi$ in Eq. (4.7) represents a projection upon the direction of propagation, Eq. (4.7) is replaced by

$$\delta = \left(\frac{dZ}{dz}\right) a \cos\theta.$$

(4.12)

We can follow through the calculation as for the transverse waves, and in place of (4.8) we have

$$\left[\left(\frac{dZ}{dz}\right) a \overline{\cos^2\theta} + \frac{1}{2}\left(\frac{dZ}{dz}\right)^2 a \overline{\cos^2\theta\sin^2\theta}\right]\frac{d\epsilon_p}{dr} + \frac{1}{2}\left(\frac{dZ}{dz}\right)^2 a^2 \overline{\cos^4\theta}\frac{d^2\epsilon_p}{dr^2}$$

$$= \frac{1}{3}\left(\frac{dZ}{dz}\right) a \frac{d\epsilon_p}{dr} + \frac{1}{15}\left(\frac{dZ}{dz}\right)^2 a \frac{d\epsilon_p}{dr} + \frac{1}{10}\left(\frac{dZ}{dz}\right)^2 a^2 \frac{d^2\epsilon_p}{dr^2}.$$

(4.13)

We must now proceed to average over values in the direction of propagation z, and $\overline{dZ/dz}$ vanishes. For the other terms we may use Eq. (4.9), replacing dZ/dx by dZ/dz, and we obtain an expression just like Eq. (4.10) except for the numerical coefficients, which will be $\frac{1}{15}$ and $\frac{1}{10}$ instead of $\frac{2}{15}$ and $\frac{1}{30}$. The final result will be like Eq. (4.11) except for the same change in coefficients:

$$u_1 = a \left(\frac{\sum_i \frac{1}{10}\alpha_i^2[\frac{2}{3}a_i^{-1}(d\epsilon_p/dr)_{r=a_i} + (d^2\epsilon_p/dr^2)_{r=a_i}]n_i}{m}\right)^{1/2}.$$

(4.14)

Let us define the quantity $\zeta_j(a_i)$ thus:

$$\zeta_j(a_i) = \left[ja_i^{-1}\left(\frac{d\epsilon_p}{dr}\right)_{r=a_i} + \left(\frac{d^2\epsilon_p}{dr^2}\right)_{r=a_i} \right]\frac{n_i}{m}. \tag{4.15}$$

Then we may use Eq. (2.9) to obtain an expression for $\Theta_0 = h\nu_m/k$ in a compact form. In doing so we use the relation for cubic close-packing, $V/N = a^3/2^{1/2}$. The result is

$$\Theta_0 = \left(\frac{9\cdot 2^{1/2}}{4\pi}\right)^{1/3}\frac{h}{k}\frac{[\frac{1}{10}\sum_i \alpha_i^2\zeta_{2/3}(a_i)]^{1/2}[\frac{1}{30}\sum_i \alpha_i^2\zeta_4(a_i)]^{1/2}}{\{[\frac{1}{30}\sum_i \alpha_i^2\zeta_4(a_i)]^{3/2} + 2[\frac{1}{10}\sum_i \alpha_i^2\zeta_{2/3}(a_i)]^{3/2}\}^{1/3}}. \tag{4.16}$$

In general, $a_i^{-1}d\epsilon_p/dr$ will be much less than $d^2\epsilon_p/dr^2$, especially in the most important case, that of nearest neighbors, where $a_i = a$. In this case the ratio will, from Eq. (3.5) be roughly $(a - r_e)/a$, and previous calculations have shown that, in the position of equilibrium, at temperatures between 0°K and the melting point for argon, $a - r_e$ is very small compared with a. These calculations will be discussed later; in the meantime we may set as an approximation

$$\zeta_j(a_i) = \zeta(a_i), \tag{4.17}$$

where $\zeta(a_i)$ does not depend on j. Then it is found that

$$\Theta_0 \approx 0.141\,\frac{h}{k}\,[\sum_i \alpha_i^2\zeta(a_i)]^{1/2}. \tag{4.18}$$

On the other hand, in this approximation, we find from Eq. (3.13)

$$\Theta \approx 0.119\,\frac{h}{k}\,[\sum_i \zeta(a_i)]^{1/2}. \tag{4.19}$$

From the coefficients alone we would conclude that Θ_0 is about 19% greater than Θ. Actually the difference will be slightly less than this because of the greater weight given in Eq. (4.18) to the more distant neighbors, on account of the factor α_i^2. The value of $d^2\epsilon_p/dr^2$ is positive for the nearest neighbors, but negative for all more distant. Calculations [4, 13]† of the actual spectrum of frequencies indicate that Θ_0/Θ should be about 1.15 rather than 1.19. The difference seems to be some-

---

† It should be noted that the trend of Θ with T is relatively simple in the case of a cubic close-packed crystal. With crystals of lower symmetry the trend can be more complicated.

what greater than can be accounted for by the more distant neighbors, but in any event the agreement is reasonably good.

9-5. *Estimate of* Θ *as a Function of Temperature*

Once $\overline{\nu^2}$ is fixed, the thermodynamic functions are reasonably independent of the true distribution of frequencies, provided that T/Θ is greater than about 0.25. On the other hand, at very low temperatures the thermodynamic quantities are such as conform to a Debye characteristic temperature equal to Θ_0. There will, therefore, be a change in the apparent value of Θ somewhere in the low-temperature range. To find the exact course of this change, we need to know the exact distribution of frequencies. We may, however, reproduce it approximately by a very rough guess about the nature of the frequency distribution.

The distribution at the low-frequency end would correspond, if the Debye frequency distribution were followed, to a maximum frequency $\nu_{m,0} = \Theta_0 k/h$, which is larger than $\nu_m = \Theta k/h$, where $\nu_m^2 = \frac{5}{3}\overline{\nu}^2$. Since the limiting value Θ_0 depends only on the low frequencies, and since at high temperatures the properties depend almost entirely on ν_m or Θ, we attempt to represent the situation by assuming that the Debye distribution characterized by Θ_0 is cut off at the frequency ν_m. Then all the frequencies which would lie between $\nu_{m,0}$ and ν_m, equal in number to $\int_{\nu_m}^{\nu_{m,0}} N_\nu\, d\nu$ $[= 3N(\nu_{m,0}^3 - \nu_m^3)/\nu_{m,0}^3$, by Eq. (2.10)] are reassigned and assumed to be equal to the Einstein frequency, namely, $(\frac{3}{5})^{1/2}\nu_m$. The fraction of the frequencies in the Debye distribution is $\nu_m^3/\nu_{m,0}^3$. Let us assume that $\nu_{m,0} = 1.15\nu_m$; then 0.657 of the frequencies are in the new Debye distribution, and 0.343 of them are in the Einstein "distribution." If we let C_v be the molal specific heat at constant volume, $C_{v,D}$ be the molal specific heat for the Debye distribution (maximum frequency ν_m), and $C_{v,E}$ that for the Einstein frequency $[= (\frac{3}{5})^{1/2}\nu_m]$, then

$$C_v = 0.657C_{v,D} + 0.343C_{v,E}.$$

Also, for the entropy we have

$$S = 0.657S_D + 0.343S_E.$$

We may thus calculate C_v and S as a function of T/Θ, where Θ is the high-temperature value. We can then calculate the value of T/Θ which would give any value of C_v or of S on the basis of the Debye theory. These values of T/Θ we will call T/Θ_C, and T/Θ_S; by comparison with

TABLE 9-1

Change in Effective Values of Θ with Temperature

$(C_v$ and S in cal mole^{-1} deg$^{-1})$

T/Θ	$C_{v,\mathrm{D}}$	$C_{v,\mathrm{E}}$	Θ_{C_v}/Θ	S_D	S_E	Θ_S/Θ
0.05	0.0581	0.0006	1.148	. . . . . .	. . . . . .	. . . . .
0.1	.4520	.1551	1.093	0.1536	0.0231	1.124
0.1333	.9667	.609	1.056	.3503	.123	1.094
0.2	2.197	1.941	1.026	.9750	.618	1.060
0.3	3.623	3.516	1.011	2.160	1.728	1.042
0.4	4.446	4.401	1.006	3.325	2.874	1.036
0.5	4.920	4.899	1.004	4.373	3.915	1.033
1.0	5.673	5.670	1.002	8.094	7.626	1.030

the originally assigned T/Θ we may get the effective value, Θ_C, or Θ_S, based on specific heat or entropy. This calculation is shown in Table 9-1.

The more precise calculation, based on a more nearly correct distribution function [4], shows the decrease in Θ_C, occurring at a value of T/Θ about 60% of that shown in Table 9-1. This difference arises because the deviation from the frequency distribution with Debye characteristic temperature Θ_0 begins to occur at lower frequencies than the Einstein frequency.

It appears that Θ_{C_v}/Θ approaches unity in the high-temperature limit, but that Θ_S/Θ does not. This occurs because the entropy is expressible as an integral, $\int (C_v/T)\, dT$, and residual effects remain even at high temperatures, arising from the low-temperature departures of C_v from the values which would be characteristic of Θ, the high-temperature value.

An integration similar to Eq. (2.23), but expressing ϵ_t in the form given by Eq. (2.22) and allowing the frequency distribution function $N_\nu\, d\nu$ to remain unspecified, can be used to find out about the high-temperature behavior of an assembly having an arbitrary frequency distribution [14]. On the basis of Eq. (2.22) we have

$$E_t = \int \frac{h\nu}{\exp\{h\nu/kT\} - 1}\, N_\nu\, d\nu, \tag{5.1}$$

the integration being taken, of course, over all possible frequencies. Expansion of the exponential and division by the resulting series yields

$$E_t = kT \int \left(1 - \frac{h\nu}{2kT} + \frac{(h\nu)^2}{12(kT)^2} - \frac{(h\nu)^4}{720(kT)^4} + \cdots \right) N_\nu \, d\nu$$

$$= 3NkT - \int \frac{h\nu}{2} N_\nu \, d\nu + \int \left(\frac{(h\nu)^2}{12kT} - \frac{(h\nu)^4}{720(kT)^3} + \cdots \right) N_\nu \, d\nu,$$

$$(5.2)$$

since $\int N_\nu \, d\nu = 3N$. Differentiation gives

$$C_\nu = 3Nk - k \int \left(\frac{(h\nu)^2}{12(kT)^2} - \frac{(h\nu)^4}{240(kT)^4} + \cdots \right) N_\nu \, d\nu. \qquad (5.3)$$

This gives C_ν as a high-temperature expansion whose coefficients involve the moment integrals of the frequency distribution. ($\int \nu^2 N_\nu \, d\nu / 3N$ is the second moment of the distribution, $\int \nu^4 N_\nu \, d\nu / 3N$ the fourth moment, and so on.) Of course, $3Nk$ is the expected high-temperature limit of C_ν, and it is observed that $C_\nu - 3Nk$ depends in the limit on $\int (h\nu/k)^2 N_\nu \, d\nu$, which is just equal to $3N \cdot \frac{3}{5}\Theta^2$. This relation holds regardless of the frequency distribution, in particular for the Debye distribution. At high T, then, any frequency distribution should have the effective Debye temperature corresponding to $(\frac{5}{3})^{1/2}$ times the root-mean-square frequency.

The difference which arises when an effective Θ is calculated from the entropy can be brought out by setting up an expression for the entropy in a similar way. From Eq. (3.12) of Chap. 2,

$$S = \int \left[\frac{h\nu/T}{\exp\{h\nu/kT\} - 1} - k \ln \left(1 - \exp\left\{ -\frac{h\nu}{kT} \right\} \right) \right] N_\nu \, d\nu. \quad (5.4)$$

Expansion of the exponentials and subsequent expansion of the logarithm yield

$$S = 3Nk + 3Nk \ln \frac{kT}{h} - k \int \left(\ln \nu - \frac{h\nu}{kT} + \frac{(h\nu)^2}{8(kT)^2} + \cdots \right) N_\nu \, d\nu.$$

$$(5.5)$$

The high-temperature behavior of S depends on the logarithmic average of ν rather than the root mean square. The effective value of Θ from the entropy might therefore be expected to approach a slightly different limit from that calculated from the specific heat. Nevertheless it will sometimes be desirable, as we shall see, to calculate effective Θ's from the entropy.

9-6. *Effect of Thermal Expansion*

The changes in Θ with temperature which were examined in Sec. 9-5 were the changes that would occur if the volume of the solid did not change. In general, there will be some expansion of the solid and this will result in a further lowering of Θ. This will in general only occur at a temperature higher than that at which the decrease in Θ discussed in Sec. 9-5 is virtually complete. This effect of temperature on Θ was analyzed by Grüneisen [15] whose theory is based upon the relation, which is true in the Debye theory, that the entropy S is a function only of Θ/T, in this combination. Using Eq. (2.15) we have, from the general definition of pressure,

$$P = -\left(\frac{\partial E}{\partial V}\right)_S = -\frac{dE_z}{dV} - \left(\frac{\partial E_t}{\partial V}\right)_S - \frac{dE_0}{dV}, \tag{6.1}$$

in which E_z and E_0 are, of course, functions only of V. Since E_t/T depends only on Θ/T it is also true that $E_t/\Theta = (E_t/T)(T/\Theta)$ is a function of Θ/T and does not change if S remains constant. Hence we have

$$\left(\frac{\partial E_t}{\partial V}\right)_S = \left[\frac{\partial \Theta(E_t/\Theta)}{\partial V}\right]_S = \frac{E_t}{\Theta}\frac{d\Theta}{dV}. \tag{6.2}$$

Thus we may write

$$P = -\frac{E_t}{\Theta}\frac{d\Theta}{dV} - \frac{dE_z}{dV} - \frac{dE_0}{dV}. \tag{6.3}$$

From Eq. (2.16) we readily see that this may also be written

$$P = -\frac{E_t + E_z}{\Theta}\frac{d\Theta}{dV} - \frac{dE_0}{dV}. \tag{6.4}$$

For a solid under its own vapor pressure, we may ordinarily replace P on the left-hand side of Eq. (6.3) or (6.4) by 0, since the pressures involved are small compared with the terms on the right-hand side. Under these conditions we may write

$$\left(\frac{\partial P}{\partial T}\right)_V dT + \left(\frac{\partial P}{\partial V}\right)_T dV = 0 \tag{6.5}$$

or

$$\frac{dV}{dT} = -\frac{(\partial P/\partial T)_V}{(\partial P/\partial V)_T},$$ (6.6)

from which an expression for the coefficient of expansion may be obtained. Since E_z, E_0, and Θ are functions of V only, we see at once from Eq. (6.4) that

$$\left(\frac{\partial P}{\partial T}\right)_V = -\frac{C_v}{\Theta}\frac{d\Theta}{dV}.$$ (6.7)

In obtaining $(\partial P/\partial V)_T$ we note first that, from Eq. (2.16), E_z/Θ is independent of V, and also we note that

$$\left(\frac{\partial (E_t/\Theta)}{\partial V}\right)_T = \frac{d(E_t/\Theta)}{d(\Theta/T)}\left(\frac{\partial(\Theta/T)}{\partial V}\right)_T = \frac{1}{T}\frac{d(E_t/\Theta)}{d(\Theta/T)}\frac{d\Theta}{dV}.$$

At the same time we see that

$$C_v = \Theta\left(\frac{\partial(E_t/\Theta)}{\partial T}\right)_V = \Theta\frac{d(E_t/\Theta)}{d(\Theta/T)}\left(\frac{\partial(\Theta/T)}{\partial T}\right)_V$$

$$= -\left(\frac{\Theta}{T}\right)^2\frac{d(E_t/\Theta)}{d(\Theta/T)}.$$ (6.8)

Thus we get

$$\left(\frac{\partial(E_t/\Theta)}{\partial V}\right)_T = -\frac{TC_v}{\Theta^2}\frac{d\Theta}{dV},$$ (6.9)

and, from Eq. (6.4),

$$\left(\frac{\partial P}{\partial V}\right)_T = \frac{TC_v}{\Theta^2}\left(\frac{d\Theta}{dV}\right)^2 - \frac{E_t + E_z}{\Theta}\frac{d^2\Theta}{dV^2} - \frac{d^2E_0}{dV^2}.$$ (6.10)

Usually the last term in Eq. (6.10) is the dominant one. Therefore, we may write an approximation for $\alpha = V^{-1}\,dV/dT$, the expansion coefficient, using Eqs. (6.6), (6.7), and (6.10), as follows:

$$\alpha \approx -\frac{C_v(d\Theta/dV)}{V\Theta(d^2E_0/dV^2)}.$$ (6.11)

Of the quantities in this equation, C_v changes most rapidly as the temperature of a solid is increased at essentially constant volume. Thus, roughly speaking, α will parallel C_v. In the regions in which Θ is changing on account of the factors discussed in Sec. 9-5, T/Θ and therefore C_v are small, the coefficient of expansion will be small, and changes in Θ due to expansion will be negligible. As previously stated, only when the temperature has increased further will changes in Θ due to expansion be important.

Data on the compressibility of a substance generally come in the form of measurements of the pressure at various volumes. Equation (6.10) could be applied to these data; however, often it is more convenient to apply an equation in which the differentiation has not been carried out. For this purpose a modification of Eq. (6.4) is useful. If we subtract the equation for $P = 0$, evaluated at the same volume, (but, of course, at a different temperature) from the original Eq. (6.4), we note that, since E_z, $d\Theta/dV$, and dE_0/dV depend on V only,

$$ P = \frac{1}{\Theta}\left(\frac{d\Theta}{dV}\right)[E_t(0) - E_t], \tag{6.12} $$

where $E_t(0)$ stands for the value of E_t at zero pressure, but with the volume equal to V.

9-7. *The Thermodynamic Properties of Solid Argon*

We now apply the results of this chapter to a specific case. These results are based on the Debye theory, and we shall ignore the deviations arising from the true distribution of frequencies which produce the high apparent Θ values at low temperatures. These effects are largely negligible if $T/\Theta > 0.2$, and above such a temperature we may assume that the Debye Θ calculable from Eq. (3.13) can be used. As already noted, because the entropy represents an integral of C_v/T or C_p/T, some residual effects will remain, owing to the deviations in the specific heat at low temperatures, but these will be small.

Solid argon is a useful example, since a considerable amount of data is available. Accurate measurements of the specific heat have recently been made by Flubacher, Leadbetter, and Morrison [16]. Integration of C_p will give the enthalpy (in practice, the energy, since the measurements were made under the vapor pressure, which is essentially zero), as a function of temperature, and integration of C_p/T will give the entropy. From the entropy, using Eq. (2.20) (or tabulated values of S as a function of Θ/T), the Debye temperature Θ may be calculated. If Θ is known, E_z may be found from Eq. (2.16) and E_t from Eq. (2.17) (or from tables). Combining these with the values of the energy, we may obtain the potential energy E_0 from Eq. (2.15), and C_v from Θ/T. These quantities are now all known at various values of T, and the molal volumes V corresponding to various values of T are also known from measurements of Figgins, of Piercey, and of Clusius and Weigand.[†] The mean distance a between nearest neighbors in the crystal is given for a face-centered cubic crystal like argon in terms of the molal volume by

$$V = \frac{Na^3}{2^{1/2}}, \tag{7.1}$$

where N is Avogadro's number.

The various quantities, directly observed and derived, are tabulated in Table 9-2, and in Fig. 9-8 we have plotted Θ as a function of V and as a function of a.

TABLE 9-2

The Thermodynamic Properties of Solid Argon

(T and Θ in °K; C_p, C_v, and S in cal mole^{-1} deg^{-1}; energies in cal mole^{-1}; V in cc mole^{-1}.)

T	C_p	S	Θ	$E - E(0°)$	E_z	E_t	$E_0 - E_0(0°)$	V	$C_p - C_v$
10	0.7900	0.2588	83.54	1.975	186.74	1.93	.....	22.60	.....
20	2.990	1.502	$\begin{cases}81.44\\81.31*\end{cases}$	21.21	$\begin{cases}182.05\\181.76*\end{cases}$	20.99	$\begin{cases}0.93\\1.22*\end{cases}$	22.65	0.054
30	4.463	3.020	80.46	59.15	179.86	58.42	3.63	22.79	.196
40	5.387	4.441	78.92	108.79	176.42	106.43	8.70	23.02	.443
50	6.006	5.711	77.00	165.82	172.12	160.31	16.15	23.31	.696
60	6.528	6.854	74.88	228.56	167.39	217.63	26.3	23.62	1.007
70	7.100	7.900	72.44	296.47	161.39	277.41	39.9	23.99	1.447
80	7.928	8.899	69.48	371.43	155.31	339.39	59.5	24.44	2.186
83	8.327	9.198	68.42	395.76	152.94	358.50	67.1	24.60	2.564

* Calculated using the extrapolation of the line Θ versus V of Fig. 9-8.

It is seen that Θ is linear with respect to either of these quantities within limits of experimental error (it is believed that the linearity is best with V), except at the lowest temperatures. The increase in the apparent value of Θ at low temperatures is due to the effects discussed in Sec. 9-4.

[†] For the handling of these data and for references see [17]. Tables 9-2, 9-3, and 9-4 and Figs. 9-8, 9-9, and 9-10 have been taken from this article.

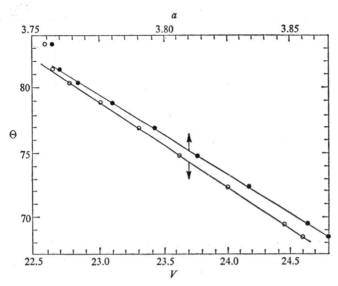

Figure 9-8. Debye temperature $\Theta(°K)$ of argon as a function of volume (cc mole^{-1}) or of interatomic distance (Å).

It may be shown that E_0 is essentially quadratic in V, for dE_0/dV is virtually linear and may be found by taking differences in Table 9-2. If the quotient of differences is $\Delta E_0/\Delta V$, this may be taken to be the value of dE_0/dV at the value of V halfway between the tabulated values. Thus Fig. 9-9 is obtained, the curve shown being a straight line.

We could verify Eq. (6.4) for $P = 0$; however, this would serve only as a check on the accuracy of our calculations, for it can be shown that if $dE = T\,dS$ (as it does when $P = 0$, though not in general), then Eq. (6.4) with $P = 0$ follows directly from Eq. (2.15), if the Debye theory is used (even if it is not correct), regardless of the dependence of Θ on T or V. Since the Debye theory is used to obtain Θ from S, and then to calculate E_z, E_t, and thus, indirectly, E_0, these quantities *have* to be consistent with this theory, as does E if $dE = T\,dS$; so, at $P = 0$, Eq. (6.4) is not an independent relation.

Equation (6.12) may, however, be applied at higher pressures. Stewart [**18, 19**]† has measured the compressibility of argon at 65°K and 77°K. These results may be expressed by giving the volume at certain pressures. With V known, Θ can be found, and the temperature for which this volume would occur at $P = 0$. Thus the quantities in Eq. (6.12) can be found, and P(calc.) compared with P(obs.).

---

† Stewart also has unpublished data modifying the results at 77°. See also [**4,** p. 554, and **20**]. Stewart's changes are included in Table 9-3.

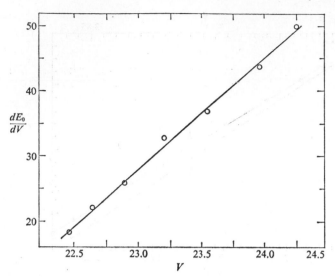

Figure 9-9.

The results of this calculation are shown in Table 9-3. The agreement is not too good. But we can now calculate $C_p - C_v$ from the thermodynamic formula

$$C_p - C_v = -T \left(\frac{\partial V}{\partial T}\right)_P^2 \left(\frac{\partial P}{\partial V}\right)_T \tag{7.2}$$

using Stewart's data and the observed coefficient of expansion. It is found to be 1.43 at 65° and 2.5 at 77°; these are larger than expected from Table 9-2, which reflects the small compressibility found by Stewart.†
The discrepancies between Stewart's data and the theory may arise from deviations from the simple picture of the solid. The low compressibility could possibly be associated with anharmonicity [10–12, 21] in the vibrations [i.e., higher terms in δ than those shown in Eq. (3.14)].

Another manifestation of the difficulty mentioned in the preceding paragraph is observed in the calculation made by Beaumont, Chihara and Morrison [22]. These writers have estimated compressibilities and thermal expansions at low temperatures and have calculated C_v from the observed values of C_p, using Eq. (7.2). The values of Θ calculated by use of the Debye theory from the values of C_v so obtained show a marked increase with temperature in spite of the thermal

† Previous conclusions [17] are changed somewhat by Stewart's recent data at 77°.

TABLE 9-3

Compressibility

(Units as in Table 9-2; P in cal cc^{-1})

T	V	Θ	$T(P = 0)$	$P(\text{calc})$	$P(\text{obs})$
	23.80	73.72	65	0	0
	23.54	75.46	57.5	3.65	4.69
	23.30	77.04	49.6	7.05	9.37
65	23.21	77.62	46.6	8.53	11.71
	23.09	78.44	42.5	10.2	14.06
	22.69	81.09	23.4	16.65	23.43
	24.30	70.41	77	0	0
	23.89	73.11	67.3	5.00	6.52
	23.57	75.24	58.4	9.20	12.23
77	23.43	76.17	54.0	11.18	14.96
	23.31	76.98	50.0	12.89	17.49
	22.87	79.89	34.1	18.90	27.74

expansion. However, calculated in this way, Θ is so exceedingly sensitive to small errors in C_v that it has little significance.

If, despite the discrepancies, we believe that the Debye theory offers a reasonably adequate rough approximation, the values of E_0 offer an opportunity to obtain the interatomic potential-energy curve near its minimum. To get this curve, we assume that the potential energies are pairwise additive and subtract out the effects of neighbors other than nearest neighbors. We make use of Eq. (3.6) with

$$c_6 = 8.64 \times 10^5 \text{ cal mole}^{-1} \text{ Å}^6,$$
$$c_8 = 2.59 \times 10^6 \text{ cal mole}^{-1} \text{ Å}^8, \tag{7.3}$$

as suggested from quantum mechanical considerations [8, 23]. When ϵ_p is added up for all neighbors other than nearest neighbors, following results of Jones and Ingham [9], we get

$$E_0' = -\frac{1.060 \times 10^6}{a^6} - \frac{1.039 \times 10^6}{a^8}. \tag{7.4}$$

The units are as in Eq. (7.3) and a is, as before, the distance between equilibrium positions of nearest neighbors. Equation (7.4) agrees fairly well with the estimate of Guggenheim and McGlashan [24] and the empirical inference of Munn [25]. We subtract E_0' from E_0 to get E_n, the total potential energy of nearest neighbors at their equilibrium positions, which is of course equal to $6N\epsilon_p$, where ϵ_p is the potential energy function for a pair of atoms, in this case nearest neighbors. Then $E_n - E_{n,0}$ (where $E_{n,0}$ is the value of E_n at $0°K$, at which temperature $V = 22.590$ cc mole^{-1}) is plotted against a in Fig. 9-10. We see that ϵ_p has the expected unsymmetrical shape, being steeper for $a < r_0$ than for $a > r_0$, although the shape is not in all details as one should expect, in particular the rather steep rise at large a. Since E_0 versus V is essentially a quadratic function, the lack of symmetry must be canceled out by the effects of the other than nearest neighbors (one notes also that the independent variable is different).

This cancellation does not mean that the lack of symmetry in the potential-energy curve is unimportant. As may be seen from Eq. (7.6), below, it is largely this asymmetry which causes Θ to change with V, and if Θ were independent of V there would be no thermal expansion of the solid, as may be seen from Eq. (6.11), which is exact if $d\Theta/dV = 0$.

We now wish to see how well the pair potential energy ϵ_p and Θ can be correlated by means of Eqs. (3.5) and (3.16). We use Eq. (3.16) to find b_2, b_3 and b_4 from Θ and its derivatives. We find from Fig. 9-8 or the data of Table 9-2 that $d\Theta/dV$ is equal to about 6.64 deg mole^{-1}

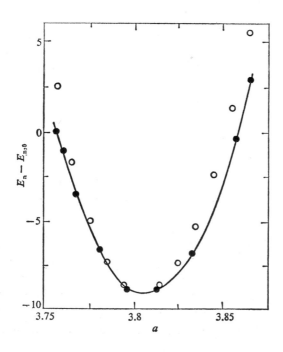

Figure 9-10. Potential energy due to nearest neighbors, $E_n - E_{n,0}$, in cal mole^{-1}, against interatomic distance a in angstroms. Black circles, calculated from Table 9-2 corrected by use of Eq. (7.4). Open circles from the middle column of Table 9-4.

cc^{-1} and $d^2\Theta/dV^2$ is about zero. The derivatives of Θ can be related to those of B through Eq. (3.15) and derivatives with respect to V can be related to derivatives with respect to a through Eq. (7.1).

The minimum in Fig. 9-10 occurs at $a = r_e$, so r_e is determined by this figure, and it is very much easier to apply Eq. (3.16) and its derivatives at $a = r_e$. Indeed, at $a = r_e$ we have

$$B = b_2 - \beta, \tag{7.5}$$

$$\frac{dB}{da} = -3b_3 + \frac{2b_2}{a} - \frac{d\beta}{da}, \tag{7.6}$$

$$\frac{d^2B}{da^2} = 12b_4 - \frac{6b_3}{a} - \frac{4b_2}{a^2} - \frac{d^2\beta}{da^2}, \tag{7.7}$$

where β stands for the last two terms of Eq. (3.16), representing effects of more distant neighbors, and B can be expressed in terms of Θ by Eq. (3.15), dB/da can be expressed in terms of Θ and $d\Theta/dV$, and d^2B/da^2 in terms of Θ, $d\Theta/dV$, and $d^2\Theta/dV^2$. Thus Θ and its successive derivatives give successively b_2, b_3, and b_4. The values thus obtained are given in Table 9-4, where they are compared with values corresponding to the Lennard-Jones potential $-c_6/r^6 + c_{12}/r^{12}$, with the values for the parameters which are usually assumed.

TABLE 9-4

Constants in Eq. (3.16)

(Energy units, cal mole^{-1}; units of length, Å)

Constant	Rice (1964)	Lennard-Jones
b_2	731	596
b_3	907	1092
b_4	354	1270
r_0	3.805	3.82

In Fig. 9-10 we have included points calculated from our values of b_2, b_3, b_4. It is to be observed that the agreement is not perfect; that is to say, ϵ_p and Θ are not correlated perfectly by the same set of parameters. In addition to the possible effects of anharmonicity [higher powers of δ in Eq. (3.14)], errors may arise from vacancies in the lattice and incorrectness of the assumption that the interatomic potential energies are pairwise additive. Indeed, recent work [26] indicates that the latter is an important cause of discrepancies. In view of the approximations made, the agreement seems reasonably good. It is, of course, to be recognized that if one attempts to take account of the effects of anharmonicity, some apparently fairly drastic modifications in Fig. 9-10 may be expected. There could be a rather large shift in the position of the minimum, for example, but probably not much change in the curvature, and I believe that the rough consistency between the curve for $E_n - E_{n,0}$ and the calculation based on the values of the b's is significant.

REFERENCES

1. M. Blackman, *Specific Heat of Solids* in *Handbuch der Physik*, rev. ed., Band VII, Teil 1, Berlin, Springer, 1955, pp. 325–82.

2. J. M. Ziman, *Principles of the Theory of Solids*, Cambridge, Eng., Cambridge Univ. Press, 1964, Chap. 2.

3. M. Born and K. Huang, *Dynamical Theory of Crystal Lattices*, Oxford, Eng., Clarendon Press, 1954.

4. E. R. Dobbs and G. O. Jones, *Rep. Prog. Phys.* (The Physical Society, London), **20**, 516 (1957), esp. pp. 528–32.

5. Landolt-Börnstcin, *Zahlenwerte und Funktionen*, Aufl. 6, Band II, Teil 4, Berlin, Springer, 1961, pp. 742–49.

6. Jahnke-Emde-Lösch, *Tables of Higher Functions*, 6th ed., Stuttgart, Teubner (or New York, McGraw-Hill), 1960, pp. 293–94. [Entries for $\theta/T = 4.7$ are slightly in error.]

7. R. H. Fowler, *Statistical Mechanics*, 2d ed., Cambridge, Eng., Cambridge Univ. Press, 1936, p. 126.

8. O. K. Rice, *J. Am. Chem. Soc.*, **63**, 3 (1941).

9. J. E. Jones and A. E. Ingham, *Proc. Roy. Soc.* (London), **A107**, 636, (1925).

10. J. H. Henkel, *J. Chem. Phys.*, **23**, 681 (1955).

11. I. J. Zucker, *J. Chem. Phys.*, **25**, 915 (1956).

12. G. Leibfried and W. Ludwig, "Theory of Anharmonic Effects in Crystals," in *Solid State Physics*, Vol. 12, Eds., F. Seitz and D. Turnbull, New York, Academic, 1961, pp. 275–444.

13. R. B. Leighton, *Rev. Mod. Phys.*, **20**, 165 (1948).

14. E. W. Montroll and D. C. Peaslee, *J. Chem. Phys.*, **12**, 98 (1944).

15. E. Grüneisen, *Handbuch der Physik*, Band X, Kap. 1, Berlin, Springer-Verlag, 1926.

16. P. Flubacher, A. J. Leadbetter, and J. A. Morrison, *Proc. Phys. Soc.* (London), **78**, 1449 (1961).

17. O. K. Rice, *J. Elisha Mitchell Sci. Soc.*, **80**, 120 (1964).

18. J. W. Stewart, *Phys. Rev.*, **97**, 578 (1955).

19. J. W. Stewart, *J. Chem. Phys. Solids*, **1**, 146 (1956).

20. B. L. Smith and C. J. Pings, *J. Chem. Phys.*, **38**, 825 (1963).
21. J. Kuebler and M. P. Tosi, *Phys. Rev.*, **137**, A1617 (1965).
22. R. H. Beaumont, H. Chihara, and J. A. Morrison, *Proc. Phys. Soc.* (London), **78**, 1462 (1961).
23. R. A. Buckingham, *Proc. Roy. Soc.* (London), **A160**, 94, 113 (1937).
24. E. A. Guggenheim and M. L. McGlashan, *Proc. Roy. Soc.* (London), **A255**, 456 (1960).
25. R. J. Munn, *J. Chem. Phys.*, **40**, 1439 (1964).
26. L. Jansen and E. Lombardi, *Disc. Faraday Soc.*, **40**, 78 (1965).

PROBLEMS

9.1. From Eqs. (1.5) and (1.6) find an expression for the chemical potential of an Einstein solid, neglecting the pressure–volume term and the dependence of Θ_E on N/V. From this and the chemical potential of the vapor find an expression for the density of the vapor in equilibrium with the solid, and show that it is equivalent to Eq. (9.4) of Chap. 7. Now take into account the pressure–volume term, using $\mu = (\partial G/\partial N)_{P,T}$, and show that Eq. (9.5) of Chap. 7 follows. Express the results in terms of Θ_E.

9.2. Find the chemical potential of the Debye solid from Eq. (2.13), neglecting the pressure–volume term and the dependence of Θ on N/V. Show that the same result is obtained by use of Eqs. (2.14) and (2.20). Calculate the vapor density for the Debye solid and compare the result term by term with that obtained in Prob. 9.1.

9.3. A two-dimensional Debye solid would have $a\nu d\nu$ frequencies in the range ν to $\nu + d\nu$, where a is a constant. Find a, and the zero-point energy in terms of ν_m and N, and show how to set up (P.F.) in this case.

9.4. For the Debye solid, find out, from Eq. (5.5), in terms of the Debye Θ, how much the high-temperature entropy differs from that of an Einstein solid with frequency equal to the root-mean-square frequency $\overline{(\nu^2)}^{1/2} = (\tfrac{3}{5}\nu_m^2)^{1/2}$ of the Debye solid.

9.5. An *Einstein* solid will have under any given conditions, an effective *Debye* Θ. Find how much the effective value of the Debye Θ based on entropy will differ from that based on the specific heat at high temperatures.

9.6. From Table 9-2 make an estimate of the terms on the right-hand side of Eq. (6.10) at 40°K and indicate to what extent the last term is the dominant one at this temperature. Will it dominate more or less strongly at lower temperatures?

9.7. Using the tables [5, 6] check the values of E_t, and $C_p - C_v$ listed in Table 9-2 for 60° and 70°. Apply Eq. (7.2) to show that the calculated values of P at 65° in Table 9-3 give a value of $C_p - C_v$ consistent with those given in Table 9-2.

Chapter 10

The Grand Partition Function

10-1. *Grand Ensembles*

In the earlier chapters we have assumed that each of the assemblies in an ensemble has a fixed number of particles. We now consider the possibility that assemblies exchange molecules with each other; such assemblies are called "open." The techniques developed to determine fluctuations in the number of particles in assemblies can also be used to study fluctuations in a part of an assembly. That is, the assembly can be thought of as divided into many subassemblies, and the entire assembly is then treated as an ensemble of these subassemblies.

An ensemble in which the assemblies can exchange molecules is called a grand ensemble. First we need to discuss the fluctuations in numbers of particles between these assemblies. We shall find, as a sort of by-product, that we can define two new kinds of partition functions, the ensemble partition function (E.P.F.) and the grand partition function (G.P.F.), the latter of which is extremely useful in the calculation of thermodynamic properties.

Suppose that in the ensemble at any given instant there are m_1 assemblies with one molecule, m_2 with two molecules, $\cdots$, m_N with N molecules. We assume that there are M assemblies, and that the number of molecules in the entire ensemble is fixed and equal to $M\bar{N}$, where $\bar{N}$ is the average number of molecules in an assembly. We can then set

$$M = \sum_N m_N,$$ (1.1)

and

$$M\bar{N} = \sum_N N m_N.$$ (1.2)

We want to know about the state of the ensemble of M assemblies and $M\bar{N}$ molecules. To do this we suppose the ensemble itself to be a part of a superensemble. It is then at a fixed temperature, and its properties may be investigated by setting up a canonical partition function of the whole ensemble, designated as (E.P.F.). We now evaluate (E.P.F.) in steps. If the values of N were fixed individually for every assembly in the ensemble, we would have (E.P.F.) $= \prod_i$ (P.F.)$_i$ where the index i goes over all assemblies, (P.F.)$_i$ being the ordinary canonical partition function of the ith assembly. Since (P.F.)$_i$ depends only on the number N_i of molecules in the ith assembly, this product can be rewritten $\prod_N$ (P.F.)$_N^{m_N}$. We now go one step further in relaxing the restrictions placed on the ensemble. If the only requirement is that the number m_N of assemblies having N molecules must be fixed, then there are $M!/\prod_N m_N!$ ways of setting up the ensemble, and the product will have to be multiplied by this factor, since every one of the $M!/\prod_N m_N!$ ways has its own set of energy levels. Finally we have to add up all such terms for every possible combination of m_N's obeying Eqs. (1.1) and (1.2). Thus we have

$$\text{(E.P.F.)} = M! \sum_{(m_N)} \frac{\displaystyle\prod_N (\text{P.F.})_N^{m_N}}{\displaystyle\prod_N m_N!}, \tag{1.3}$$

and, in the usual way, we evaluate (E.P.F.) by setting it equal to the maximum of the terms in the sum on the right-hand side of Eq. (1.3). That this procedure is legitimate may be easily seen in the following way. $M\bar{N}$ molecules can be distributed among M distinguishable boxes in

$$\frac{(M\bar{N} + M - 1)!}{(M - 1)!(M\bar{N})!} \approx \frac{(M\bar{N} + M)!}{M!(M\bar{N})!}$$

ways.† Many of these terms have already been combined before setting up the sum of Eq. (1.3). Hence (E.P.F.) must be less than $(M + \bar{N}M)!/M!(M\bar{N})!$ times the maximum term of Eq. (1.3). But we have

---

† The number of ways of arranging N objects in C groups is the same as that of arranging N objects of one kind and $C - 1$ of another on a straight line. The latter serve as dividers to separate the first kind into C groups. If all objects were distinguishable the number of arrangements would be $(N + C - 1)!$, but this must be divided by the number of exchanges of each type of objects, since those of each are indistinguishable among themselves.

$$\ln \frac{(M\bar{N} + M)!}{M!(M\bar{N})!}$$

$$\approx (M\bar{N} + M) \ln (M\bar{N} + M) - M \ln M - M\bar{N} \ln (M\bar{N})$$

$$= M\bar{N} \ln \frac{M\bar{N} + M}{M\bar{N}} + M \ln \frac{M\bar{N} + M}{M}$$

$$= M\bar{N} \ln \left(1 + \frac{1}{\bar{N}}\right) + M \ln (\bar{N} + 1)$$

$$\approx M(1 + \ln \bar{N}).$$

This term will be negligible, since we will in general be interested in quantities which are proportional to $M\bar{N}$.

We determine the values of m_N which give the maximum term in Eq. (1.3) by setting allowable variations of the logarithm of the term equal to zero, thus, using the Stirling approximation:

$$\sum_N \delta m_N [\ln (\text{P.F.})_N - \ln m_N] = 0. \tag{1.4}$$

From Eqs. (1.1) and (1.2) we have

$$\sum_N \delta m_N = 0, \tag{1.5}$$

and

$$\sum_N N \delta m_N = 0. \tag{1.6}$$

We now multiply Eq. (1.5) by ζ/kT and Eq. (1.6) by μ_{max}/kT (where ζ and μ_{max} are undetermined constants, and T is, of course, also constant under the conditions of the problem) and add the results to Eq. (1.4), which gives

$$\sum_N \delta m_N \left[\ln (\text{P.F.})_N - \ln m_N + \frac{\zeta}{kT} + \frac{N\mu_{max}}{kT} \right] = 0. \tag{1.7}$$

This yields, in the usual manner,

$$m_N = (\text{P.F.})_N \exp \left\{ \frac{N\mu_{max}}{kT} \right\} \exp \left\{ \frac{\zeta}{kT} \right\}. \tag{1.8}$$

These values, then, are substituted into the equation

$$(\text{E.P.F.}) = \frac{M! \displaystyle\prod_N (\text{P.F.})_N^{m_N}}{\displaystyle\prod_N m_N!} \tag{1.9}$$

to give the approximate value of (E.P.F.).

Before evaluating (E.P.F.), it will be advantageous to discuss the constants μ_{max} and ζ. This will also involve a discussion of the values of m_N given by Eq. (1.8). Finding the maximum term in Eq. (1.3) may be considered equivalent to finding the state of equilibrium in the ensemble, provided that deviations from this state are improbable.

From Eq. (1.8) we may write

$$M = \sum_N m_N = \exp\left\{\frac{\zeta}{kT}\right\} \sum_N (P.F.)_N \exp\left\{\frac{N\mu_{max}}{kT}\right\}. \tag{1.10}$$

The sum in Eq. (1.10) is the grand partition function (G.P.F.). We write

$$(G.P.F.) = \sum_N (P.F.)_N \exp\left\{\frac{N\mu_{max}}{kT}\right\} = \sum_N (P.F.)_N \lambda^N, \tag{1.11}$$

where the activity λ is defined by the equation. This gives, then,

$$\exp\left\{\frac{\zeta}{kT}\right\} = \frac{M}{(G.P.F.)}, \tag{1.12}$$

and

$$m_N = M \frac{(P.F.)_N \exp\{N\mu_{max}/kT\}}{(G.P.F.)}. \tag{1.13}$$

We turn now to the interpretation of μ_{max}, which involves the distribution of the values of m_N. Certain values of N occur much more frequently than others. We obtain the value of N which makes m_N a maximum by differentiating Eq. (1.8) or Eq. (1.13) logarithmically with respect to N, and setting the result equal to zero. We find that

$$\left(\frac{\partial \ln m_N}{\partial N}\right)_{T,V,max} = \left(\frac{\partial \ln (P.F.)_N}{\partial N}\right)_{T,V,max} + \frac{\mu_{max}}{kT} = 0,$$

or

$$\mu_{max} = -kT \left(\frac{\partial \ln (P.F.)_N}{\partial N}\right)_{T,V,max}. \tag{1.14}$$

Therefore μ_{max} is equal to the chemical potential of the assembly having the most probable number of molecules.

10-2. *Fluctuations*

Since the assemblies in the ensemble all have a fixed volume, increasing N is equivalent to increasing the concentration. As shown in Sec. 7-11, for the assemblies to be stable, μ must increase with concentration if there is a single phase. But if a change of phase is occurring, there is a range of concentrations or densities over which μ remains constant. Therefore, with a fixed value of μ_{max} characteristic of the ensemble there will be one value of N or one range of values of N for which $\mu = \mu_{max}$. We will now see how m_N changes with N as N departs from N_{max}. If there is a range of N for which Eq. (1.14) holds, the manner in which m_N changes as N goes out of the range will closely resemble the manner in which it changes when N departs from a single N_{max}.

Since $(\partial \ln m_N / \partial N)_{T,V,max}$ vanishes, we have to use the second derivative. We have

$$\left(\frac{\partial^2 \ln m_N}{\partial N^2}\right)_{T,V,max} = \left(\frac{\partial^2 \ln (\text{P.F.})_N}{\partial N^2}\right)_{T,V,max}$$

$$= -\frac{1}{kT}\left(\frac{\partial \mu}{\partial N}\right)_{T,V,max}, \tag{2.1}$$

and we can write approximately

$$\ln m_N = \ln m_{N,max} - \frac{1}{2kT}\left(\frac{\partial \mu}{\partial N}\right)_{T,V,max} (\Delta N)^2, \tag{2.2}$$

where $\Delta N = N - N_{max}$.

When we increase N with V constant we increase the pressure. Consequently we may write

$$\left(\frac{\partial \mu}{\partial N}\right)_{T,V} = \left(\frac{\partial \mu}{\partial P}\right)_{T,V}\left(\frac{\partial P}{\partial N}\right)_{T,V} \tag{2.3}$$

At constant temperature, P is a function of V and N only, while at constant pressure (except in a range of constant μ) V/N is constant. Therefore

$$\left(\frac{\partial P}{\partial N}\right)_{V,T} = -\left(\frac{\partial P}{\partial V}\right)_{N,T}\left(\frac{\partial V}{\partial N}\right)_{P,T}$$

$$= -\left(\frac{\partial P}{\partial V}\right)_{N,T}\frac{V}{N}$$

$$= \frac{1}{\beta N}, \tag{2.4}$$

where β is the compressibility. Also, according to a well-known thermodynamic relation† [see Eq. (10.7) of Chap. 7]

---

† The thermodynamic relation is usually written $(\partial \mu / \partial P)_{T,N} = V/N$. However $(\partial \mu / \partial P)_{T,V} = (\partial \mu / \partial P)_{T,N} + (\partial \mu / \partial N)_{T,P}(\partial N / \partial P)_{T,V}$, and since μ depends only on T and P we see that $(\partial \mu / \partial N)_{T,P} = 0$.

$$\left(\frac{\partial \mu}{\partial P}\right)_{T,V} = \frac{V}{N}. \tag{2.5}$$

Substituting from Eqs. (2.3), (2.4), and (2.5) in Eq. (2.2) and changing to the exponential form, we have

$$m_N = m_{N,\max} \exp\left\{\frac{-(\Delta N/N_{\max})^2 V}{2kT\beta_{\max}}\right\}. \tag{2.6}$$

This equation gives the probability of fluctuation in the number of molecules from its most probable value $N_{\max}$, in a region in which β is not infinite. To get an idea of the orders of magnitude involved, let us evaluate Eq. (2.6) for a perfect gas. For a perfect gas, $\beta = V/NkT$, and we have

$$m_N = m_{N,\max} \exp\left\{\frac{-\Delta N^2}{2N_{\max}}\right\}. \tag{2.7}$$

There is thus little chance of finding an assembly with a deviation from $N_{\max}$ greater than $N_{\max}^{1/2}$, which, since $N_{\max}$ is very large, is a very small relative deviation.

Over a region in which a phase change is occurring, μ is constant and $(\partial \mu/\partial N)_{T,V}$, therefore, is zero. One would then predict from Eq. (2.2) that all values of N in the range of the phase change would be equally probable, and this would be confirmed by Eq. (1.13), taken together with Sec. 7-10. But even within the range of the phase change, it cannot be strictly true that all values of N are equally likely, for this would lead to a single fixed value of $\bar{N}$. If $\bar{N}/V$ were much nearer to the density of one of the phases than that of the other, it is obvious that values of N near $\bar{N}$ would have to be favored. The necessary adjustment of the relative probabilities of different values of N could be accomplished by changes in (P.F.)$_N$ which are within the usual accuracy by which (P.F.)$_N$ is determined, since even multiplication of (P.F.)$_N$ by N itself would not affect the thermodynamic functions within the limits of physical observation. And it will be recalled that the conclusions of Sec. 7-10 depended upon taking the largest term in a sum. Effects of interfacial tension are ignored in this discussion.

In the immediate neighborhood of a critical point, β is very large, and we note also that the smaller the V the greater the fluctuations. We may apply Eq. (2.6) to determine fluctuations within an assembly, by dividing the assembly into subassemblies, and treating these as a grand ensemble. But if β is very large, Eq. (2.6) will not be sufficiently accurate; one would suppose, then, that it would be necessary to go to higher-order terms in the expansion of Eq. (2.2). The next term in this expansion is equal to

$$-\frac{1}{6kT}\left(\frac{\partial^2\mu}{\partial N^2}\right)_{T,V,\max}(\Delta N)^3 = -\frac{1}{6kT}\left[\frac{\partial}{\partial N}\left(\frac{V}{\beta N^2}\right)\right]_{T,V,\max}(\Delta N)^3$$

[by Eqs. (2.3), (2.4) and (2.5)]

$$= \frac{V}{6kT}\left[\frac{2}{\beta N^3} + \frac{1}{\beta^2 N^2}\left(\frac{\partial\beta}{\partial N}\right)_{T,V,\max}\right](\Delta N)^3.$$

Since $\partial\beta/\partial N$ is not expected to exceed β/N in absolute order of magnitude, this new term is of the order of $(V/\beta kT)(\Delta N/N)^3$, and will not be important compared with the second-degree term unless $\Delta N \approx N$. However, right in the critical region, where β is large, β will change very rapidly with the density. So $\Delta N \approx N$ should perhaps be interpreted as $|\Delta N|$ not less than $0.1N$ to $0.01N$.

10-3. *The Thermodynamic Functions*

It is often advantageous to express the thermodynamic properties of a system in terms of the grand partition function. First we evaluate Eq. (1.9). If we substitute Eq. (1.13) in Eq. (1.9), using the Stirling approximation, it is readily seen that

$$\ln \text{(E.P.F.)} = M \ln \text{(G.P.F.)} - \frac{M\bar{N}\mu_{\max}}{kT}. \tag{3.1}$$

Introducing the definition of (G.P.F.) from Eq. (1.11), we have

$$\ln \text{(E.P.F.)} = M \ln\left[\sum_N \text{(P.F.)}_N \exp\left\{\frac{N\mu_{\max}}{kT}\right\}\right] - \frac{M\bar{N}\mu_{\max}}{kT}$$

$$= M \ln\left[\sum_N \text{(P.F.)}_N \exp\left\{\frac{N\mu_{\max}}{kT}\right\}\right] - M\bar{N}\ln\lambda. \tag{3.2}$$

The term under the summation sign has a maximum value when N has a value given by Eq. (1.14). It should be legitimate to replace the sum by its maximum value. (The sum certainly cannot exceed in order of magnitude $\bar{N}\text{(P.F.)}_{N,\max}\exp\{\mu_{\max}N_{\max}/kT\}$, and $\ln\bar{N}$ will give a negligible contribution.) We then obtain

$$\ln \text{(E.P.F.)} = M \ln \text{(P.F.)}_{N,\max} + \frac{M\mu_{\max}(N_{\max} - \bar{N})}{kT}.$$

If there is no appreciable range of values of N for which $(\partial \ln m_N/\partial N)_{T,V} = 0$, then $N_{max} = \bar{N}$ and the last term vanishes. Therefore, except when we are in a transition range or very close to a critical point we can write

$$\ln (E.P.F.) = M \ln (P.F.)_{N.max}, \tag{3.3}$$

which simply indicates that the Helmholtz free energy of a system of M assemblies, even though they can exchange molecules, is M times the Helmholtz free energy of one of them, as might have been expected. Of course, then, energies and entropies will also be additive. This actually gives us nothing new, and there are some advantages in leaving the expression for (E.P.F.) in the more general form of Eq. (3.2). We will see that it may be used to get expressions for the thermodynamic functions in terms of (G.P.F.).

Before proceeding, it is necessary to consider the functional make-up of (G.P.F.). Since all the $(P.F.)_N$ are functions of V and T, we see that (G.P.F.) is a function of these variables. It is also a function of μ_{max} or λ [Eq. (1.11)]. Since the $(P.F.)_N$ do not depend on μ_{max} or λ, a partial differentiation of (G.P.F.) with respect to T or V, holding μ_{max} or λ constant, involves only differentiation of the $(P.F.)_N$, as appears from Eq. (1.11). In general, (G.P.F.) is a function of three variables. Other independent sets of variables may be chosen, such as V, T, and $\bar{N}$, but the relationships involved in the differentiation may be more complex. Whenever we perform a partial differentiation on (G.P.F.) without noting the variables which are held constant, it will be understood that we are considering T, V, and λ to be the three independent variables, two of them being held constant.

We are now in a position to get one of the essential relationships. Noting that

$$\frac{\lambda \, \partial(G.P.F.)}{\partial \lambda} = \sum_N N(P.F.)_N \lambda^N, \tag{3.4}$$

we readily see from Eqs. (1.13) and (1.2) and the definition of λ that

$$\bar{N} = \frac{\lambda \, \partial \ln (G.P.F.)}{\partial \lambda}. \tag{3.5}$$

Next we attempt to calculate the average energy $\bar{E}$ of the assemblies. Since (E.P.F.) is the canonical partition function for the whole ensemble, we can obtain the energy of the ensemble, $M\bar{E}$, by differentiating (E.P.F.) in the usual manner, making use of Eq. (3.1), thus:

$$M\overline{E} = kT^2 \left[\frac{\partial \ln \text{(E.P.F.)}}{\partial T}\right]_{V,\overline{N}}$$

$$= kT^2 M \left[\frac{\partial \ln \text{(G.P.F.)}}{\partial T}\right]_{V,\overline{N}} - kT^2 M\overline{N} \left(\frac{\partial \ln \lambda}{\partial T}\right)_{V,\overline{N}}$$

$$= kT^2 M \frac{\partial \ln \text{(G.P.F.)}}{\partial T} + kT^2 M \frac{\partial \ln \text{(G.P.F.)}}{\partial \lambda} \left(\frac{\partial \lambda}{\partial T}\right)_{V,\overline{N}}$$

$$- kT^2 \frac{M\overline{N}}{\lambda} \left(\frac{\partial \lambda}{\partial T}\right)_{V,\overline{N}}.$$

From Eq. (3.5) it is seen that the last two terms cancel. Hence we arrive at the important relationship [which could also be obtained from Eqs. (1.13) of this chapter and (1.9) of Chap. 3],

$$\overline{E} = kT^2 \frac{\partial \ln \text{(G.P.F.)}}{\partial T}. \tag{3.6}$$

The importance of this equation lies in the fact that it is often possible to find (G.P.F.) explicitly as a function of T, V, and λ. Equation (3.3) shows that, at least in a one-phase system, $\overline{E}$ has the same value as that found for a constant-temperature ensemble without exchange of molecules. In any event, use of Eq. (3.6) avoids the necessity of evaluating (P.F.) by finding the largest term in a sum.

The Helmholtz free energy of the grand ensemble will be given by

$$M\overline{A} = -kT \ln \text{(E.P.F.)}$$

$$= -MkT \ln \text{(G.P.F.)} + M\overline{N}\mu_{\max},$$

or

$$\overline{A} = -kT \ln \text{(G.P.F.)} + \overline{N}\mu_{\max}. \tag{3.7}$$

We have previously shown that $\mu_{\max}$ is the chemical potential of an assembly having the most probable number of molecules. We would then also expect it to be equal to the chemical potential of the ensemble, which is defined as $[\partial(M\overline{A})/\partial(M\overline{N})]_{T,V}$ or $(\partial\overline{A}/\partial\overline{N})_{T,V}$. From Eq. (3.7), we have

$$\left(\frac{\partial\overline{A}}{\partial\overline{N}}\right)_{T,V} = -kT \left[\frac{\partial \ln \text{(G.P.F.)}}{\partial\overline{N}}\right]_{T,V} + \overline{N}\left(\frac{\partial\mu_{\max}}{\partial\overline{N}}\right)_{T,V} + \mu_{\max}$$

$$= -kT \left[\frac{\partial \ln \text{(G.P.F.)}}{\partial\lambda}\right]\lambda\left(\frac{\partial \ln \lambda}{\partial\overline{N}}\right)_{T,V}$$

$$+ \overline{N}\left(\frac{\partial\mu_{\max}}{\partial\overline{N}}\right)_{T,V} + \mu_{\max}.$$

Since $kT(\partial \ln \lambda / \partial \overline{N})_{T,V}$ is equal to $(\partial \mu_{\max} / \partial \overline{N})_{T,V}$, it is seen from Eq. (3.5) the first two terms on the right-hand side cancel, and

$$\left(\frac{\partial \overline{A}}{\partial \overline{N}}\right)_{T,V} = \mu_{\max}, \tag{3.8}$$

as expected.

Since $\overline{N}\mu_{\max}$ is the average Gibbs free energy $\overline{A} + \overline{P}V$ [see Eq. (8.12) of Chap. 7], we have

$$\overline{P} = \frac{kT}{V} \ln \text{(G.P.F.)} \tag{3.9}$$

another very important relationship.

Another expression can be found for the pressure from the equation

$$\overline{P} = -\left(\frac{\partial \overline{A}}{\partial V}\right)_{T,\overline{N}}.$$

Using Eq. (3.7) we get

$$\overline{P} = kT\frac{\partial \ln \text{(G.P.F.)}}{\partial V} + kT\left[\frac{\partial \ln \text{(G.P.F.)}}{\partial \lambda}\right]\left(\frac{\partial \lambda}{\partial V}\right)_{T,\overline{N}} - \overline{N}\left(\frac{\partial \mu_{\max}}{\partial V}\right)_{T,\overline{N}}.$$

By Eq. (3.5) and the relation between $\mu_{\max}$ and λ, the last two terms cancel, so

$$\overline{P} = kT\frac{\partial \ln \text{(G.P.F.)}}{\partial V}. \tag{3.10}$$

Comparing Eqs. (3.9) and (3.10), we have

$$\frac{\partial \ln \text{(G.P.F.)}}{\partial V} = V^{-1} \ln \text{(G.P.F.)}. \tag{3.11}$$

The solution of this differential equation is

$$\ln \left[\ln \text{(G.P.F.)}\right] = \ln V + \ln \gamma,$$

where γ is a function of T and λ only. The equation may be written in the form

$$\ln \text{(G.P.F.)} = \gamma V, \tag{3.12}$$

or

$$\text{(G.P.F.)} = \exp \{\gamma V\}. \tag{3.13}$$

On comparing Eqs. (3.9) and (3.13) it is seen that $\gamma = \bar{P}/kT$, so that $\bar{P}$ is a function of T and λ. Differentiating Eq. (3.9) with respect to λ, and holding V constant, which may be done if $\bar{P}$ is considered as a function of T and λ, we find

$$\left(\frac{\partial \bar{P}}{\partial \lambda}\right)_T = \frac{kT}{V} \frac{\partial \ln (\text{G.P.F.})}{\partial \lambda}$$

$$= \frac{\bar{N}kT}{V\lambda},$$

or

$$\left(\frac{\partial \bar{P}}{\partial \ln \lambda}\right)_T = \frac{\bar{N}kT}{V}. \tag{3.14}$$

Recalling that $\ln \lambda = \mu_{\text{max}}/kT$, we can write

$$\left(\frac{\partial \bar{P}}{\partial \mu_{\text{max}}}\right)_T = \frac{\bar{N}}{V} \tag{3.15}$$

which is a familiar thermodynamic equation.

The formalism of the grand partition function can be used to show that when λ and T are constant, $\bar{N}$ is proportional to V. For we have

$$\left(\frac{\partial \bar{N}}{\partial V}\right)_{\lambda,T} = \frac{\lambda \, \partial^2 \ln (\text{G.P.F.})}{\partial \lambda \partial V} \qquad \text{[by Eq. (3.5)]}$$

$$= \frac{\lambda}{V} \frac{\partial \ln (\text{G.P.F.})}{\partial \lambda} \qquad \text{[by Eq. (3.11)]}$$

$$= \frac{\bar{N}}{V}. \tag{3.16}$$

Thus λ, and hence μ_{max} and $\bar{P}$ [by Eq. (3.15)] must be functions only of $\bar{N}/V$, the density, at constant T. This property has been discussed in Sec. 7-8, which was used in the derivation of Eqs. (3.9) and (3.11). So the present deduction is not independent of the previous one, but has some interest in itself.

Equation (3.15) does not, however, hold in a region of phase transition, since differentiation with respect to μ_{max} loses its meaning in a region where μ_{max} is constant, except in the sense that when a change in μ_{max} is zero, the corresponding change in $\bar{P}$ is also zero, and vice versa. Equations (3.5) and (3.6) likewise cannot be used in such a region. However, Eq. (3.9), which requires no differentiation, will remain valid, and Eq. (3.10) will also, as may be seen by multiplying

Eq. (3.9) by V and differentiating with respect to V while holding $\bar{P}$ and λ constant.

10-4. *Further Analysis of Density Fluctuations*

The grand partition function is especially suited to the analysis of density fluctuations. We can extend the discussion of Sec. 10-2, for we are now in a position to make a direct calculation of the mean square of the fluctuation,

$$\overline{(N - \bar{N})^2} = \overline{N^2} - \bar{N}^2. \tag{4.1}$$

Consider the evaluation of $\overline{N^2}$. We have noted that

$$\lambda \frac{\partial(\text{G.P.F.})}{\partial \lambda} = \sum_N N(\text{P.F.})_N \lambda^N, \tag{4.2}$$

and hence

$$\lambda \frac{\partial}{\partial \lambda} \left[\lambda \frac{\partial(\text{G.P.F.})}{\partial \lambda} \right] = \sum_N N^2 (\text{P.F.})_N \lambda^N. \tag{4.3}$$

$\overline{N^2}$ will be given by (4.3) divided by (G.P.F.). Hence, carrying out the indicated operations, we have

$$\overline{N^2} = \lambda \frac{\partial \ln (\text{G.P.F.})}{\partial \lambda} + \frac{\lambda^2}{(\text{G.P.F.})} \frac{\partial^2(\text{G.P.F.})}{\partial \lambda^2}$$

$$= \bar{N} + \frac{\lambda^2}{(\text{G.P.F.})} \frac{\partial}{\partial \lambda} \left[\bar{N} \frac{(\text{G.P.F.})}{\lambda} \right] \quad \text{[by Eq. (3.5)]}$$

$$= \bar{N} + \lambda \frac{\partial \bar{N}}{\partial \lambda} + \frac{\lambda \bar{N}}{(\text{G.P.F.})} \frac{\partial(\text{G.P.F.})}{\partial \lambda} - \bar{N}$$

$$= \lambda \frac{\partial \bar{N}}{\partial \lambda} + \bar{N}^2, \tag{4.4}$$

again by Eq. (3.5). Equation (4.4) may be rewritten

$$\overline{N^2} - \bar{N}^2 = \lambda \frac{\partial \bar{N}}{\partial \lambda}. \tag{4.5}$$

It must be borne in mind that in the differentiation with respect to λ the other variables T and V are held constant. From the relation between λ and μ_{max}, Eq. (4.5) may be written

$$\overline{N^2} - \overline{N}^2 = kT\left(\frac{\partial \overline{N}}{\partial \mu_{\max}}\right)_{V,T}$$

$$= -kT\left(\frac{\partial \overline{N}}{\partial V}\right)_{\mu_{\max},T}\left(\frac{\partial V}{\partial \mu_{\max}}\right)_{\overline{N},T}. \qquad (4.6)$$

However, by Eq. (3.16)

$$\left(\frac{\partial \overline{N}}{\partial V}\right)_{\mu_{\max},T} = \frac{\overline{N}}{V}. \qquad (4.7)$$

Also

$$\left(\frac{\partial V}{\partial \mu_{\max}}\right)_{\overline{N},T} = \left(\frac{\partial V}{\partial \overline{P}}\right)_{\overline{N},T}\left(\frac{\partial \overline{P}}{\partial \mu_{\max}}\right)_{\overline{N},T}$$

$$= \frac{\overline{N}}{V}\left(\frac{\partial V}{\partial \overline{P}}\right)_{\overline{N},T}$$

$$= -\overline{N}\bar{\beta}, \qquad (4.8)$$

by Eq. (3.15). Equation (4.6), then, gives

$$\overline{N^2} - \overline{N}^2 = \frac{\overline{N}^2\bar{\beta}kT}{V}. \qquad (4.9)$$

If $N_{\max} = \overline{N}$ the average value of $(\Delta N)^2$ from Eq. (2.6) coincides with Eq. (4.9). As was pointed out in Sec. 10-2, Eq. (2.6) breaks down at a phase transition, when β becomes infinite. It also breaks down if β becomes so large that higher terms in the expansion of Eq. (2.2) become important. We noted in 10-2 that this occurs when $\Delta N \approx N$. Only in this case can $N_{\max}$ not equal $\overline{N}$.

Equation (4.9) also must break down in any region in which β becomes large enough for $\overline{N^2} - \overline{N}^2$ to become of the order of $\overline{N}^2$. For the fluctuations to become this large, β must become of the order of V/kT, which is $\overline{N}$ times the value for a perfect gas. This statement implies that a pressure must have significance when it is only $1/\overline{N}$ times the pressure of a perfect gas, but thermodynamic quantities will not in general be determined to such an accuracy by the equations of statistical mechanics. Even before this breakdown occurs, however, one may expect the fluctuations themselves to have an influence upon β. In the present formulation, $\bar{\beta}$, which is defined by Eq. (4.8) in terms of an average pressure, includes effects of the fluctuations. This effect remains implicit in Eq. (4.9) and can be made explicit only if the precise functional dependence of (G.P.F.) on λ can be found. In the formulation of Sec. 10-2, $\beta_{\max}$ is defined in terms of the properties of the individual assemblies having N very near N_{max}. This formulation may also include effects of the fluctuations implicitly.

Where fluctuations are large and β varies greatly, $\bar{\beta}$ and β_{max} will not be equal to each other.

10-5. *The Perfect Gas*

As an illustration, we apply the (G.P.F.) to a perfect gas. In this case $(P.F.)_N = (p.f.)^N/N!$. Thus

$$(G.P.F.) = \sum_N \frac{(p.f.)^N \lambda^N}{N!} = \exp\{(p.f.)\lambda\}. \tag{5.1}$$

From this and from Eq. (3.5) we see at once that

$$\bar{N} = (p.f.)\lambda = \ln (G.P.F.). \tag{5.2}$$

Then from Eq. (3.9) we have

$$\bar{P} = \frac{\bar{N}kT}{V}. \tag{5.3}$$

which is the perfect gas law. From Eq. (5.2), setting $(p.f.) = (p.f.)^0 V$ we get

$$(p.f.)^0\lambda = \frac{\bar{N}}{V}, \tag{5.4}$$

showing that in this case the activity λ is proportional to the density. Using this fact, we could also get Eq. (5.3) by integrating Eq. (3.14), evaluating the integration constant by setting $P = 0$ when $\bar{N}/V = 0$. Equation (3.14) is, of course, more general than (5.3), and is in a certain sense the generalization of the ideal gas law.

Equation (3.6) gives

$$\bar{E} = kT^2\lambda \frac{\partial(p.f.)}{\partial T} = \bar{N}kT^2 \frac{\partial \ln (p.f.)}{\partial T}. \tag{5.5}$$

From Eqs. (5.4) and (5.5), recalling the relation between λ and μ_{max}, all the thermodynamic equations can be derived. We have, of course, obtained nothing new, but the familiar relations appear directly and easily.

10-6. *Many-Component Systems*

If we have a number of different species of molecules, A, B, C, $\cdots$, with respective numbers, N_A, N_B, N_C, $\cdots$, the canonical partition function (P.F.) will be a function of the N's. To indicate this functional dependence we may write $(P.F.)_{N_A,N_B,\ldots}$. The procedure of the earlier sections of this chapter will go through just as before, except that there are a number of conditions

$$\sum_{N_A,N_B,\cdots} N_A m_{N_A,N_B,\cdots} = M\bar{N}_A,$$

$$\sum_{N_A,N_B,\cdots} N_B m_{N_A,N_B,\cdots} = M\bar{N}_B, \tag{6.1}$$

$$\cdot \quad \cdot \quad \cdot \quad \cdot \quad \cdot \quad \cdot \quad \cdot \quad \cdot \quad \cdot$$

replacing Eq. (1.2). A number of Lagrange multipliers will be required, and we find

$$m_{N_A,N_B,\cdots} = (P.F.)_{N_A,N_B,\cdots} \exp\left\{\frac{\mu_{A,\max}N_A}{kT}\right\} \exp\left\{\frac{\mu_{B,\max}N_B}{kT}\right\} \cdots \exp\left\{\frac{\zeta}{kT}\right\}. \tag{6.2}$$

This suggests the definition

$$(G.P.F.) = \sum_{N_A,N_B,\cdots} (P.F.)_{N_A,N_B,\cdots} \lambda_A^{N_A} \lambda_B^{N_B} \cdots . \tag{6.3}$$

It may be readily shown that we can use Eqs. (3.6), (3.9), (3.10) unchanged. Equation (3.7) becomes

$$\bar{A} = -kT \ln (G.P.F.) + \bar{N}_A \mu_{A,\max} + \bar{N}_B \mu_{B,\max} + \cdots, \tag{6.4}$$

and in place of Eq. (3.5) we obtain a series of equations,

$$\bar{N}_A = \lambda_A \frac{\partial \ln (G.P.F.)}{\partial \lambda_A}$$

$$\bar{N}_B = \lambda_B \frac{\partial \ln (G.P.F.)}{\partial \lambda_B} \tag{6.5}$$

$$\cdot \quad \cdot \quad \cdot \quad \cdot \quad \cdot \quad \cdot \quad \cdot$$

This (G.P.F.) is a function of T, V, λ_A, λ_B, $\cdots$, and in an unmarked partial derivative all those quantities not indicated in the differentiation are assumed to be held constant.

In a case in which an equilibrium is established, say

$$A + B \rightleftarrows AB$$

a somewhat similar formalism can be set up. We can, in this case, consider (P.F.) to be a function $(\text{P.F.})_{N_A, N_B, N_{AB}}$ of N_A, N_B, and N_{AB}. However, we have only two conditions on the total numbers $M(\bar{N}_A + \bar{N}_{AB})$ and $M(\bar{N}_B + \bar{N}_{AB})$ of the A's and B's, whether combined or uncombined. Carrying out the maximization of (E.P.F.) under these conditions, we get

$$m_{N_A, N_B, N_{AB}} = (\text{P.F.})_{N_A, N_B, N_{AB}} \exp\left\{\frac{(N_A + N_{AB})\mu_{A,\max}}{kT}\right\}$$

$$\times \exp\left\{\frac{(N_B + N_{AB})\mu_{B,\max}}{kT}\right\} \exp\left\{\frac{\varsigma}{kT}\right\} \tag{6.6}$$

and we therefore write

$$(\text{G.P.F.}) = \sum_{N_A, N_B, N_{AB}} (\text{P.F.})_{N_A, N_B, N_{AB}} \lambda_A^{N_A + N_{AB}} \lambda_B^{N_B + N_{AB}}. \tag{6.7}$$

By differentiating logarithmically with respect to λ_A and λ_B, we obtain

$$\bar{N}_A + \bar{N}_{AB} = \lambda_A \left[\frac{\partial \ln (\text{G.P.F.})}{\partial \lambda_A}\right]_{T,V,\lambda_B},$$
$$\bar{N}_B + \bar{N}_{AB} = \lambda_B \left[\frac{\partial \ln (\text{G.P.F.})}{\partial \lambda_B}\right]_{T,V,\lambda_A}. \tag{6.8}$$

It is readily shown that Eqs. (3.6), (3.9), (3.10), hold, and

$$\bar{A} = -kT \ln (\text{G.P.F.}) + (\bar{N}_A + \bar{N}_{AB})\mu_{A,\max} + (\bar{N}_B + \bar{N}_{AB})\mu_{B,\max} \tag{6.9}$$

If we treated our system as though equilibrium were not established then we would have, of course,

$$(\text{G.P.F.}) = \sum_{N_A, N_B, N_{AB}} (\text{P.F.})_{N_A, N_B, N_{AB}} \lambda_A^{N_A} \lambda_B^{N_B} \lambda_{AB}^{N_{AB}}, \tag{6.10}$$

and

$$\bar{N}_A = \lambda_A \left[\frac{\partial \ln (\text{G.P.F.})}{\partial \lambda_A}\right]_{T,V,\lambda_B,\lambda_{AB}},$$
$$\bar{N}_B = \lambda_B \left[\frac{\partial \ln (\text{G.P.F.})}{\partial \lambda_B}\right]_{T,V,\lambda_A,\lambda_{AB}}, \tag{6.11}$$
$$\bar{N}_{AB} = \lambda_{AB} \left[\frac{\partial \ln (\text{G.P.F.})}{\partial \lambda_{AB}}\right]_{T,V,\lambda_A,\lambda_B},$$

also

$$\bar{A} = -kT \ln (\text{G.P.F.}) + \bar{N}_A \mu_{A,\text{max}} + \bar{N}_B \mu_{B,\text{max}} + \bar{N}_{AB} \mu_{AB,\text{max}} \qquad (6.12)$$

Now it can be shown from Eq. (6.9), in much the same manner that Eq. (3.8) was derived from Eq. (3.7), that

$$\left[\frac{\partial \bar{A}}{\partial (\bar{N}_A + \bar{N}_{AB})} \right]_{N_B + N_{AB}} = \mu_{A,\text{max}}. \qquad (6.13)$$

In obtaining this expression it is necessary to remember that (G.P.F.) is a function of both $\bar{N}_A + \bar{N}_{AB}$ and $\bar{N}_B + \bar{N}_{AB}$ and that $\mu_{A,\text{max}}$ and $\mu_{B,\text{max}}$ are functions of both these variables.

Quite similarly it may be shown from Eq. (6.12) that

$$\left(\frac{\partial \bar{A}}{\partial \bar{N}_A} \right)_{N_B, N_{AB}} = \mu_{A,\text{max}}. \qquad (6.14)$$

If equilibrium is established, $\bar{N}_A + \bar{N}_{AB}$ may be changed by adding molecules of A only, allowing adjustment to occur afterwards. In this adjustment there will be no further change in $\bar{A}$, since this quantity is at a minimal value. Thus if $\bar{N}_A$, $\bar{N}_B$, and $\bar{N}_{AB}$ do represent the equilibrium numbers corresponding to $\bar{N}_A + \bar{N}_{AB}$ and $\bar{N}_B + \bar{N}_{AB}$, the left-hand sides of Eqs. (6.13) and (6.14) are identical. Also if $\bar{N}_A$, $\bar{N}_B$, and $\bar{N}_{AB}$ are equilibrium values, the value of $\bar{P}$ corresponding to the (G.P.F.) of Eq. (6.10) will (within the usual limits of accuracy) be equal to that corresponding to Eq. (6.7). Thus the (G.P.F.)'s will be equal in the two cases, as the $\bar{A}$'s will also (see Prob. 10.9). From these equalities, it can be seen by comparison of Eq. (6.9) and (6.12) that, at equilibrium,

$$\mu_{A,\text{max}} + \mu_{B,\text{max}} = \mu_{AB,\text{max}}, \qquad (6.15)$$

or

$$\lambda_A \lambda_B = \lambda_{AB}. \qquad (6.16)$$

Applying this now to a perfect gas, where

$$(\text{P.F.})_{N_A, N_B, N_{AB}} = \frac{(\text{p.f.})_A^{N_A}}{N_A!} \frac{(\text{p.f.})_B^{N_B}}{N_B!} \frac{(\text{p.f.})_{AB}^{N_{AB}}}{N_{AB}!}, \qquad (6.17)$$

we see that Eqs. (6.7) and (6.10) give, respectively,

$$(\text{G.P.F.}) = \exp \{(\text{p.f.})_A \lambda_A\} \exp \{(\text{p.f.})_B \lambda_B\} \exp \{(\text{p.f.})_{AB} \lambda_A \lambda_B\}, \qquad (6.18)$$

and

$$(\text{G.P.F.}) = \exp\{(\text{p.f.})_A \lambda_A\} \exp\{(\text{p.f.})_B \lambda_B\} \exp\{(\text{p.f.})_{AB} \lambda_{AB}\}. \qquad (6.19)$$

By applying Eqs. (6.8) to Eq. (6.18) we get

$$
\begin{aligned}
\bar{N}_A + \bar{N}_{AB} &= (\text{p.f.})_A \lambda_A + (\text{p.f.})_{AB} \lambda_A \lambda_B \\
\bar{N}_B + \bar{N}_{AB} &= (\text{p.f.})_B \lambda_B + (\text{p.f.})_{AB} \lambda_A \lambda_B
\end{aligned}
\qquad (6.20)
$$

and applying Eqs. (6.11) to (6.19) gives

$$\bar{N}_A = (\text{p.f.})_A \lambda_A \qquad \bar{N}_B = (\text{p.f.})_B \lambda_B \qquad \bar{N}_{AB} = (\text{p.f.})_{AB} \lambda_{AB}, \qquad (6.21)$$

and so, by Eq. (6.16) [or simply using the fact that λ_A and λ_B have, respectively, the same values in Eqs. (6.20) and (6.21)],

$$\bar{N}_{AB} = (\text{p.f.})_{AB} \lambda_A \lambda_B. \qquad (6.22)$$

Equations (6.21) and (6.22) immediately give

$$\frac{\bar{N}_{AB}}{\bar{N}_A \bar{N}_B} = \frac{(\text{p.f.})_{AB}}{(\text{p.f.})_A (\text{p.f.})_B}. \qquad (6.23)$$

Applying Eq. (3.9) to Eq. (6.18) gives,

$$\bar{P} = \frac{kT}{V} \left[(\text{p.f.})_A \lambda_A + (\text{p.f.})_B \lambda_B + (\text{p.f.})_{AB} \lambda_A \lambda_B \right], \qquad (6.24)$$

or we can also write from Eq. (6.19)

$$\bar{P} = \frac{kT}{V} \left[(\text{p.f.})_A \lambda_A + (\text{p.f.})_B \lambda_B + (\text{p.f.})_{AB} \lambda_{AB} \right]. \qquad (6.25)$$

It is of interest that the identity of λ_A and λ_B in Eqs. (6.20) and (6.24) with the λ_A and λ_B in Eqs. (6.21) and (6.25), and also the relation $\lambda_A \lambda_B = \lambda_{AB}$ follows from Eqs. (6.20), (6.21), (6.24) and (6.25) alone, in this case, without the intervention of the arguments based on Eqs. (6.13) and (6.14), since there is a sufficient number of relations involved so that only in this way can the two sets of values of $\bar{N}_A$, $\bar{N}_B$, $\bar{N}_{AB}$, and $\bar{P}$ be identical.

Again we have derived only familiar equations, but we have done it without invoking the use of the largest term in a sum, except insofar as this was used in the original handling of (E.P.F.). We shall find that the grand partition function is often a powerful tool in evaluating thermodynamic functions in less trivial cases.

PROBLEMS

10.1. Show from Eq. (2.6) that the average value of $(\Delta N)^2$ is $\beta k T N_{max}^2/V$.

10.2. From the definition of (G.P.F.) find an expression for $[\partial \ln (G.P.F.)/\partial \bar{N}]_{T,V}$ and show that in the region of a phase change (G.P.F.) does not change with $\bar{N}$ at constant V and T. Express the first result in a form involving β, the compressibility. How does (G.P.F.) change with V over a phase change?

10.3. Find an expression for $(\partial \bar{P}/\partial V)_{T,\bar{N}}$ and from it derive Eq. (3.14).

10.4. Derive Eq. (3.6) from Eq. (1.13) of this chapter and Eq. (1.9) of Chap. 3.

10.5. Derive Eq. (4.4) by direct differentiation of the right-hand side of Eq. (4.2), noting that the right-hand side is equal to $\bar{N}$(G.P.F.), and using any other necessary relations later.

10.6. Show that, in general, if (P.F.) can be written in the form $(P.F.)_t(p.f.)_0^N$, where $(p.f.)_0$ is an internal partition function (see Prob. 3.2), the grand partition function is independent of $(p.f.)_0$, and hence the pressure is also.

10.7. Derive an expression for $\bar{A}$ for a perfect gas as a function of T, V, and N, using Eq. (3.7) and the equations of Sec. 5.

10.8. Verify Eqs. (6.2), (6.6), and (6.4).

10.9. Write the total differential for $\bar{A}$ for constant T, when the equilibrium $A + B \rightleftarrows AB$ is established, treating $\bar{A}$ as a function of $\overline{N_A + N_{AB}}$, $\overline{N_B + N_{AB}}$, and V. Integrate this expression with respect to these variables, holding their ratios (i.e., the composition) constant, and show that Eq. (3.9) holds.

10.10. Apply the method of the grand partition function to the reaction $2A \rightleftarrows A_2$.

10.11. Using Eq. (6.6) show that the conditions that $m_{N_A,N_B,N_{AB}}$ have the largest value are that $\mu_A = \mu_{A,max}$, $\mu_B = \mu_{B,max}$, and $\mu_{AB} = \mu_{A,max} + \mu_{B,max}$.

10.12. An ideal gas consists of atoms with spin $\frac{1}{2}$, which have a component of magnetic moment $\boldsymbol{\mu}_z$ in the z direction if they are oriented with the magnetic field H in the z direction, and component $-\boldsymbol{\mu}_z$ if oriented in the opposite direction. Suppose that there are arbitrary numbers $\bar{N}_+$ and $\bar{N}_-$ oriented in the two directions, and that these are not in equilibrium. Show how to write out (G.P.F.) for this case, and find expressions for $\bar{N}_+$ and $\bar{N}_-$. Then consider the case of equilibrium, using the method of the grand partition function and find the equilibrium ratio $\bar{N}_+/\bar{N}_-$. Find $\overline{M}_z$, where M_z is the total magnetic moment of an assembly, and find $\overline{(M_z - \overline{M}_z)^2}$. [Hint: $\overline{M_z^2}$ is proportional to $\overline{(N_+ - N_-)^2}$, which may be found by twofold differentiation of (G.P.F.) with respect to the proper variable. This may be seen by leaving (G.P.F.) as a sum. (G.P.F.) may then be evaluated analytically and the differentiation performed.]

10.13. The partition function of a solid has been written in the form $(P.F.)_N = (p.f.)^N$, so that in this case $(G.P.F.) = \Sigma_N (p.f.)^N \lambda^N$. By logarithmic differentiation find the condition for the largest term in the sum, and thus get an expression for $\ln \lambda$. Remember that (p.f.) will depend upon the density N/V or the molecular volume v, and since V is constant, (p.f.) will depend upon N. Express $\ln \lambda$ in terms of $[\partial \ln (p.f.)/\partial v]_{T,\mathrm{max}}$ and show that

$$\lambda = \frac{1}{(p.f.)_{\mathrm{max}}} \exp\left\{ \frac{P_{\mathrm{max}} V}{N_{\mathrm{max}} k T} \right\},$$

where P is the pressure and where the subscript "max" refers to the situation corresponding to the maximum term in the sum for (G.P.F.). Show that Eq. (3.9) follows if it is legitimate to set (G.P.F.) equal to its largest term, and give arguments justifying this procedure.

Chapter 11

Cluster Expansions for Imperfect Gases

11-1. *The Virial Expansion and the Irreducible Integrals*

The discussion of the second virial coefficient in Chap. 8 was based on the previously developed theory of the equilibrium between pairs of interacting molecules. A more general treatment of gas imperfections, capable in principle of including virial coefficients beyond the second, can be given by direct use of the phase integral.† In this application we shall for simplicity consider only spherically symmetrical classical molecules; this will include, however, molecules which, although having internal degrees of freedom, are still essentially spherical. In this case the internal degrees of freedom are not appreciably affected by the molecular interaction; we need consider only the partition function for the translational degrees of freedom. If there are N molecules, all of one kind,

$$(\text{P.F.}) = \frac{1}{N!\,h^{3N}} \int \cdots \int \exp\left\{\frac{-E}{kT}\right\} dp_{x,1}dp_{y,1} \cdots dp_{z,N}dx_1 dy_1 \cdots dz_N,$$

$$(1.1)$$

where E, the total energy, is given by

$$E = \frac{1}{2m}\left(p_{x,1}^2 + p_{y,1}^2 + \cdots p_{z,N}^2\right) + E_p,$$

---

† The material in this chapter was originally worked out largely by J. E. Mayer and collaborators, and a detailed account from a slightly different point of view from this chapter is given Mayer and Mayer [1]. The same general methods can also be extended to the study of solutions [2, 3].

and E_p is the potential energy, depending only on the coordinates. Integration over the momenta, as in Sec. 3-4, gives

$$\text{(P.F.)} = \frac{1}{N!} \left(\frac{2\pi mkT}{h^2} \right)^{3N/2} Q_\tau, \tag{1.2}$$

where

$$Q_\tau = \int \cdots \int \exp\left\{ \frac{-E_p}{kT} \right\} dx_1 dy_1 \cdots dz_N. \tag{1.3}$$

Our problem resolves itself into evaluation of this integral, the configuration integral. We shall consider the special case in which the potential energy is the sum of potentials between pairs of molecules. Thus we write

$$E_p = \sum_{\substack{\text{all pairs}}} \epsilon_{ij} = \sum_{\substack{i,j \\ j>i}} \epsilon_{ij}, \tag{1.4}$$

where each ϵ_{ij} is a function only of the distance r_{ij} between the molecules i and j, and is taken to vanish when r_{ij} becomes very large. Then Q_τ becomes

$$Q_\tau = \int \cdots \int \prod_{\substack{i,j \\ j>i}} \exp\left\{ \frac{-\epsilon_{ij}}{kT} \right\} d\tau_1 d\tau_2 \cdots d\tau_N, \tag{1.5}$$

where we abbreviate by writing $d\tau_i = dx_i dy_i dz_i$. We now define

$$f_{ij} = \exp\left\{ \frac{-\epsilon_{ij}}{kT} \right\} - 1. \tag{1.6}$$

We note that f_{ij} is a quantity which vanishes when ϵ_{ij} vanishes, and therefore goes to zero asymptotically as r_{ij} goes to infinity. In the region in which attractive forces predominate, f_{ij} is positive, at low temperatures strongly positive, but at smaller values of r_{ij} it approaches -1.

Substituting Eq. (1.6) in Eq. (1.5) we obtain

$$Q_\tau = \int \cdots \int \prod_{\substack{i,j \\ j>i}} (1 + f_{ij}) \, d\tau_1 d\tau_2 \cdots d\tau_N$$

$$= \int \cdots \int \left(1 + \sum_{\substack{i,j \\ j>i}} f_{ij} + \sum_{\substack{i',j',i,j \\ \left(\substack{j'>i',i' \geq i, j>i \\ j'>j \text{ if } i'=i} \right)}} f_{i'j'} f_{ij} + \cdots \right) d\tau_1 d\tau_2 \cdots d\tau_N. \tag{1.7}$$

In expanding the product in the first line of Eq. (1.7) we need to remember that there will be *one* f_{ij} for every pair. The inequality signs on the summations are intended to ensure that all combinations will be included but none duplicated. For example, no term like $f_{12}f_{12}$ will occur when the product is expanded, and if a term like $f_{34}f_{12}$ ($i' = 3$, $j' = 4$, $i = 1$, $j = 2$) occurs, there will not be *another* term $f_{12}f_{34}$ ($i' = 1$, $j' = 2$, $i = 3$, $j = 4$), the latter being excluded by the conditions on the sum. †

In an integral of the type $\int \cdots \int f_{ij} d\tau_1 d\tau_2 \cdots d\tau_i d\tau_j \cdots d\tau_N$, integration over each of the volume elements except $d\tau_i$ and $d\tau_j$ yields a factor V, the volume of the assembly, so that the integral reduces to $V^{N-2} \int\int f_{ij} d\tau_j d\tau_i$. If we now hold x_j, y_j and z_j fixed and integrate over $d\tau_i$, we see that we will have a contribution to the integrand only if x_i, y_i, and z_i are close to x_j, y_j, and z_j. The result of this integration will be independent of x_j, y_j, and z_j, provided the corresponding volume element is not too close to the edge of the volume V. If V is large enough, this edge effect can be neglected. We may write

$$\int f_{ij} \, d\tau_i = \int_0^\infty f_{ij} \cdot 4\pi r_{ij}^2 \, dr_{ij} = \beta_1,$$

thus defining β_1. In rewriting this integral we have recast the volume element into the form $4\pi r_{ij}^2 dr_{ij}$. We must remember that f_{ij} is a function of r_{ij}. Final integration‡ over $d\tau_j$ yields another factor V, so that the complete integral over all the $d\tau$ becomes, finally, $V^{N-1}\beta_1$. Because of the edge effects, the value of β_1 will actually depend very slightly on V. This dependence will not be noticeable unless V is of the same order of magnitude as the actual extension in space of the two molecules. For integrals in which the interactions of only two or a few molecules are involved, this will never be of importance. Since there are $N(N - 1)/2 \approx N^2/2$ possible pairs of systems, the second term in the summation in Eq. (1.7) will be equal to $N^2 V^{N-1}\beta_1/2$.

We now consider integrals of the form

$$\iiiint f_{i'j'} f_{ij} \, d\tau_{i'} d\tau_{j'} d\tau_i d\tau_j,$$

---

† The discussion of Eq. (1.7) follows to a large extent the treatment which I gave in Sec. E.7 of *Thermodynamics and Physics of Matter*, [4]. The four paragraphs following this one are taken, almost without revision, from this work.

‡ This procedure amounts to a change of the variables of integration from x_i, y_i, z_i, x_j, y_j, z_j to $x_i - x_j$, $y_i - y_j$, $z_i - z_j$, x_j, y_j, z_j (the Jacobian of which is 1), and subsequent transformation of $x_i - x_j$, $y_i - y_j$, $z_i - z_j$ to polar coordinates.

where i', j', i, and j are all different. It is clear that this integral will be $\beta_1^2 V^2$. The other volume elements will contribute a factor V^{N-4}, so the value of the entire integral will be $V^{N-2}\beta_1^2$. If $i' = i$, however, we must consider $\int\int\int f_{ij'}f_{ij}d\tau_{j'}d\tau_i d\tau_j$. By first holding x_i, y_i, z_i fixed and integrating successively with respect to $d\tau_{j'}$ and $d\tau_j$, then finally integrating with respect to $d\tau_i$, we see that this integral is equal to $V\beta_1^2$, and again the complete integral will be $V^{N-2}\beta_1^2$.

In a similar manner, most of the terms in the next sum, containing three f_{ij} terms, will yield on integration $V^{N-3}\beta_1^3$. However, there will be some combinations like $f_{23}f_{13}f_{12}$ which on integrating will give

$$V^{N-3}\int\int\int f_{23}f_{13}f_{12}\,d\tau_1 d\tau_2 d\tau_3 = 2V^N\frac{\beta_2}{V^2}.$$

The final integration, as usual, yields another factor V, and β_2 is defined by the equation. It will be seen that the first two integrations, with respect to $d\tau_1$ and $d\tau_2$, cannot be made independently of each other, since the suffixes 1 and 2 each occur in more than one of the f_{ij}, and so $2\beta_2$ is not equal to β_1^2.

We may now summarize our definitions of β_1 and β_2 and add one more, from which we may infer how all the β's go.

$$\beta_1 = \frac{1}{V}\int\int f_{12}\,d\tau_1 d\tau_2, \tag{1.8}$$

$$\beta_2 = \frac{1}{2!V}\int\int\int f_{23}f_{13}f_{12}\,d\tau_1 d\tau_2 d\tau_3, \tag{1.9}$$

$$\beta_3 = \frac{1}{3!V}\int\int\int\int (3f_{34}f_{23}f_{14}f_{12} + 6f_{34}f_{23}f_{14}f_{13}f_{12} + f_{34}f_{24}f_{23}f_{14}f_{13}f_{12})d\tau_1 d\tau_2 d\tau_3 d\tau_4. \tag{1.10}$$

In the definition of β_3, the factors 3 and 6 are the number of ways in which the numbers can be cross-connected by, respectively, four and five f links, as illustrated in Fig. 11-1.[†] The three integrands, $f_{34}f_{23}f_{14}f_{12}$, $f_{24}f_{23}f_{14}f_{13}$, and $f_{34}f_{24}f_{13}f_{12}$ are all distinct and must all contribute to Q_τ but will yield integrals with the same value. It is necessary to write down only one of them, if the factor 3 is included.

It is characteristic of these combinations that all combinations of linkages are part of a cycle. If this is not the case, one can decompose the integrals into simpler ones. For example, consider the linkage

---

† Diagrams of this sort have been extensively used in recent applications of statistical mechanics. Sometimes such diagrams are used as symbols to represent integrals [5].

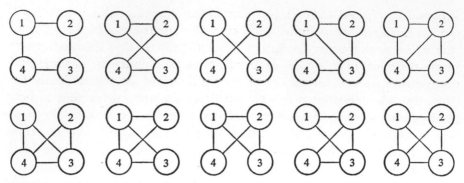

Figure 11-1. (Reproduced from Rice [4].)

shown in Fig. 11-2, where the link between 2 and 5 is not part of a
cycle, nor, for example, does the set of linkages 568 form part of a
cycle. Before integrating we can make a change of variables, expressing
$d\tau_1$ in terms of the distance to point 2 (this means explicitly in terms
of $x_1 - x_2$, $y_1 - y_2$, and $z_1 - z_2$), $d\tau_3$ in terms of distance to 2, $d\tau_2$, $d\tau_4$,
and $d\tau_6$ in terms of distances to 5, and $d\tau_7$, $d\tau_8$, $d\tau_9$ and $d\tau_{10}$ in terms
of distances to 6. We may then integrate with respect to $d\tau_1$ and $d\tau_3$,
with respect to $d\tau_4$ and $d\tau_6$, with respect to $d\tau_7$ and $d\tau_8$, and with
respect to $d\tau_9$ and $d\tau_{10}$, in pairs, obtaining four factors $2!\beta_2$, then with
respect to $d\tau_2$ obtaining a factor β_1, finally with respect to $d\tau_5$ obtaining

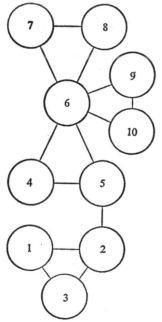

Figure 11-2.

a factor V. We may say that each factor corresponds to a "rigid" group. If there were a link 1 to 4, then the whole set 1 to 6 would be "rigid" by our definition (despite the fact that the square 1254 could be distorted without changing the lengths of the "bonds"), and integration with respect to five of the six $d\tau$'s would lead to one of the terms in β_5. We see that β_3 contains all terms arising from all cyclic connections (giving a "rigid" configuration) of four numbers, β_4 the factors arising from all cyclic connections of five numbers, β_5 those of six numbers, etc. These integrals, which cannot be broken up into simpler integrals, are called the irreducible integrals.

Examining Eq. (1.7), we have already seen that the second term in the last form of the integrand, that is, the sum over pairs $\sum\limits_{j>i} f_{ij}$ is equal to the number of possible pairs, approximately $N^2/2$, times $V^N(\beta_1/V)$. In the next term, the quadruple sum, all the terms will be equal to $V^N(\beta_1/V)^2$, and the number of such terms will be equal to the number of pairs, times the number of pairs left after one pair is taken out, divided by two (since the restriction on the sum sets a certain order for the appearance of the pairs). This is very approximately † $(N^2/2)^2/2$. In the next sum (the sextuple sum not shown) *almost* all the summands will be $V^N(\beta_1/V)^3$, and, neglecting those which involve β_2, their number will be approximately $(N^2/2)^3/3!$. Continuing, we see that, insofar as the appearance of β_2, β_3, $\cdots$ can be neglected,

$$Q_\tau = V^N \left[1 + \frac{1}{2}\left(\frac{N^2}{2}\right)^2\left(\frac{\beta_1}{V}\right)^2 + \frac{1}{3!}\left(\frac{N^2}{2}\right)^3\left(\frac{\beta_1}{V}\right)^3 \right.$$
$$\left. + \frac{1}{4!}\left(\frac{N^2}{2}\right)^4\left(\frac{\beta_1}{V}\right)^4 + \cdots \right]. \qquad (1.11)$$

If the series converges rapidly enough so that it is not necessary to go so high that the approximations concerning the number of terms break down (i.e., if the required number of terms in the series is very much less than N), we may write

$$Q_\tau = V^N \exp\left\{\frac{N^2\beta_1}{2V}\right\}. \qquad (1.12)$$

We recall that $P = kT\, \partial \ln (\text{P.F.})/\partial V$. Since Q_τ is the only part of (P.F.) which contains V,

$$P = \frac{NkT}{V}\left(1 - \frac{N\beta_1}{2V}\right). \qquad (1.13)$$

† See footnote p. 169.

Comparing Eq. (1.13) with Eq. (1.2) of Chap. 8 shows that this gives at least an approximate expression (it actually turns out to be exact) for the second virial coefficient:

$$B = -\frac{\beta_1}{2}. \tag{1.14}$$

Looking at Eq. (1.8), for β_1, and remembering the definition of f_{12}, we see that Eq. (1.14) is indeed identical to Eq. (2.3) of Chap. 8.

We may obtain all the other virial coefficients in terms of the higher β's. Let us first consider all the terms which give rise to β_2's, still neglecting all higher β's. These terms first appear in the sextuple sum containing terms with three f_{ij} factors; in this case the term is equal† to $V^N(2!\beta_2/V^2)$. The number of such terms occurring in the sextuple sum is equal to the number of triplets, namely $N(N-1)(N-2)/3! \approx N^3/3!$. In the sum containing four f_{ij}, there will also be a single factor $2!\beta_2/V^2$ in $N^3/3!$ combinations, each one combined with a single β_1/V factor ($N^2/2$ combinations); $N^3/3!$ factors $2!\beta_2/V^2$ combined with two (β_1/V)'s [approximately $(N^2/2)^2/2$ combinations] in the sum containing five f_{ij}, and so on. In writing down these numbers of combinations, we assume that taking out one triplet does not appreciably decrease the number of pairs available; this is true if N is large enough (and will, indeed, continue to be true for two triplets, and so on). As we proceed we find $2!\beta_2/V^2$ combined with three (β_1/V)'s [approximately $(N^2/2)^3/3! \times N^3/3!$ combinations], etc. In short, we find a term, which, when all the integrations have been performed, turns out to be

$$V^N \frac{N^3}{3!} \frac{2!\beta_2}{V^2} \exp\left\{\frac{N^2\beta_1}{2V}\right\}.$$

When we come to the sum involving six f_{ij}'s we can have some factors of the form $(2!\beta_2/V^2)^2$, involving pairs of triplets. The number of pairs of triplets will be $(N^3/3!)^2/2$, the factor $\frac{1}{2}$ appearing because the order of the triplets cannot be reversed; the reversals which would appear if we took them at random have to be removed. Each pair of

---

† More precisely, since the terms which result in a β_2 factor have already been included among the array of β_1^3 terms, we might write the effective value as $2!\beta_2/V^2 - \beta_1^3/V^3$. This will be true in all combinations in which $2!\beta_2/V^2$ appears. β_1^3/V^3 can, of course, be made negligible compared to $2!\beta_2/V^2$, if the specific volume $v = V/N$ is held fixed, by making N and V large enough, and since they always occur in the same combination the term β_1^3/V_1^3 can here be neglected.

triplets would also be multiplied by various powers of β_1/V, thus giving a term

$$\frac{V^N (N^3/3!)^2}{2} \left(\frac{2!\beta_2}{V^2}\right)^2 \exp\left\{\frac{N^2\beta_1}{2V}\right\}.$$

It will be seen that we have a general term†

$$\frac{V^N}{n!} \left(\frac{N^3}{3!}\right)^n \left(\frac{2!\beta_2}{V^2}\right)^n \exp\left\{\frac{N^2\beta_1}{2V}\right\}, \tag{1.15}$$

and that the sum over n of all terms like (1.15) will give as the second approximation

$$Q_\tau = V^N \exp\left\{\frac{N^2\beta_1}{2V}\right\} \exp\left\{\frac{N^3\beta_2}{3V^2}\right\}. \tag{1.16}$$

The analysis can be continued to get the terms involving‡ $3!\beta_3/V^3$. It is true that the various parts of the integrand for β_3 will appear first in different sums in Eq. (1.7). However, regardless of this, the number of quartets is approximately $N^4/4!$, the number of pairs of quartets approximately $(N^4/4!)^2/2$, and so on. The number of terms involving $(3!\beta_3/V^3)^n$ is approximately $(N^4/4!)^n/n!$. Such a term will eventually be multiplied by every possible combination of β_1 and β_2 terms, the number of these combinations being essentially the same as before, provided $N \gg n$. Carrying this out for all subsequent β_κ up to some κ which is still small compared with N, we have the general expression

---

† As noted, this combination is not quite precise because the number of pairs is decreased by first taking out triplets. In fact, each triplet effectively removes three pairs from further consideration. The general term (1.15) should, therefore, be replaced by

$$\frac{V^N}{n!} \left(\frac{N^3}{3!}\right)^n \left(\frac{2!\beta_2}{V^2}\right)^n \exp\left\{\left(\frac{N^2}{2} - 3n\right)\frac{\beta_1}{V}\right\},$$

and Eq. (1.16), then, would be

$$Q_\tau = V^N \exp\left\{\frac{N^2\beta_1}{2V}\right\} \exp\left\{\frac{N^3\beta_2}{3V^2} \exp\left\{-\frac{3\beta_1}{V}\right\}\right\}$$

The extra factor $\exp\{-3\beta_1/V\}$ is very close to 1, and its effect would be negligible. A more complicated, but similar situation arises with higher terms.

‡ In the same way that it was necessary, in order to be more precise, to subtract from $2!\beta_2/V^2$ the term which it replaced, it will be necessary to subtract from $3!\beta_3/V^3$ several terms which it replaces, and which were previously retained. However, once again, these terms will occur in the same way in all combinations of $3!\beta_3/V^3$, and will be negligible. Similar remarks hold for the higher-order terms.

$$Q_\tau = V^N \prod_{\kappa \geqq 1} \exp\left\{\frac{N^{\kappa+1}\beta_\kappa}{(\kappa+1)V^\kappa}\right\} = V^N \exp\left\{\sum_\kappa \frac{N^{\kappa+1}\beta_\kappa}{(\kappa+1)V^\kappa}\right\}. \tag{1.17}$$

From this we obtain

$$P = \frac{NkT}{V}\left[1 - \sum_{\kappa \geqq 1} \frac{\kappa\beta_\kappa}{\kappa+1}\left(\frac{N}{V}\right)^\kappa\right]. \tag{1.18}$$

Again comparing with Eq. (1.2) of Chap. 8, we see that the successive virial coefficients are given by $-\kappa\beta_\kappa/(\kappa+1)$.

By accurate measurements of the pressure over a sufficient range of volume, experimental values for the third virial coefficient may be obtained, although these are subject to some uncertainty. Some comparisons between experimental and theoretical values have been made by Bird, Spotz, and Hirschfelder [6]. The theoretical values were obtained by numerical evaluation of β_2, employing punched-card methods and using the Lennard-Jones potential, Eq. (3.2) of Chap. 8. It can be shown that a reduced virial coefficient $C^* = C/(\frac{2}{3}\pi r_0^3)^2$ depends only on the reduced temperature T^*. The results for some reasonably spherically symmetrical molecules, argon† and nitrogen, which are not subject to appreciable quantum deviations, are shown in Fig. 11-3. The reduced quantities were obtained by using in all cases the same constants for the potential-energy curve as were used for the second virial coefficient by Bird, Spotz, and Hirschfelder. Deviations noted in the figure may reflect difficulties in the experimental determinations, may indicate that Eq. (3.2) of Chap. 8 is not too exact a representation of the facts, or may be due to lack of additivity of the pair potentials.

The expression for Q_τ which we have obtained can of course be used to obtain the thermodynamic functions of the imperfect gas in terms of the irreducible integrals. We have, from Eqs. (1.2), and (1.17),

$$(\text{P.F.}) = \frac{\eta^N V^N}{N!} \exp\left\{\sum_{\kappa \geqq 1} \frac{N^{\kappa+1}\beta_\kappa}{(\kappa+1)V^\kappa}\right\}, \tag{1.19}$$

where $\eta = (2\pi mkT/h^2)^{3/2}$. From this the thermodynamic functions can

---

† The data used by Bird, Spotz, and Hirschfelder have been supplemented by some at lower temperatures, but from the same source (Michels, *et. al.*, tabulated in [7]). No data below $-100°C$ have been included, however, for the measurements below this temperature were fitted by a virial expansion which was carried only to lower powers of $1/V$, so the resulting values of the third virial coefficient were not comparable.

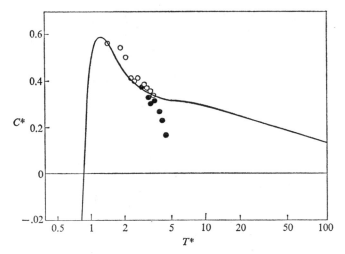

Figure 11-3. Reduced value of the third virial coefficient *vs.* reduced temperature, based on the Lennard-Jones potential. Theoretical curve after Table I-C of Hirschfelder, Curtiss, and Bird (Chap. 8, [1]). Open circles, argon; black circles, nitrogen.

be obtained in the usual way. We content ourselves with writing out the chemical potential. We have

$$\mu = -kT \frac{\partial \ln (\text{P.F.})}{\partial N}$$

$$= kT \ln \frac{N}{\eta V} - kT \sum_{\kappa \geq 1} \beta_\kappa \left(\frac{N}{V}\right)^\kappa.$$

(1.20)

For the derived quantity λ, the activity, we have

$$\lambda = \exp\left\{\frac{\mu}{kT}\right\} = \frac{N}{\eta V} \exp\left\{-\sum_{\kappa \geq 1} \beta_\kappa \left(\frac{N}{V}\right)^\kappa\right\},$$

(1.21)

and we define a reduced activity, or activity on the basis of density,

$$z = \eta\lambda = \frac{N}{V} \exp\left\{-\sum_{\kappa \geq 1} \beta_\kappa \left(\frac{N}{V}\right)^\kappa\right\}.$$

(1.22)

This becomes equal to the density when the latter is low.

11-2. *The Cluster Integrals*

Instead of being decomposed in terms of the irreducible integrals, the integral which appears in Eq. (1.7) can also be expressed in terms of so-called cluster integrals. The nature of the cluster integrals can be inferred from the definitions of the first three:

$$b_1 = \frac{1}{V} \int d\tau_1 = 1, \tag{2.1}$$

$$b_2 = \frac{1}{2!V} \iint f_{12}\, d\tau_1 d\tau_2$$
$$= \frac{1}{2} \beta_1 = \frac{b_2'}{2!}, \tag{2.2}$$

$$b_3 = \frac{1}{3!V} \iiint (f_{13}f_{12} + f_{23}f_{13} + f_{23}f_{12} + f_{23}f_{13}f_{12})\, d\tau_1 d\tau_2 d\tau_3$$
$$= \frac{1}{2} \beta_1^2 + \frac{1}{3} \beta_2 = \frac{b_3'}{3!}. \tag{2.3}$$

The b_l are the cluster integrals, where l designates the running subscript; we have introduced the b_l' because they are somewhat simpler to discuss in certain circumstances. In general $l!Vb_l$ or Vb_l' will be a $3l$-fold integral (each integral sign actually stands for a 3-fold integration), involving the volume elements of l elementary particles, e.g., $d\tau_1 d\tau_2 \cdots d\tau_l$, with products of f_{ij} in the integral containing every possible combination of these l subscripts such that each f_{ij} has at least one cross-connection with another. Figure 11-2 is a diagram corresponding to one term in b_{10}. In the integral in Eq. (1.7), every possible combination of Vb_l' of the form $\prod_l (Vb_l')^{m_l}$ will occur which satisfies the condition $\sum_l m_l l = N$, where m_l is an integer which gives the number of factors for which there is $3l$-fold integration. We may now ask how many times a particular set of m_l can occur, since l actually measures only the *number* of integrations which occur in b_l, and there are many possible ways to select the particular l molecules which are involved. Suppose for example a given term contains m_1 "clusters" of 1 molecule each, m_2 clusters of 2 each, and so on. There are N ways to pick the first molecule, $N - 1$ ways to pick the second (the first one being no longer available), $\cdots$, $N - m_1 + 1$ ways to pick the m_1th molecule. It might thus be supposed that there would be $N(N - 1) \cdots (N - m_1 + 1)$ ways to pick the set of clusters of single molecules. However, a particular set of m_1 single molecules occurs in $m_1!$ different orders. The order in which the molecules are brought into the integral does not matter, so the actual number of distinct ways m_1 single molecules will be picked is $N(N - 1) \cdots (N - m_1 + 1)/m_1!$. Having picked these out, we next pick out a pair of molecules, from the $(N - m_1)(N - m_1 - 1)/2!$ pairs left. After this there are $(N - m_1 - 2)(N - m_1 - 3)/2!$ pairs left. Altogether, there are

$$\frac{(N - m_1)(N - m_1 - 1) \cdots (N - m_1 - 2m_2 + 1)}{(2!)^{m_2} m_2!}$$

distinct ways of picking the m_2 pairs, and

$$\frac{N(N - 1) \cdots (N - m_1 - 2m_2 + 1)}{m_1!(2!)^{m_2} m_2!}$$

distinct ways of picking both singles and pairs. Continuing this reasoning, we see that the number of ways of getting a particular set of clusters from the N molecules is

$$\frac{N!}{\prod_l (l!)^{m_l} m_l!},$$

and

$$Q_r = \sum_{(m_l)} N! \prod_l \frac{(Vb_l')^{m_l}}{(l!)^{m_l} m_l!} = \sum_{(m_l)} N! \prod_l \frac{(Vb_l)^{m_l}}{m_l!}, \qquad (2.4)$$

the sum being taken over all sets of m_l satisfying the condition $\sum_l m_l l = N$.

In order to express the thermodynamic functions in terms of the cluster integrals, it is expeditious to use the grand partition function.[†] To do this, we first find (P.F.), which, by Eq. (1.2) and (2.4), is given by

$$\text{(P.F.)} = \eta^N \sum_{(m_l)} \prod_l \frac{(Vb_l)^{m_l}}{m_l!}. \qquad (2.5)$$

From this we have, by Eq. (1.11) of Chap. 10,

$$\text{(G.P.F.)} = \sum_N (\eta\lambda)^N \sum_{(m_l)} \prod_l \frac{(Vb_l)^{m_l}}{m_l!}$$

$$= \sum_N \sum_{(m_l)} \prod_l \frac{(\eta\lambda)^{m_l l}(Vb_l)^{m_l}}{m_l!},$$

[†] We saw in the footnote on p. 246 that the β_2/V^2 terms arising in some of the integrals effectively replaced some β_1^3/V^3 terms which were negligible in comparison. In this present situation, however, we are putting into b_3/V^2 some β_1^2/V^2 terms which are not negligible compared with the β_2/V^2 terms. This precludes us from developing the partition function in terms of the b's in the same way that we developed it in terms of the β's.

the second form following because $\sum_l m_l l = N$. The effect of the summation over N is to remove the condition $\sum_l m_l l = N$, since now, somewhere in the sum, $\sum_l m_l l$ can have any value whatsoever. Thus

$$\text{(G.P.F.)} = \sum_{\substack{(m_l) \\ \text{all sets}}} \prod_l \frac{(\eta\lambda)^{m_l l}(Vb_l)^{m_l}}{m_l!}. \tag{2.6}$$

As in Eq. (1.5) of Chap. 3, the order of summation and multiplication can be interchanged, so

$$\text{(G.P.F.)} = \prod_l \sum_{m_l} \frac{[(\eta\lambda)^l Vb_l]^{m_l}}{m_l!}$$

$$= \prod_l \exp\{(\eta\lambda)^l Vb_l\} = \exp\left\{\sum_l (\eta\lambda)^l Vb_l\right\}$$

$$= \exp\left\{\sum_l Vb_l z^l\right\}, \tag{2.7}$$

where $z = \eta\lambda$.

From Eq. (3.5) of Chap. 10, we now find

$$\bar{N} = \lambda\frac{\partial \ln (\text{G.P.F.})}{\partial\lambda} = z\frac{\partial \ln (\text{G.P.F.})}{\partial z}$$

$$= \sum_l l Vb_l z^l. \tag{2.8}$$

and from Eq. (3.9) of Chap. 10,

$$\bar{P} = \frac{kT}{V}\ln (\text{G.P.F.})$$

$$= kT\sum_l b_l z^l. \tag{2.9}$$

We may interpret Eq. (2.8) in the following rather fanciful way. Given that l is the number of molecules involved in a cluster, of the $\bar{N}$ molecules, $l Vb_l z^l$ are involved in clusters of size l, hence Vbz^l must be the average number of clusters of size l. In any given term in the integral a molecule can be involved in only one cluster. The average, therefore, is a properly weighted one over all terms in Eq. (1.7). With this understanding, then, we may write

$$\bar{N} = \sum_l l N_l, \tag{2.10}$$

with

$$N_l = Vb_l z^l. \tag{2.11}$$

Hence Eq. (2.9) becomes

$$\bar{P} = \frac{kT}{V} \sum_l N_l. \tag{2.12}$$

Each average number N_l contributes to the pressure as though it were the number of molecules in a perfect gas!

The expressions derived here for the pressure of an imperfect gas can be converted to those of the preceding section. By inverting Eq. (2.8) one can express z as a series in $\bar{N}/V$ or v^{-1}. This expression for z can then be introduced into Eq. (2.9), yielding the pressure in the virial form. By comparison with Eq. (1.18) one can then find the relations between the b_l and the β_κ. These can be derived independently; the first three are given already in Eqs. (2.1), (2.2), and (2.3). Historically, Eq. (2.9) was first derived, and these relations were then used to obtain Eq. (1.18).

The case in which the forces cannot be considered additive two-body forces can be readily handled by generalizing Eq. (1.4), writing

$$E_p = \sum_{\text{all pairs}} \epsilon_{ij} + \sum_{\text{all triples}} \epsilon_{ijk} + \cdots, \tag{2.13}$$

and defining

$$f_{ijk} = \exp\left\{\frac{-\epsilon_{ijk}}{kT}\right\} - 1, \tag{2.14}$$

and so on. A correction term must then be added to b_3, namely

$$\frac{1}{3!V} \iiint f_{123} \, d\tau_1 d\tau_2 d\tau_3. \tag{2.15}$$

The correction to b_4 will be considerably more complicated.

11-3. *The Relation between the Cluster Integrals and the Irreducible Integrals*

Before going further into the nature of the series obtained in the last two sections, we need the general relation between the cluster integrals and the irreducible integrals. We have noted how this relation might be obtained in Sec. 11-2; however, it will be easier to solve this problem directly. The relation between a single term in an integral and the irreducible integrals in that term is, as should be clear from the discussion of Fig. 11-2, the same as the relation between a set of connected points, and the subsets of "rigidly" connected points within that set. Each rigid subset, if there is more than one, has at least one point in common with another rigid subset, but not more than one point with any given rigid subset. Let us start with the first rigid subset, using the coordinates of one point as the variables of integration to give the factor V. Integration of an appropriate combination of the f_{ij} with respect to the rest of the variables will give some term in β_{κ_i} if there are $\kappa_1 + 1$ points in the subset. Consider now the rigid subsets which have a point in common with subset 1. Integration with respect to the other points (not in common with 1) will give terms in $\beta_{\kappa_2}, \beta_{\kappa_3}, \cdots$. If connections are made in all possible ways within a rigid subset, leaving it rigid, and the resulting integrals added, we get $\kappa! \beta_\kappa$ when there are $\kappa + 1$ points in the subset. As we proceed with the third group of subsets, those which are connected to the second group, it is seen that more factors $\kappa! \beta_\kappa$ will arise. Further, we see that *each* rigid subset has one point in common with a subset that precedes it, so for each subset except the first one there is one "common point," or link. Nevertheless, we will make the convention that any common point is assigned to the subset which is the *earlier* in the sequence. The net result of the division into subsets is an integral whose value is $V\kappa_1! \beta_{\kappa_1} \kappa_2! \beta_{\kappa_2} \cdots$. As we have seen, the factor V results from one variable of integration, and each β_{κ_i} from κ_i additional ones. Therefore $\kappa_1 + \kappa_2 + \cdots + 1 = l$. Some of the κ_i may be identical; suppose there are n_κ factors with a particular κ. Then the value of a particular integral in the expression for $Vb_l l!$ may be written

$$V \prod_\kappa (\kappa! \beta_\kappa)^{n_\kappa}. \tag{3.1}$$

where the product is over the particular set of κ's.

We are now interested in the number of different ways a particular set of κ's can be obtained for a given l. Since $\sum_\kappa \kappa n_\kappa = l - 1$, let us arbitrarily set aside one molecule from the group of l molecules. Of the $l - 1$ remaining, there are $(l - 1)!/\prod_\kappa (\kappa!)^{n_\kappa} n_\kappa!$ different ways of dividing them into subsets with n_κ subsets for each particular κ. The order within a subset does not matter, nor does it matter if two subsets of the same size are interchanged (i.e., after such changes we will have the same integral), hence the factors in the denominator.

Having selected one of the $(l - 1)!/\prod_\kappa (\kappa!)^{n_\kappa} n_\kappa!$ different ways of dividing the group into particular subsets, we must find out how many ways this particular set of subsets can be linked together. The number of ways depends upon which molecules are chosen as links and in which order. Any molecule can be a link any number of times. Therefore there are l ways of choosing any link, and since the number of links will be one less than the number of subsets, i.e., $(\sum_{\kappa} n_{\kappa}) - 1$, the total number of possibilities will be

$$l^{(\sum_{\kappa} n_{\kappa}) - 1}.$$

It is necessary to examine this process of choice a little more closely to be sure that the molecule which was arbitrarily set aside in the first place is properly included, and that there are no duplications or omissions. Provisionally we may say that there are

$$\frac{(l-1)!}{\prod_{\kappa} (\kappa!)^{n_{\kappa}} n_{\kappa}!} l^{(\sum_{\kappa} n_{\kappa}) - 1} \tag{3.2}$$

different ways of getting a term equal to $V \prod_{\kappa} (\kappa! \beta_{\kappa})^{n_{\kappa}}$ into the expression for $V b_l l!$, and we have

$$V b_l l! = V \sum_{(n_{\kappa})} \frac{(l-1)! l^{(\sum_{\kappa} n_{\kappa}) - 1}}{\prod_{\kappa} (\kappa!)^{n_{\kappa}} n_{\kappa}!} \prod_{\kappa} (\kappa! \beta_{\kappa})^{n_{\kappa}},$$

where the sum is taken over all sets of n_{κ} consistent with the conditions $\sum_{\kappa} \kappa n_{\kappa} = l - 1$ (κ being equal to or greater than 1). Therefore

$$b_l = \frac{1}{l^2} \sum_{(n_{\kappa})} \prod_{\kappa} \frac{(l \beta_{\kappa})^{n_{\kappa}}}{n_{\kappa}!}. \tag{3.3}$$

Let us now consider more carefully the basis of the combinatorial factor (3.2). Having chosen one molecule to set aside, which we call molecule 1, we will chose one of the $(l-1)!/\prod_{\kappa} (\kappa!)^{n_{\kappa}} n_{\kappa}!$ distinct arrangements. We will put the subsets having the various values of κ in some fixed preliminary order. Remember that a subset contains κ molecules and is linked by a molecule that is not part of it to some other subset.

Let us now choose some particular molecule, other than 1, as our first link; this is in some subset A. Since subset A is not linked to any preceding one, it is short one molecule, and we attach molecule 1 to it. We now choose link 2, thus automatically choosing subset B, to be linked on to subset A (via link 1 in A already chosen), unless link 2 is also in subset A. If link 2 is in subset A we choose link 3; the first link not in subset A selects subset B, which is attached to link 1. This process continues. After all the links are chosen, any remaining subsets are attached to the successive links in the order in which they were originally placed. It is to be noted that molecule 1 can be used as a link, once it is put in a subset (what happens if it is chosen as the first link will be considered later). Molecule 1 can thus be incorporated in any subset, and it can be used as a link any number of times once it is in. Thus, except when it is the first link, all possibilities are covered. Furthermore, any change in the order in which the links are chosen will cause a change in the diagram, so there are no duplications. †

If molecule 1 is chosen as the first link, the situation needs special consideration. *All* the links might be 1, in which case each subset connects to all others through 1. If this is not the case, we must wait until some other molecule is chosen; this then determines subset A, to which molecule 1 is then added, and we then proceed as before. After 1 is chosen as the first link, it can be made a part of any subset, all possibilities are covered, and no duplications with the previous cases occur (see Prob. 11.6).

It may also be seen that it does not matter which molecule is set aside. Suppose, for example, molecule 2 were selected. In some particular configuration, we relabel the subset in which 1 happens to appear (or, if 1 is a link, one of the subsets which has another link) as A. If we now remove molecule 1, and dismantle the group into new subsets, we see that we have left one of the $(l-1)!/\prod_{\kappa}(\kappa!)^{n_\kappa}n_\kappa!$ combinations. In other words, the group based on molecule 2 was one of those enumerated in (3.2). One will thus get everything by choosing an arbitrary molecule to start with, and there will be as many diagrams for any combination of κ's as there are ways of selecting and ordering the links, as assumed in Eq. (3.2).

11-4. *Some Properties of the Expansions: Condensation*

We shall presently be concerned with the behavior with increasing density, of the series derived in the last two sections, and in particular with the apparent "divergence" of the expansions at a certain density,

---

† By carefully selecting the order of the links, one sequence can be caused to give a diagram which appears to be coming out identical to that produced by another, but when one comes to the remaining subsets which do not have further links this breaks down, for these must go in the order in which the subsets were originally arbitrarily placed. See Prob. 11.6.

which we shall identify as a description of the process of condensation. †
This is actually a somewhat controversial subject, and will require careful consideration of the behavior of the β_κ and the b_l at large κ and l.
First we must make some general observations.

We have obtained two expressions for the pressure, Eqs. (1.18) and (2.9). For given values of the density and temperature these should, indeed, give identical values. Through the use of Eqs. (1.22) and (3.3) in Eq. (2.9) the latter should reduce to (1.18). However, there are apparently different limits to the validity of Eqs. (1.18) and (2.9). Equation (2.9) comes from an exact calculation of the grand partition function, and so should be exact to the extent that the pressure calculated from the grand partition function gives the measured pressure of one of the assemblies. Equation (1.18), on the other hand, depends on the assumption that the κ for any term which contributes appreciably is very small compared with N. Thus, in just the circumstances that the series "diverges" and higher-order terms become important, Eq. (1.18) might be expected to break down. Equation (1.22) will break down under the same circumstances, so just under these conditions one cannot develop the relation between Eqs. (1.18) and (2.9).

The sum in Eq. (1.18) is a finite sum, since κ cannot be greater than N; on the other hand, the sum in Eq. (2.9) is an infinite sum. By taking the volume V in Eq. (1.18) arbitrarily large, one can make the value of N for a given density also arbitrarily large. One can thus extend the validity of Eqs. (1.18) and (1.22) to higher-order terms, and by continuing this process we can approach a situation in which the sum in Eq. (1.18) can be taken as an infinite sum. Under these circumstances Eqs. (1.18) and (2.9) must be exactly equivalent, since the use of the grand partition function implies that there is effectively no limitation on the number of particles involved, inasmuch as the total number of assemblies in the ensemble can be made as large as we please. Furthermore, we note that Eq. (3.3) gives a definite algebraic form for the conversion of the b_l to the β_κ. Thus Eq. (1.18), with an infinite sum, is also an expression for the pressure of the grand ensemble. Difficulties, to be sure, might arise in a region in which either of the series diverged in the true sense, but we shall introduce arguments to show that true divergence of these series, in contrast to apparent divergence, does not occur in any range of the variables we need to consider.

Let us look at the behavior of β_κ for large κ, at very low tem-

† For a detailed discussion of condensation see [8, 9].

peratures. We recall that there is a range of r_{ij}, around a few Ångstroms, for which the interatomic potential is noticeably negative and for which f_{ij} is positive. Indeed, at very low temperatures, f_{ij} is large and positive in most of this range. On the other hand, in the range of smaller r_{ij}, where the interatomic potential becomes repulsive, f_{ij} becomes negative, but it can never go below -1. At low temperatures, then, we may conjecture that positive values predominate. However, β_κ will consist of large numbers of positive and negative contributions. There will be a positive contribution from the part of the integral in which no r_{ij} is small enough for the corresponding f_{ij} to be negative, a negative contribution from the part with one negative f_{ij}, a positive contribution from the part with two negative f_{ij}'s, and so on.

Let us consider the first positive contribution. If any r_{ij} that represents two points which are connected in the linkage diagram becomes large, the value of the integrand becomes small. In general, then, this contribution comes mostly from linkages such that no molecule is cross-connected to more than about twelve other molecules, since a given (spherical) molecule cannot have more molecules at the right distance from it than about the number that can be close-packed about it. We can obtain, then, all the appreciable terms coming from all possible sets of cross connections derived from all possible close-packed, or nearly close-packed, arrangements by connecting some or all of the nearest neighbors. An integral β_κ corresponding to a close-packed structure has approximately κ elements of volume in the integration, each of which would be expected to contribute almost the same factor. Thus one might expect the first positive contribution to be expressible as some quantity raised to the κ power, say Λ^κ. If, however, one is permitted any given way of making the connections, there will be $\kappa!$ ways of arranging the atoms in the close-packed array, all of which give rise to distinct contributions to the integral, so the total first positive contribution is written $\kappa!\Lambda^\kappa$.

The first negative contribution occurs when one pair of molecules is very close. We can think of a close-packed structure of $\kappa - 1$ molecules, with one selected molecule coinciding or nearly coinciding with one of the $\kappa - 1$. We have κ choices for the selected molecule, $\kappa - 1$ positions for it [actually $\kappa(\kappa - 1)/2$ possible pairs, since when two molecules are in a given position it does not matter which one was selected] and $(\kappa - 1)!$ different ways of arranging in close-packed order the molecules which were not selected. Thus there are $\frac{1}{2}\kappa(\kappa - 1)(\kappa - 1)! = \frac{1}{2}(\kappa - 1)\kappa!$ ways of getting a negative contribution, which may be taken as $-\Lambda^\kappa\lambda$. The factor λ depends only on a change in the contribution to the integrand of a few pairs involving the selected molecule, and is not expected to depend on κ. The net first negative contribution is

$$-\frac{1}{2}(\kappa - 1)\kappa!\Lambda^\kappa\lambda \approx -\frac{\kappa\lambda}{2}\kappa!\Lambda^\kappa.$$

In the second positive contribution there are two selected molecules on a substrate of $\kappa - 2$. There are $\kappa(\kappa - 1)/2$ ways of choosing the first selected molecule and its position and $(\kappa - 2)(\kappa - 3)/2$ choices for the second, while the substrate can be arranged in $(\kappa - 2)!$ ways. Thus there are $[\kappa(\kappa - 1)(\kappa - 2)(\kappa - 3)/2^3](\kappa - 2)! \approx (\kappa!/2)(\kappa/2)^2$ ways of getting a contribution of $\Lambda^\kappa\lambda^2$ (the extra division by 2 occurs because it does not matter which of the selected molecules is chosen first). The total contribution then is approximately $(\kappa\lambda/2)^2\kappa!\Lambda^\kappa/2$.

The second negative contribution will be

$$-\frac{\kappa(\kappa - 1)\cdots(\kappa - 5)}{2^3\cdot 3!}(\kappa - 3)!\Lambda^\kappa\lambda^3 \approx -\left(\frac{\kappa\lambda}{2}\right)^3\frac{\kappa!\Lambda^\kappa}{3!},$$

and the total contribution then,

$$\kappa!\Lambda^\kappa\left[1 - \frac{\kappa\lambda}{2} + \frac{(\kappa\lambda/2)^2}{2} - \frac{(\kappa\lambda/2)^3}{3!} + \cdots\right] = \kappa!\Lambda^\kappa\exp\left\{\frac{-\kappa\lambda}{2}\right\}.$$

Since the expression for β_κ contains a factor $1/\kappa!$ [Eqs. (1.8) to (1.10)], we have

$$\beta_\kappa \approx \Lambda^\kappa\exp\left\{\frac{-\kappa\lambda}{2}\right\}.$$

This expression contains several implicit approximations. Perhaps the most important is that of the independence of the effects of two or more selected molecules producing negative factors—surely these are not independent if they are superimposed on close neighbors in the close-packed array. A further influence will arise from edge effects in the close-packed array. Nevertheless the above expression suggests that we can write

$$\beta_\kappa = f_\beta(\kappa)\beta_0^\kappa, \tag{4.1}$$

where β_0 is independent of κ and $f_\beta(\kappa)$ is a function which depends on κ less strongly than does β_0^κ.

The factor $f_\beta(\kappa)$ may be expected to *decrease* with increasing κ, for it must take care of the edge effects. Some of the κ factors in β_0^κ actually will fail to appear for molecules near the surface of the close-packed array, and the number left out because of the lack of neighbors to interact with will be proportional to $\kappa^{2/3}$. Thus we may suppose that β_κ would be expressible as $\beta_0^{\kappa - c\kappa^{2/3}}$, where c is a constant, so that $f_\beta(\kappa)$ would then be equal to $\beta_0^{-c\kappa^{2/3}}$ or $\beta_0'^{-\kappa^{2/3}}$, where $\beta_0' = \beta_0^c$. In contrast to β_0, note that β_0' is a dimensionless quantity, which is of the order of magnitude of $\exp\{-\epsilon_{12}/kT\} - 1$ raised to a small power, since this is the type of term left out at the boundary. Since ϵ_{12} is negative near the minimum, β_0' will be large at low temperatures.

The argument by which we arrived at Eq. (4.1) has the status of a plausibility argument. If we are at a low temperature where the values of f_{ij} in the positive region become very large, we should expect a small factor $\lambda(\ll 1)$ to arise when we go into the negative region of one of them. At higher temperatures, λ is not necessarily small, the series converges less rapidly, and the approximations will become more important.[†] Indeed, we must eventually get negative values for some of the β_κ. But even at low temperatures the series converges only slowly for large κ, and doubts have been expressed that all β_κ remain always positive. Indeed, for an artificial type of very long range potential-energy function, it can be shown that some of them become negative for any fixed T, however low [10]. Nevertheless, for a normal type of potential-energy function, the argument given seems sufficiently convincing to make it appear worthwhile to investigate the consequences of assuming that Eq. (4.1) holds at a sufficiently low temperature.

If all the β_κ are positive, we can obtain an approximate expression for b_l (large l) from Eq. (3.3) by finding the maximum term in Eq. (3.3) with respect to variation of the n_κ under the condition

$$\sum_\kappa \kappa n_\kappa = l - 1 \tag{4.2}$$

and multiplying this value by the total number Δ of terms having values comparable to this maximum. Let us first transform Eq. (3.3) by substituting the more precise form of the Stirling approximation [11]

$$n_\kappa! = \exp\{-n_\kappa\} n_\kappa^{n_\kappa} (2\pi n_\kappa)^{1/2}.$$

[†] It is now generally believed that the conclusions of Mayer and his collaborators concerning phenomena in the neighborhood of the critical point (see [1]) are not valid.

Equation (3.3) then becomes

$$b_l = \frac{1}{l^2} \left[\prod_{\kappa=1}^{l-1} \frac{(el\beta_\kappa/n_\kappa)^{n_\kappa}}{(2\pi n_\kappa)^{1/2}} \right]_{\max} \Delta$$

$$= \frac{1}{l^2} B_{\max}\Delta. \tag{4.3}$$

where, as usual, $e \equiv \exp\{1\}$, and

$$B = \prod_{\kappa=1}^{l-1} \frac{(el\beta_\kappa/n_\kappa)^{n_\kappa}}{(2\pi n_\kappa)^{1/2}}. \tag{4.4}$$

Differentiating the logarithm of B, setting the result equal to zero, and taking care of the condition Eq. (4.2) by means of a Lagrange multiplier, which we shall call $\ln \rho_0$, we see that the n_κ in $B_{\max}$ must satisfy the equation

$$\ln (l\beta_\kappa) - \ln n_\kappa - \frac{1}{2n_\kappa} + \kappa \ln \rho_0 = 0.$$

In solving for n_κ the term $1/2n_\kappa$ may be neglected, so

$$n_\kappa = l\beta_\kappa\rho_0^\kappa, \tag{4.5}$$

which gives the number of factors involving β_κ in the greatest term in the sum of Eq. (3.3). Substituting this back into Eq. (4.2), neglecting the difference between l and $l-1$, we have the condition which can be used to determine ρ_0,

$$\sum_{\kappa=1}^{l} \kappa\beta_\kappa\rho_0^\kappa = 1. \tag{4.6}$$

In all that has been done in the last paragraph, it is implied that T is low and all β_κ are positive. Then the average value of the terms in the sum in Eq. (4.6) will be very much less than 1; indeed, the average value will be l^{-1}. If we use Eq. (4.1) in Eq. (4.6) we obtain

$$\sum_{\kappa=1}^{l} \kappa f_\beta(\kappa)(\beta_0\rho_0)^\kappa = 1. \tag{4.7}$$

If $\sum_\kappa \kappa f_\beta(\kappa) \approx \sum_\kappa \kappa(\beta_0')^{-\kappa^{2/3}}$ [see the paragraph following Eq. (4.1)], we may evaluate it roughly by changing it to an integral:

$$\sum_\kappa \kappa(\beta_0')^{-\kappa^{2/3}} \approx \int_0^\infty \kappa \exp\left\{-\kappa^{2/3} \ln \beta_0'\right\} d\kappa$$

$$= \frac{3}{2} \int_0^\infty x^2 \exp\left\{-x \ln \beta_0'\right\} dx \qquad \text{(substituting } x = \kappa^{2/3})$$

$$= \frac{3}{(\ln \beta_0')^3}. \tag{4.8}$$

Since β_0' is very large at low temperatures, our conjecture is that $\sum_\kappa \kappa f_\beta(\kappa) \ll 1$. From this inequality we see that, in order to satisfy Eq. (4.7), ρ_0 must be greater than $1/\beta_0$. If l is large ρ_0 does not need to be much greater than $1/\beta_0$; indeed, it must be very close, and if the series were an infinite one $\rho_0 > 1/\beta_0$ would cause it to diverge. Having ρ_0 even slightly larger than $1/\beta_0$ throws weight on the higher terms in Eq. (4.6) or (4.7).

However, in order to understand these relationships properly, we must recognize that our representation of $f_\beta(\kappa)$ as $(\beta_0')^{-\kappa^{2/3}}$ cannot be correct for small κ, and, on the other hand, that Eq. (4.5) cannot hold for κ of the order of magnitude of l, and hence the terms in the summations we are considering will be modified for the small and the large values of κ. The expression $(\beta_0')^{-\kappa^{2/3}}$ for $f_\beta(\kappa)$ breaks down at small κ because, when only a small number of corrections are involved, the correction for edge effects will be even more important than indicated. The maximum in the integrand in Eq. (4.8) occurs at a value of κ less than 1, which obviously cannot be significant. The true maximum will occur at a higher term, the first terms in the sum $\sum_\kappa \kappa f_\beta(\kappa)$ being smaller than $\kappa(\beta_0')^{-\kappa^{2/3}}$. This, of course, can only mean that the sum is even smaller than the value given by Eq. (4.8).

The expression for n_κ breaks down for $\kappa \approx l$, because the derivation of Eq. (4.5) is based on the assumption that n_κ is large enough to use the Stirling approximation for $n_\kappa!$. It is obvious, from the condition, Eq. (4.2), that the value of n_κ in the largest term in Eq. (3.3) must actually be zero if κ is large. Recall that n_κ must be an integer, and that even $n_\kappa = 1$ is too large for large κ, because $n_\kappa = 1$ (large κ) would preclude a large combinatorial factor in the term in Eq. (3.3). Thus the factor $(\beta_0 \rho_0)^\kappa$, which is large if κ is large even though $\beta_0 \rho_0$ is only slightly larger than 1, cannot affect n_κ's for which $\kappa \approx l$, for these terms vanish in any case, but it will affect terms for which κ is large but still not comparable with l.

We now attempt to find the number of terms Δ comparable in size to that of the maximum. This may be done by finding the second variation of $\ln B$ with respect to n_κ. We find from Eq. (4.4)

$$\ln B - \ln B_{\max} = -\sum_\kappa \frac{1}{2} \frac{(\delta n_\kappa)^2}{n_{\kappa,\max}}, \tag{4.9}$$

or

$$B = B_{\max} \exp\left\{-\frac{1}{2}\sum_\kappa \frac{(\delta n_\kappa)^2}{n_{\kappa,\max}}\right\}, \tag{4.10}$$

and we wish to find the number of terms for which

$$\frac{1}{2}\sum_\kappa \frac{(\delta n_\kappa)^2}{n_{\kappa,\max}} < 1. \tag{4.11}$$

The inequality implies that we need, roughly, all the values of δn_κ which occur within an l-dimensional hyperellipsoid with semi-axes (analogous to radii) of $(2n_\kappa)^{1/2}$ (we drop the subscript "max," which will hereafter be understood) in the l-dimensional space in which the δn_κ are measured along the axes. The l-dimensional volume of such a hyperellipsoid is (and hence Δ is roughly) equal to $\prod_\kappa (2\pi n_\kappa)^{1/2}/\Gamma(r+1)$ where r is half the number of factors in the product [12]. Actually the allowable values of δn_κ must conform to Eq. (4.2), which reduces the dimensionality by one. We must, of course, recall that our equations hold only if n_κ is large. Thus we should take the product only over those κ's for which n_κ is large, and so we have replaced $l/2$ by r. Since there are many values of κ for which n_κ is large, r will be a large number, although much smaller than $l/2$. In view of the fact that Eq. (4.5) makes n_κ proportional to l, we expect r to increase with l. It still seems reasonable to suppose that the condition, Eq. (4.2), causes there to be one less factor in Δ than there is in the product $\prod_\kappa (2\pi n_\kappa)^{-1/2}$ of Eq. (4.3). We thus write

$$\frac{\Delta}{\prod\limits_\kappa (2\pi n_\kappa)^{1/2}} \approx \frac{1}{l^{1/2} r! (2\pi\beta_{\kappa'}\rho_0^{\kappa'})^{1/2}}, \tag{4.12}$$

where $l\beta_{\kappa'}\rho_0^{\kappa'}$ is a typical value for n_κ [see Eq. (4.5)]. Using Eq. (4.12) and Eq. (4.5) in Eq. (4.3), we obtain

$$b_l = \frac{\prod\limits_{\kappa=1}^{2r} (e/\rho_0^\kappa)^{n_\kappa}}{l^{5/2} r! (2\pi\beta_{\kappa'}\rho_0^{\kappa'})^{1/2}}$$

$$= \frac{\rho_0}{r!(2\pi\beta_{\kappa'}\rho_0^{\kappa'})^{1/2} l^{5/2}} \frac{\exp\left\{\sum\limits_{\kappa=1}^{l} n_\kappa\right\}}{\rho_0^l} \quad \text{[by Eq. (4.2)]}$$

$$= \frac{\rho_0}{r!(2\pi\beta_{\kappa'}\rho_0^{\kappa'})^{1/2} l^{5/2}} \left(\frac{\exp\left\{\sum\limits_{\kappa=1}^{l} \beta_\kappa\rho_0^\kappa\right\}}{\rho_0}\right)^l \quad \text{[by Eq. (4.5)]}$$

$$= f_b(l) b_0^l, \tag{4.13}$$

defining † $f_b(l)$ and b_0. Since ρ_0 is defined by Eq. (4.6), it will decrease slightly as l increases and therefore $\sum_\kappa \beta_\kappa \rho_0^\kappa$ will also decrease slightly from this cause. It tends to increase with l because of the inclusion of more terms, but this must be overcompensated by the other effect, because Eq. (4.6) must always hold, ‡ and the larger the value of l the greater the values of κ by which the terms of Eq. (4.6) must be divided to get $\sum_\kappa \beta_\kappa \rho_0^\kappa$. So $\sum_\kappa \beta_\kappa \rho_0^\kappa$ will tend to a limit for large l. In defining b_0 we take this limiting value, allowing any discrepancy to be absorbed in $f_0(l)$. The latter quantity is very small compared to $\rho_0/l^{5/2}$ because of the factor $r!$ in the denominator ($\beta_{\kappa'} \rho_0^{\kappa'}$ is a small factor in the denominator but is more than compensated by $r!$). Because of the dependence of r on l, we expect $f_b(l)$ to decrease more rapidly with l than as $1/l^{5/2}$.

In the foregoing discussion we have dealt with the behavior of b_l at large l, but we have still to deal with its behavior at *very* large l. Let us consider a grand canonical ensemble with vessels of fixed volume V. In such a system we are forced to think of the possibility of a very large number of particles entering any given vessel, resulting in a large value of the number density $\rho = N/V$, of particles in that vessel. This is reflected in the fact that the various series which occur in Sec. 11-2 are infinite series. We will have to deal with b_l's for which l is so large that if l particles were packed into a vessel of size V, the resulting density $\rho_l = l/V$ would be comparable to the density of a fluid (liquid) in which all particles were close enough to interact with their neighbors. The variables of integration which appear in the integrals involved in b_l are, of course, restricted to regions within the volume V. If l is small, this restriction has an effect only on the last integration, which explicitly introduces the factor V. The effective range of the other integrations is limited by the range of the interatomic forces. But if ρ_l becomes comparable to the density of the liquid, it will not be possible to develop many of the integrations to the extent which would be allowed by the interatomic forces; they, too, will be limited

---

† It has been shown rigorously [13, 14] that for large l

$$f_b(l) = \frac{\rho_0}{(2\pi \sum_\kappa \kappa^2 \beta_\kappa \rho_0^\kappa)^{1/2} l^{5/2}}$$

as long as $\sum_\kappa \kappa^2 \beta_\kappa \rho_0^\kappa$ converges, even if some of the β_κ are negative. However, since ρ_0 has to be slightly greater than β_0, and $\sum_\kappa \kappa^2 \beta_\kappa \rho_0^\kappa$ must, therefore, increase with l, application of the theorem seems questionable.

‡ Equation (4.2) will hold approximately even if the sum is cut off at $\kappa = 2r$, since only small terms are left out. Since it makes very little difference we continue the sum to l in Eq. (4.13) and take Eq. (4.6) as defining ρ_0. In this sense Eq. (4.6) is exact.

on account of the size of the vessel. Thus, while for large values of l the value of b_l will be given by Eq. (4.13), for *very* large values it will fall below this. Indeed, there is no guarantee that it will not become negative for some values of l, even at very low temperatures, but there will be an effective upper limit for b_l so far as absolute value is concerned. A similar statement can be made concerning the β_κ. Indeed, it is perhaps more obvious for these simple integrals.

Let us now turn our attention to Eqs. (2.8) and (2.9). The first of these can be written

$$\bar{\rho} = \sum_l l b_l z^l. \tag{4.14}$$

It is an infinite series, and may be considered to be an equation for the determination of z as a function of $\bar{\rho}$; of course z increases with $\bar{\rho}$. As long as z is smaller than b_0^{-1}, Eq. (4.14) can be written

$$\bar{\rho} = \sum_l l f_b(l) b_0^l z^l. \tag{4.15}$$

We will also need, for reference, the expressions for $\partial P/\partial \rho$, which can be obtained from Eqs. (2.9) and (1.18). We do not need to distinguish between ρ and $\bar{\rho}$. From Eq. (2.9), we find

$$\frac{\partial P}{\partial \rho} = kT \sum_l l b_l z^l \frac{\partial \ln z}{\partial \rho}$$

$$= kT\rho \frac{\partial \ln z}{\partial \rho}, \tag{4.16}$$

using Eq. (4.14). From Eq. (4.14) we also find

$$1 = \sum_l l^2 b_l z^l \frac{\partial \ln z}{\partial \rho}; \tag{4.17}$$

hence

$$\frac{\partial P}{\partial \rho} = \frac{kT\rho}{\sum_l l^2 b_l z^l}. \tag{4.18}$$

Now as long as ρ is less than ρ_0 [defined as the limiting value— see following Eq. (4.13)] there will be no question about the validity of Eq. (1.22), since as explained following Eq. (4.13), $\sum_\kappa \beta_\kappa \rho_0^\kappa$ has a definite limiting value. If, therefore, we substitute from Eq. (1.22) into Eq. (4.15), and also use Eq. (4.13) for b_0, we obtain

$$\rho = \sum_l l f_b(l) \exp\left\{l \sum_{\kappa=1}^{l} \beta_\kappa(\rho_0^\kappa - \rho^\kappa)\right\} \left(\frac{\rho}{\rho_0}\right)^l. \tag{4.19}$$

Since this is an identity in ρ, it must actually determine the coefficients $f_b(l)$. As ρ approaches ρ_0, the left-hand side of the equation must also approach ρ_0, and the equation will be valid, since $\sum_\kappa \beta_\kappa \rho_0^\kappa$ converges. Thus we have

$$\rho_0 = \sum_l l f_b(l). \tag{4.20}$$

This equality again means that $f_b(l)$ must be a decreasing function of l, in the range of l for which Eq. (4.13) holds (and by taking a large V, this range may be made as large as we wish); otherwise by getting ρ very close to ρ_0, the sum could be made too large.

Thus when ρ approaches ρ_0, we see from Eq. (4.15) that z approaches b_0^{-1}. When z becomes very slightly greater than b_0^{-1}, the higher terms in Eq. (4.14) become suddenly very much more important. Over an exceedingly small range of z, as these terms come in ever more powerfully, ρ will increase beyond ρ_0. This increase will continue for a very small range of z, (indeed, so small that z can be considered virtually constant), then the terms for which Eq. (4.13) is no longer valid will begin to be important, and the behavior will change.

The region over which z remains virtually constant, but ρ increases, is interpreted as the region of condensation. In this region $\partial P/\partial \rho$ will essentially vanish, as may be seen from Eq. (4.18), since for a large term we will have

$$l^2 b_l z^l \gg l b_l z^l \tag{4.21}$$

and hence

$$\sum_l l^2 b_l z^l \gg \sum_l l b_l z^l = \rho. \tag{4.22}$$

Since terms for which l is of the order of Avogadro's number can still be described by Eq. (4.13) and will, of course, appear in the sum, the inequality of (4.21) can be a very marked inequality indeed, and if these large terms are at all important the factor, $\rho/\sum_l l^2 b_l z^l$ which appears in Eq. (4.18) will be very small indeed. Thus the behavior of the system when ρ just exceeds ρ_0 is exactly what is encountered in condensation.

One point remains to be clarified: the reason that $\partial P/\partial \rho$ vanishes suddenly, and more or less discontinuously. This behavior depends on the properties of the higher β_κ, and it is not possible to deduce the character of the transition without more information. However, we may proceed inversely, and from the fact that $\partial P/\partial \rho$ shows a sudden change to zero at the transition, we may infer certain properties of the series involving β_κ.

From Eq. (1.18), which may be written

$$P = kT \left(\rho - \sum_\kappa \frac{\kappa \beta_\kappa}{\kappa + 1} \rho^{\kappa+1} \right),$$ (4.23)

we find

$$\frac{\partial P}{\partial \rho} = kT \left(1 - \sum_\kappa \kappa \beta_\kappa \rho^\kappa \right)$$

$$= kT \left(1 - \sum_\kappa \kappa f_\beta(\kappa) \beta_0^\kappa \rho^\kappa \right).$$ (4.24)

In the several pages preceding we have treated sums over κ, such as the one appearing in Eq. (4.24) as infinite sums, even if ρ is as great as ρ_0. This is satisfactory as long as the convergence is sufficiently rapid; however, when ρ approaches β_0^{-1}, some further scrutiny is needed. If $\sum_\kappa \kappa f_\beta(\kappa) < 1$, then Eq. (4.24) can hold up to and including $\rho = \beta_0^{-1}$. This inequality is the necessary and sufficient condition that there should be a sudden change in $\partial P/\partial \rho$. As soon as ρ exceeds β_0^{-1} the series will diverge. For some value of ρ very slightly greater than β_0^{-1} the sum $\sum_\kappa \kappa \beta_\kappa \rho^\kappa$ will pass the value 1, at which point $\rho = \rho_0$. If the series is infinite, we have no way of finding ρ_0, except to note that it is indefinitely close to β_0^{-1}. Our original definition of ρ_0 came from Eq. (4.6), and we have already noted that the value of ρ_0, then, will depend on l; we may write it $\rho_0(l)$ and, as before, consider ρ_0 without the designation as a limiting value.

Let us now consider the other expression for $\partial P/\partial \rho$, namely Eq. (4.18), which may be written in the form

$$\frac{\partial P}{\partial \rho} = \frac{kT\rho}{\sum_l l^2 f_b(l) b_0^l z^l}.$$ (4.25)

So long as z is not too close to b_0^{-1}, no difficulty will arise. But when z approaches b_0^{-1} there is an apparent difficulty. If $f_b(l)$ were proportional to $l^{-5/2}$ for large l, the sum of the higher-order terms would be proportional to $\sum_\kappa l^{-1/2}(b_0 z)^l$. As $b_0 z$ approaches 1 this sum approaches infinity not suddenly but gradually. For $\sum_\kappa l^{-1/2}(b_0 z)^l$ can be replaced by the integral

$$\int_0^\infty \frac{1}{l^{1/2}} \exp\left\{l \ln (b_0 z)\right\} dl \approx \int_0^\infty \frac{1}{l^{1/2}} \exp\left\{-l(1 - b_0 z)\right\} dl$$

$$= \frac{\Gamma(\tfrac{1}{2})}{(1 - b_0 z)^{1/2}}. \tag{4.26}$$

which approaches infinity continuously [15]. However, as indicated following Eq. (4.13), $f_b(l)$ is expected to decrease more rapidly with l than as $1/l^{5/2}$. In any event, the higher-order terms in the sum in Eq. (4.13) have an extremely large number in the denominator. Ordinarily the sum in Eq. (4.25) will be essentially determined by the first few terms. Even if Eq. (4.26) properly described the contribution of the higher-order terms, only when z got extremely close to b_0^{-1} would the large size of the integral evaluated in Eq. (4.26) become important, and then its effect would come in very suddenly. This is equivalent to saying that up to the condensation point large clusters play no role, then their effect suddenly becomes evident.

REFERENCES

1. J. E. Mayer and M. G. Mayer, *Statistical Mechanics*, New York, Wiley, 1940, Chaps. 12, 13, 14.
2. W. G. McMillan, Jr. and J. E. Mayer, *J. Chem. Phys.*, **13**, 276 (1945).
3. T. L. Hill, *An Introduction to Statistical Thermodynamics*, Reading, Mass., Addison-Wesley, 1960, Chap. 19.
4. O. K. Rice, in F. D. Rossini, ed., *Thermodynamics and Physics of Matter*, Princeton, N.J., Princeton Univ. Press, ©1955.
5. G. E. Uhlenbeck and G. W. Ford, in J. de Boer and G. E. Uhlenbeck, eds., *Studies in Statistical Mechanics*, Vol. 1, Amsterdam, North-Holland, 1962, part B.
6. R. B. Bird, E. L. Spots, and J. O. Hirschfelder, *J. Chem. Phys.*, **18**, 1395 (1950).
7. J. A. Beattie, in G. A. Cook, ed., *Argon, Helium and the Rare Gases*, New York, Interscience, 1961, Chap. 8.
8. K. Ikeda, *Prog. Theor. Phys.*, **16**, 341 (1956).
9. T. Yosida and K. Ikeda, *Prog. Theor. Phys.*, **27**, 1025 (1962).
10. H. N. V. Temperley, *Proc. Phys. Soc.* (London), **A67**, 233 (1954).
11. H. Margenau and G. M. Murphy, *The Mathematics of Physics and Chemistry*, 2d ed., Princeton, N.J., Van Nostrand, 1956, p. 97.
12. R. C. Tolman, *Statistical Mechanics with Application to Physics and Chemistry*, New York, Chemical Catalog Co., 1927, pp. 128–30.
13. J. E. Mayer and S. F. Harrison, *J. Chem. Phys.*, **6**, 87 (1938).

14. M. Born and K. Fuchs, *Proc. Roy. Soc.* (London), **A166,** 391 (1938).
15. B. O. Peirce, *A Short Table of Integrals*, 3d ed., Boston, Ginn, 1929, Nos. 481 and 493.

PROBLEMS

11.1. According to the statement made in explanation of Fig. 9-2, we transformed $d\tau_1 = dx_1 dy_1 dz_1$ to $d(x_1 - x_2)d(y_1 - y_2)d(z_1 - z_2)$; that is to say, part of the change of variables consisted of the transformation $x_1' = x_1 - x_2$, $y_1' = y_1 - y_2$, $z_1' = z_1 - z_2$. Write out the complete transformation as described in the paragraph explaining Fig. 9-2, and show that the Jacobian is equal to 1.

11.2. From Eqs. (1.9) and (1.18) with Eq. (3.2) of Chap. 8, show, with the aid of a proper change of variables, that $C/(\frac{2}{3}\pi r_0^3)^2$ depends only on T^* of Chap. 8. C is the third virial coefficient.

11.3. Evaluate (P.F.) roughly by assuming that the sum in Eq. (2.5) can be replaced by its largest term under the condition $\sum_l m_l l = N$. Then obtain Eq. (2.9) from this approximate value of (P.F.). [Evaluate the Lagrange multiplier from the condition and compare with Eq. (2.8).]

11.4. By starting to solve Eq. (2.8) for z, to get a series in $\bar{N}/V$, find the first terms in the series expansion of P as a function of $\bar{N}/V$, and show that the terms up to the third virial coefficient agree with Eq. (1.18).

11.5. Consider the contribution of the term involving β_2^2 to b_5. Set up the various combinations of suffixes giving distinct terms in the integrand of Eq. (1.7) and show that Eq. (3.2) does indeed give the number of different ways of getting a term equal to $V(2!\beta_2)^2$ into the expression for $5!Vb_5$.

11.6. Consider the linkages in a term $\beta_3\beta_2^4$ in which two of the β_2 groups have only one linkage, and therefore will come at the end of the sequence described after Eq. (3.3). Number the molecules arbitrarily. Arrange the subsets in a fixed preliminary order, which is not to be changed. Show that you can find two distinct orders for the linkages which give the same diagram up to the point at which the last two groups are attached, so that the contributions to the integrand differ only in that part. Work this out for a pair of diagrams in which 1 is not a linkage, and for a pair in which 1 is the first linkage.

Chapter 12

Mixtures: Order–Disorder Phenomena

12-1. *Ideal Solutions*

In earlier chapters we have at a number of points noted how our equations must be modified in order that they might apply to mixtures. We have dealt in detail only with ideal gases. In particular, we have noted that, if N_A molecules of one species of gas are mixed with N_B molecules of another species (both samples and the final mixture at the same pressure), there is an entropy of mixing given by

$$\Delta S_m = -kN_A \ln \frac{N_A}{N} - kN_B \ln \frac{N_B}{N}$$
$$= -kN(x_A \ln x_A + x_B \ln x_B), \tag{1.1}$$

where $N = N_A + N_B$, and where x_A and x_B are the mole fractions. This of course, as noted before, represents an increase in entropy ($x_A < 1$ and $x_B < 1$) that arises from the increase in available volume for each type of molecule when the mixing occurs. It would not occur if the A species and B species were identical, for it would be cancelled out because the factor $N!$ would then appear in the denominator of the partition function for the mixture, replacing the factor $N_A!N_B!$ which occurs in the denominator of the product of the partition functions of the separate gases. Conversely, we may think of the partition function of the mixture as being formed from the partition function which would exist if A and B were identical, by multiplication by the factor $N!/N_A!N_B!$, which is the total number of distinguishable arrangements of N_A molecules of type A and N_B molecules of type B.

One of the characteristics of an ideal-gas mixture is the fact that the mixing takes place without change of energy, i.e., $\Delta E_m = 0$. Furthermore, if the entropy of mixing arises from the term $N!/N_A!N_B!$ (the number of distinguishable exchanges), we can say that, aside from any effect arising from this term, each molecule has the same free volume in the mixture as it had in the pure gas at the same pressure. A similar situation will occur in a liquid or solid mixture if two molecules A and B are so nearly alike that the force fields are virtually identical (also the force field for A–B is the same as that for A–A and B–B). In this case the free volume for A in either pure A or an A–B mixture will be the same as that of B in pure B or an A–B mixture. The free volumes of A and B will not change from one composition to another, and the only change in entropy will be due to the exchange factor $N!/N_A!N_B!$, and ΔS_m will be given by Eq. (1.1). A solution of this type is called an "ideal" or "perfect" solution.

Relatively few pairs of molecular species (outside of those which differ only in their isotopic composition) are so nearly alike as to form an ideal or nearly ideal solution. Nevertheless, the ideal solution is a useful standard, and we shall derive some of its properties.

We define $(\text{p.f.})_A$ and $(\text{p.f.})_B$ by the equations, which apply to the pure liquids:

$$(\text{P.F.})_A = (\text{p.f.})_A^{N_A}, \quad \text{and} \quad (\text{P.F.})_B = (\text{p.f.})_B^{N_B};\tag{1.2}$$

$(\text{p.f.})_A$ and $(\text{p.f.})_B$ are, of course, proportional to the respective free volumes (see Sec. 3-5). We do not need to divide through by $N_A!$ and $N_B!$, since $(\text{p.f.})_A$ and $(\text{p.f.})_B$ are localized partition functions, as explained in Sec. 7-9. Since in an ideal solution the free volumes do not depend on the composition, we can write for the partition function of the solution

$$(\text{P.F.}) = (\text{p.f.})_A^{N_A}(\text{p.f.})_B^{N_B} \frac{N!}{N_A!N_B!}.\tag{1.3}$$

We then find

$$\mu_A = -kT\left(\frac{\partial \ln(\text{P.F.})}{\partial N_A}\right)_{T,V,N_B}$$

$$= -kT \ln(\text{p.f.})_A + kT \ln\left(\frac{N_A}{N}\right)$$

$$= \mu_A^0 + kT \ln x_A,\tag{1.4}$$

where x_A is the mole fraction of species A and μ_A^0 is the chemical potential of pure A. In obtaining Eq. (1.4), we remember that $N = N_A + N_B$ and changes when N_A changes if N_B is held fixed. Similarly, we have

$$\mu_B = \mu_B^0 + kT \ln x_B. \tag{1.5}$$

In carrying out the differentiation to obtain Eq. (1.4) we have neglected the terms

$$-N_A kT \left[\frac{\partial \ln (\text{p.f.})_A}{\partial N_A} \right]_{T,V,N_B} - N_B kT \left[\frac{\partial \ln (\text{p.f.})_B}{\partial N_A} \right]_{T,V,N_B}.$$

In an ideal solution $(\text{p.f.})_A$ and $(\text{p.f.})_B$ are independent of the composition, but may be expected to depend on the density, which changes if N_A changes at constant V. Further addition of B molecules at constant volume will have the same or nearly the same effect as addition of A molecules. Thus we can replace these terms by

$$-N_A kT \left[\frac{\partial \ln (\text{p.f.})_A}{\partial N_A} \right]_{T,V,N_B} - N_B kT \left[\frac{\partial \ln (\text{p.f.})_B}{\partial N_B} \right]_{T,V,N_A}$$

$$= -\frac{N_A}{V} kT \left[\frac{\partial \ln (\text{p.f.})_A}{\partial (N_A/V_A)} \right]_{T,V_A} - \frac{N_B}{V} kT \left[\frac{\partial \ln (\text{p.f.})_B}{\partial (N_B/V_D)} \right]_{T,V_B},$$

where V_A or V_B is the volume of N_A or N_B molecules of pure A or pure B. The change of $\ln (\text{p.f.})_A$, for example, with a given change in N_A will depend inversely on the volume in which the change occurs, thus the correction factor V_A/V must be included. If $(\text{p.f.})_A$ depends only on N_A/V_A and $(\text{p.f.})_B$ on N_B/V_B, the expression may be rewritten

$$-\frac{kT}{V} \left[\frac{\partial \ln (\text{p.f.})_A}{\partial (1/V_A)} \right]_{T,N_A} - \frac{kT}{V} \left[\frac{\partial \ln (\text{p.f.})_B}{\partial (1/V_B)} \right]_{T,N_B}$$

$$= \frac{V_A^2}{V} kT \left[\frac{\partial \ln (\text{p.f.})_A}{\partial V_A} \right]_{T,N_A} + \frac{V_B^2}{V} kT \left[\frac{\partial \ln (\text{p.f.})_B}{\partial V_B} \right]_{T,N_B}$$

$$= -\frac{V_A^2}{V N_A} \left(\frac{\partial A_A}{\partial V_A} \right)_{T,N_A} - \frac{V_B^2}{V N_B} \left(\frac{\partial A_B}{\partial V_B} \right)_{T,N_B}$$

$$= \frac{P V_A^2}{V N_A} + \frac{P V_B^2}{V N_B}.$$

For liquids under ordinary conditions, the products $P V_A/N_A$ and $P V_B/N_B$ are always small compared with kT. Therefore the neglected terms are negligible.

At equilibrium, the chemical potential of the vapor of species A must be equal to the chemical potential of A in the solution. Let us suppose the vapor to be an ideal gas, and let us set the vapor pressure of the pure liquid A equal to P_A^0. For the vapor (see Sec. 6-3, remembering that (p.f.) is proportional to the volume)

$$\mu_A = kT \ln \frac{N_A}{V_A} + \text{const.}$$

$$= kT \ln P_A - kT \ln kT + \text{const.},$$

where here N_A, V_A and P_A refer to the vapor phase. Hence

$$\mu_A - \mu_A^0 = kT(\ln P_A - \ln P_A^0)$$

$$= kT \ln \frac{P_A}{P_A^0}. \tag{1.6}$$

From Eq. (1.4), then, for an ideal solution, the vapor pressure is given by

$$\frac{P_A}{P_A^0} = x_A \tag{1.7}$$

and, similarly,

$$\frac{P_B}{P_B^0} = x_B. \tag{1.8}$$

These equations give rise to the typical vapor-pressure diagram for an ideal solution (a solution obeying Raoult's law), as shown in Fig. 12-1.

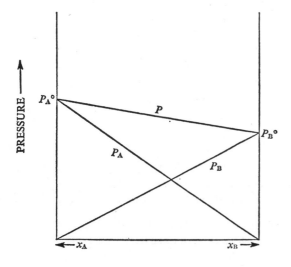

Figure 12-1. Vapor pressure and partial vapor pressures of an ideal solution.

12-2. *Regular Solutions*

Although two kinds of molecules are seldom so much alike that we can use the ideal-solution law, the molecules are often similar enough so that we can use Eq. (1.1) to get an approximate value for ΔS_m, even though we cannot set ΔE_m equal to zero. Such solutions are called regular solutions.

These assumptions are equivalent to setting

$$(\text{P.F.}) = (\text{p.f.})_A^{N_A}(\text{p.f.})_B^{N_B} \exp\left\{\frac{-\Delta E_m}{kT}\right\} \frac{N!}{N_A!N_B!}. \tag{2.1}$$

There are several inconsistencies involved here. In the first place, if the interactions A–A, B–B, and A–B are different, one could hardly expect $(\text{p.f.})_A$ and $(\text{p.f.})_B$ to remain independent of concentration, as is implied here. Second, since the various ones of the $N!/N_A!N_B!$ arrangements will correspond to different numbers of A–A, B–B, and A–B contacts between neighboring molecules, they will not all have the same energy, and should be weighted accordingly. Nevertheless the approximation is a useful one, and its utility has been shown in an extensive series of investigations by Hildebrand and his collaborators [1].†

To use Eq. (2.1) for calculating properties of solutions, we need to make some estimate of ΔE_m as a function of the concentration. Let us suppose that A and B are sufficiently similar in size so that the average number of nearest neighbors of a molecule either of type A or type B, is z, and that this does not depend on composition or temperature. There will, then, be a total of $zN/2$ nearest-neighbor contacts of which we will say that $N_{\alpha\alpha}$ are A–A contacts, $N_{\beta\beta}$ are B–B contacts, and $N_{\alpha\beta}$ are A–B contacts. The N_A molecules of type A will have altogether $N_{\alpha\alpha} + N_{\alpha\beta}$ nearest-neighbor contacts and the N_B of type B will have $N_{\beta\beta} + N_{\alpha\beta}$. Since the A–A and B–B contacts are shared between two like molecules, it may be seen that

$$zN_A = 2N_{\alpha\alpha} + N_{\alpha\beta}, \quad \text{and} \quad zN_B = 2N_{\beta\beta} + N_{\alpha\beta}. \tag{2.2}$$

We shall assume that the potential energy (i.e., the energy the system would have if all atoms were in their equilibrium positions) depends only upon the nearest-neighbor contacts, and that each A–A contact has on the average a potential energy $\epsilon_{\alpha\alpha}$, each B–B a potential

---

† A number of books and articles deal with various aspects of the theory discussed in the present chapter and with the relevant experimental material, for example, [2, 3].

energy $\epsilon_{\mathcal{BB}}$, and each A–B a potential energy $\epsilon_{\alpha\mathcal{B}}$. If the N_A molecules of type A and the N_B molecules of type B formed pure liquids the total energies would be, respectively,

$$E_A = \frac{zN_A}{2}\epsilon_{\alpha\alpha} \quad \text{and} \quad E_B = \frac{zN_B}{2}\epsilon_{\mathcal{BB}}. \tag{2.3}$$

The energy of the mixture (aside from the local thermal energy implied in $(\text{p.f.})_A$ and $(\text{p.f.})_B$, which does not change on mixing) will be

$$E = N_{\alpha\alpha}\epsilon_{\alpha\alpha} + N_{\mathcal{BB}}\epsilon_{\mathcal{BB}} + N_{\alpha\mathcal{B}}\epsilon_{\alpha\mathcal{B}}, \tag{2.4}$$

and for the energy of mixing we will have

$$\begin{aligned}
\Delta E_m &= E - E_A - E_B \\
&= N_{\alpha\alpha}\epsilon_{\alpha\alpha} + N_{\mathcal{BB}}\epsilon_{\mathcal{BB}} + N_{\alpha\mathcal{B}}\epsilon_{\alpha\mathcal{B}} - \frac{zN_A}{2}\epsilon_{\alpha\alpha} - \frac{zN_B}{2}\epsilon_{\mathcal{BB}} \\
&= N_{\alpha\mathcal{B}}\left(\epsilon_{\alpha\mathcal{B}} - \frac{\epsilon_{\alpha\alpha} + \epsilon_{\mathcal{BB}}}{2}\right),
\end{aligned} \tag{2.5}$$

by Eqs. (2.2). If the mixing is random, as supposed for a regular solution, we may find an average value for $N_{\alpha\mathcal{B}}$. Of the z molecules surrounding an A molecule, on the average a fraction N_B/N will be of type B. There will, therefore, be altogether zN_AN_B/N contacts of the A–B type, and we will have

$$\begin{aligned}
\Delta E_m &= \frac{zN_AN_B\Delta\epsilon}{N} \\
&= zNx_Ax_B\Delta\epsilon,
\end{aligned} \tag{2.6}$$

where

$$\Delta\epsilon = \epsilon_{\alpha\mathcal{B}} - \frac{\epsilon_{\alpha\alpha} + \epsilon_{\mathcal{BB}}}{2} \tag{2.7}$$

is the excess of energy of a contact of the A–B type over the average for the A–A and B–B types. If $\Delta\epsilon$ is negative, there tends to be more attraction between unlike than between like molecules, while if $\Delta\epsilon$ is positive the reverse is true. If the latter is true, there can be a tendency for separation of phases.

Equation (2.6) clearly gives the required relation between ΔE_m and the composition. It can be combined with Eq. (1.1) to obtain a relation for the excess free energy,

$$\Delta A_m = N_A kT \ln \frac{N_A}{N} + N_B kT \ln \frac{N_B}{N} + \frac{zN_A N_B \Delta \epsilon}{N}$$

$$= NkT(x_A \ln x_A + x_B \ln x_B) + zN x_A x_B \Delta \epsilon. \tag{2.8}$$

The only difference between ΔA_m for a regular solution and ΔA_m for an ideal solution is the last term in Eq. (2.8). The chemical potentials will therefore differ from those for an ideal solution only through terms derived from this last part of Eq. (2.8). We find

$$\mu_A = \mu_A^0 + kT \ln x_A + zx_B^2 \Delta \epsilon$$

$$\mu_B = \mu_B^0 + kT \ln x_B + zx_A^2 \Delta \epsilon. \tag{2.9}$$

The corresponding vapor pressures, assuming an ideal gas, are [see Eq. (1.6)]

$$\frac{P_A}{P_A^0} = x_A \exp\left\{\frac{zx_B^2 \Delta \epsilon}{kT}\right\},$$

$$\frac{P_B}{P_B^0} = x_B \exp\left\{\frac{zx_A^2 \Delta \epsilon}{kT}\right\}. \tag{2.10}$$

It is clear that if $\Delta \epsilon > 0$, then P_A/P_A^0 and P_B/P_B^0 are greater than their ideal values; this is described as a positive deviation from Raoult's law. Conversely, $\Delta \epsilon < 0$ results in a negative deviation from Raoult's law.

Partial pressures for regular solutions are plotted as functions of x_B in Figs. 12-2 and 12-3.

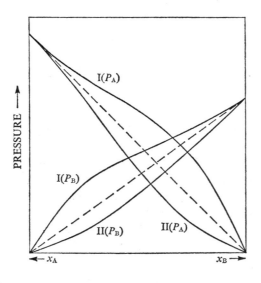

Figure 12-2. Partial vapor pressures of a solution (I) showing positive deviations from Raoult's law, and of a solution (II) showing negative deviations.

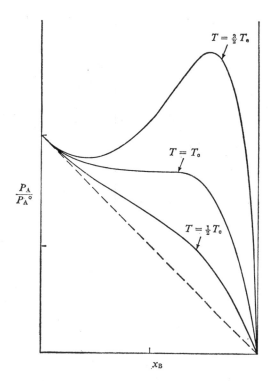

$$T = \tfrac{3}{2} T_\circ$$

$$T = T_\circ$$

$$T = \tfrac{1}{2} T_\circ$$

$\dfrac{P_A}{P_A{}^\circ}$

x_B

Figure 12-3. Partial vapor pressures of component A of a solution showing positive deviations from Raoult's law, at several temperatures.

If $\Delta\epsilon/kT$ is positive and large enough, there will be conditions under which dP_A/dx_A, for example, is negative; this represents an unstable condition and will result in the separation of two phases, as mentioned above. Indeed, we find from Eq. (2.10), recalling that dx_A is always equal to $-dx_B$,

$$\frac{d(P_A/P_A^0)}{dx_A} = \left(1 - 2zx_Ax_B \frac{\Delta\epsilon}{kT}\right) \exp\left\{\frac{zx_B^2\Delta\epsilon}{kT}\right\}. \tag{2.11}$$

For that portion (if any) of the range of concentrations for which

$$2zx_Ax_B \frac{\Delta\epsilon}{kT} > 1 \tag{2.12}$$

this derivative will be negative. The curve for P_A/P_A^0 against x_B will have an inflection somewhere in this range. When $T = z\Delta\epsilon/2k$, the inflection point and the one point (since $x_Ax_B \leq \tfrac{1}{4}$) where the derivative vanishes coincide. For T greater than this value the derivative will be always positive. Thus the condition for the critical point is

$$T_c = \frac{z\Delta\epsilon}{2k}. \tag{2.13}$$

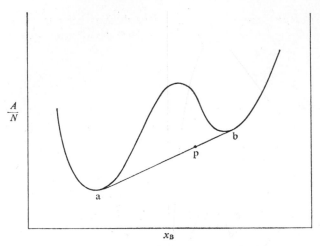

Figure 12-4. Illustrating determination of phase equilibrium using curve of average molecular free energy *vs.* mole fraction, at constant volume.

The conditions for equilibrium between coexisting phases is illustrated in Fig. 12-4, in which † A/N is plotted against x_B. This figure does not presuppose the symmetry with respect to concentration which appears in the equations of this section, which arises from the symmetry which we have put into our assumptions, and which does not necessarily hold in actual cases. Any point p on the common tangent to the points a and b gives the free energy per molecule [i.e., $A_{tot}/(N_{A,tot} + N_{B,tot})$] of the two phases having the compositions indicated by a and b, whose over-all composition is that of p. It will be observed that the free energy for this two-phase system is less than that of the one-phase system given by the original curve; therefore the two-phase system will be the more stable.

When the curve is symmetrical with respect to the composition, the common tangent will touch the A/N curve at its minima. Since ΔA_m is the only concentration-dependent contribution to the free energy of the mixture, we may differentiate $\Delta A_m/N$ with respect to x_A (remembering that $x_B = 1 - x_A$). From Eq. (2.8), then, we find for the condition that a phase be capable of coexistence with another phase,

$$\frac{\partial(\Delta A_m/N)}{dx_A} = kT \ln \frac{x_A}{x_B} + z(x_B - x_A)\Delta\epsilon = 0. \tag{2.14}$$

† More properly, G/N should be plotted against x_B at constant pressure, but in a condensed phase at low pressure, A/N at constant density may be used instead.

Note that this equation always has a solution at $x_A = x_B = \frac{1}{2}$. Its more general behavior can be deduced from the second derivative

$$\frac{\partial^2(\Delta A_m/N)}{\partial x_A^2} = \frac{kT}{x_A x_B} - 2z\Delta\epsilon. \tag{2.15}$$

If T is greater than $T_c = z\Delta\epsilon/2k$, this derivative will be positive at the midpoint, $x_A = x_B = \frac{1}{2}$, and a minimum will occur there. Since $x_A x_B$ has its greatest value at $x_A = x_B = \frac{1}{2}$, the curvature of the ΔA_m curve will always be positive if $T > T_c$, and there will be but one minimum. If $T < T_c$, there will be a *maximum* at the midpoint of the concentration range, but, because of the decreasing value of $x_A x_B$ as $x_A \longrightarrow 0$ or as $x_A \longrightarrow 1$, the curvature of ΔA_m will eventually change signs on both sides of the midpoint. Since $\partial(\Delta A_m/N)/\partial x_A$ is clearly negative at $x_A = 0$ (indeed has a logarithmic negative infinity), and similarly for $\partial(\Delta A_m/N)/\partial x_B$ at $x_B = 0$, it is seen that $\Delta A_m/N$ will in this case have two minima symmetrically placed with respect to the middle of the concentration range. The values of x_A at these minima will give the compositions of the coexisting phases.

If we replace $\Delta\epsilon$ in Eq. (2.14) by the value obtained from Eq. (2.13), then Eq. (2.14) can be reduced to

$$\frac{T}{T_c} = \frac{2(x_B - x_A)}{\ln x_B - \ln x_A}. \tag{2.16}$$

At $x_A = x_B = \frac{1}{2}$ the right-hand side of Eq. (2.16) is an indeterminate form. It can be readily evaluated by differentiating numerator and denominator, and gives $T/T_c = 1$ at $x_A = x_B = \frac{1}{2}$, as it should. In general, Eq. (2.16) can be solved for T/T_c as a function of x_A, so that the coexistence curve can be obtained. To see the nature of these solutions, it is best to expand the two terms in the denominator as Taylor series about the point $x_A = x_B = \frac{1}{2}$. Since $x_B - x_A = 2(x_B - \frac{1}{2}) = -2(x_A - \frac{1}{2})$, this may readily be seen to give

$$\frac{T}{T_c} = \frac{2(x_B - x_A)}{2(x_B - x_A) + \frac{2}{3}(x_B - x_A)^3 + \frac{2}{5}(x_B - x_A)^5 + \cdots}$$

$$= 1 - \frac{1}{3}(x_B - x_A)^2 - \frac{4}{45}(x_B - x_A)^4 + \cdots$$

or

$$\frac{T_c - T}{T_c} = \frac{1}{3}(x_B - x_A)^2 + \frac{4}{45}(x_B - x_A)^4 + \cdots. \tag{2.17}$$

At any given temperature less than T_c this equation has two solutions, with $x_B - x_A$ positive or negative, which correspond to the compositions of the two coexisting phases. Because of the complete symmetry it is seen that $(x_B - x_A)^2$ for either of the phases is equal to $(x_A'' - x_A')^2$, where x_A'' is the mole fraction of A in one of the phases and x_A' is that in the other. Thus we may write Eq. (2.17) in the form

$$\frac{T_c - T}{T_c} = \frac{1}{3}(x_A'' - x_A')^2 + \frac{4}{45}(x_A'' - x_A')^4 + \cdots. \tag{2.18}$$

In addition to the fact that, in general, solubility curves are not symmetrical with respect to the concentration axis, this result has one fundamental defect—it does not give even a qualitatively correct description of the experimentally determined solubility curves in the neighborhood of the critical point. These curves have almost invariably a form which is closely described by setting $T_c - T$ proportional to $|(x_A'' - x_A')^3|$. Since $(x_A'' - x_A')^3$ changes sign at $x_A'' = x_A' = \frac{1}{2}$, the absolute value sign is needed, and a discontinuity is implied at the critical point.

In spite of these deficiencies, the theory does at least give the phase separation and a critical point. We shall now examine further the predicted values of certain thermodynamic quantities. Let us consider a solution of equimolar composition, so that $x_A = x_B = \frac{1}{2}$. As long as we have a homogeneous phase, the specific heat of mixing, ΔC_m, will be zero, provided $\Delta\epsilon$ is temperature independent, as may be seen from Eq. (2.6). Below the critical temperature, however, we have two coexisting phases of different composition. The total energy of mixing, which is divided equally between the two phases, is

$$\Delta E_m = \tfrac{1}{2}zN(x_A' x_B' + x_A'' x_B'')\Delta\epsilon, \tag{2.19}$$

and the resulting specific heat of mixing of the two phases will be

$$\Delta C_m = \frac{d\Delta E_m}{dT} = \frac{1}{2}zN\Delta\epsilon\left[(x_B' - x_A')\frac{dx_A'}{dT} + (x_A'' - x_B'')\frac{dx_B''}{dT}\right]$$

$$= zN\Delta\epsilon(x_B' - x_A')\frac{dx_A'}{dT}. \tag{2.20}$$

The two terms in the bracket are equal because of the symmetry with respect to concentration. From Eq. (2.17), we get

$$\frac{1}{T_c} = \frac{4}{3}(x_B' - x_A')\frac{dx_A'}{dT} + \frac{32}{45}(x_B' - x_A')^3\frac{dx_A'}{dT} + \cdots,$$

which can be written, using Eq. (2.17) again to get an approximate expression for $(x'_B - x'_A)^2$ to substitute in the second term on the right-hand side,

$$\frac{1}{T_c} = \frac{4}{3}(x'_B - x'_A)\frac{dx'_A}{dT}\left(1 + \frac{8}{5}\frac{T_c - T}{T_c} + \cdots\right),$$

which gives

$$(x'_B - x'_A)\frac{dx'_A}{dT} = \frac{3}{4T_c}\left(1 - \frac{8}{5}\frac{T_c - T}{T_c} + \cdots\right),$$

whence, for T less than T_c

$$\Delta C_m = \frac{3}{4}\frac{zN\Delta\epsilon}{T_c}\left(1 - \frac{8}{5}\frac{T_c - T}{T_c} + \cdots\right), \tag{2.21}$$

and a discontinuity will occur at T_c. A more general expression could be obtained from Eqs. (2.16) and (2.20), but it is quite complicated, and we will not write it down. The general trend of the specific-heat curve, with a comparison with some more exact calculations, is shown in Fig. 12-5.

12-3. *The Quasi-chemical Approximation*

In the preceding section we have proceeded on the assumption that all possible arrangements of the molecules are equally probable. Actually, some of the possible arrangements of molecules are more probable than others because their energies differ. Thus, instead of the purely random arrangement assumed in Sec. 12-2, there will be a more ordered one. As a matter of fact, a certain amount of order did appear in the calculations of Sec. 12-2 in spite of our assumptions, because of the separation of phases at low temperatures. This separation occurs, however, only when $\Delta\epsilon$ is positive. When $\Delta\epsilon$ is negative, however, a tendency toward an ordered state will also exist at low temperatures. In this state the molecules A and B tend to be arranged alternately, especially if they are present in equal numbers.

The energy of any arrangement depends upon the numbers, $N_{\alpha\alpha}$, $N_{\beta\beta}$, and $N_{\alpha\beta}$, of the various kinds of contact. If we let $g(N_{\alpha\alpha}, N_{\beta\beta}, N_{\alpha\beta})$ be the number of possible arrangements having the

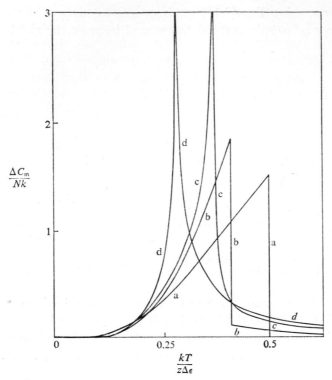

Figure 12-5. Theoretical specific-heat curve for regular solution (a), compared to various other cases and approximations which will be considered later in this chapter: (b) quasi-chemical approximation, $z = 6$; (c) simple cubic lattice $z = 6$, series approximation, after Wakefield [18]; (d) exact solution for two-dimensional square lattice. All are for the case $x_A = x_B = 0.5$, or for the Ising lattice with $H = 0$ (see Sec. 12-8).

specified number of contacts, and $E(N_{\alpha\alpha}, N_{\beta\beta}, N_{\alpha\beta})$ be the corresponding energy, then

$$(\text{P.F.}) = \sum_{N_{\alpha\alpha}, N_{\beta\beta}, N_{\alpha\beta}} \left[(\text{p.f.})_A^{N_A} (\text{p.f.})_B^{N_B} g(N_{\alpha\alpha}, N_{\beta\beta}, N_{\alpha\beta}) \right.$$

$$\left. \times \exp \left\{ \frac{-E(N_{\alpha\alpha}, N_{\beta\beta}, N_{\alpha\beta})}{kT} \right\} \right], \qquad (3.1)$$

where the sum is to be taken over all possible values of $N_{\alpha\alpha}$, $N_{\beta\beta}$, and $N_{\alpha\beta}$, as controlled by Eqs. (2.2). This form is very general, and in order to make calculations it is necessary to specify the model more precisely. According to the model used in Sec. 12-2, in which the two species A and B have essentially the same size (having the same coordination numbers) and can be freely exchanged one for the other, the energy of mixing, ΔE_m, depends only on $N_{\alpha\beta}$, because of Eqs. (2.2). Using this model, then, we may, from Eqs. (2.5) and (2.7) write for the partition function of mixing† (that is, the partition function based on the energy of the separate liquids, with N_A molecules of A and N_B of B, respectively, as the zero of energy, and omitting the internal partition functions of A and B, which are thus assumed to be independent of the composition and configuration.)

$$(\text{P.F.})_m = \sum_{N_{\alpha\beta}} g(N_A, N_B, N_{\alpha\beta}) \exp\left\{\frac{-N_{\alpha\beta}\Delta\epsilon}{kT}\right\}. \tag{3.2}$$

In Eq. (3.2) we changed the designated variables in g from $N_{\alpha\alpha}$, $N_{\beta\beta}$, and $N_{\alpha\beta}$ to N_A, N_B, and $N_{\alpha\beta}$, as may be done by use of Eqs. (2.2). If $g(N_A, N_B, N_{\alpha\beta})$ could be determined, the largest term in the summation of Eq. (3.2) could be taken to approximate $(\text{P.F.})_m$, and the problem would be solved. However, the determination of g is a very difficult problem, and we must consider approximate evaluations.

In Sec. 12-2 we said in effect that the value of $N_{\alpha\beta}$ for this maximum term is given by

$$N_{\alpha\beta} = \frac{zN_AN_B}{N} \tag{3.3}$$

[see the deduction leading to Eq. (2.6)], and that g for this value of $N_{\alpha\beta}$ is equal to $N!/N_A!N_B!$. By using Eqs. (2.2), Eq. (3.3) can be written

$$N_{\alpha\beta} = \frac{(2N_{\alpha\alpha} + N_{\alpha\beta})(2N_{\beta\beta} + N_{\alpha\beta})}{(2N_{\alpha\alpha} + 2N_{\beta\beta} + 2N_{\alpha\beta})},$$

which, solved for $N_{\alpha\beta}$, gives

$$N_{\alpha\beta}^2 = 4N_{\alpha\alpha}N_{\beta\beta}, \tag{3.4}$$

or

$$x_{\alpha\beta}^2 = 4x_{\alpha\alpha}x_{\beta\beta} \tag{3.4a}$$

where $x_{\alpha\beta} = N_{\alpha\beta}/N$, etc. This looks like an equilibrium equation for the "reaction"

$$\text{A–A} + \text{B–B} \longrightarrow 2\text{A–B},$$

† Although it has not been formally so described, what we are presenting is in effect a lattice theory of liquid mixtures. Some different points of view and some attention to theories not covered here may be found in references [4–10].

the "equilibrium constant" being 4. It will be seen, from the definition of $\Delta\epsilon$, that the energy of this reaction is $2\Delta\epsilon$. Equation (3.4) is the correct result if $\Delta\epsilon = 0$. Therefore, by analogy with the case of chemical equilibrium, it suggests itself that we write as an approximation, instead of Eq. (3.4)

$$N_{\alpha\beta}^2 = 4N_{\alpha\alpha}N_{\beta\beta} \exp\left\{\frac{-2\Delta\epsilon}{kT}\right\}. \tag{3.5}$$

This can be only an approximation, since not all individual exchanges of A–A and B–B linkages for A–B linkages can take place independently, there being many more linkages than molecules, which are the primary exchanging entities [11]. It is obvious why Eq. (3.5) is called the quasi-chemical approximation.

Used together with Eqs. (2.2), Eq. (3.5) determines $N_{\alpha\beta}$ for any given values of N_A and N_B; in turn $N_{\alpha\beta}$ determines the thermodynamic properties of the assembly, since the energy of an assembly with a given value of N_A and N_B depends solely on $N_{\alpha\beta}$. Since we are always considering mixtures at low (essentially zero) pressure, the only independent variable, aside from the concentration, is the temperature. In the quasi-chemical approximation $N_{\alpha\beta}$ will depend on the temperature. It

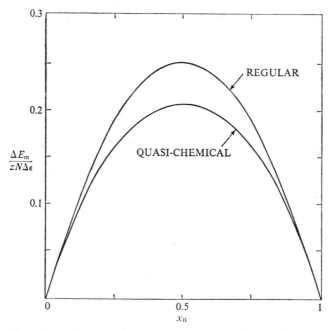

Figure 12-6. Energy of mixing for regular and quasi-chemical solutions.

is also possible that $\epsilon_{\alpha\beta}$, $\epsilon_{\alpha\alpha}$, and $\epsilon_{\beta\beta}$ might depend on the temperature, although $\Delta\epsilon$ is generally taken as temperature independent. With the energy—for practical purposes ΔE_m—determined as a function of temperature, so is ΔC_m, and the changes of ΔS_m with temperature are then also determined. In Fig. 12-6 we show $\Delta E_m/zN\Delta\epsilon$ as a function of x_B for the special case $\exp\{-2\Delta\epsilon/kT\} = \frac{1}{2}$, and contrast it with the same quantity for the regular solution.

If we can set up $(\text{P.F.})_m$ as a sum of terms such that the condition for the maximum term yields Eq. (3.5), and such that the limiting value when $\Delta\epsilon/kT = 0$ is simply the total number of random arrangements, $N!/N_A!N_B!$, we will have a satisfactory description of the quasi-chemical approximation. Such a partition function, which can be found by generalization of a one-dimensional case that can be worked out exactly, is†

$$(\text{P.F.})_m = \sum_{N_{\alpha\beta}} \frac{N!}{N_A!N_B!} \left[\left(\frac{\dfrac{N_A!N_B!}{(2N_{\alpha\alpha}/z)!(2N_{\beta\beta}/z)!(N_{\alpha\beta}/z)!^2}}{N!/N_A!N_B!} \right) \right]^{z/2} \exp\left\{ \frac{-N_{\alpha\beta}\Delta\epsilon}{kT} \right\}.$$
(3.6)

The largest term in the sum is given by differentiating logarithmically with respect to $N_{\alpha\beta}$, noting that N, N_A, and N_B are fixed, and, by Eqs. (2.2) and consistently with the quasi-chemical reaction, that $dN_{\alpha\alpha} = dN_{\beta\beta} = -\frac{1}{2}dN_{\alpha\beta}$. The condition for a maximum is then

$$\left[\frac{1}{2}\ln\frac{2N_{\alpha\alpha}}{z} + \frac{1}{2}\ln\frac{2N_{\beta\beta}}{z} - \ln\frac{N_{\alpha\beta}}{z} - \frac{\Delta\epsilon}{kT} \right] \delta N_{\alpha\beta} = 0.$$
(3.7)

It is readily seen that this reduces to Eq. (3.5).

We shall now show that, if $\Delta\epsilon = 0$, the quantity inside the brackets for the largest term in Eq. (3.6) is equal to 1, or at least that the logarithm vanishes to the degree of accuracy required. Writing out the logarithm of the factor within the brackets, using the Stirling approximation for the factorials, we find

$$2N_A \ln N_A - 2N_A + 2N_B \ln N_B - 2N_B - \frac{2N_{\alpha\alpha}}{z}\ln\frac{2N_{\alpha\alpha}}{z} + \frac{2N_{\alpha\alpha}}{z}$$

$$- \frac{2N_{\beta\beta}}{z}\ln\frac{2N_{\beta\beta}}{z} + \frac{2N_{\beta\beta}}{z} - \frac{2N_{\alpha\beta}}{z}\ln\frac{N_{\alpha\beta}}{z} + \frac{2N_{\alpha\beta}}{z}$$

$$- N \ln N + N.$$
(3.8)

† See [5, pp. 318–21; 12]. Based on Ising [13].

Recalling that $N = N_A + N_B$ and using Eqs. (2.2), we get

$$2N_A \ln N_A + 2N_B \ln N_B - N \ln N$$
$$- \frac{2N_{\alpha\alpha}}{z} \ln \frac{2N_{\alpha\alpha}}{z} - \frac{2N_{\beta\beta}}{z} \ln \frac{2N_{\beta\beta}}{z} - \frac{N_{\alpha\beta}}{z} \ln \left(\frac{N_{\alpha\beta}}{z}\right)^2. \tag{3.9}$$

For the maximum term, Eq. (3.7) holds and permits a further reduction to

$$2N_A \ln N_A + 2N_B \ln N_B - N \ln N$$
$$- \frac{2N_{\alpha\alpha} + N_{\alpha\beta}}{z} \ln \frac{2N_{\alpha\alpha}}{z} - \frac{2N_{\beta\beta} + N_{\alpha\beta}}{z} \ln \frac{2N_{\beta\beta}}{z} + \frac{2N_{\alpha\beta}}{z} \frac{\Delta\epsilon}{kT}$$
$$= 2N_A \ln N_A + 2N_B \ln N_B - N \ln N$$
$$- N_A \ln \frac{2N_{\alpha\alpha}}{z} - N_B \ln \frac{2N_{\beta\beta}}{z} + \frac{2N_{\alpha\beta}}{z} \frac{\Delta\epsilon}{kT} \tag{3.10}$$

by Eqs. (2.2). If $\Delta\epsilon/kT = 0$ we have random mixing and we may set $N_{\alpha\alpha} = zN_A$ times fraction of A neighbors divided by $2 = (zN_A/2)N_A/N = zN_A^2/2N$, and similarly $N_{\beta\beta} = zN_B^2/2N$. With this substitution the last expression is seen to vanish so, thus far, Eq. (3.6) has the required properties.

We can now verify that $\ln (\text{P.F.})_m$ has the right temperature coefficient; then it must have the correct value at all temperatures, at least as long as $N_{\alpha\alpha}$, $N_{\beta\beta}$, and $N_{\alpha\beta}$ are all large enough to use the Stirling approximation. We know that ΔE_m is equal to $N_{\alpha\beta}\Delta\epsilon$. We also know that

$$kT^2 \frac{\partial \ln (\text{P.F.})_m}{\partial T} = \Delta E_m. \tag{3.11}$$

Differentiating the largest term in the sum in Eq. (3.6), we have

$$\frac{\partial \ln (\text{P.F.})_m}{\partial T} = -\frac{dN_{\alpha\alpha}}{dT} \ln \frac{2N_{\alpha\alpha}}{z} - \frac{dN_{\beta\beta}}{dT} \ln \frac{2N_{\beta\beta}}{z}$$
$$- \frac{dN_{\alpha\beta}}{dT} \ln \frac{N_{\alpha\beta}}{z} - \frac{dN_{\alpha\beta}}{dT} \frac{\Delta\epsilon}{kT} + \frac{N_{\alpha\beta}\Delta\epsilon}{kT^2}. \tag{3.12}$$

By Eqs. (2.2),

$$\frac{dN_{\alpha\alpha}}{dT} = \frac{dN_{\beta\beta}}{dT} = -\frac{1}{2}\frac{dN_{\alpha\beta}}{dT}. \tag{3.13}$$

Substituting for $dN_{\alpha\alpha}/dT$ and $dN_{\beta\beta}/dT$ in Eq. (3.12), we see from

Eq. (3.7) that all the terms on the right-hand side of Eq. (3.12) cancel except the last. Therefore ΔE_m does come out to be equal to $N_{\alpha\beta}\Delta\epsilon$, and $\ln$ (P.F.)$_m$ has the proper temperature dependence.

The expression for (P.F.)$_m$ can be used to calculate the thermodynamic properties of the system, it being essentially equivalent to Eq. (3.5), which, as we have seen, determines all the properties except the absolute value of the entropy, which is determined by assuming random mixing at high temperatures ($\Delta\epsilon/kT = 0$).

We shall use (P.F.)$_m$ to determine the critical temperature for the quasi-chemical approximation. To do this, it is simplest to go back to Eq. (3.6), writing out the logarithm of the largest term, which gives the equilibrium values of $N_{\alpha\alpha}$, $N_{\beta\beta}$, and $N_{\alpha\beta}$. We find

$$\ln \text{(P.F.)}_m = \left(1 - \frac{z}{2}\right) \ln N! - (1 - z) \ln N_A! - (1 - z) \ln N_B!$$

$$- \frac{z}{2} \ln \left(\frac{2N_{\alpha\alpha}}{z}\right)! - \frac{z}{2} \ln \left(\frac{2N_{\beta\beta}}{z}\right)! - z \ln \left(\frac{N_{\alpha\beta}}{z}\right)! - \frac{N_{\alpha\beta}\Delta\epsilon}{kT}. \quad (3.14)$$

Since this is the largest term, $N_{\alpha\alpha}$, $N_{\beta\beta}$, and $N_{\alpha\beta}$ will satisfy Eq. (3.5) as well as Eqs. (2.2).

We wish to find the maxima of Eq. (3.14) with respect to N_A, holding N constant, so that $dN_A = -dN_B$. (This is equivalent to expressing $\ln$ (P.F.)$_m/N$ as a function of x_A and x_B and allowing them to vary.) Because of symmetry, $\ln$ (P.F.)$_m$ will have a maximum or a minimum at $N_A = N_B = N/2$. Differentiating Eq. (3.14), using the Stirling approximation, we find

$$\frac{d \ln \text{(P.F.)}_m}{dN_A} = -(1 - z) \ln N_A + (1 - z) \ln N_B$$

$$- \frac{dN_{\alpha\alpha}}{dN_A} \ln \frac{2N_{\alpha\alpha}}{z} - \frac{dN_{\beta\beta}}{dN_A} \ln \frac{2N_{\beta\beta}}{z} - \frac{dN_{\alpha\beta}}{dN_A} \ln \frac{N_{\alpha\beta}}{z} - \frac{dN_{\alpha\beta}}{dN_A} \frac{\Delta\epsilon}{kT}. \quad (3.15)$$

By Eqs. (2.2)

$$2\frac{dN_{\alpha\alpha}}{dN_A} = z - \frac{dN_{\alpha\beta}}{dN_A}, \quad \text{and} \quad 2\frac{dN_{\beta\beta}}{dN_A} = -z - \frac{dN_{\alpha\beta}}{dN_A}. \quad (3.16)$$

If these are used to eliminate $dN_{\alpha\alpha}/dN_A$ and $dN_{\beta\beta}/dN_A$ from Eq. (3.15), it will be observed that the factor multiplying $dN_{\alpha\beta}/dN_A$ vanishes because of Eq. (3.5) or (3.7), and Eq. (3.15) reduces to

$$\frac{d \ln \text{(P.F.)}_m}{dN_A} = (1 - z) \ln \frac{N_B}{N_A} + \frac{z}{2} \ln \frac{N_{\beta\beta}}{N_{\alpha\alpha}}. \quad (3.17)$$

Differentiating this once more, still taking $dN_A = -dN_B$

$$\frac{d^2 \ln (\text{P.F.})_m}{dN_A^2} = \frac{z-1}{N_A} + \frac{z-1}{N_B} - \frac{z}{2N_{\alpha\alpha}}\frac{dN_{\alpha\alpha}}{dN_A} + \frac{z}{2N_{\beta\beta}}\frac{dN_{\beta\beta}}{dN_A}. \tag{3.18}$$

We are interested in these derivatives when $N_A = N_B = N/2$. It is seen that $d \ln (\text{P.F.})_m/dN_A$ vanishes at the midpoint, since $N_{\alpha\alpha}$ and $N_{\beta\beta}$ will also be equal there, so $(\text{P.F.})_m$ is either a maximum or a minimum. Also, by the symmetry, $N_{\alpha\beta}$ must have a maximum where $N_A = N_B$, so $dN_{\alpha\beta}/dN_A = 0$. Thus $dN_{\alpha\alpha}/dN_A = -dN_{\beta\beta}/dN_A = z/2$, by Eqs. (3.16). If these relations are substituted in Eq. (3.18) it becomes

$$\left[\frac{d^2 \ln (\text{P.F.})_m}{dN_A^2}\right]_{N_A = N_B} = \frac{4(z-1)}{N} - \frac{z^2}{2N_{\alpha\alpha}}. \tag{3.19}$$

$N_{\alpha\alpha}$ can be found by solving Eqs. (2.2) and (3.5) simultaneously. This solution is specially easy when $N_A = N_B = N/2$, and at this point it gives

$$N_{\alpha\alpha} = \frac{zN}{4(1 + \exp\{-\Delta\epsilon/kT\})}. \tag{3.20}$$

Thus, finally

$$\left[\frac{d^2 \ln (\text{P.F.})_m}{dN_A^2}\right]_{N_A = N_B} = \frac{2(z-2)}{N} - \frac{2z \exp\{-\Delta\epsilon/kT\}}{N}. \tag{3.21}$$

We will have separation of phases if the free energy is a maximum (and hence $(\text{P.F.})_m$ is a minimum) at $N_A = N_B$. It will occur, therefore, if $d^2 \ln (\text{P.F.})_m/dN_A^2$ is positive, which by Eq. (3.21) will occur if $\Delta\epsilon$ is positive and if T is small. T_c will be given by

$$\exp\left\{\frac{\Delta\epsilon}{kT_c}\right\} = \frac{z}{z-2},$$

or

$$T_c = \frac{\Delta\epsilon/k}{\ln\left[z/(z-2)\right]}. \tag{3.22}$$

Note that Eq. (3.22) will in general give a lower value of T_c than Eq. (2.13). A schematic drawing, illustrating the determination of T_c, is given in Fig. 12-7.

In order to get information about the coexistence curve, it is of course necessary to consider the points other than $N_A = N_B$ at

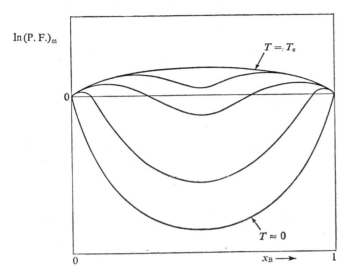

Figure 12-7. Schematic representation of ln $(P.F.)_m$ as a function of mole fraction for the quasi-chemical approximation, for various temperatures, showing the approach to the critical temperature.

which $d \ln (P.F.)_m / dN_A$ vanishes. The two logarithms in Eq. (3.17) may be expanded about the midpoint [much as was the denominator of Eq. (2.16)] to yield

$$\frac{d \ln (P.F.)_m}{dN_A} = 2(1 - z) \frac{N_B - N_A}{N_A + N_B} + z \frac{N_{BB} - N_{\alpha\alpha}}{N_{\alpha\alpha} + N_{BB}}$$

$$+ \frac{2(1 - z)}{3} \left(\frac{N_B - N_A}{N_A + N_B} \right)^3 + \frac{z}{3} \left(\frac{N_{BB} - N_{\alpha\alpha}}{N_{\alpha\alpha} + N_{BB}} \right)^3 + \cdots = 0. \qquad (3.23)$$

Considering only the situation very close to the critical point, we break off the series with the terms shown in Eq. (3.23), use the relation from Eqs. (2.2), $N_{BB} - N_{\alpha\alpha} = (z/2)(N_B - N_A)$, and solve Eq. (3.23) to get the roots that are different from zero. We find

$$(N_B - N_A)^2 = -\frac{[2(1 - z)/N] + [z^2/2(N_{\alpha\alpha} + N_{BB})]}{[2(1 - z)/3N^3] + [z^4/24(N_{\alpha\alpha} + N_{BB})^3]}. \qquad (3.24)$$

By using Eqs. (3.20) and (3.22), we find that the numerator of Eq. (3.24) vanishes at T_c when $N_A = N_B$. Thus $N_B - N_A = 0$ is a solution of Eq. (3.24) when $T = T_c$. When $T = T_c$ but $N_A \neq N_B$, the value of $N_{\alpha\alpha} + N_{BB}$ will differ from its minimum value at $N_B = N_A$ by an amount proportional to $(N_B - N_A)^2$ if $N_B - N_A$ is not too great. Thus the numerator of Eq. (3.24) will be proportional to $(N_B - N_A)^2$, but the proportionality constant will not be equal to 1, so the only solution at $T = T_c$ will be $N_B - N_A = 0$. At T close to but not equal to T_c, the numerator of Eq. (3.24) will not be equal to zero when $N_A = N_B$, but will be proportional to $T_c - T$ [since, by Eq. (3.20), its derivative with respect to T will be finite but nonzero]. Thus $(N_B - N_A)^2$ will be proportional to $T_c - T$, and we have the quadratic coexistence curve, which is always given by approximate treatments of this sort.

The specific-heat curve for $N_A = N_B$ can be calculated for the quasi-chemical approximation in much the same way that it was calculated for the regular solution, and the results, while differing in quantitative details, are much the same qualitatively. The specific heat rises sharply, then drops discontinuously to a lower value. In this case, however, there is a further change with temperature. The curve is shown schematically in Fig. 12-5.

12-4. *The Case with $\Delta\epsilon$ Negative*

If $\Delta\epsilon$ is positive, like molecules attract each other more than unlike molecules, and we have seen that this results in a tendency for a system to separate into two phases at low temperatures. On the basis of some rather rough assumptions we have in certain simple cases been able to calculate an approximate value for the critical mixing temperature.

If $\Delta\epsilon$ is negative, then the situation is reversed: unlike molecules attract each other more than like molecules. We then suppose that at the lowest temperatures there would be a considerable tendency for A molecules to be surrounded by B's, and vice versa. What might ultimately be expected can be seen better for a solid lattice, rather than a liquid. There is, indeed, no reason why the theories developed in this chapter should not hold as well for a solid as for a liquid, or even better. If we have $N_A = N_B$ and certain simple structures, such as a simple cubic lattice or a body-centered cubic lattice, we can readily visualize a situation in which all the nearest neighbors of any given molecule are molecules of the other kind. If $\Delta\epsilon < 0$, this is the structure of lowest energy, and so would be expected to occur at low temperatures. However, it can be shown that the circumstances described lead to difficulties. If we substitute $N_A = N_B = N/2$, $N_{\alpha\alpha} = N_{\beta\beta} = 0$, and hence $N_{\alpha\beta} = zN/2$ into a term of the sum in Eq. (3.6), with $z > 2$ the approximate $g(N_A, N_B, N_{\alpha\beta})$ factor becomes much less than 1. These values of $N_{\alpha\alpha}$, $N_{\beta\beta}$, and $N_{\alpha\beta}$ are, however, the limiting values to be expected when $\Delta\epsilon < 0$ and $T \longrightarrow 0$. We must conclude, therefore, that the form of $g(N_A, N_B, N_{\alpha\beta})$ used in Eq. (3.6) breaks down badly when $N_{\alpha\alpha}$ and

$N_{\mathfrak{B}\mathfrak{B}}$ are small. We ought (if $N_A = N_B$) always have a term in the sum of Eq. (3.6) arising from the one configuration in which all A's are surrounded by B's and all B's by A's. This term will be equal to

$$\exp\left\{\frac{-N_{\alpha\mathfrak{B}}\Delta\epsilon}{kT}\right\} = \exp\left\{\frac{-zN\Delta\epsilon}{2kT}\right\}. \tag{4.1}$$

The maximum term in the sum is obtained by finding an extremum with respect to variation of $N_{\alpha\mathfrak{B}}$, $N_{\alpha\alpha}$, and $N_{\mathfrak{B}\mathfrak{B}}$. Such variations will not in general lead us to a term like (4.1), in which these variables are at the ends of their ranges, and such a term can be larger than the maximum term found by the variation procedure. But so long as it is the largest term in the sum, it will constitute an approximation to the partition function. This suggests, that as a new approximation we simply add the term (4.1) to the sum in Eq. (3.6). At low temperatures, as long as this term remains the predominant one, the specific heat will be zero. When the maximum term from the rest of the sum becomes equal to (4.1) a first-order transition will be predicted, in which a measure of disorder will appear.

If we look critically at the case where $\Delta\epsilon > 0$ and phase separation occurs, we see that a similar situation exists. At very low temperatures the assembly is separated into two phases, in which only A–A or B–B contacts occur. At $0°K$, there is only one state of the system, and again one might think that it would be the stable state until it was overtaken by the state at which $(P.F.)_m$ is maximized. This would have to be true, if only one homogeneous mixed phase were possible. But other conditions of greater stability at the intermediate temperatures become possible through the mutual solubilities. One must, then, inquire whether something similar happens in the case where $\Delta\epsilon$ is negative.

As a matter of fact, in the special case we are considering ($N_A = N_B$ and a simple lattice), there is complete symmetry between the system with $\Delta\epsilon$ positive or negative, and the temperature variation of the thermodynamic properties of the whole system (including both phases if the phases are separated) depends only on the *absolute value* of $\Delta\epsilon$. By using Eqs. (2.2) we may re-express the energy of mixing of such a system:

$$\Delta E_m = N_{\alpha\mathfrak{B}}\Delta\epsilon = \left(\frac{zN}{2} - N_{\alpha\alpha} - N_{\mathfrak{B}\mathfrak{B}}\right)\Delta\epsilon. \tag{4.2}$$

Thus with a given absolute value of $\Delta\epsilon$ the system with negative $\Delta\epsilon$

has the same ΔC_m as a system with positive $\Delta \epsilon$, provided that the number of ways an assembly can be set up with $N_{\alpha\alpha} + N_{\beta\beta}$ equal to some given value, **N**, say, is the same as the number in which it can be set up with $N_{\alpha\beta} = $ **N**. That this will be true will be evident if we can bring systems with a fixed value of $N_{\alpha\alpha} + N_{\beta\beta}$ into one-to-one correspondence with those having the same value of $N_{\alpha\beta}$.

   With a simple lattice, and with $N_A = N_B$, this correspondence can be demonstrated, as illustrated by a two-dimensional case in Fig. 12-8. A simple lattice is one in which the nearest neighbors of a given molecule are not nearest neighbors of each other. We can divide the molecules in such a lattice into groups, such that within any group all molecules are of the same kind and any molecule can be joined to any other molecule by a path consisting of bonds joining nearest neighbors. (Thus the fourth molecule in the bottom row in Fig. 12-8a and the fifth one in the row just above are not in the same group because they are not nearest neighbors, and there is no way to get from one to the other by "stepping on" nearest neighbors of the same kind only.) The number of A–A and B–B contacts is determined within the groups; the number of A–B contacts is determined by the connection with nearest neighbors across the boundaries. Now it will be possible to divide N molecules into groups of the same shape and size, but having alternate A's and B's in the groups (Fig. 12-8b), and groups having a common boundary will be set up to be "out of phase," and if they are out of phase at one place on the boundary they will be out of phase at all points. And if Group I and Group II, say, each have a common boundary with Group III, they cannot have a common boundary with each other—if they did they would not be out of phase (or would not have molecules of different kinds in the first representation—Fig. 12-8a). It is clear that as between these two different arrangements, illustrated by Figs. 12-8a and 12-8b, $N_{\alpha\beta}$ in a is replaced

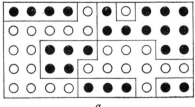

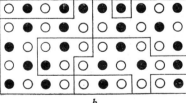

Figure 12-8.

by $N_{\alpha\alpha} + N_{\beta\beta}$ in *b*, and vice versa. Since this correspondence can be set up for any possible arrangement of the assembly as a whole (including an arrangement in which it is split into two phases), the number of different ways in which an assembly can be set up with $N_{\alpha\beta}$ having a given value is equal to the number in which it can be set up with $N_{\alpha\alpha} + N_{\beta\beta}$ having the same given value. It may also be noted that the case in which a system is split up into two different phases having different ratios of N_A and N_B; is paralleled in the case where $\Delta\epsilon < 0$ by a split into two different phases which are predominantly out of phase with each other. Such a difference, of course, would not be noticed physically.

It must be noted, however, that the correspondence between the two arrangements, such as those shown in Fig. 12-8, may not be perfect in all respects. For examples, although there are equal numbers of the two kinds of molecule in Fig. 12-8*a*, this is not quite true in Fig. 12-8*b*. In general, however, one may expect that for virtually all cases, and especially if the total number of molecules is very large, there will be practically equal numbers of A and B. If one considers the total number of configurations over a small range of N_A and N_B, they should be essentially the same in the two cases. Thus the course of the specific heat curve should be the same for $\Delta\epsilon > 0$ and $\Delta\epsilon < 0$.

A somewhat more rigorous demonstration of this result can be given by considering an ensemble of assemblies in which the assemblies are allowed to exchange molecules, but in which the total number N of molecules is held fixed in each assembly. This would result if there is a set of boxes all the same size having a fixed number of lattice positions, with each box completely filled. Then A's could exchange with B's, but for each A added in any box a B would have to be removed. If m_{N_A} is the number of assemblies with N_A molecules of type A (the particular assemblies with a given value of N_A being unspecified), the ensemble partition function, in analogy to Eq. (1.3) of Chap. 10, is

$$(\text{E.P.F.}) = M! \sum_{(m_{N_A})} \frac{\prod_{N_A} (\text{P.F.})_{N_A}^{m_{N_A}}}{\prod_{N_A} m_{N_A}!} \tag{4.3}$$

with

$$\sum_{N_A} m_{N_A} = M. \tag{4.4}$$

We may now use Eq. (3.1), noting that because of Eqs. (2.2)

$g(N_{\alpha\alpha}, N_{\beta\beta}, N_{\alpha\beta})$ can just as well be written for fixed N as $g(N_A, N_{\alpha\beta})$, and that $E(N_{\alpha\alpha}, N_{\beta\beta}, N_{\alpha\beta})$ is given by Eq. (2.5):

$$E(N_{\alpha\alpha}, N_{\beta\beta}, N_{\alpha\beta}) = \Delta E_m + E_A + E_B$$

$$= N_{\alpha\beta}\Delta\epsilon + \frac{zN_A}{2}\epsilon_{\alpha\alpha} + \frac{zN_B}{2}\epsilon_{\beta\beta}, \qquad (4.5)$$

by Eqs. (2.3) and (2.7). We shall also write $(\text{p.f.})'_A = (\text{p.f.})_A \exp\{-z\epsilon_{AA}/2kT\}$ and $(\text{p.f.})'_B = (\text{p.f.})_B \exp\{-z\epsilon_{BB}/2kT\}$. Equation (3.1) then gives

$$(\text{E.P.F.}) = M! \sum_{(m_{N_A})} \frac{\prod_{N_A} (\text{p.f.})_A'^{N_A m_{N_A}} (\text{p.f.})_B'^{N_B m_{N_A}} [(\text{P.F.})_{m,N_A}]^{m_{N_A}}}{\prod_{N_A} m_{N_A}!} \qquad (4.6)$$

where $(\text{P.F.})_{m,N_A}$, a function of N_A only, is identical to $(\text{P.F.})_m$ of Eq. (3.2). Setting

$$\sum_{N_A} N_A m_{N_A} = M\bar{N}_A, \qquad (4.7)$$

and since

$$\sum_{N_A} N_B m_{N_A} = \sum_{N_A} (N - N_A) m_{N_A} = M(N - \bar{N}_A) = M\bar{N}_B, \qquad (4.8)$$

Eq. (4.6) may be written

$$(\text{E.P.F.}) = \sum_{(m_{N_A})} \frac{M!(\text{p.f.})_A'^{M\bar{N}_A} (\text{p.f.})_B'^{M\bar{N}_B} \prod_{N_A} [(\text{P.F.})_{m,N_A}]^{m_{N_A}}}{\prod_{N_A} m_{N_A}!}. \qquad (4.9)$$

The values of m_{N_A} which are to be selected in setting up the sum in Eq. (4.9) have two independent conditions upon them, Eqs. (4.4) and (4.7). One could find the largest term in the sum under these conditions, but for $\bar{N}_A = \bar{N}_B$ another procedure is more expeditious. On account of the symmetry, in the maximum term $m_{N_A} = m_{N'_A}$, where $N'_A = N - N_A = N_B$. Therefore, we have $m_{N_A} = m_{N-N_A}$, where m_{N-N_A} gives the number of boxes in which the number of A molecules is $N - N_A$. Instead of confining ourselves to the maximum term, we will select *all* terms for which $m_{N_A} = m_{N-N_A}$, and within these terms we will pair the factors for which the numbers of A molecules are related in this way. We can then characterize the pairs by an N_A less than $N/2$ and we note that *any* set of values of m_{N_A}, with N_A less than

$N/2$, provided $\sum\limits_{N_A=0}^{N/2} m_{N_A} = M/2$, will automatically satisfy Eq. (4.7). By the symmetry we will also have $g(N_A, N_{\alpha\mathfrak{B}}) = g(N - N_A, N_{\alpha\mathfrak{B}})$, and the factors in the product in Eq. (4.9) for which $N_A < N/2$ and for which $N_A > N/2$ will contribute two equal partial products. Thus we have

$$(\text{E.P.F.}) = \sum_{(m_{N_A})} \frac{M!(\text{p.f.})_A'^{MN/2}(\text{p.f.})_B'^{MN/2} \{\prod\limits_{N_A} [(\text{P.F.})_{m,N_A}]^{m_{N_A}}\}^2}{(\prod\limits_{N_A} m_{N_A}!)^2},$$

$$(4.10)$$

with

$$N_A \leqq N/2.$$

At this point we find the largest term in Eq. (4.10). This may easily be done by maximizing

$$\sum_{N_A=0}^{N/2} \ln [(\text{P.F.})_{m,N_A}]^{m_{N_A}} - \sum_{N_A}^{N/2} \ln m_{N_A}!$$

Under the condition noted:

$$\sum_{N_A=0}^{N/2} m_{N_A} = \frac{M}{2}.$$

$$(4.11)$$

Variation of m_{N_A}, according to the usual procedure, yields

$$\ln (\text{P.F.})_{m,N_A} - \ln m_{N_A} - \ln a = 0,$$

$$(4.12)$$

where $-\ln a$ is the Lagrange multiplier. From Eq. (4.12), it is seen that

$$a \sum_{N_A=0}^{N/2} m_{N_A} = \sum_{N_A=0}^{N/2} (\text{P.F.})_{m,N_A};$$

therefore

$$a = 2 \sum_{N_A=0}^{N/2} \frac{(\text{P.F.})_{m,N_A}}{M}.$$

$$(4.13)$$

We now use Eq. (4.12) to transform Eq. (4.10), by substitution into the largest term. First we note that the factor $(\text{p.f.})_A'^{MN/2}(\text{p.f.})_B'^{MN/2}$ is what would be found for the separate pure constituents; the rest is the mixing part, $(\text{E.P.F.})_m$. We find, with the Stirling approximation, making use first of Eq. (4.12), then of Eq. (4.11), and, eventually, of Eq. (4.13),

$$\ln (\text{E.P.F.})_m$$

$$= M \ln M - 2 \sum_{N_A=0}^{N/2} m_{N_A} \ln m_{N_A} + 2 \sum_{N_A=0}^{N/2} m_{N_A} \ln (\text{P.F.})_{m,N_A}$$

$$= M \ln M + 2 \sum_{N_A=0}^{N/2} m_{N_A} \ln a = M \ln M + M \ln a$$

$$= M \ln \left[2 \sum_{N_A=0}^{N/2} (\text{P.F.})_{m,N_A} \right] = M \ln \sum_{N_A=0}^{N} (\text{P.F.})_{m,N_A}. \tag{4.14}$$

Using the equation preceding Eq. (3.7) of Chap. 10, adapted to the mixing part ΔA_m of the Helmholtz free energy, we find

$$- M \overline{\Delta A_m} = kT \ln (\text{E.P.F.})_m$$

$$= MkT \sum_{N_A=0}^{N} \sum_{N_{\alpha\beta}} g(N_A, N_{\alpha\beta}) \exp \left\{ -\frac{N_{\alpha\beta} \Delta \epsilon}{kT} \right\} \tag{4.15}$$

where we have again written out $(\text{P.F.})_{m,N_A}$. We can perform the summation over N_A first and define

$$G(N_{\alpha\beta}) = \sum_{N_A=0}^{N} g(N_A, N_{\alpha\beta}) = 2 \sum_{N_A=0}^{N/2} g(N_A, N_{\alpha\beta}) \tag{4.16}$$

this being the total number of states for a given $N_{\alpha\beta}$ regardless of N_A. Then, for the case we are considering ($\overline{N}_A = \overline{N}_B$),

$$- \overline{\Delta A_m} = kT \ln \sum_{N_{\alpha\beta}} G(N_{\alpha\beta}) \exp \left\{ -\frac{N_{\alpha\beta} \Delta \epsilon}{kT} \right\}. \tag{4.17}$$

Now we can get a one-to-one correspondence between states having a given $N_{\alpha\beta}$ and states having the same value of $N_{\alpha\alpha} + N_{\beta\beta}$ in the case of a simple lattice. We designate half of the lattice sites as α sites, and the other half (the nearest neighbors of the α sites) as β sites. If we take all A molecules on α sites and change them to B, and all B molecules on α sites and change them to A, then it is seen that we have changed all A–A and B–B contacts to A–B and all A–B to A–A or B–B. Thus we now have a system designated by primes, in which $N'_{\alpha\alpha} + N'_{\beta\beta} = N_{\alpha\beta}$ and $N'_{\alpha\beta} = N_{\alpha\alpha} + N_{\beta\beta}$, and it follows that $G(N_{\alpha\beta}) = G(N'_{\alpha\beta})$. Thus

$$\overline{\Delta A_m'} = kT \ln \sum_{N'_{\alpha\mathfrak{B}}} G(N'_{\alpha\mathfrak{B}}) \exp\left\{\frac{-N'_{\alpha\mathfrak{B}}\Delta\epsilon'}{kT}\right\}$$

$$= kT \ln \sum_{N_{\alpha\mathfrak{B}}} G(N_{\alpha\mathfrak{B}}) \exp\left\{\frac{-(N_{\alpha\alpha} + N_{\mathfrak{B}\mathfrak{B}})\Delta\epsilon'}{kT}\right\}$$

$$= kT \ln \sum_{N_{\alpha\mathfrak{B}}} G(N_{\alpha\mathfrak{B}}) \exp\left\{\frac{(N_{\alpha\mathfrak{B}} - zN/2)\Delta\epsilon'}{kT}\right\} \qquad (4.18)$$

by Eqs. (2.2). Aside from an additive constant, $(zN/2)\Delta\epsilon$, the value of $\overline{\Delta A_m'}$ will be the same as that of $\overline{\Delta A_m}$ if $\Delta\epsilon' = -\Delta\epsilon$. Thus the course of $\overline{\Delta C_m}$ as a function of temperature will be the same for the two cases.

The difficulty (similar to that arising in connection with Fig. 12-8) that, if there are not equal numbers of A and B on α sites, the number of A's and B's is changed in the process of setting up the correspondence between $N_{\alpha\mathfrak{B}}$ and $N_{\alpha\alpha} + N_{\mathfrak{B}\mathfrak{B}}$ is avoided, because here we sum over all possible values of $N_{\alpha\mathfrak{B}}$ and [in Eq. (4.16)] over all values of N_A.

The case in which $\Delta\epsilon < 0$, is a good model for the situation which occurs with a number of binary alloys, for example, β-brass, which consists, in the ideal case, of an equimolecular mixture of Cu and Zn. At low temperatures the Cu and Zn tend to occupy alternate places in the lattice, and the arrangement is ordered. As the temperature is raised, some of the Cu and Zn atoms exchange positions in the lattice and Cu–Cu and Zn–Zn contacts appear. The specific heat shows an anomaly over a certain temperature range, above which most of the order in the mixture has disappeared. However, the character of the anomaly is somewhat different from what would be expected from the quasi-chemical approximation. Actually the specific heat rises to a very high value and then falls rapidly, but without any definite discontinuity. This suggests that a more precise calculation might give a different result, and indeed this is true. It is possible to solve the problem for a one-dimensional lattice;[†] in this case there is no singularity, although the specific heat shows a maximum. The only example of real interest in which an exact solution has been obtained is that of a simple two-dimensional lattice with $N_A = N_B$, for which Onsager [14], by a mathematical *tour de force*, was able to give what is in effect an exact evaluation of $g(N_A, N_{\alpha\mathfrak{B}})$. The specific heat was found to have a logarithmic infinity at the critical temperature.[‡]

† In this case the quasi-chemical approximation is exact. See Prob. 12.7.
‡ In addition to the original paper, various accounts are available, *e.g.* [8; **9**, pp. 581–592; **15**; **16**].

This result has aroused great interest, since it is the only model which yields a phase transition which can be characterized precisely. The mathematics is so complicated that we will not attempt to go through it here. Instead we shall, in some of the following sections, consider certain expansions, some of which resemble in some respects the virial expansion of a gas. They are of more general application, and can also be used to characterize the transition, although not with the precision of Onsager's solution of the two-dimensional lattice.

12-5. *The Grand Partition Function of Mixing*

We shall next get an expression for (E.P.F.) which is valid even though $\overline{N}_A \neq N/2$. In doing this, our only interest will lie in (E.P.F.)$_m$ which is given by

$$(\text{E.P.F.})_m = M! \sum_{(m_{N_A})} \frac{\prod_{N_A} [\sum_{N_{\alpha\beta}} g(N_A, N_{\alpha\beta}) \exp\{-N_{\alpha\beta}\Delta\epsilon/kT\}]^{m_{N_A}}}{\prod_{N_A} m_{N_A}!}$$

$$= M! \sum_{(m_{N_A})} \frac{\prod_{N_A} [(\text{P.F.})_{m,N_A}]^{m_{N_A}}}{\prod_{N_A} m_{N_A}!}. \tag{5.1}$$

This is the same as Eq. (4.9) except that it leaves out the factor

$$(\text{p.f.})_A'^{M\overline{N}_A}(\text{p.f.})_B'^{M\overline{N}_B} = (\text{p.f.})_A'^{NMx_A}(\text{p.f.})_B'^{NMx_B},$$

which is the partition function for Mx_A boxes having only A molecules and Mx_B boxes having only B molecules. There would, to be sure, be $M!/(Mx_A)!(Mx_B)!$ ways to choose these boxes, but the logarithm of this is by Stirling's approximation, equal to $-Mx_A \ln x_A - Mx_B \ln x_B$ and so is negligible, since it is not multiplied by a factor like N. Thus (E.P.F.)$_m$ may be called the ensemble partition function of mixing.

We evaluate (E.P.F.)$_m$ in the usual way by selecting the largest term in the sum, obtained by maximizing with respect to the values of m_{N_A} under the conditions expressed by Eqs. (4.4) and (4.7). This gives (cf. Sec. 10-1)

$$m_{N_A} = (\text{P.F.})_{m,N_A} \exp\left\{\frac{N_A \mu_{max}}{kT}\right\} \exp\frac{\zeta}{kT}, \tag{5.2}$$

where μ_{max}/kT and ζ/kT are Lagrange multipliers. By putting (5.2) into Eq. (4.4) we can evaluate $\exp\{\zeta/kT\}$, and we then obtain

$$m_{N_A} = \frac{M(\text{P.F.})_{\text{m},N_A} \exp\{N_A \mu_{\text{max}}/kT\}}{\sum_{N_A} (\text{P.F.})_{\text{m},N_A} \exp\{N_A \mu_{\text{max}}/kT\}}. \tag{5.3}$$

The interpretation of μ_{max} is somewhat different from that in Chap. 10. The largest value of m_{N_A} is found by differentiating the numerator in Eq. (5.3) with respect to N_A, holding N constant. First we note that

$$\left[\frac{\partial \ln (\text{P.F.})_{\text{m},N_A}}{\partial N_A}\right]_{T,N}$$

$$= \left[\frac{\partial \ln (\text{P.F.})_{\text{m},N_A}}{\partial N_A}\right]_{T,N_B} + \left[\frac{\partial \ln (\text{P.F.})_{\text{m},N_A}}{\partial N_B}\right]_{T,N_A}\left(\frac{\partial N_B}{\partial N_A}\right)_N$$

$$= \left[\frac{\partial \ln (\text{P.F.})_{\text{m},N_A}}{\partial N_A}\right]_{T,N_B} - \left[\frac{\partial \ln (\text{P.F.})_{\text{m},N_A}}{\partial N_B}\right]_{T,N_A}. \tag{5.4}$$

In holding N_B or N_A constant in the last partial derivatives, it would seem best also to hold the density constant; thus they will have the character of derivatives at constant pressure, and one might write

$$\left[\frac{\partial \ln (\text{P.F.})_{\text{m},N_A}}{\partial N_A}\right]_{T,N_B} = \frac{-\mu_{\text{m},A}}{kT},$$

and

$$\left[\frac{\partial \ln (\text{P.F.})_{\text{m},N_A}}{\partial N_B}\right]_{T,N_A} = \frac{-\mu_{\text{m},B}}{kT}. \tag{5.5}$$

These "chemical potentials," however, are affected only by the mixing terms, and so are not chemical potentials in the ordinary sense. The condition for the largest value of m_{N_A} yields

$$\mu_{\text{max}} = \mu_{\text{m},A} - \mu_{\text{m},B}, \tag{5.6}$$

where $\mu_{\text{m},A}$ and $\mu_{\text{m},B}$ are evaluated for $N_A - N_{A,\text{max}}$, which means essentially for $N_A = \bar{N}_A$.

The value of m_{N_A} given in Eq. (5.3) can be inserted into Eq. (5.1), after taking the logarithm. This yields, after some simplification,

$$\ln (\text{E.P.F.})_{\text{m}} = -\frac{M\bar{N}_A\mu_{\text{max}}}{kT} + M \ln \sum_{N_A} (\text{P.F.})_{\text{m},N_A} \exp\left\{\frac{N_A\mu_{\text{max}}}{kT}\right\}, \tag{5.7}$$

which gives

$$\overline{\Delta A_{\text{m}}} = \bar{N}_A\mu_{\text{max}} - kT \ln \sum_{N_A} (\text{P.F.})_{\text{m},N_A} \exp\left\{\frac{N_A\mu_{\text{max}}}{kT}\right\}. \tag{5.8}$$

Equation (5.7), with $\mu_{\text{max}} = 0$, may be compared with Eq. (4.14).

Evaluation of $g(N_A, N_{\alpha\beta})$ and consequent evaluation of $(P.F.)_{m,N_A}$ would now allow one to determine the thermodynamic properties of the system in terms of μ_{max}/kT and T. Use of Eqs. (5.5) and (5.6) would, in principle, allow the determination of $\bar{N}_A$ in terms of μ_{max}/kT and T; thus $\bar{N}_A$ and T could, if desired, be used as independent variables. In a sense this is a circular argument, for if $g(N_A, N_{\alpha\beta})$ were known, the thermodynamic functions could be obtained as functions of N_A and T by use of $(P.F.)_{m,N_A}$ alone. The advantage of Eq. (5.8), which will soon become apparent, is that in the sum (which we shall call the grand partition function of mixing) it is possible to sum over N_A first. Thus we write

$$
\begin{aligned}
(G.P.F.)_m &= \sum_{N_A} (P.F.)_{m,N_A} \exp\left\{\frac{N_A\mu_{max}}{kT}\right\} \\
&= \sum_{N_A}\sum_{N_{\alpha\beta}} g(N_A, N_{\alpha\beta}) \exp\left\{\frac{-N_{\alpha\beta}\Delta\epsilon}{kT}\right\} \exp\left\{\frac{N_A\mu_{max}}{kT}\right\} \\
&= \sum_{N_{\alpha\beta}} \exp\left\{\frac{-N_{\alpha\beta}\Delta\epsilon}{kT}\right\} \sum_{N_A} g(N_A, N_{\alpha\beta}) \exp\left\{\frac{N_A\mu_{max}}{kT}\right\} \\
&= \sum_{N_{\alpha\beta}} x^{N_{\alpha\beta}} \sum_{N_A} g(N_A, N_{\alpha\beta})\lambda_A^{N_A},
\end{aligned}
\tag{5.9}
$$

where $x = \exp\{-\Delta\epsilon/kT\}$ and $\lambda_A = \exp\{\mu_{max}/kT\}$.

12-6. *Series Expansions*

If $\Delta\epsilon > 0$, Eq. (5.9) lends itself to a low temperature-expansion by considering the situations encountered when $N_{AB} = 0, 1, 2, \cdots$ [5, 7, 17–21]. To illustrate this we start the development of the series for a simple, square, two-dimensional lattice.

There are only two ways for $N_{\alpha\beta}$ to be zero: N_A must be either 0 or N. Thus we have

$$
\sum_{N_A} g(N_A, 0)\lambda_A^{N_A} = 1 + \lambda_A^N.
\tag{6.1}
$$

From Eqs. (2.2), since z is even (4 in this instance), we see that $N_{\alpha\beta}$ can never be odd. It is also clear that it cannot be equal to 2. It can be equal to 4 by having $N_A = 1$ or $N_B = 1$, and since the one A or the one B could be on any of the N lattice spaces, there are $2N$ ways for this to occur. Thus

$$
\sum_{N_A} g(N_A, 4)\lambda_A^{N_A} = N\lambda_A + N\lambda_A^{N-1},
\tag{6.2}
$$

We can get $N_{\alpha\beta}$ equal to 6 by having $N_A = 2$ or $N_B = 2$, the two A's or two B's being side-by-side. There are very approximately $4N/2 = 2N$ ways for two A's to be side-by-side.† Thus

$$\sum_{N_A} g(N_A, 6)\lambda_A^{N_A} = 2N\lambda_A^2 + 2N\lambda_A^{N-2}. \tag{6.3}$$

We can get $N_{\alpha\beta} = 8$ by having two A's or two B's, but not side-by-side. One A can be placed on N spaces, the second then on $N - 5$ remaining spaces (*not* on the already occupied space or its neighbors), there being thus $N(N - 5)/2$ possibilities with $N_A = 2$. We also get $N_{\alpha\beta} = 8$ by having three A's or B's arranged either straight, ∘∘∘, or bent, °°°. There are (very approximately) N spaces for the first atom, 4 for the second, 3 for the third, the number of possibilities then being $12N/2 = 6N$ (the division by 2 occurs because one might get the same configuration by starting at either end—one never starts in the middle, however). Finally, the configuration °° can also give 8 unlike contacts, and there are N ways to set down the lower left-hand corner. In this case, therefore,

$$\sum_{N_A} g(N_A, 8)\lambda_A^{N_A} = \tfrac{1}{2}N(N - 5)(\lambda_A^2 + \lambda_A^{N-2})$$
$$+ 6N(\lambda_A^3 + \lambda_A^{N-3}) + N(\lambda_A^4 + \lambda_A^{N-4}). \tag{6.4}$$

We have thus found the coefficients of the powers of x up to x^8. This process can, of course, be continued, but naturally becomes more difficult the greater the value of $N_{\alpha\beta}$. By systematization of the procedure, however, and by the use of certain combinatorial theorems, it has been possible to extend the series to much higher terms, not only for the square planar lattice, but for various other types of lattice, including some three-dimensional ones. Since we are mainly interested in the principles involved we will refer the reader to the literature [17–21] for these details. If $\lambda_A < 1$, which occurs [by Eq. (5.6)] if $\mu_{m,A} < \mu_{m,B}$ (or $N_A < N_B$), the terms λ_A^N, λ_A^{N-2}, $\cdots$ can be neglected in Eqs. (6.2), (6.3), and (6.4) and the series becomes

$$(\text{G.P.F.})_m = 1 + N\lambda_A x^4 + 2N\lambda_A^2 x^6$$
$$+ [\tfrac{1}{2}N(N - 5)\lambda_A^2 + 6N\lambda_A^3 + N\lambda_A^4]x^8 + \cdots. \tag{6.5}$$

If $\lambda_A > 1$, then the terms λ_A^N, λ_A^{N-2}, $\cdots$ become the predominant

---

† See footnote on p. 169. The approximation, which is more important for $N_{\alpha\beta} \geqq 8$, arises from edge effects. The elimination of this difficulty is considered in the discussion of Eq. (6.6).

terms, and if we set $\lambda_B = \exp\{-\mu_{max}/kT\} = \lambda_A^{-1}$, the expression for (G.P.F.)$_m$ has the same form as Eq. (6.5) but with λ_A replaced by λ_B and multiplied by a factor λ_A^N. When (G.P.F.)$_m$ is introduced into Eq. (5.8), this factor λ_A^N causes the first term $N_A\mu_{max}$ to be replaced by $(N - N_A)(-\mu_{max}) = N_B(-\mu_{max})$. Thus the lack of symmetry between A and B, which arises from the way we set up the original variation problem and choose the Lagrange multipliers, does not result in any lack of symmetry in the thermodynamic functions. We may note that when $N_A = N_B$, the expression in Eq. (6.5) is incorrect by a factor of 2, which is unimportant.

As already mentioned, the series in Eq. (6.5) can be and has been carried to much higher powers of x. It might seem that it would be impossible to carry it far enough for it to be valid at any but the very smallest values of x, because the coefficients contain powers of N, and because all contributions from significant values of $N_{\alpha\beta}$ (i.e., values of $N_{\alpha\beta}$ at all comparable to N) occur in the coefficients of extremely high powers of x. It is possible, however, to extract the Nth root of (G.P.F.)$_m$, by using the binomial theorem. Thus we get a molecular grand partition function from which the thermodynamic functions can be derived. This procedure requires only the lower-order terms in the series. If it is carried out we obtain

$$(G.P.F.)_m^{1/N} = 1 + \lambda_A x^4 + 2\lambda_A^2 x^6 + (-2\lambda_A^2 + 6\lambda_A^3 + \lambda_A^4)x^8 + \cdots.$$

$$(6.6)$$

The validity of this procedure may perhaps be indicated in the following way. If we had a system with a small value of N, then we could reach a reasonable value of $N_{\alpha\beta}/N$ with a small value of $N_{\alpha\beta}$. Since we are considering an ensemble of such systems this result would be valid except for edge effects. But the edge effects may be largely eliminated by means of periodic boundary conditions. We suppose that our assembly is surrounded by replicas of itself which interact with it, but in which not only the gross thermodynamic variables but the exact arrangement of the molecules is the same. Thus, in Fig. 12-9 the molecule A which is next to the boundary causes an interaction at all the lattice points marked with a cross. If, in setting up Eq. (6.4) we wish to place another molecule on the lattice to produce altogether $N_{\alpha\beta} = 8$, the first molecule removes 5 possible places even if it is near the boundary. And the lower left-hand corner of the configuration ⚇ can be placed in exactly N positions, for it does not matter if it overlaps the boundary. Thus the coefficients in the lower-order terms of the series will be for-

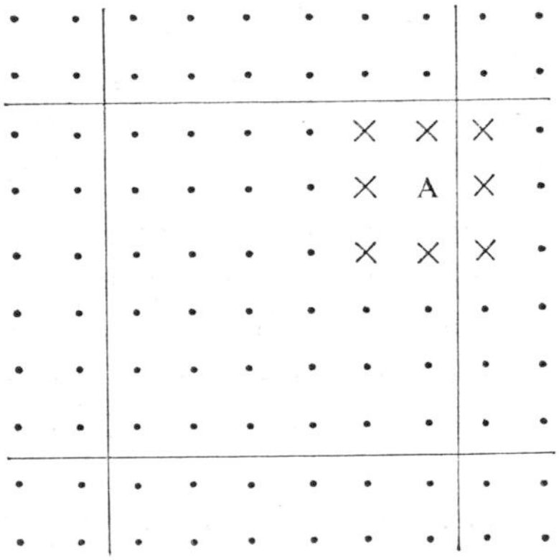

Figure 12-9.

mally just as they are in Eq. (6.5), even if N is relatively small. It does not, then, seem so strange that they can determine the thermodynamic properties of the system over a range of x and λ_A. The extraction of the Nth root of Eq. (6.5) to give Eq. (6.6) involves what seems to be an almost miraculous cancellation of terms having powers of N as a factor. If such cancellation did not occur, however, the expected additive property of the thermodynamic functions (e.g., doubling of S or A if N is doubled, keeping N_A/N constant) would not be valid.

If $\Delta\epsilon < 0$, then the low-temperature configuration will be one in which A and B occupy alternate places on the lattice to the greatest extent possible, tending to give $N_{\alpha\mathcal{B}}$ as great a value as possible. The greatest value of $N_{\alpha\mathcal{B}}$ is $zN/2$, occurring when $N_A = N_B = N/2$. Let us write

$$N'_{\alpha\mathcal{B}} = \frac{zN}{2} - N_{\alpha\mathcal{B}}, \tag{6.7}$$

and

$$N'_A = \frac{N}{2} - N_A. \tag{6.8}$$

Then Eq. (5.9) takes the form

$$(\text{G.P.F.})_m = \exp\left\{\frac{-zN\Delta\epsilon}{2kT}\right\} \exp\left\{\frac{N\mu_{\max}}{2kT}\right\}$$

$$\times \sum_{N'_{\alpha\mathcal{B}}} \exp\left\{\frac{-N'_{\alpha\mathcal{B}}(-\Delta\epsilon)}{kT}\right\} \sum_{N'_A} g(N'_A,\ N'_{\alpha\mathcal{B}}) \exp\left\{\frac{-N'_A\mu_{\max}}{kT}\right\}$$

$$= y^{-zN/2}\lambda_A^{N/2} \sum_{N'_{\alpha\mathcal{B}}} y^{N'_{\alpha\mathcal{B}}} \sum_{N'_A} g(N'_A,\ N'_{\alpha\mathcal{B}})\lambda_A^{-N'_A} \tag{6.9}$$

where $y = \exp\{\Delta\epsilon/kT\}$.

We find $g(N_A', N_{\alpha\beta}')$ for the plane square lattice at different values of $N_{\alpha\beta}'$ in the same way that we evaluated $g(N_A, N_{\alpha\beta})$ for different values of $N_{\alpha\beta}$. There are two ways to have $N_{\alpha\beta}' = 0$ (this requires alternate A and B in the lattice—*two* ways since all A's and B's can be interchanged). By replacing one A by one B or *vice versa* in either of the first two configurations we increase $N_{\alpha\beta}'$ to 4; there are thus $2N$ ways to do this. In half of the ways, N_A' is 1, in the other half it is -1. If we change one A and one B, side-by-side, to a B and an A respectively, we get a situation in which $N_{\alpha\beta}' = 6$; in this case, however, $N_A' = 0$. This procedure can continue, as for $\Delta\epsilon > 0$. The count of configurations for various values of $N_{\alpha\beta}'$ is the same as the former count for $N_{\alpha\beta}$, but the values of N_A' do not match those of N_A in the other case. In place of Eq. (6.5) we obtain, taking $z = 4$,

$$(\text{G.P.F.})_m = \frac{\lambda_A^{N/2}}{y^{2N}} \left\{ 2 + N\left(\lambda_A + \frac{1}{\lambda_A}\right) y^4 + 4Ny^6 \right.$$

$$+ \left[N\left(\frac{N}{2} - 4\right) + \frac{N}{2}\left(\frac{N}{2} - 1\right)\left(\lambda_A^2 + \frac{1}{\lambda_A^2}\right) \right.$$

$$\left. \left. + 6N\left(\lambda_A + \frac{1}{\lambda_A}\right) + 2N \right] y^8 + \cdots \right\}. \qquad (6.10)$$

Extracting the Nth root gives, leaving out a factor $2^{1/N}$, we get

$$(\text{G.P.F.})_m^{1/N} = \frac{\lambda_A^{1/2}}{y^2} \left\{ 1 + \frac{1}{2}\left(\lambda_A + \frac{1}{\lambda_A}\right) y^4 + 2y^6 \right.$$

$$\left. + \left[-\frac{1}{8}\left(\lambda_A^2 + \frac{1}{\lambda_A^2}\right) + 3\left(\lambda_A + \frac{1}{\lambda_A}\right) - \frac{3}{4} \right] y^8 + \cdots \right\}. \qquad (6.11)$$

In the special case of $\mu_{\max} = 0$, we have $\lambda_A = \lambda_B = 1$ and, as noted, we may substitute this value in Eq. (6.6). Carried somewhat beyond the terms shown in Eq. (6.6), this substitution gives

$$(\text{G.P.F.})_m^{1/N} = 1 + x^4 + 2x^6 + 5x^8 + 14x^{10}$$

$$+ 44x^{12} + 152x^{14} + \cdots. \qquad (6.12)$$

If we substitute $\lambda_A = 1$ in Eq. (6.11), we get the same function of y except for the factor $1/y^2$. Since $y = 1/x$, it will be seen, using Prob. 12.13 and Eq. (2.5), that the effect of the factor $1/y^2$ is to add to the energy a temperature-independent increment, which will not affect the specific heat. The specific heat and most other properties will thus not be dependent on the sign of $\Delta\epsilon$ when $\lambda_A = 1$.

Certain characteristics of the assemblies which we have been considering can be seen immediately from the equations which we have derived. If the relation derived in Prob. 12.12 is applied to Eq. (6.6), we can obtain an expression for $\overline{N}_A/N$ as follows:

$$\frac{\overline{N}_A}{N} = \frac{\lambda_A x^4 + 4\lambda_A^2 x^6 + (-4\lambda_A^2 + 18\lambda_A^3 + 4\lambda_A^4)x^8 + \cdots}{1 + \lambda_A x^4 + 2\lambda_A^2 x^6 + (-2\lambda_A^2 + 6\lambda_A^3 + \lambda_A^4)x^8 + \cdots}. \tag{6.13}$$

We are interested in the value of $\overline{N}_A/N$ when $\lambda_A = 1$. When $\lambda_A = 1$, we have $\mu_{m,A} = \mu_{m,B}$. If we have another solution, designated with a prime, with a value of $\overline{N}_B'/N'$ equal to $\overline{N}_A/N$ of the original solution, we see by the symmetry of the problem that, if x is the same for the two solutions, $\mu_{m,A} = \mu_{m,B}'$ and $\mu_{m,B} = \mu_{m,A}'$, whence $\mu_{m,A} = \mu_{m,A}'$ and $\mu_{m,B} = \mu_{m,B}'$, so that these two solutions will be in equilibrium. Thus $\lambda_A = 1$ defines the locus of the coexistence curve for the two phases in equilibrium.

We see from Eq. (6.13) that $\overline{N}_A/N = 0$ at $x = 0$, and as x increases, the value of $\overline{N}_A/N$ along the coexistence curve increases as x^4. This means at first a slow, but then a much more rapid, increase in $\overline{N}_A/N$, which at higher x is augmented by the higher-order terms in the series. Eventually $\overline{N}_A/N$ will reach $\frac{1}{2}$, which marks the critical point. If Eq. (6.13) still converges it can be used to find x_c.

An expression for $\overline{N}_{\alpha\beta}$ also can be found. Application of Prob. 12.13 to Eq. (6.6) gives

$$\frac{\overline{N}_{\alpha\beta}}{N} = \frac{4\lambda_A x^4 + 12\lambda_A^2 x^6 + 8(-2\lambda_A^2 + 6\lambda_A^3 + \lambda_A^4)x^8 + \cdots}{1 + \lambda_A x^4 + 2\lambda_A^2 x^6 + (-2\lambda_A^2 + 6\lambda_A^3 + \lambda_A^4)x^8 + \cdots}. \tag{6.14}$$

If we set $\lambda_A = 1$ in this equation, we will have the expression for $N_{\alpha\beta}$ along the coexistence curve, which is closely related to the energy of mixing, ΔE_m. Differentiation of the expression so obtained with respect to T will give ΔC_m for a two-phase system in equilibrium. Because the system is symmetrical with respect to A and B, the energy per molecule of either A or B will be the same for either of the two phases in equilibrium, or for any mixture of them. Thus it is legitimate to obtain the thermodynamic properties from a single phase with $\lambda_A = 1$.

Expansions of the type just considered may, however, be expected to exhibit convergence difficulties, and Eq. (6.12) certainly diverges before x reaches its limiting value 1. It is, however, possible to order the terms in Eq. (6.6) differently, and set up the equation as a series in λ_A rather than in x. If we do this, we find

$$(\text{G.P.F.})_m^{1/N} = 1 + x^4\lambda_A + (2x^6 - 2x^8)\lambda_A^2$$
$$+ (6x^8 - 14x^{10} + 8x^{12})\lambda_A^3 + \cdots. \tag{6.15}$$

This expression includes some terms not shown in Eq. (6.6). If $x = 1$, its limiting high-temperature value, the coefficients of all terms beyond the term in λ_A are zero, and $(\text{G.P.F.})_m = (1 + \lambda_A)^N$. This is the correct value, because at high temperatures

$$\sum_{N_{a\text{ⓑ}}} g(N_A, N_{a\text{ⓑ}}) = \frac{N!}{N_A!(N - N_A)!},$$

and this inserted into Eq. (5.9) gives $(\text{G.P.F.})_m = (1 + \lambda_A)^N$ by use of the binomial theorem. The form (6.15), then may be expected to be usable at both high and low temperatures.

Domb and Sykes [21] have used this series to investigate the properties of an assembly near its critical point. If we simply break off the series after, say, λ_A^n, we can calculate $\Delta C_m^{(n)}$ on this basis. For any finite n, $\Delta C_m^{(n)}$ plotted as a function of x for $\lambda_A = 1$ does not have a singularity, but it does have a maximum. This maximum grows sharper as n increases and finally approaches the singular value of ΔC_m. By extrapolating the value of $\Delta C_m^{(n)}$ to $n = \infty$ an estimate can be made of x_c and hence T_c.

Once one has obtained x_c, one can return to the series expansion of ΔC_m as a function of x for $\lambda_A = 1$ and recast it as a series in x/x_c (simply by dividing x^n, where it occurs, by x_c^n and multiplying its coefficient by x_c^n). Examination of such a series shows that the ratio of the coefficients of successive terms approaches some degree of regularity in the higher terms, and approaches a correspondence to the ratio of a known function. The series for $\bar{N}_A/N$ as a function of x for $\lambda_A = 1$ can be handled in the same way, thus characterizing the coexistence curve.

These procedures were carried out for the two-dimensional case, for which an exact solution is known through the work of Onsager, and comparison showed that the series expansion and the inferences based upon it gave the correct qualitative picture and a very close quantitative agreement with the exact result. In the two-dimensional lattice the specific heat has a logarithmic infinity; it is proportional to $\ln(T_c - T)$ or $\ln(T - T_c)$ below or above the critical point. Along the coexistence curve it is found that $T_c - T$ is proportional to $[(\bar{N}_A/N) - \frac{1}{2}]^8$; thus the coexistence curve is very flat at the top.

In the application of similar methods to three-dimensional cases, convergence difficulties arise, especially in the low-temperature expansion. The equation analogous to Eq. (6.12) contains some negative terms, and the expansion diverges suddenly before the singularity in the specific heat is reached, so more powerful mathematical methods are needed to continue the $(G.P.F.)_m$ into the region of the singularity. The method of the Padé approximant [22–24] has been found useful. An $[M, N]$ Padé approximant is a ratio $P(z)/Q(z)$ of two polynomials $P(z) = \sum_{r=0}^{M} p_r z^r$ and $Q(z) = \sum_{s=0}^{N} q_s z^s$, where z is the independent variable ($p_0 = q_0 = 1$). The coefficients p_r and q_s are fixed by allowing the first $M + N$ terms of the expansion of $P(z)/Q(z)$ to be equal to the first $M + N$ terms of the function to be represented. These approximants can be computed by digital computers and will give good approximations, if enough terms are available, even close to a singularity, which may occur at $z = z_c$. If, for example, it is thought that a function $F(z)$ has a form roughly equal to $A(z - z_c)^\alpha$ near such a singular point, we may find a Padé approximant to $d \ln F(z)/dz$ which approaches $\alpha/(z - z_c)$ at the singularity. This would serve to locate z_c approximately, and α could be estimated by finding the residue of the pole of $d \ln F(z)/dz$ considered as a function of a complex variable. Or if z_c is known accurately one could find a Padé approximant to $(z - z_c) d \ln F(z)/dz$. From calculations of this sort it has been concluded [23, 24] that in the three-dimensional model $T_c - T$ is approximately proportional to $[(N_A/N) - \frac{1}{2}]^{16/5}$ and that the singularity in the specific heat at the critical point may possibly be very slightly sharper than logarithmic.

12-7. *The Lattice Gas*

As noted in the introduction to this chapter, there are a number of other problems which are mathematically equivalent [7] to the problem of mixtures we have just considered. A very closely related problem is that of the lattice gas—a system in which we have N_A molecules of type A resting on N_A lattice points in a lattice which has altogether N spaces. Any spaces not occupied by molecules of this one type are left vacant, and are called holes. There are $N - N_A$ holes, and this number corresponds to N_B in the case of the mixtures.

In this case we set $\epsilon_{\mathcal{B}\mathcal{B}}$ and $\epsilon_{\alpha\mathcal{B}}$ equal to zero, and then, from Eq. (2.7),

$$\Delta\epsilon = -\frac{\epsilon_{\alpha\alpha}}{2}. \tag{7.1}$$

The combinatorial problem will be the same as before, and the grand partition function for the mixing of holes and molecules will have the same form as before. Only the interpretation of $\mu_{\max}$ will now be more conventional, since now, clearly (N being the total number of lattice spaces, filled or vacant)

$$\left[\frac{\partial (P.F.)_m}{\partial N_A}\right]_{T,N} = \left[\frac{\partial (P.F.)_m}{\partial N_A}\right]_{T,V},$$ (7.2)

and thus μ_{max} is the ordinary chemical potential of mixing. All the equations will be identical, and at phase equilibrium we will have $\mu_{max} = 0$, as before.

We are, however, concerned with one property of the lattice gas, namely its pressure, which is not of interest in the discussion of the binary mixtures. The pressure can, of course, be calculated directly from (P.F.) according to the usual formula

$$P = -\left(\frac{\partial A}{\partial V}\right)_{T,N_A} = kT\left[\frac{\partial \ln (P.F.)}{\partial V}\right]_{T,N_A}.$$ (7.3)

We note that in this case $V = v_0 N$, where v_0 is the volume per lattice space and is taken as constant. Furthermore $(P.F.) = (P.F.)_m (p.f.)_A^{N_A}$, and since $(p.f.)_A^{N_A}$ does not depend on N, we could just as well write Eq. (7.3) as

$$Pv_0 = kT\left[\frac{\partial \ln (P.F.)_m}{\partial N}\right]_{T,N_A}.$$ (7.4)

Thus, the pressure of a lattice gas depends only on the mixing properties; at least this is true if v_0 is constant, as we have assumed.

It is convenient to use the grand partition function to calculate the pressure, and we shall now develop the necessary formulas. We have already seen that μ_{max} is the chemical potential of mixing. If we define the Gibbs free energy in the usual manner,

$$G = A + PV,$$ (7.5)

we have

$$G = A - V\left(\frac{\partial \Delta A_m}{\partial V}\right)_{T,N_A} = A - N\left(\frac{\partial \Delta A_m}{\partial N}\right)_{T,N_A}.$$ (7.6)

We expect the derivative to be infinite when $N \longrightarrow N_A$ (see Prob. 12.14), so the natural definition of the ΔG of mixing would contain an infinite term. Therefore we arbitrarily define

$$\Delta G_m = \Delta A_m + PV = \Delta A_m - N\left(\frac{\partial \Delta A_m}{\partial N}\right)_{T,N_A}.$$ (7.7)

Since ΔA_m is an extensive property and $\Delta A_m/N$ depends only on the composition of the assembly, it is seen that $(\partial\Delta A_m/\partial N)_{T,N_A}$ itself depends only on the concentration, or on N_A/N. With this in mind we will show that, as usual,

$$\mu_{max} = \left(\frac{\partial\Delta G_m}{\partial N_A}\right)_{T,P,\,max} = \left(\frac{\partial\Delta G_m}{\partial N_A}\right)_{T,N_A/N,\,max} = \left(\frac{\Delta G_m}{N_A}\right)_{max}. \qquad (7.8)$$

From Eq. (7.7), we have

$$\left(\frac{\partial\Delta G_m}{\partial N_A}\right)_{T,N_A/N} = \left(\frac{\partial\Delta A_m}{\partial N_A}\right)_{T,N_A/N} - \frac{N}{N_A}\left(\frac{\partial\Delta A_m}{\partial N}\right)_{T,N_A}, \qquad (7.9)$$

since $(\partial N/\partial N_A)_{N_A/N} = N/N_A$ and since $(\partial\Delta A_m/\partial N)_{T,N_A}$ will not change with N if N/N_A is constant. But

$$\left(\frac{\partial\Delta A_m}{\partial N_A}\right)_{T,N_A/N} = \left(\frac{\partial\Delta A_m}{\partial N_A}\right)_{T,N} + \left(\frac{\partial\Delta A_m}{\partial N}\right)_{T,N_A}\left(\frac{\partial N}{\partial N_A}\right)_{N_A/N}. \qquad (7.10)$$

From Eqs. (7.9) and (7.10), we have

$$\left(\frac{\partial\Delta G_m}{\partial N_A}\right)_{T,N_A/N} = \left(\frac{\partial\Delta A_m}{\partial N_A}\right)_{T,N}, \qquad (7.11)$$

so that Eq. (7.8) follows by the definition of μ_{max}. This being the case, we have from Eqs. (7.7), (5.8), and the first part of (5.9), assuming $\overline{\Delta G_m} = \Delta G_{m,max}$,

$$PV = kT \ln (\text{G.P.F.})_m. \qquad (7.12)$$

In the case of the lattice gas, the two-phase situation in which we have one phase rich in molecules and the other phase rich in holes, resembles the liquid–vapor equilibrium of a real substance. With the equations which have been developed, it is possible to find the vapor pressure as a function of temperatures and to find the various properties of this equilibrium, insofar as the real systems are truly represented by the lattice gas. Application of these results will be made in Sec. 13.3.

12-8. *The Ising Lattice*

The Ising lattice [13] is a model which was set up to investigate the behavior of substances whose molecules possess a magnetic moment.

It is a rather specialized model of this type, but because of its relative simplicity it has been extensively treated theoretically. It also can be shown to be mathematically equivalent to the mixing problem, and, indeed, most of the investigations published on this subject have been couched in terms of the language of the Ising lattice. It is thus especially important that the relation of our notation to the Ising lattice be understood.

Suppose that we have N particles arranged in a lattice and suppose that these particles have a spin with a magnetic moment, the spins being capable of being oriented in one of two directions, either up, A, or down, B. We can let the respective numbers be N_A and N_B, with $N_A + N_B = N$. Let the interaction energy (we consider nearest neighbors only) of a pair of two adjacent A's, or of two adjacent B's, be equal to $\epsilon_{\alpha\alpha}$. Let the energy of an adjacent A and B be taken as 0 (thus fixing the zero of energy). Now we have,[†] from Eq. (2.7),

$$\Delta\epsilon = -\epsilon_{\alpha\alpha}. \tag{8.1}$$

Again the combinatorial problem is the same; that is, $g(N_A, N_{\alpha\beta})$ has the same value as before. The total energy of mixing of the system will be $N_{\alpha\beta}\Delta\epsilon$. If N_A is fixed, the partition function of mixing will be $\sum_{N_{\alpha\beta}} g(N_A, N_{\alpha\beta}) \exp\{-N_{\alpha\beta}\Delta\epsilon/kT\}$. However, N_A is not necessarily fixed, only N being held constant. Thus the general form is

$$(\text{P.F.})_m = \sum_{N_A} \sum_{N_{\alpha\beta}} g(N_A, N_{\alpha\beta}) \exp\left\{\frac{-N_{\alpha\beta}\Delta\epsilon}{kT}\right\}. \tag{8.2}$$

So far we have tacitly assumed that the magnetic field is zero. If there is a magnetic field equal to H in such a direction that the spins tend to orient in the direction A, then there will be an additional energy of interaction with the field equal to

$$(N_B - N_A)\mu H = (N - 2N_A)\mu H, \tag{8.3}$$

where μ is the magnetic moment. Thus the $(\text{P.F.})_m$ needs an additional factor, and we have

$$(\text{P.F.})_m = \exp\left\{\frac{-N\mu H}{kT}\right\} \sum_{N_A} \sum_{N_{\alpha\beta}} g(N_A, N_{\alpha\beta}) \exp\left\{-\frac{N_{\alpha\beta}\Delta\epsilon}{kT}\right\} \exp\left\{\frac{2N_A\mu H}{kT}\right\}$$

$$= \lambda^{-N/2} \sum_{N_{\alpha\beta}} x^{N_{\alpha\beta}} \sum_{N_A} g(N_A, N_{\alpha\beta})\lambda^{N_A}; \tag{8.4}$$

[†] In the literature $\Delta\epsilon$ is usually referred to as $2J$.

here $\lambda = \exp\{2\mu H/kT\}$ and, as before, $x = \exp\{-\Delta\epsilon/kT\}$. Comparison with Eq. (5.9) shows that, aside from the factor $\lambda^{-N/2}$, this $(\text{P.F.})_m$ has the same form as the $(\text{G.P.F.})_m$ for the mixture of A and B molecules. If we write

$$(\text{P.F.})'_m = (\text{P.F.})_m \lambda^{N/2}, \tag{8.5}$$

then we may solve problems analogous to Probs. 12.12 and 12.13, with λ substituted for λ_A and $(\text{P.F.})'_m$ substituted for $(\text{G.P.F.})_m$. Thus we may work with the canonical partition function in just the same way that we previously worked with the grand partition function. With $\lambda = 1$, we may calculate the specific heat of the Ising lattice and the magnetization, which, per spin, is given by

$$\mu \frac{\bar{N}_A - \bar{N}_B}{N} = \mu \left(\frac{2\bar{N}_A}{N} - 1 \right)$$

by using the results of the previous sections.

As noted at the beginning of this section, the Ising model is a rather oversimplified picture of the magnetic case. Some progress has been made for a more general Ising model [25], in which the spin component can take on several values and in which the interaction energy between adjacent spins is proportional to $s_z s'_z$, where s_z and s'_z are the respective components. Also, some attention has been given to the Heisenberg model [25, 26], in which the interaction is proportional to $s_x s'_x + s_y s'_y + s_z s'_z$, where the spin components are quantum mechanical operators.

REFERENCES

1. J. H. Hildebrand and R. L. Scott, *Regular Solutions*, Englewood Cliffs, N.J., Prentice-Hall, 1962.
2. E. A. Guggenheim, *Mixtures*, Oxford, Eng., Clarendon Press, 1952.
3. I. Prigogine, *The Molecular Theory of Solutions*, New York, Interscience, 1957.
4. T. L. Hill, *An Introduction to Statistical Thermodynamics*, Reading, Mass., Addison-Wesley, 1960, Chap. 20.
5. T. L. Hill, *Statistical Mechanics*, New York, McGraw-Hill, 1956, Chap. 7.
6. F. C. Nix and W. Shockley, *Rev. Mod. Phys.*, **10**, 1 (1938).
7. G. S. Rushbrooke in *Changements de Phases*, Paris, Société de Chimie Physique, 1952, pp. 177–91.
8. G. F. Newell and E. W. Montroll, *Rev. Mod. Phys.*, **25**, 353 (1953).
9. A. Münster, *Statistische Thermodynamik*, Berlin, Springer, 1956, Kap. 16, 17, 18, and 20.

10. H. S. Green and C. A. Hurst, *Order-Disorder Phenomena*, New York, Interscience, 1964.

11. R. H. Fowler and E. A. Guggenheim, *Statistical Thermodynamics*, Cambridge, Eng., Cambridge Univ. Press, 1939, pp. 350–66.

12. G. S. Rushbrooke, *Introduction to Statistical Mechanics*, Oxford, Eng., Clarendon Press, 1949, pp. 296–310.

13. E. Ising, *Z. Physik*, **31**, 253 (1925).

14. L. Onsager, *Phys. Rev.*, **65**, 117 (1944).

15. B. Kaufman, *Phys. Rev.*, **76**, 1232 (1949).

16. M. Kac and J. C. Ward, *Phys. Rev.*, **88**, 1332 (1952).

17. C. Domb, *Proc. Roy. Soc.* (London), **A199**, 199 (1949).

18. A. J. Wakefield, *Proc. Camb. Phil. Soc.*, **47**, 419, 799 (1951).

19. E. Trefftz, *Z. Physik*, **127**, 371 (1950).

20. T. Tanaka, H. Katsumori, and S. Toshima, *Prog. Theor. Phys.*, **6**, 17 (1951).

21. C. Domb and M. F. Sykes, *Proc. Roy. Soc.* (London), **A235**, 247 (1956).

22. G. A. Baker, Jr., *Phys. Rev.*, **124**, 768 (1961).

23. J. W. Essam and M. E. Fisher, *J. Chem. Phys.*, **38**, 802 (1963).

24. M. E. Fisher, *J. Math. Phys.*, **4**, 278 (1963), **5**, 944 (1964).

25. C. Domb and M. F. Sykes, *Phys. Rev.*, **128**, 168 (1962).

26. J. M. Ziman, *Principles of the Theory of Solids*, Cambridge, Eng., Cambridge Univ. Press, 1964, pp. 291–95.

PROBLEMS

12.1. Consider the solid–vapor equilibrium discussed in Sec. 7-9. Suppose the solid to be an ideal solution of two types of atom, A and B, which replace each other on the lattice. Show how (P.F.), Eq. (9.1) of Chap. 7, will be modified, assuming there to be N_A molecules of A and N_B of B divided between the solid and vapor phases. Find the partial vapor pressures by finding the maximum term in (P.F.), under the proper constraints, and show how they depend on the mole fractions in the solid phase. Find the analogue of Eq. (9.5) of Chap. 7.

12.2. Suppose we have a surface with N sites upon which may be adsorbed molecules either of type A or type B. Let the energies of adsorption (the energy necessary to just remove a molecule from the minimum of the potential energy curve at the site) be ϵ_A and ϵ_B, respectively, let the free volumes of adsorbed molecules be $v_{f,A}$ and $v_{f,B}$, respectively, let the total number of A be N_A and the total number of B be N_B, and let the gas phase volume be V. Assume that the adsorbed molecules do not interact with each other, so that A, B, and the vacant spaces form essentially a ternary ideal solution. Find expressions for the numbers of A and B adsorbed, and their concentrations in the vapor phase.

12.3. An assembly of interacting magnetic dipoles is a system that exhibits a critical point, which is brought out by the following very crude model. Suppose the dipoles have a magnetic moment μ, and suppose that the resultant dipole moment of all the dipoles is in the z direction, and has a value $N\bar{\mu}_z$, where $\bar{\mu}_z$ is the average value of $\mu \cos \theta$, where θ is the angle made by any given magnetic dipole with the z direction. Suppose that the local field at any instant is also in the z direction and is given by $c\bar{\mu}_z$, where c is a constant, the energy of interaction of the dipole with the field thus being $-c\bar{\mu}_z\mu \cos \theta$. Set up an expression for $\bar{\mu}_z$ where the right-hand side will also involve $\bar{\mu}_z$, giving thus an implicit equation for $\bar{\mu}_z$. Plot the right-hand side as a function of $\bar{\mu}_z$. What is the condition that the implicit equation have a solution other than $\bar{\mu}_z = 0$? Show that no such solution will be possible if $kT > \frac{1}{3}c\mu^2$.

12.4. Calculate $\Delta E_m/zN\Delta\epsilon$ for a regular solution, and for the quasi-chemical solution with $\exp\{-2\Delta\epsilon/kT\} = \frac{1}{2}$, at $x_A = \frac{1}{3}$. Explain in qualitative physical terms why ΔE_m is less for the quasi-chemical than for the regular solution.

12.5. If $N_{\alpha\alpha}$, $N_{\beta\beta}$, and $N_{\alpha\beta}$ were independent of each other except for the "stoichiometric" relations implied in the "chemical" equation, A–A + B–B $\longrightarrow$ 2A–B, the number of possible arrangements would be $(zN/2)!/N_{\alpha\alpha}!N_{\beta\beta}!N_{\alpha\beta}!$ and we would have

$$(\text{P.F.})_m = \sum_{N_{\alpha\beta}} \frac{(zN/2)!}{N_{\alpha\alpha}!N_{\beta\beta}!N_{\alpha\beta}!} \exp\left\{-\frac{N_{\alpha\beta}\Delta\epsilon}{kT}\right\}.$$

Why is this not a satisfactory form for the quasi-chemical approximation? Show which of the necessary relations would not be obeyed.

12.6. In a one-dimensional row of molecules of types A and B we may assume that the A–B linkages divide the row into (almost exactly) $N_{\alpha\beta}/2$ boxes containing A–A linkages and $N_{\alpha\beta}/2$ boxes containing B–B linkages, each type being distributed at random in its own particular set of boxes. Show that $(\text{P.F.})_m$ is correctly and precisely given in this case by Eq. (3.6) with z set equal to 2.

12.7. Show that in the one-dimensional case considered in Prob. 12.6 there is never any separation of phases.

12.8. Show that Eq. (3.14) can be reduced to

$$\ln (\text{P.F.})_m = \left(1 - \frac{z}{2}\right) N \ln N - (1 - z)N_A \ln N_A$$

$$- (1 - z)N_B \ln N_B - \frac{zN_A}{2} \ln \frac{2N_{\alpha\alpha}}{z} - \frac{zN_B}{2} \ln \frac{2N_{\beta\beta}}{z}.$$

12.9. Show, using Eq. (3.5), that the limiting value of Eq. (3.18) as $N_A \longrightarrow 0$ is $-1/N_A$.

12.10. Evaluate Eq. (5.9) for an ideal solution, and find an analytic form for $(\text{G.P.F.})_m$ by applying the binomial theorem. Use the results of Problem 12.12 to find $\bar{N}_A$ and show that $\bar{N}_A/\bar{N}_B = \exp\{\mu_{m,A}/kT\}/\exp\{\mu_{m,B}/kT\}$. Show that this relation is consistent with Eqs. (1.4) and (1.5).

12.11. In the evaluation of Eq. (6.4) count up the number of possibilities for $N_{\alpha\mathfrak{B}} = 8$ with $N_A = 3$ by choosing the middle A first.

12.12. Show that $\bar{N}_A = \lambda_A \partial \ln (\text{G.P.F.})_m/\partial\lambda_A$.

12.13. Show that $\bar{N}_{\alpha\mathfrak{B}} = x \, \partial \ln (\text{G.P.F.})_m/\partial x$. (Note: There are two distinct parts to this proof.)

12.14. Write the expression for ΔS_m for the lattice gas, assuming it to be an ideal lattice gas ($\Delta\epsilon = 0$), and show that $(\partial\Delta S_m/\partial N)_{T,N_A}$ becomes infinite as N_A approaches N.

12.15. Suppose that N molecules of HCl are arranged in a plane with the Cl atoms in a square array, and that the H atom belonging to a particular Cl atom is on one of the lines joining the Cl's, but that an arrangement in which both H's are on the same line between the same two Cl's is excluded.

   a. Indicate what you would need to know in order to calculate the entropy due to the random placing of the H's.

   b. Make an attempt at an approximate evaluation.

13

The Liquid State

13-1. *Introduction*

It is possible to give a complete statistical mechanical description of an ideal gas, in which there are negligible interactions between the molecules, and a reasonably satisfactory description of a simple solid consisting of atoms arranged in a regular lattice. On the other hand, a liquid, even one consisting of simple, spherically symmetrical molecules, presents a much more difficult problem, for it has neither the regular arrangement nor the simplicity which comes from lack of interaction between the molecules. As a result it is necessary to make various approximations in order to obtain usable results.

Among the approximate theories which have been developed are the cell theory and the lattice theory. In the cell theory one attempts to calculate a partition function for a single, usually spherical molecule in the field of its neighbors, much as one does in the Einstein theory of solids. Essentially, then, one considers the liquid to be like a solid and attempts to introduce into this picture features which will take care of the disorder which is present in the liquid.

In a lattice theory it is assumed that there are certain lattice points upon which the molecules may be placed and about which they vibrate. Disorder is introduced by allowing some of the lattice points to be vacant, and expansion of the liquid is taken care of by increasing the number of vacancies. This is the situation with the lattice gas, which was considered in the preceding chapter, provided one can neglect all but nearest-neighbor interactions. Indeed, we shall see later in this chapter that the theory of the lattice gas can be adapted to describe roughly the equilibrium between a liquid and its vapor.

A lattice theory may, in principle, be made as exact as desired by increasing the number of, and decreasing the spacing between, the lattice points. This means, of course, that only a small fraction of the lattice points is occupied, and it complicates the calculation. If the distance between lattice points is the same as the intermolecular distance, we can in first approximation, as we have noted, neglect interactions between atoms which are not on adjacent lattice points. If, on the other hand, the lattice points are much more closely spaced, this will not be possible.

According to the simple lattice theory, the number of close neighbors of any given molecule (the coordination number) continually decreases as the liquid expands, since expansion is considered to be caused solely by creation of vacancies. In a cell theory, this is not necessarily so, since the expansion can occur by an increase of intermolecular distance, leaving the mean positions of the molecules relative to each other unaltered except in scale. In actual fact, changes of both kinds take place. The average coordination number decreases and the intermolecular distance increases as the liquid expands. The regularity implied by the lattice theory is, of course, not found. Although a certain amount of order is found by X-ray examination of liquids, in the sense that certain intermolecular distances occur more frequently than others, actually one is measuring merely average locations, and the details of the surroundings of any given molecule will at any instant differ from those of its neighbors.

There are, indeed, a number of discussions of the liquid state which revolve around consideration of the distribution of molecules around a central molecule. If this distribution function could be found precisely, then the problem of the liquid state could be solved completely for spherical molecules. Since this approach involves many points of interest from the viewpoint of statistical mechanics, we will deal with it in detail later in this chapter.

13-2. *Cell Theories and Communal Entropy*

One of the difficulties of the cell theory arises because, with liquids, one cannot consider the cell to be fixed in position. Even if we could assume that the surroundings of any given molecule were exactly like those of any other, we would have to recognize that these surroundings can be displaced somewhat without actual interchange of molecules. Interchange of identical molecules would of course produce no change in configuration, but fluctuations in position which do not involve interchange will produce a contribution to the entropy which is known as "communal" [1] or "fluctuation" † entropy. Although some theories of the liquid state in principle include the communal entropy without its being explicitly mentioned, in a cell theory it must be calculated separately. This is often difficult to do, and in most cases resort is made to some, hopefully intelligent, guesswork.

The name communal entropy came from some considerations in the calculation of the entropy of a perfect gas. The configuration integral (translational part) is actually equal to $V^N/N!$. But let us suppose the volume V to be divided into N cells of volume V/N, and that one molecule is confined to each of these cells. In this case, the configuration integral for the assembly would be $(V/N)^N$. Because, in the real gas, a molecule is not confined to its own cell but the volume of the entire container is held in common, the assembly possesses an extra entropy, or communal entropy, given by

$$S_c = k \ln \frac{V^N}{N!} - k \ln \left(\frac{V}{N}\right)^N \approx kN. \tag{2.1}$$

Per molecule, the communal entropy is equal to $k = k \ln e$, and each molecule has effectively an available volume e-fold greater than if each molecule were confined to its cell. It may be said that the molecule may range, on the average, over a volume e-fold greater than V/N before it has in effect exchanged places with another molecule.

Exactly the same result will hold for a one-dimensional case [3] in which point molecules are constrained to move along a line of length L. It is necessary only to replace V by L in Eq. (2.1). The configuration integral $(L/N)^N$ for the case of each molecule confined to its cell is obvious. The configuration integral for the case of free motion along the line $L^N/N!$ can be obtained by introducing the divisor $N!$ to take care of the exchange of like molecules. Alternatively it can be set up as an integral in which no exchange is allowed, in which the Nth molecule is allowed to go from $x_N = 0$ to $x_N = L$, the $(N-1)$th can go from $x_{N-1} = 0$ to $x_{N-1} = x_N$, and so on. The integral then becomes

---

† The term "fluctuation entropy" was introduced by Frank [2]; as used by him it did not mean quite the same thing as "communal entropy." We shall later use the term in still a different sense.

$$\int_0^{x_2} dx_1 \int_0^{x_3} dx_2 \int_0^{x_4} dx_3 \cdots \int_0^L dx_N = \int_0^{x_3} x_2\, dx_2 \int_0^{x_4} dx_3 \cdots \int_0^L dx_N$$

$$= \int_0^{x_4} \frac{x_3^2}{2}\, dx_3 \cdots \int_0^L dx_N = \int_0^{x_5} \frac{x_4^3}{3!}\, dx_4 \cdots \int_0^L dx_N$$

$$\cdot \quad \cdot \quad \cdot \quad \cdot \quad \cdot \quad \cdot \quad \cdot \quad \cdot \quad \cdot \quad \cdot \quad \cdot \quad \cdot$$

$$= \frac{L^N}{N!}. \tag{2.2}$$

This latter method of deduction is of some interest because it can be applied at once to an assembly of N spheres of radius σ constrained to move with their centers on a straight line of length L. The Nth sphere can move from $x_N = (N-1)\sigma + \frac{1}{2}\sigma$ (with all the other spheres piled together at one end of the line) to $x_N = L - \frac{1}{2}\sigma$, the $(N-1)$th sphere can move from $x_{N-1} = (N-2)\sigma + \frac{1}{2}\sigma$ to $x_{N-1} = x_N - \sigma$, etc., and the integral becomes

$$\int_{\sigma/2}^{x_2-\sigma} dx_1 \int_{3\sigma/2}^{x_3-\sigma} dx_2 \int_{5\sigma/2}^{x_4-\sigma} dx_3 \cdots \int_{(N-\frac{1}{2})\sigma}^{L-\sigma/2} dx_N = \frac{(L-N\sigma)^N}{N!}. \tag{2.3}$$

The spheres thus have the same configuration integral as would point particles on the free length $L - N\sigma$. If each sphere is confined to its cell of length L/N and *no part of it is allowed to overlap* into the next cell (see Fig. 13-1) then the free length available to each sphere is $L/N - \sigma = (L - N\sigma)/N$, and the configuration integral is $(L - N\sigma)^N/N^N$. Thus, once again, the communal entropy is equal to kN.

This result can be used to learn something about the communal entropy of a three-dimensional assembly of hard spheres, which has some resemblance to a fluid [4–6]. Let us take such an assembly with a simple cubic arrangement of the spheres, each sphere having six nearest neighbors and being part of three rows which extend in the x, y, and z directions, respectively. If the spheres are close enough together, almost touching each other, motion in one direction will not appreciably interfere with motion in the other two directions. Thus there will be a communal entropy of k for each direction of motion of each sphere, or $3k$

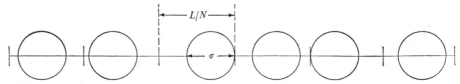

Figure 13-1. One-dimensional distribution of spheres along a line, each in its own cell.

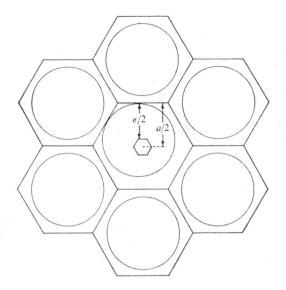

Figure 13-2. Two-dimensional lattice. Each sphere, except the center one, is shown at the center of its cell. The center sphere is at the edge of its cell.

per sphere, altogether. We can think of the whole space as being divided into N cubic cells, one for each sphere, the center of the cell being called the lattice point. The communal entropy is the difference in entropy between the actual system and the entropy which would be found if each sphere were confined to its cell and were not allowed to overlap in any part into an adjacent cell.

In a close-packed lattice, each sphere would be confined to a cell each face of which bisected the line joining the lattice point of a sphere and that of a neighbor. Because of the close-packed lines of spheres, motions of a given sphere in a given line would be interfered with by spheres in adjacent lines, and the communal entropy would be somewhat less than $3k$.

If each sphere were confined to its own cell, the free volume would consist of a solid figure having the same shape as the cell, but with the distance from the center to a face reduced to $a/2 - \sigma/2$ instead of $a/2$ (see Fig. 13-2 for a two-dimensional analogy), where a is the distance between lattice points of adjacent spheres. Thus the free volume would bear to the total volume the ratio $(a - \sigma)^3 : a^3$. In actuality, however, even if we suppose that all the neighbors are held fixed at their lattice positions, the central sphere would (in a densely packed assembly) be able to travel twice the distance $a/2 - \sigma/2$ (or even very slightly more at some points if the free volume is not very small) before it collided with the adjoining sphere, since the face of a cell bisects the line joining lattice points of adjacent spheres. This would result in the effective free volume's being multiplied by a factor 2^3, or 8, thus already accounting for a fairly large portion of the communal entropy. This factor is almost exactly equal to e^2, so the remaining communal entropy is equal approximately to $k \ln e = k$ per molecule. This final part of the communal entropy has sometimes itself been called the communal entropy, and this usage is, of course, to some extent a matter of definition. If we choose as the standard of comparison a situation in which the center of the molecule is not allowed to leave its cell, rather than one in which the edges of the molecules cannot overlap into the next cell, then the extra entropy will, indeed, be that arising from the effects of fluctuations in the positions of the neighbors on the motion of a central molecule. This extra entropy is, more or less fortuitously, almost exactly the same, for a set of closely spaced hard spheres in simple cubic array, as the communal entropy of an ideal gas, and, to avoid confusion, we shall call it the *fluctuation* entropy (which is now different from the communal entropy). Thus the fluctuation entropy of a three-dimensional, closely spaced assembly of hard spheres goes more or less smoothly into the communal entropy of the ideal gas, which in this case is identical to the fluctuation entropy. In general the fluctuation entropy will be less than the communal entropy. In the ideal gas it is, of course, possible for a given molecule to penetrate far into its neighbor's territory, but if the latter simultaneously penetrates into the territory of the first molecule, the effect on the phase integral cancels out, for this movement amounts to exchange of the two identical molecules. It is this exchange effect which prevents the free transfer of molecules in the gas from producing a communal entropy greater than k per molecule.

We are more interested in a system in which the molecules have attractive forces than we are in an assembly consisting of hard spheres. For a solid composed of spherical molecules, the difference in entropy between a Debye solid (assuming that this represents fairly accurately the true situation) and the corresponding Einstein solid (in which any given particle moves in the field of its *fixed* neighbors) is just the fluctuation entropy.

From Table 2.1 [Sec. 2-3] we see that the high-temperature limit for the entropy of an Einstein solid with N molecules having three vibrational degrees of freedom is (where $e \equiv \exp\{1\}$)

$$S_\mathrm{E} \approx 3Nk \ln \frac{ekT}{h\nu} = 3Nk \ln \frac{eT}{\Theta_\mathrm{E}},\qquad(2.4)$$

whereas, from Eq. (2.20) of Chap. 9, since $D(\Theta_\mathrm{D}/T) \longrightarrow 1$ as $T \longrightarrow \infty$, we have

$$S_D \approx 4Nk - 3Nk \ln \left(1 - \exp \left\{ \frac{-\Theta_D}{T} \right\} \right)$$

$$\approx 3Nk \ln \frac{eT}{\Theta_D} + Nk, \tag{2.5}$$

corresponding to

$$(\text{p.f.}) = e \left(\frac{T}{\Theta_D} \right)^3. \tag{2.6}$$

Thus the fluctuation entropy will be

$$S_F = S_D - S_E = 3Nk \ln \frac{\Theta_E}{\Theta_D} + Nk = Nk \left(1 - \frac{3}{2} \ln \frac{5}{3} \right) \tag{2.7}$$

$$= 0.234Nk,$$

by Eq. (3.4) of Chap. 9. In this case the fluctuation entropy is considerably less than k per molecule.

If we write the partition function of a fluid in the form

$$(\text{P.F.}) = (\text{p.f.})^N = (\text{p.f.})_0^N \exp \left\{ \frac{S_F}{k} \right\}, \tag{2.8}$$

then a cell theory may be characterized by the fact that it attempts to make a direct estimate of $(\text{p.f.})_0$ and S_F, or of (p.f.), which then includes the communal entropy. Such a partition function will have some of the characteristics of the partition function for a solid and some of that for a gas. For the molecules move in the fields of their neighbors, and their motion has some of the characteristics of vibrational motion, but sometimes, in a fluid, they can also slip past each other without excessive change in potential energy. Thus they engage in something resembling translational motion. We may expect, also, that the effective frequency for the vibrational motion in a liquid will be lowered from that of the solid, not only because the average coordination number is lower in a liquid, but also because the various neighbors are not so definitely fixed in position.

The force on a spherical molecule in a solid, which arises when it is displaced from its equilibrium along the line joining it with the two neighbor molecules lying on either side of it, is due not only to these two neighbors, but also to the neighbors which lie somewhat to the side of the direction of motion (as in Fig. 9-6). Indeed, the force constant for the vibration of an atom surrounded by other atoms in a cubic close-packed array is approximately twice as great as the force constant for the vibration in a simple cubic lattice with the same lattice distance. This follows from Eq. (3.11) of Chap. 9, simply because the close-packed lattice has twice as many nearest neighbors. Thus a simple cubic lattice would have a Debye Θ reduced by a factor approximately $2^{1/2}$ below that of a close-packed lattice.

In a liquid the packing resembles a close-packed lattice more closely than it does a simple cubic lattice. However, the side-atoms are not in fixed positions, and it seems reasonable to suppose that they do not greatly affect the motion of a central atom, so that a liquid acts more like interpenetrating rows of spheres, and thus resembles a simple cubic lattice to some extent. However, the side atoms do occupy space [the molecular volume of a cubic close-packed lattice is $(a/2^{1/6})^3$, where a is the distance of closest lattice points, whereas that of a simple cubic lattice is a^3, and the free volumes may be supposed to be in proportion]. To allow for this it is suggested that the effective Debye Θ for the liquid should be taken as $2^{1/6}\Theta/2^{1/2}$ or $\Theta/2^{1/3}$ rather than $\Theta/2^{1/2}$. If it were legitimate to suppose that only the vibrational motion need be included, we would then write $[2^{1/3} e^{1/3} T/\Theta(a_0)]^3$, for the partition function (p.f.) of the liquid, following Eq. (2.6). Here $\Theta(a_0)$ is the Debye temperature for the solid for an intermolecular distance a_0 corresponding closely to the actual average closest intermolecular distance in the disordered liquid.

The partition function for an interpenetrating row of hard spheres (which has only translational motion) would have been written $[(2\pi m k T/h^2)^{1/2}2^{-1/6}e(a - \sigma)]^3$. The factor $2^{-1/6}$ again takes care of the space-filling properties of the side-atoms, the factor e takes care of the communal entropy, and $a - \sigma$ is the free length. A reasonable compromise between the vibrational and translational motion might be reached by writing

$$(\text{p.f.}) = \left[\frac{2^{1/3}e^{1/3}T}{\Theta(a_0)} + \left(\frac{2\pi m k T}{h^2}\right)^{1/2}2^{-1/6}e(a - a_0)\right]^3, \tag{2.9}$$

which in effect takes the distance a_0 as a kind of boundary between the types of motion. Of course, this is only an estimate and it has the disadvantage that a_0 must be determined empirically.

To get the thermodynamic quantities we write

$$A = -RT \ln (\text{p.f.}) + E_p, \tag{2.10}$$

which takes explicit account of the potential energy E_p, since (p.f.) is reckoned from the zero of energy defined by the configuration of minimum potential energy for any given volume V. We can use the thermo-dynamic equation

$$S = -\left(\frac{\partial A}{\partial T}\right)_V \qquad (2.11)$$

to get the entropy; then, on assuming a_0 is a function of V (or a) only,

$$S = R \ln (\text{p.f.}) + RT \left[\frac{\partial \ln (\text{p.f.})}{\partial T}\right]_{a,a_0}. \qquad (2.12)$$

An attempt was made to use these equations to correlate data on liquid (or fluid) argon for volumes near that of the normal liquid up to high pressures [7, 8]. It was found best to replace the coefficient $2^{1/3} e^{1/3}$ in Eq. (2.9) by one about 8% larger. Next, a value of a_0 (ranging from 3.806 Å when a was 3.94 to 3.891 Å when a was 4.15 Å), was chosen to fit the entropy fairly well at any given V or a, up to pressures of several thousand atmospheres and $\Theta(a_0)$ was estimated by using data from the solid. Then the thermodynamic data could be correlated; a_0 appeared to increase with a, but more and more slowly as a grew larger. Thus as the volume increases, the vibrational part of the motion becomes less and less important, as is to be expected. However, the data on argon which were used were probably not very accurate, so details will not be given here. The equations undoubtedly describe the situation qualitatively, but one could not expect them to be quantitatively correct.

A number of modified cell theories have been proposed [9–12]. A cell-lattice theory has been developed by Eyring and his collaborators [13] and seems to have had a considerable measure of empirical success, although the basis of some of the assumptions may not be entirely clear.

13-3. *Modified Lattice Theory of a Liquid*

In this section we deal with a simple lattice theory of a liquid, modified to some extent by what might be called an admixture of cell theory.†
Our model of a liquid is actually a lattice gas. We assume that we have a regular lattice, with N lattice points. On this lattice there will be placed N_A molecules, leaving then $N - N_A = N_B$ empty places or holes. This is the same problem that was treated in the preceding chapter.

---

† For general references on lattice theories see [9, 12]. For a theory more specifically related to Sec. 13-3 see [14, 15], also O. K. Rice in [10, pp. 439–44].

The partition function, then [following Eq. (3.1) of Chap. 12 and in the light of Eqs. (2.2) of Chap. 12, setting $g(N_A, N_{\alpha\beta}) \equiv g(N_{\alpha\alpha}, N_{\beta\beta}, N_{\alpha\beta})$], can be written for fixed N

$$\text{(P.F.)} = \sum_{N_{\alpha\beta}} \text{(p.f.)}_A^{N_A} g(N_A, N_{\alpha\beta}) \exp\left\{\frac{-E}{kT}\right\}; \tag{3.1}$$

(p.f.)_A is the local partition function of a molecule (the partition function for the holes is of course 1) and E is given by

$$E = \Delta E_m + E_A$$
$$= N_{\alpha\beta}\Delta\epsilon + \frac{zN_A}{2}\epsilon_{\alpha\alpha} \tag{3.2}$$

[compare Eqs. (2.5) and (2.7) of Chap. 12 with $\epsilon_{\beta\beta} = \epsilon_{\alpha\beta} = 0$]. This model really treats the liquid as if it were a solid. As noted in Sec. 12-7, it can account for the equilibrium between the condensed phase and the vapor, as a sort of mixing phenomenon between molecules and holes, but does not account for the transition between liquid and solid. We may take some account of the liquid-like nature of a lattice with some holes, by considering the possible variation of (p.f.)_A with the surroundings of a molecule. Let us suppose that (p.f.)_A is increased by a factor $\exp\{\phi\}$ for each neighboring lattice space not occupied by another molecule, i.e., for each A–B contact. This factor implies a gas-like character of (p.f.)_A introduced by the ability to move into an adjoining space. There will be altogether $N_{\alpha\beta}$ such contacts in the assembly, or, on the average, $N_{\alpha\beta}/N_A$ per molecule. Thus we can write

$$\text{(p.f.)}_A = \text{(p.f.)}_{\alpha\alpha} \exp\left\{\frac{N_{\alpha\beta}\phi}{N_A}\right\}, \tag{3.3}$$

where $\text{(p.f.)}_{\alpha\alpha}$ is the value of (p.f.)_A when all the contacts are of the A–A type. On introducing this and Eq. (3.2) into Eq. (3.1), the latter becomes

$$\text{(P.F.)} = \text{(p.f.)}_{\alpha\alpha}^{N_A} \exp\left\{\frac{-zN_A\epsilon_{\alpha\alpha}}{2kT}\right\} \sum_{N_{\alpha\beta}} g(N_A, N_{\alpha\beta}) \exp\left\{\frac{-N_{\alpha\beta}(\Delta\epsilon - \phi kT)}{kT}\right\}. \tag{3.4}$$

The factor in front of the summation sign depends only on the molecules, not the holes, and we may write

$$\text{(P.F.)}_m = \sum_{N_{\alpha\beta}} g(N_A, N_{\alpha\beta}) \exp\left\{\frac{-N_{\alpha\beta}\Delta\epsilon}{kT}\right\} \exp\{N_{\alpha\beta}\phi\}. \tag{3.5}$$

This has the same form as Eq. (3.2) of Chap. 12, except that $\Delta\epsilon - \phi kT$ replaces $\Delta\epsilon$, and it completely determines the phase relationships to be expected from the model used. If we can find the proper values of z, $\Delta\epsilon$, and ϕ, all the results of the preceding chapter can be taken over immediately.

To illustrate the application of these results we take argon, which crystallizes in the face-centered cubic structure. It would seem reasonable, therefore, to set $z = 12$; here $\Delta\epsilon = -\epsilon_{\alpha\alpha}/2$ [Eq. (7.1) of Chap. 12], and it may be obtained from the energy of vaporization of the crystal, say at the normal melting point. In a crystal there are $zN_A/2$ bonds or contacts. In evaporation, $z/2$ contacts per molecule are broken, if we neglect the small number of holes in the solid. Thus the heat ΔH of vaporization is equal to $-z\epsilon_{\alpha\alpha}/2 - kT/2$ per molecule. (The term $-kT/2$ enters because the thermal energy per molecule in the solid† is $3kT$, whereas in the vapor it is only $3kT/2$, but on the other hand the PV term in the enthalpy of the vapor is equal to kT.) The heat of sublimation of argon at its melting point is about 1,857 cal mole^{-1} [16, Band II, Teil 4, p. 399], and $\epsilon_{\alpha\alpha}$ is thus equal to -326 cal mole^{-1}, so $\Delta\epsilon$ is 163 cal mole^{-1}.

The evaluation of ϕ is slightly more involved but can be carried out by considering a vapor so dilute that it can be treated as an ideal gas. For an ideal gas with N_A molecules in a volume V, the configurational part of the partition function will be $V^{N_A}/N_A! = (NV_0)^{N_A}/N_A!$, where N is the total number of lattice points and V_0 is the volume per lattice point (i.e., essentially the molecular volume of the solid).

In a very dilute gas the molecules are in contact only a negligible fraction of the time. From the lattice-gas point of view, this means that $N_{\alpha\beta}$ is almost always equal to one value, namely, zN_A, and $g(N_A, N_{\alpha\beta})$ for this value of $N_{\alpha\beta}$ is equal to $\sum_{N_{\alpha\beta}} g(N_A, N_{\alpha\beta})$, or the total possible number of configurations: $N!/N_A!(N - N_A)!$. We will, therefore, have for $N_A \ll N$

$$(\text{P.F.}) = (\text{p.f.})_{\alpha\alpha}^{N_A} \exp\left\{\frac{-zN_A\epsilon_{\alpha\alpha}}{2kT}\right\} \left[\frac{N!}{N_A!(N - N_A)!}\right]$$

$$\times \exp\{zN_A\phi\} \exp\left\{\frac{-zN_A\Delta\epsilon}{kT}\right\}. \qquad (3.6)$$

Since for an ideal gas $E = N_{\alpha\beta}\Delta\epsilon + (zN_A/2)\epsilon_{\alpha\alpha}$ is taken as zero, the factor $\exp\{-zN_A\epsilon_{\alpha\alpha}/2kT\} \exp\{-zN_A\Delta\epsilon/kT\}$ is simply unity. The

---

† $E_z + E_t$ is actually about 16 cal per mole larger than $3kT$ at the melting point (see Table 9-2). This has been allowed for.

configuration part of (P.F.) will be obtained by leaving out the momentum factor which occurs in $(p.f.)_{aa}$, thus replacing $(p.f.)_{aa}$ by v_f, the corresponding free volume.

Equating the logarithm of the configurational parts of the two forms of partition function, we have

$$N_A \ln N + N_A \ln V_0 - N_A \ln N_A + N_A = N \ln N - N_A \ln N_A$$
$$- (N - N_A) \ln (N - N_A) + N_A \ln v_f + N_A z\phi. \quad (3.7)$$

Since for a dilute gas $N \gg N_A$ we may write

$$\ln (N - N_A) = \ln N + \ln \left(1 - \frac{N_A}{N}\right) \approx \ln N - \frac{N_A}{N},$$

we see that Eq. (3.7) reduces to

$$z\phi \approx \ln \frac{V_0}{v_f}. \quad (3.8)$$

That is to say, $\exp\{z\phi\}$ is the ratio of the volume occupied by a molecule in a solid lattice to its free volume. At very low temperatures where there are few holes in the condensed phase and few molecules in the vapor, the number of vapor molecules $N_{A,v}$ in a volume V_v of vapor is given by [Eq. (9.4) of Chap. 7]

$$N_{A,v} = \frac{V_v}{v_f} \exp \left\{ \frac{(z/2)\epsilon_{aa}}{kT} \right\}$$
$$= \frac{V_v}{v_f} \exp \left\{ \frac{-z\Delta\epsilon}{kT} \right\}, \quad (3.9)$$

since, as noted above, $\Delta\epsilon$ is equal to $-\epsilon_{aa}/2$ in this case. Thus we have

$$\ln v_f = \ln \frac{V_v}{N_{A,v}} - \frac{z\Delta\epsilon}{kT}, \quad (3.10)$$

and therefore

$$z\phi = \ln \frac{N_{A,v}}{V_v} + \ln V_0 + \frac{z\Delta\epsilon}{kT}$$
$$= \ln \frac{\rho_v}{\rho_s} + \frac{z\Delta\epsilon}{kT}, \quad (3.11)$$

where ρ_v is the density of the vapor and ρ_s is the density of the solid (neglecting any holes in it), which is in equilibrium with it.

Equation (3.11) may also be derived by considering the solid – vapor equilibrium directly on the basis of the lattice theory, applied to a dilute gas, on the one hand, and a solid with few holes on the other. For the vapor we obtain, from Eq. (3.6) [omitting the factor $(\text{p.f.})_{\alpha\alpha}^{N_A} \exp\{-zN_A\epsilon_{\alpha\alpha}/kT\}$ to get $(\text{P.F.})_m$],

$$\mu_{A,m,v} = -kT\left[\frac{\partial \ln (\text{P.F.})_m}{\partial N_{A,v}}\right]_{T,N}$$

(since holding N constant is equivalent to holding V constant)

$$= kT \ln N_{A,v} - kT \ln (N_v - N_{A,v}) - z\phi + \frac{z\Delta\epsilon}{kT}. \qquad (3.12)$$

For the solid, with $N - N_A$ very small, we have $N_{\alpha\beta} = z(N - N_A)$, instead of zN_A. However, $\sum_{N_{\alpha\beta}} g(N_A, N_{\alpha\beta})$ will still be equal to $N!/N_A!(N - N_A)!$, and therefore from Eq. (3.5)

$$\mu_{A,m,s} = kT \ln N_{A,s} - kT \ln (N_s - N_{A,s}) + z\phi - \frac{z\Delta\epsilon}{kT}. \qquad (3.13)$$

Because of the symmetry between holes in the solid and molecules in the vapor, we will have

$$\frac{N_{A,v}}{N_v - N_{A,v}} = \frac{N_s - N_{A,s}}{N_{A,s}} \approx \frac{N_{A,v}}{N_v} = \frac{\rho_v}{\rho_s},$$

since the density of lattice spaces in the vapor is approximately equal to the density of the solid. Equating $\mu_{A,m,v}$ and $\mu_{A,m,s}$, we obtain Eq. (3.11).

We may use Eq. (3.11) to evaluate ϕ for argon by taking the equilibrium between solid and vapor at the normal melting point. We have $\rho_s = 0.0405$ (from Table 9.2), and $\rho_v = 0.990 \times 10^{-4}$ moles cc^{-1}.[†] As already noted $z = 12$ and $\Delta\epsilon = 163$ cal mole^{-1}; thus $\phi = 0.48$. Taking ϕ to be independent of temperature, we note that $kT\phi$ behaves differently from $\Delta\epsilon$, and we recall that $\Delta\epsilon - \phi kT$ replaces $\Delta\epsilon$ in the theory developed in the preceding chapter. However, this difference in temperature dependence will not affect the phase equilibrium at a given temperature. It may affect the specific-heat curve slightly, but it cannot affect the singularity in this curve. In other words, the value of T_c will bear the same relation to $\Delta\epsilon - \phi kT$ as it bore to $\Delta\epsilon$ in the theory of

---

† From the vapor pressure at the triple point (see [**16**, Band II, Teil 2a, p. 4]), assuming the ideal gas law.

Chap. 12. The temperature dependence of the coexistence curve in the immediate neighborhood of the critical point will have the same general character as it had in Chap. 12.

We may now compare experimental results with the theoretical deductions. In the first place, it is known that the coexistence curve is approximately cubic, that is, $|\rho - \rho_c|$ is proportional to $(T_c - T)^{1/3}$. This agrees very well with the theoretical prediction, which as we saw in the last chapter would make $|\rho - \rho_c|$ proportional to approximately $(T_c - T)^{5/16}$. Whether the slight discrepancy is within experimental error is difficult to say. However, it also is difficult to decide just how significant is the rather good agreement, since a lattice model does not too closely resemble an actual liquid, because it places molecules on specific lattice points, allows only for holes of molecular size, and permits only nearest-neighbor interactions. The theory predicts a symmetrical coexistence curve, because of the more-or-less artificial symmetry between holes and molecules, but this of course is not observed in practice. Because of this symmetry, the molecular volume at the critical point, where there are equal numbers of holes and molecules, should be twice that of the solid. In practice it turns out to be more nearly three times as large.

From the lattice theory of Chap. 12, Domb and Sykes [17] found that the critical temperature for a face-centered cubic lattice was given by $kT_c = 0.402 \, z\Delta\epsilon$. For the liquid-vapor critical point this will become

$$kT_c = 0.402 \, z(\Delta\epsilon - \phi kT_c),$$

or

$$kT_c = \frac{0.402 \, z\Delta\epsilon}{1 + 0.402 \, z\phi}. \tag{3.14}$$

This gives $T_c = 119°\mathrm{K}$ for argon, which may be compared with the experimental value of $151°\mathrm{K}$ [16, Band II, Teil 2a, pp. 17, 186].

Finally we evaluate the critical ratio, $P_c v_c / kT_c$, where P_c and v_c are pressure and molecular volume, respectively, at the critical point. We saw in Sec. 12-7 that

$$PV = kT \ln (\text{G.P.F.})_m$$
$$= NkT \ln (\text{G.P.F.})_m^{1/N}. \tag{3.15}$$

Since $N = 2N_A$ at the critical point, this gives

$$\frac{P_c V_c}{N_{A,c} kT_c} = \frac{P_c v_c}{kT_c} = 2 \ln (\text{G.P.F.})_{m,c}^{1/N}, \tag{3.16}$$

Domb and Skyes [17] have evaluated $(\text{G.P.F.})_m^{1/N}$ for a face-centered cubic lattice at the critical point by consideration of a series expansion of the type discussed in Sec. 12-6; it turns out to be 1.131, which gives

$$\frac{P_c v_c}{kT_c} = 0.246.$$

This may be compared with the experimental value, which for argon is 0.291 [16, Band II, Teil 2a, pp. 17, 186]. Thus the lattice-gas model, in spite of its crudity, gives critical constants which are at least of the right order of magnitude.

13-4. *The Radial Distribution Function*

Some of the most powerful methods of investigating classical liquids involve the radial distribution function, which expresses the probability that the positions of two molecules bear a certain relation to each other. If we consider a liquid, such as the inert-gas liquids, composed of spherically symmetrical molecules whose positions are defined by the rectangular coordinates x, y, and z, we may define a function $g^{(2)}(x_1, y_1, z_1, x_2, y_2, z_2) \, dx_1 dy_1 dz_1 \, dx_2 dy_2 dz_2$ which is proportional to the probability of finding molecule 1 in the element of volume x_1 to $x_1 + dx_1$, etc., and, simultaneously, molecule 2 in the volume element x_2 to $x_2 + dx_2$, etc. The notation is often abbreviated by writing $g^{(2)}(\mathbf{r}_1, \mathbf{r}_2)$, where $\mathbf{r}_1$ and $\mathbf{r}_2$ are vectors with components x_1, y_1, z_1 and x_2, y_2, z_2, respectively.

If the two molecules are very far apart, the simultaneous probabilities of finding them in certain positions will be independent, and $g^{(2)}$ will approach a constant value; we may conveniently normalize $g^{(2)}$ by letting this value be 1. Since the liquids of the type considered are isotropic, $g^{(2)}$ will be a function $g^{(2)}(r)$ only of the distance r between the two molecules.

If one of the molecules is thought of as fixed in position, the probability of finding any other molecule at a given position will be proportional to $g^{(2)}(r)$. The density of molecules at any point at a distance r from the first one will be $\rho g^{(2)}(r)$, where ρ is the average number density of the liquid.† Of course, $\rho g^{(2)}(r)$ must approach ρ at large r. The quantity $g^{(2)}(r)$ can be determined experimentally by X-ray or neutron diffraction from liquids and will approach zero for very

† But see the discussion in the paragraph following Eq. (9.16).

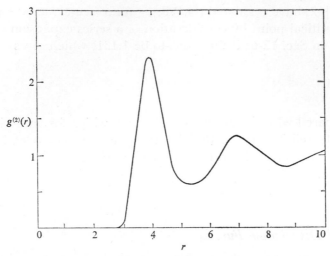

Figure 13-3. Radial distribution function of argon at 84°K, according to neutron diffraction measurements of D. G. Henshaw [18].

small r where the repulsive potential becomes very large. It rises to a maximum near the average intermolecular distance in a liquid, usually shows several maxima and minima, and eventually approaches 1. A typical curve is shown in Fig. 13-3.

The usefulness of the function $g^{(2)}(r)$ in the determination of thermodynamic functions may be shown by a simple example. If the mutual potential energy of a pair of molecules is $\epsilon_p(r)$, and if the potential energy of a given pair is independent of the presence of other molecules (i.e., if the potential is additive), the total potential energy of an atom in the field of its neighbors will clearly be $\int \epsilon_p(r)\rho g^{(2)}(r)\,d\tau$. Here, as usual, $d\tau \equiv dxdydz$. The total potential energy of N atoms will be given by

$$E_p = \tfrac{1}{2}N \int \epsilon_p(r)\rho g^{(2)}(r)\,d\tau. \tag{4.1}$$

The factor $\tfrac{1}{2}$ is included so as not to count mutual potentials of pairs twice, and $d\tau$ may of course be replaced by $4\pi r^2\,dr$, in which case r may be carried from 0 to ∞.

The total energy of the system is found by adding $\tfrac{3}{2}NkT$ to E_p:

$$E = \frac{3}{2}NkT + \frac{1}{2}N \int \epsilon_p(r)\rho g^{(2)}(r)\,d\tau. \tag{4.2}$$

13-5. *The Virial Theorem of Clausius*

The pressure may also be found if $g^{(2)}(r)$ is known. This follows for classical liquids from the virial theorem of Clausius, which is based rather directly upon Newton's laws of motion by use of the function $x_i f_{x_i} + y_i f_{y_i} + z_i f_{z_i}$, where x_i, y_i, z_i are the positional rectangular coordinates of the ith molecule, and f_{x_i}, f_{y_i}, f_{z_i} are the components of the force exerted upon it. Note that

$$x_i f_{x_i} = x_i \frac{d(m\dot{x}_i)}{dt} = \frac{d(x_i m \dot{x}_i)}{dt} - m\dot{x}_i^2. \tag{5.1}$$

If we average over the molecules in an assembly which are at or near some specific value of x_i, we see that $\overline{m\dot{x}_i}$ must be zero[†] (unless the molecules have a net momentum in some direction—in a stationary container, this would normally happen only if a sound wave were passing through the system). Thus the sum over *all* molecules $\sum x_i m \dot{x}_i$ must vanish, as must its time derivative, which is equal to $\sum_i d(x_i m \dot{x}_i)/dt$. Thus we have

$$\sum_i x_i f_{x_i} = -\sum_i m\dot{x}_i^2 = -NkT, \tag{5.2}$$

making use of the well-known expression for the average translational kinetic energy of the molecules of a classical gas.

That the term $d(x_i m \dot{x}_i)/dt$ drops out if we average for a *single* molecule over time may also be seen by integrating Eq. (5.1) over a large period of time Δt. This gives

$$\overline{x_i f_{x_i}} = \frac{(x_i m \dot{x}_i)_{t=\Delta t} - (x_i m \dot{x}_i)_{t=0}}{\Delta t} - \overline{m\dot{x}_i^2},$$

where the bars now indicate time averages. Since $x_i m \dot{x}_i$ will not increase indefinitely, the term arising from it will vanish as $\Delta t \longrightarrow \infty$.

If now we add in the y and z components, and add over all molecules, N in number, we may write

$$\sum_i (x_i f_{x_i} + y_i f_{y_i} + z_i f_{z_i}) = -3NkT. \tag{5.3}$$

[†] Although $\overline{m\dot{x}_i}$, for any specific x_i, is zero, $\overline{d(m\dot{x})/dt} = \overline{m\ddot{x}_i}$ is not. The constancy of $\overline{m\dot{x}_i}$ is maintained by the flow of molecules into and out of the particular region of space. Consider, for example, what happens close to a wall. In deriving Eq. (5.2) we take advantage of the constancy of $x_i m \dot{x}_i$ summed over *all* molecules. The dot, as usual, means differentiation with respect to time.

The virial of Clausius is the left-hand side of this equation; to analyze it let us suppose that we have our assembly in a rectangular container of volume V with edges which extend from the origin to a, b, c, in the x, y, z directions, respectively. The forces will be of two kinds—intermolecular forces and forces between the molecules of the assembly and the walls. Let us take up the latter first. The total force on all the molecules near any face of the container will be equal to the pressure P times the area of the face. This force on the molecules near the three faces of the container which pass through the origin will contribute nothing to the sum of Eq. (5.3), since for every such molecule $x_i = y_i = z_i = 0$. The contribution from all the molecules near the other three faces will be

$$-aP(bc) - bP(ac) - cP(ab) = -3PV, \qquad (5.4)$$

the products in the parentheses being the areas of the faces for which $x_i = a$, $y_i = b$, and $z_i = c$, respectively. The signs are negative, since the forces on the molecules from these faces are in the negative directions.

The other contributions to the sum will come from the interactions between the molecules. The force between any pair of molecules, i and j, is assumed to be a function of the distance r_{ij}, and the force on any given molecule may be obtained by adding vectorially the forces due to all its neighbors. The component of the force f_{x_i} is given by

$$f_{x_i} = \sum_j \frac{f(r_{ij})(x_i - x_j)}{r_{ij}}, \qquad (5.5)$$

where $f(r_{ij})$ is the force between the molecules. This is positive if the force is repulsive, since then the force tends to increase r_{ij} and there is a positive contribution to f_{x_i} if $x_i > x_j$ and $f(r_{ij}) > 0$. We see that

$$\sum_i' x_i f_{x_i} = \sum_i \sum_j \frac{x_i f(r_{ij})(x_i - x_j)}{r_{ij}}. \qquad (5.6)$$

The prime on the summation sign means that the effect of the wall is not included. We may interchange i and j on the right-hand side, since they both range over all molecules. Then Eq. (5.6) becomes

$$\sum_i' x_i f_{x_i} = \sum_i \sum_j \frac{x_j f(r_{ij})(x_j - x_i)}{r_{ij}}$$

and adding the two expressions

$$\sum_i' x_i f_{x_i} = \frac{1}{2} \sum_i \sum_j \frac{(x_i - x_j) f(r_{ij})(x_i - x_j)}{r_{ij}}$$

$$= \frac{1}{2} \sum_i \sum_j \frac{(x_i - x_j)^2 f(r_{ij})}{r_{ij}}. \qquad (5.7)$$

If we add to this the similar expressions for $\sum'_i y_i f_{y_i}$ and $\sum'_i z_i f_{z_i}$ we obtain, since $(x_i - x_j)^2 + (y_i - y_j)^2 + (z_i - z_j)^2 = r^2_{ij}$,

$$\sum'_i (x_i f_{x_i} + y_i f_{y_i} + z_i f_{z_i}) = \frac{1}{2} \sum_i \sum_j r_{ij} f(r_{ij})$$

$$= \frac{1}{2} N\rho \int rf(r) g^{(2)}(r) \, d\tau. \tag{5.8}$$

In obtaining the last expression in Eq. (5.8) we have replaced the sum over j by the sum over the volume elements $d\tau$, weighting them with the probability of finding a molecule in $d\tau$; since this sum is presumably the same for all molecules, the second summation is equivalent to multiplying by the number N of molecules.

Combining Eqs. (5.3), (5.4), and (5.8) we have

$$PV = NkT + \tfrac{1}{6} N\rho \int rf(r) g^{(2)}(r) \, d\tau,$$

or

$$P = \rho kT + \tfrac{1}{6}\rho^2 \int rf(r) g^{(2)}(r) \, d\tau. \tag{5.9}$$

Of course $f(r)$ is equal to $-d\epsilon_p(r)/dr$ and $d\tau$ may, as previously noted, be replaced by $4\pi r^2 \, dr$. The integral goes over all allowed volume elements.

For future reference we shall write down the expression obtained by differentiating Eq. (5.9) with respect to ρ:

$$\left(\frac{\partial P}{\partial \rho}\right)_T = kT + \frac{1}{3} \rho \int rf(r) g^{(2)}(r) \, d\tau + \frac{1}{6} \rho^2 \int rf(r) \left(\frac{\partial g^{(2)}(r)}{\partial \rho}\right)_T d\tau$$

$$= \frac{P}{\rho} + \frac{\rho}{6} \int rf(r) \left(\frac{\partial \rho g^{(2)}(r)}{\partial \rho}\right)_T d\tau. \tag{5.10}$$

Equation (5.9) can be derived in another way from the expressions

$$P = -\left(\frac{\partial A}{\partial V}\right)_T = kT \frac{\partial \ln (\text{P.F.})}{\partial V}$$

$$= kT \left(\frac{\partial \ln Q}{\partial V}\right)_T, \tag{5.11}$$

where

$$Q = \iint \cdots \int \exp\left\{\frac{-E_p}{kT}\right\} dx_1 dy_1 \cdots dz_N \tag{5.12}$$

is the configuration integral, this being the only part of the partition function which depends on the volume. We assume E_p to have the usual form

$$E_p = \tfrac{1}{2} \sum_{i,j} \epsilon_p(r_{ij}). \tag{5.13}$$

Let us suppose as before that the system is in a container of dimensions a, b, and c in the x, y, and z directions, and let us introduce new coordinates, $\xi_i = x_i/a$, $\eta_i = y_i/b$, $\zeta = z_i/c$. Then, since $V = abc$,

$$Q = V^N \int_0^1 \int_0^1 \cdots \int_0^1 \exp\left\{\frac{-E_p}{kT}\right\} d\xi_1 d\eta_1 \cdots d\zeta_N. \tag{5.14}$$

Suppose we change V by changing a by da, so that $dV = bc\,da$. If we do this ξ_i is now equal to $x_i/(a + da)$. We can write

$$r_{ij}^2 = a^2(\xi_i - \xi_j)^2 + b^2(\eta_i - \eta_j)^2 + c^2(\zeta_i - \zeta_j)^2, \tag{5.15}$$

treating a, b, and c as parameters. Then, holding ξ_i, $\cdots$ constant,

$$\frac{\partial r_{ij}^2}{\partial a} = 2r_{ij}\frac{\partial r_{ij}}{\partial a} = 2a(\xi_i - \xi_j)^2,$$

and

$$\frac{\partial r_{ij}}{\partial a} = \frac{a}{r_{ij}}(\xi_i - \xi_j)^2. \tag{5.16}$$

Thus we have

$$\left(\frac{\partial Q}{\partial V}\right)_T = \frac{NQ}{V} - \frac{V^N}{kT}\int_0^1 \int_0^1 \cdots \int_0^1 \left(\frac{\partial E_p}{\partial a}\right)\frac{\partial a}{\partial V}\exp\left\{\frac{-E_p}{kT}\right\} d\xi_1 d\eta_1 \cdots d\zeta_N$$

$$= \frac{NQ}{V} - \frac{V^N}{2kT}\int_0^1 \int_0^1 \cdots \int_0^1 \left[\sum_{i,j}\frac{d\epsilon_p(r_{ij})}{dr_{ij}}\frac{a}{bcr_{ij}}(\xi_i - \xi_j)^2\right]$$

$$\times \exp\left\{\frac{-E_p}{kT}\right\} d\xi_1 d\eta_1 \cdots d\zeta_N$$

$$= \frac{NQ}{V} - \frac{V^{N-1}}{2kT}\int_0^1 \int_0^1 \cdots \int_0^1 \left[\sum_{i,j}\frac{d\epsilon_p(r_{ij})}{dr_{ij}}\frac{a^2}{r_{ij}}(\xi_i - \xi_j)^2\right]$$

$$\times \exp\left\{\frac{-E_p}{kT}\right\} d\xi_1 d\eta_1 \cdots d\zeta_N. \tag{5.17}$$

Had we started by changing b or c, we would have obtained the same expression with $b^2(\eta_i - \eta_j)^2$ or $c^2(\zeta_i - \zeta_j)^2$ substituted for $a^2(\xi_i - \xi_j)^2$. Since $(\partial Q/\partial V)_T$ is equal to any of these expressions, it will be equal to $\tfrac{1}{3}$

their sum, and, using Eq. (5.15), and noting that $f(r_{ij}) = -d\epsilon_{\mathrm{p}}(r_{ij})/dr_{ij}$, we obtain

$$\left(\frac{\partial Q}{\partial V}\right)_T = \frac{NQ}{V} + \frac{V^{N-1}}{6kT} \int_0^1 \int_0^1 \cdots \int_0^1 \left[\sum_{i,j} r_{ij} f(r_{ij})\right] \exp\left\{\frac{-E_{\mathrm{p}}}{kT}\right\} d\xi_1 d\eta_1 \cdots d\zeta_N.$$
(5.18)

It is clear that dividing the integral (excluding the factor in front) by Q/V^N [note Eq. (5.14)] will yield approximately N^2 times the average value of $rf(r)$; this average value is also given by $V^{-1} \int rf(r)g^{(2)}(r)\, d\tau$. Thus, by Eq. (5.11), if we divide Eq. (5.18) through by Q, we get

$$P = \frac{NkT}{V} + \frac{N^2}{6V^2} \int rf(r)g^{(2)}(r)\, d\tau,$$
(5.19)

which is identical to Eq. (5.9).

From the results of this and the previous section it is seen that if $f(r)$ is known, and if $g^{(2)}(r)$ is known as a function of T and ρ $(= N/V)$, both the energy and pressure will be known. This is sufficient for the determination of all the thermodynamic functions. For example, $(\partial S/\partial V)_{T,N} = (\partial P/\partial T)_{V,N}$ and $T(\partial S/\partial T)_{V,N} = (\partial E/\partial T)_{V,N}$. Thus the entropy can be determined, at least in principle, as a function of T and ρ, and although its absolute value cannot be found by these means, differences and changes in entropy can be found. The intimate relation between $g^{(2)}(r)$ and the thermodynamic functions is thus demonstrated. It must be emphasized, however, that these relations depend on the forces being pairwise additive.

13-6. *Determination of the Radial Distribution Function*

The exploitation of the relations developed in the last two sections will clearly depend upon some means of determining $g^{(2)}(r)$. This function may, indeed, be determined experimentally, for example, by X-ray diffraction. However, this merely stimulates the desire for a theoretical determination, for it provides something against which the theory may be compared directly. There have been a number of attempts to get an expression for the radial distribution function.† They all involve

---

† The one we shall follow is that due to J. Yvon [19], also Born and Green [20]. An alternative method [21] utilizes the concept of a coupling parameter by variation of which from 0 to 1 the force on a given molecule due to its neighbors can gradually be "turned on." For general references, see [12, Chap. 6; 22, 23]. Percus and Yevick [24] have obtained approximate expressions for the pair distribution function by the use of collective coordinates (coordinates describing modes of vibration of the liquid as a whole). See also [25].

approximations of one sort or another, and therefore do not all give precisely the same result. To illustrate the possibilities, one of the methods used is given in this section.

The theories involve a hierarchy of higher distribution functions, in particular the function $g^{(3)}(\mathbf{r}_1, \mathbf{r}_2, \mathbf{r}_3)$, which is proportional to the probability of finding three particles at the positions defined, and which is again normalized to be equal to 1 if the distances between the particles are very large. This may also be written $g^{(3)}(r_{12}, r_{13}, r_{23})$ where r_{12}, r_{13}, and r_{23} are distances between the indicated molecules. If the positions of molecules 1 and 2 are fixed, but that of 3 is variable, we write $g^{(3)}(r_{12}; r_{13}, r_{23})$. If the pair 1 and 2, is at the particular points noted, molecule 3 may range over all positions, but all the resulting configurations will have different probabilities. We see that $g^{(2)}(r_{12})$ will be proportional to $\int g^{(3)}(r_{12}; r_{13}, r_{23}) d\tau_3$, and hence, $g^{(2)}(r_{12} = \infty)$ being equal to 1, we have (integrals go over all allowed regions of the volume)

$$g^{(2)}(r_{12}) = \frac{\int g^{(3)}(r_{12}; r_{13}, r_{23}) \, d\tau_3}{\int g^{(3)}(r_{12} = \infty ; r_{13}, r_{23}) \, d\tau_3}. \tag{6.1}$$

Now if $r_{12} = \infty$ we see that $g^{(3)}$ is equal to $g^{(2)}(r_{13}) g^{(2)}(r_{23})$, since in effect molecule 3 will come under the influence of only one of 1 and 2 at a time, and we see that if all the distances are large, $g^{(2)}(r_{13})$ and $g^{(2)}(r_{23})$ are both equal to 1, and $g^{(3)}$ will be equal to 1 also. Since this is the case over most of the range of molecule 3, we may write

$$\int g^{(3)}(r_{12} = \infty ; r_{13}, r_{23}) \, d\tau \approx V. \tag{6.2}$$

Hence, to an excellent approximation,

$$g^{(2)}(r_{12}) = \frac{1}{V} \int g^{(3)}(r_{12}; r_{13}, r_{23}) \, d\tau_3. \tag{6.3}$$

The probability $w(r_{12}; r_{13}, r_{23}) d\tau_3$ that 3 will be in some specific volume element $d\tau_3$ (given that 1 and 2 are in fixed positions) is clearly

$$w(r_{12}; r_{13}, r_{23}) \, d\tau_3 = \frac{g^{(3)}(r_{12}; r_{13}, r_{23}) \, d\tau_3}{\int g^{(3)}(r_{12}; r_{13}, r_{23}) \, d\tau_3}$$

$$= \frac{g^{(3)}(r_{12}; r_{13}, r_{23}) \, d\tau_3}{V g^{(2)}(r_{12})}, \tag{6.4}$$

and the average number of molecules in this volume element is

$$n(r_{12}; r_{13}, r_{23})\, d\tau_3 = \frac{N\, d\tau_3\, g^{(3)}(r_{12}; r_{13}, r_{23})}{V g^{(2)}(r_{12})}$$

$$= \frac{\rho\, d\tau_3\, g^{(3)}(r_{12}; r_{13}, r_{23})}{g^{(2)}(r_{12})}. \tag{6.5}$$

We now can find the average force $\bar{f}_2$ exerted on molecule 2 when it is at a distance r_{12} from 1, this force being exerted not only by molecule 1 but by all the other neighbors. By obvious symmetry it will be directed along the line joining 1 and 2. Let us let this line be the x axis, the positive direction being from 1 to 2. Then we find

$$\bar{f}_2 = f(r_{12}) + \int f(r_{23})\, \frac{x_2 - x_3}{r_{23}}\, n(r_{12}; r_{13}, r_{23})\, d\tau_3$$

$$= f(r_{12}) + \rho \int f(r_{23})\, \frac{x_2 - x_3}{r_{23}}\, \frac{g^{(3)}(r_{12}; r_{13}, r_{23})}{g^{(2)}(r_{12})}\, d\tau_3, \tag{6.6}$$

the factor $(x_2 - x_3)/r_{23}$ being included in order to get the component of the force $f(r_{23})$ in the x direction. If it is repulsive, $f(r_{23})$ is positive. Suppose now we move molecule 2 very slowly (so that the forces exerted may be taken as average forces) along the x axis a distance dx_2. We will do an amount of work equal to $-\bar{f}_2\, dx_2$. If no heat is allowed to enter or escape, the energy of the assembly will change by this amount. Part of this change will go into change of kinetic energy and part into change of potential energy. Because of the first change there will be a change of temperature. If we allow heat to flow in or out to bring the assembly to its former temperature, there will be an increase in energy equal to $T\, dS$. Thus the total change in energy in an isothermal process will be given by

$$dE = T\, dS - \bar{f}_2\, dx_2, \tag{6.7}$$

whence

$$\bar{f}_2\, dx_2 = -dA. \tag{6.8}$$

The relative number of assemblies having molecules 1 and 2 in a given volume element at a distance $r_{12} + dr_{12}$, as compared with the number having them in the same-sized volume element at the distance r_{12} will be given by

$$\frac{g^{(2)}(r_{12} + dr_{12})}{g^{(2)}(r_{12})} = \exp\left\{\frac{-dA}{kT}\right\} = \exp\left\{\frac{\overline{f_2}\,dr_{12}}{kT}\right\}, \tag{6.9}$$

whence

$$\frac{1}{g^{(2)}(r_{12})}\frac{dg^{(2)}(r_{12})}{dr_{12}} = \frac{\overline{f_2}}{kT}. \tag{6.10}$$

If this is combined with Eq. (6.6), we obtain

$$kT\frac{d\ln g^{(2)}(r_{12})}{dr_{12}} = f(r_{12}) + \rho \int f(r_{23})\frac{x_2 - x_3}{r_{23}}\frac{g^{(3)}(r_{12}; r_{13}, r_{23})}{g^{(2)}(r_{12})}\,d\tau_3. \tag{6.11}$$

If $g^{(3)}$ were known we could find $g^{(2)}(r_{12})$ by solution of the integro-differential equation. A similar equation could be found giving $g^{(3)}$ in terms of $g^{(4)}$, and so on. The solution of such a set of equations would be a formidable task, to say the least. To overcome this difficulty, Kirkwood [21] has proposed an approximation known as the superposition approximation. It is proposed to set

$$g^{(3)}(r_{12}, r_{13}, r_{23}) = g^{(2)}(r_{12})g^{(2)}(r_{13})g^{(2)}(r_{23}). \tag{6.12}$$

We have already seen [following Eq. (6.1)] that this relation holds if one of the distances is large (if one distance is large, it is, indeed, true that at least two of them must be large). The proposition then, is that even if none of the distances are large, the effects of molecule 1 on 2 and 3, respectively, are independent of each other. If we insert Eq. (6.12) into Eq. (6.11), it becomes

$$kT\frac{d\ln g^{(2)}(r_{12})}{dr_{12}} = f(r_{12}) + \rho \int f(r_{23})\frac{x_2 - x_3}{r_{23}}g^{(2)}(r_{13})g^{(2)}(r_{23})\,d\tau_3. \tag{6.13}$$

Let us now convert to a set of polar coordinates (Fig. 13-4), using the line joining molecules 1 and 2 as the polar axis. (Here x rather than the usual z is measured along the polar axis.) We see then that

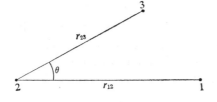

Figure 13-4. Positive values of x are to the left.

$(x_2 - x_3)/r_{23} = \cos\theta$ and Eq. (6.13) becomes, after integrating with respect to the angle ϕ,

$$
kT \frac{d \ln g^{(2)}(r_{12})}{dr_{12}}
$$

$$
= f(r_{12}) + 2\pi\rho \int_0^\infty \int_0^\pi f(r_{23})g^{(2)}(r_{13})g^{(2)}(r_{23})r_{23}^2 \cos\theta \sin\theta \, d\theta \, dr_{23}
$$

$$
= f(r_{12}) - 2\pi\rho \int_0^\infty \int_{-1}^1 f(r_{23})g^{(2)}(r_{13})g^{(2)}(r_{23})r_{23}^2 x \, dx \, dr_{23}, \qquad (6.14)
$$

letting $-\cos\theta = x$. By the law of cosines,

$$
r_{13}^2 = r_{12}^2 + r_{23}^2 - 2r_{12}r_{23}\cos\theta = r_{12}^2 + r_{23}^2 + 2r_{12}r_{23}x.
$$

We may change the variable from x to r_{13}, and in the first integration, where r_{23} is held constant, we may set $dx = (r_{13}/r_{12}r_{23}) \, dr_{13}$. Then we see that

$$
kT \frac{d \ln g^{(2)}(r_{12})}{dr_{12}}
$$

$$
= f(r_{12}) + \frac{\pi\rho}{r_{12}^2} \int_0^\infty \int_{|r_{23}-r_{12}|}^{r_{23}+r_{12}} f(r_{23})g^{(2)}(r_{13})g^{(2)}(r_{23})(r_{12}^2 + r_{23}^2 - r_{13}^2)r_{13} \, dr_{13} dr_{23}.
$$

$$(6.15)$$

It may be noted that, if we set $g^{(2)}(-r_{13}) \equiv g^{(2)}(r_{13})$, the integrand is odd with respect to r_{13}, so the integral of this integrand between $r_{23} - r_{12}$ and $r_{12} - r_{23}$ will be zero. We may, therefore, drop the absolute value sign. We integrate with respect to r_{12}, recalling that $f(r_{12}) = -d\epsilon_p(r_{12})/dr_{12}$ and that $\ln g^{(2)}(r_{12})$ and $\epsilon_p(r_{12})$ vanish when $r_{12} = \infty$ and obtain (with z substituted for r_{12} as a variable of integration) †

$$
kT \ln g^{(2)}(r_{12}) + \epsilon_p(r_{12})
$$

$$
= \pi\rho \int_0^\infty dr_{23} \int_\infty^{r_{12}} \frac{1}{z^2} dz \int_{z-r_{23}}^{z+r_{23}} f(r_{23})[g^{(2)}(r_{13}) - 1]g(r_{23})(z^2 + r_{23}^2 - r_{13}^2)r_{13} \, dr_{13}.
$$

$$(6.16)$$

Subtracting 1 from $g^{(2)}(r_{13})$ is equivalent to putting in a constant of integration, which, as will be seen, fulfills the conditions at $r_{12} = \infty$. We may change the order of integration of r_{13} and z. The expression

---

† The differential may be placed where convenient, and any expression which follows it and which is a function of the appropriate variable is also part of the integrand.

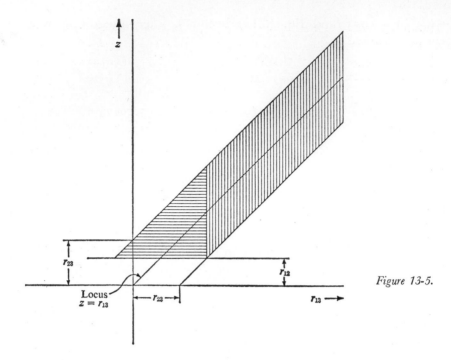

Figure 13-5.

is easily integrated with respect to z, the region of integration being divided into the shaded areas shown in Fig. 13-5. It is found that

$$\int_{r_{13}-r_{23}}^{r_{13}+r_{23}} \frac{z^2 + r_{23}^2 - r_{13}^2}{z^2} \, dz = 0,$$

so the part of the integral over the region represented by the vertical shading in Fig. 13-5 vanishes, and Eq. (6.16) reduces to

$$kT \ln g^{(2)}(r_{12}) + \epsilon_p(r_{12})$$

$$= -\pi\rho \int_0^\infty \left[dr_{23} \int_{r_{12}-r_{23}}^{r_{12}+r_{23}} r_{13} \, dr_{13} \, f(r_{23}) [g^{(2)}(r_{13}) - 1] g^{(2)}(r_{23}) \right.$$

$$\left. \int_{r_{12}}^{r_{13}+r_{23}} \frac{z^2 + r_{23}^2 - r_{13}^2}{z^2} \, dz \right]$$

$$= -\frac{\pi\rho}{r_{12}} \int_0^\infty \left[f(r_{23}) g^{(2)}(r_{23}) \, dr_{23} \right.$$

$$\left. \int_{r_{12}-r_{23}}^{r_{12}+r_{23}} [g^{(2)}(r_{13}) - 1] r_{13} [r_{23}^2 - (r_{13} - r_{12})^2] \, dr_{13} \right]. \qquad (6.17)$$

Let us now consider the effect of subtracting 1 from $g^{(2)}(r_{13})$. We note that $g^{(2)}(r_{13}) - 1$ vanishes except when r_{13} is small. If r_{12} is large, r_{13}

goes through a small value in the integration only if r_{23} is large. But if r_{23} is large, $f(r_{23})$ vanishes, so the integral with respect to dr_{23} vanishes. The right-hand side of Eq. (6.18) thus vanishes if r_{12} is large, as it should. It might be thought that the factor $1/r_{12}$ before the integral would insure this in any case. However,

$$\int_{r_{12}-r_{23}}^{r_{12}+r_{23}} r_{13}[r_{23}^2 - (r_{13} - r_{12})^2]\, dr_{13} = \tfrac{4}{3} r_{12} r_{23}^3,$$

which cancels the factor $1/r_{12}$, and of course, $\int_0^\infty f(r_{23}) g^{(2)}(r_{23}) r_{23}^2\, dr_{23}$ does not vanish. It is necessary, therefore, to subtract 1 from $g^{(2)}(r_{13})$ to provide a constant of integration which causes the boundary conditions to be satisfied.

It is seen that Eq. (6.17) is an integral equation for $g^{(2)}(r)$. If one knows the proper form of $\epsilon_p(r)$ and $f(r)$, perhaps representing these functions with the aid of the Lennard-Jones potential, and if one then can find an approximate solution for $g^{(2)}(r)$, the latter can be put into the right-hand side of Eq. (6.17), and the equation can then be used to find $g^{(2)}(r_{12})$. The resulting function can then again be used in the right-hand side, and a consistent solution can eventually be found by iteration [**26**]. In carrying out this procedure, it was found expedient to set

$$g^{(2)}(r) = \exp\left\{\frac{-\epsilon_p(r)}{kT}\right\}\left(1 + \sum_{m=1}^\infty c_m r^m\right) \qquad r < \tfrac{3}{2} r_e.$$

where r_e is the minimum of the potential-energy curve, and,

$$g^{(2)}(r) = \exp\left\{\frac{-\epsilon_p(r)}{kT}\right\} \qquad r > \tfrac{3}{2} r_e.$$

This form can be put into the equation, and values for the c_m found by an approximating procedure. These values are then used to get an approximate solution to start the iterative process. The functional form found for $g^{(2)}(r)$ has several maxima and minima and agrees reasonably well with the experimental curves found from X-ray diffraction.

Calculations of the equation of state of argon have been made by Kirkwood and collaborators [**27**], based on the pair-distribution function found by them by a slightly different procedure from that described here. A reasonably good qualitative representation of the experimental results was obtained. For example, the value of PV/RT at the critical point was found to be 0.358 as compared with the experimental value of 0.291. The results are quite sensitive to the distribution function, and a relatively small adjustment of the latter can result in considerable improvement.

13-7. *Effect of a Field of Force*

In this section we consider the behavior of a fluid in a field of force, such as a gravitational field. This will serve to elucidate some of the properties of the radial distribution function, as it will enable us to make a connection with the well-known equations of hydrostatics. Suppose that there is an external field of force, which exerts a force equal to f_0 in the z direction, on any (spherically symmetrical) molecule in the fluid. The total force on a molecule will be f_0 plus the net force exerted on it by all its neighbors. We again assume that the force between molecules will be pairwise additive, the force between molecules 1 and 2 being $f(r_{12})$. It is positive if it is repulsive.

In this case the mean density of the fluid will not be constant but will vary in the direction of the field. And the radial distribution about any molecule, say molecule 1, not only will be a function of the distance r_{12} from that molecule, but also will depend on z_1 and $z_2 - z_1$, that is, upon where the two interacting molecules (1 and 2) are located in the field of force. Thus we may now display the functional dependence of the distribution function by writing it $g^{(2)}(r_{12}, z_1, z_2 - z_1)$. It will still be assumed that $g^{(2)}$ will be equal to 1 if r_{12} is very large, no matter in which direction one goes. Thus the density at any point about molecule 1 will be given by $\rho(z_2)g^{(2)}(r_{12}, z_1, z_2 - z_1)$. The total net force on molecule 1 will, of course, be in the z direction, and it will be given by

$$f_1 = f_0 + \int f(r_{12}) \frac{z_1 - z_2}{r_{12}} \rho(z_2) g^{(2)}(r_{12}, z_1, z_2 - z_1)\, d\tau_2. \tag{7.1}$$

In order to simplify this expression we shall make certain approximations respecting $\rho(z_2)$ and $g^{(2)}(r_{12}, z_1, z_2 - z_1)$. For $\rho(z_2)$ we may in first approximation write

$$\rho(z_2) = \rho(z_1) + \left(\frac{\partial \rho}{\partial z}\right)_1 (z_2 - z_1), \tag{7.2}$$

where by $(\partial \rho / \partial z)_1$ we mean the value of $(\partial \rho / \partial z)_T$ at $z = z_1$. In similar fashion we may write

$$g^{(2)}(r_{12}, z_1, z_2 - z_1) = g^{(2)}(r_{12}, z_1) + \frac{\partial g^{(2)}(r_{12}, z_1, z_2 - z_1)}{\partial z_2} (z_2 - z_1), \quad (7.3)$$

where $g^{(2)}(r_{12}, z_1)$ is the distribution function for a fluid of uniform density with ρ equal to its value at z_1 and where the second term on the right-hand side gives the deviation of the actual distribution from the uniform density distribution.

In a system of uniform density, the second term on the right-hand side of Eq. (7.1) would vanish; hence, using Eqs. (7.2) and (7.3), retaining terms in them only to the first order in $z_2 - z_1$, we obtain

$$f_1 = f_0 - \int f(r_{12}) \frac{(z_2 - z_1)^2}{r_{12}} \left(\frac{\partial \rho}{\partial z}\right)_1 g^{(2)}(r_{12}, z_1) \, d\tau_2$$

$$- \int f(r_{12}) \frac{(z_2 - z_1)^2}{r_{12}} \rho(z_1) \frac{\partial g^{(2)}(r_{12}, z_1, z_2 - z_1)}{\partial z_2} \, d\tau_2. \quad (7.4)$$

We now make another simplification: we assume that $\partial g^{(2)}(r_{12}, z_1, z_2 - z_1)/\partial z_2$ is proportional to $\partial g^{(2)}(r_{12}, z_1)/\partial \rho$, where the derivative is evaluated for the density at z_1. The question now arises, what is the effective change of density from z_1 to z_2? We must remember that the actual change of density between z_1 and z_2 is explicitly taken into account in our expressions; only the precise distribution of the molecules in the neighborhood of molecule 1 is still to be determined in the answer to our question. The distribution of molecules at z_2 about molecule 1 is influenced not only by the density at z_2 but also by the density near molecule 1, namely that at z_1. We assume that the determining density lies halfway between molecules 1 and 2, and write

$$\frac{\partial g^{(2)}(r_{12}, z_1, z_2 - z_1)}{\partial z_2} = \frac{1}{2} \frac{\partial g^{(2)}(r_{12}, z_1)}{\partial \rho} \left(\frac{d\rho}{dz}\right)_1. \quad (7.5)$$

The subscript 1 in $(d\rho/dz)_1$ merely means that the derivative is evaluated at z_1, since only a small density gradient is being considered; the actual point of evaluation is not really important. Equation (7.5) will be substituted into Eq. (7.4). At the same time we note that if we change to polar coordinates with the polar axis in the z direction, then $(z_2 - z_1)/r_{12} = \cos \theta$. Thus we may write

$$f_1 = f_0 - \int f(r_{12}) \cos^2 \theta \left(\frac{d\rho}{dz}\right)_1 g^{(2)}(r_{12}, z_1) r_{12} \, d\tau_2$$

$$- \frac{1}{2} \int f(r_{12}) \cos^2 \theta \, \rho(z_1) \frac{\partial g^{(2)}(r_{12}, z_1)}{\partial \rho} \left(\frac{d\rho}{dz}\right)_1 r_{12} \, d\tau_2. \quad (7.6)$$

In this integration $\rho(z_1)$ and $(d\rho/dz)_1$ are constants, and, aside from $\cos^2 \theta$, the integrand depends only on r_{12}. The average value of $\cos^2 \theta$ over a sphere is $\frac{1}{3}$. Thus Eq. (7.6) becomes

$$f_1 = f_0 - \frac{1}{3} \left(\frac{d\rho}{dz} \right)_1 \int f(r_{12}) g^{(2)}(r_{12}, z_1) r_{12} \, d\tau_2$$

$$- \frac{1}{6} \rho(z_1) \left(\frac{d\rho}{dz} \right)_1 \int f(r_{12}) \frac{\partial g^{(2)}(r_{12}, z_1)}{\partial \rho} r_{12} \, d\tau_2. \qquad (7.7)$$

The force f_1 will be the average force on molecule 1, and $-\int_{z_1}^{z_2} f_1 \, dz$ is, therefore, the change in local free energy on going from z_1 to z_2. By the same reasoning as that used in Sec. 13-6 to relate the pair to the triplet distribution, we may write

$$\frac{\rho(z_2)}{\rho(z_1)} = \exp \left\{ \int_{z_1}^{z_2} \frac{f_1}{kT} \, dz \right\}, \qquad (7.8)$$

from which

$$\frac{d \ln \rho}{dz_1} = \frac{f_1}{kT}, \qquad (7.9)$$

or

$$kT \left(\frac{d\rho}{dz} \right)_1 = \rho f_1. \qquad (7.10)$$

Using this with Eq. (7.7), we find, after a slight rearrangement

$$\rho f_0 = \left(\frac{d\rho}{dz} \right)_1 \left[kT + \frac{1}{3} \rho \int f(r_{12}) g^{(2)}(r_{12}, z_1) r_{12} \, d\tau_2 \right.$$

$$\left. + \frac{1}{6} \rho^2 \int f(r_{12}) \frac{\partial g^{(2)}(r_{12}, z_1)}{\partial \rho} r_{12} \, d\tau_2 \right]. \qquad (7.11)$$

Comparing this with Eq. (5.10), we see that we may write (leaving off the subscript 1 on the derivatives)

$$\rho f_0 = \left(\frac{\partial P}{\partial \rho} \right)_T \frac{d\rho}{dz} = \frac{dP}{dz}, \qquad (7.12)$$

and thus arrive at the usual equation of hydrostatics, since ρf_0 is the force per unit volume, ρ being the number density.

The most interesting feature of this deduction is the necessity of introducing the factor $\frac{1}{2}$ in Eq. (7.5) in order to arrive at Eq. (7.12). There are, of course, a number of approximations in the deduction, but they all seem quite reasonable; it is seen, then, that the hypothesis upon which Eq. (7.5) is based is at least consistent with these approximations.

If f_0 vanishes, then, according to Eq. (7.12), $d\rho/dz$ will vanish also, giving us a fluid of uniform density. It is, however, possible to have a fluid of nonuniform density, as in a two-phase system, where there is a gradation of densities between the two phases, even though there is no external force (or, at least, the latter is relatively negligible). In such a case, however, the gradient of ρ is considerable, and the first-order approximations made in this section cannot be expected to hold. The methods used in calculating pressure can, however, be used for calculating surface tension.

13-8. *Theory of Surface Tension*

Suppose that we have a system containing two fluid phases, liquid and vapor, with a surface between these phases [28–29]. Once again we assume that the molecules are spherically symmetrical. We assume that the surface is in the xy plane, and that the system is in a rectangular box with edges parallel to the x, y, and z axes, and of lengths a, b, and c, respectively.

If the discontinuity between the two phases were sharp, and if the properties of the separate phases extended clear to the boundary, we would find that the force exerted by one of the yz faces of the container would be $F_x = Pbc$, inasmuch as the pressure would be the same for the two phases. However, in actuality the force exerted by this face will differ from Pbc by an amount ΔF_x, and the surface tension will be given by $\sigma = -\Delta F_x/b$, it being the force per unit length exerted by the wall in such a direction as to increase the size of the surface, counteracting the tendency of the surface to decrease (see Fig. 13-6).

In order to calculate ΔF_x we use the one-dimensional equations in Sec. 13-5, namely Eqs. (5.2) and (5.7), which give

$$-(F_x + \Delta F_x)a + \frac{1}{2}\sum_i \sum_j (x_i - x_j)^2 \frac{f(r_{ij})}{r_{ij}} = -NkT. \qquad (8.1)$$

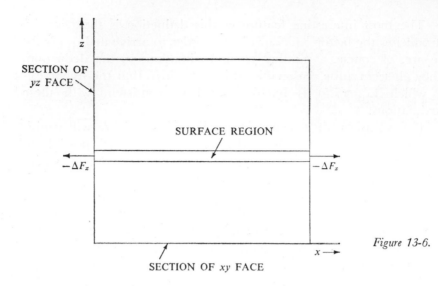

Figure 13-6.

By just the same reasoning applied to the z direction, we have

$$-cF_z + \frac{1}{2} \sum_i \sum_j (z_i - z_j)^2 \frac{f(r_{ij})}{r_{ij}} = -NkT. \tag{8.2}$$

Since $aF_x = Pabc$ and cF_z is also equal to $Pabc$ we see by subtracting Eq. (8.2) from Eq. (8.1)

$$-a\Delta F_x + \frac{1}{2} \sum_i \sum_j [(x_i - x_j)^2 - (z_i - z_j)^2] \frac{f(r_{ij})}{r_{ij}} = 0. \tag{8.3}$$

The surface tension is, therefore, given by

$$\sigma = -\frac{1}{2ab} \sum_i \sum_j [(x_i - x_j)^2 - (z_i - z_j)^2] \frac{f(r_{ij})}{r_{ij}}, \tag{8.4}$$

where it will be recognized that ab is the area of the surface. Since $f(r_{ij})$ is a short-range force, the sum over j will be the same for all the molecules whose z_i is the same, i.e., which are located at the same distance from a mathematical plane parallel to the surface. The number of such molecules in a volume equal to $ab\, dz_i$ will be equal to $ab\, \rho(z_i)\, dz_i$, where $\rho(z_i)$ is the number density at z_i. Thus Eq. (8.4) reduces to (using notation adapted from Sec. 13-7)

$$\sigma = -\frac{1}{2} \int \rho(z_i)\, dz_i \int [(x_i - x_j)^2 - (z_i - z_j)^2]\, \rho(z_j) g^{(2)}(r_{ij}, z_i, z_j - z_i) \frac{f(r_{ij})}{r_{ij}}\, d\tau_j.$$

$$\tag{8.5}$$

This equation can also be derived by applying Eq. (5.14) in a manner similar to that by which Eq. (5.19) was obtained. In doing this, the system is first expanded in the x direction to increase the surface and then compressed in the z direction, so that in the complete process there is no change in volume. The net change in free energy is thus connected with the change in the surface area. If the free-energy change is divided by the change in surface area, it gives the surface tension.

Equation (8.5) can be put into a somewhat more symmetrical form by noting that $(y_i - y_j)^2$ can be substituted for $(x_i - x_j)^2$. Adding the two expressions thus obtained, and dividing by 2, we find

$$\sigma = -\frac{1}{4} \int \rho(z_i) \, dz_i \int [(x_i - x_j)^2 + (y_i - y_j)^2 - 2(z_i - z_j)^2]$$
$$\times \rho(z_j) g^{(2)}(r_{ij}, z_i, z_j - z_i) \frac{f(r_{ij})}{r_{ij}} \, d\tau_j$$

$$= -\frac{1}{4} \int \rho(z_i) \, dz_i \int [r_{ij}^2 - 3(z_i - z_j)^2]$$
$$\times \rho(z_j) g^{(2)}(r_{ij}, z_i, z_j - z_i) \frac{f(r_{ij})}{r_{ij}} \, d\tau_j, \qquad (8.6)$$

since $r_{ij}^2 = (x_i - x_j)^2 + (y_i - y_j)^2 + (z_i - z_j)^2$. We express $d\tau_j$ in polar coordinates about the point x_i, y_i, z_i. Then $z_j - z_i = r_{ij} \cos \theta$, and we may write $g^{(2)}(r_{ij}, z_i, z_j - z_i) = g^{(2)}(r_{ij}, z_i, r_{ij} \cos \theta)$, and $\rho(z_j) = \rho(z_i + r_{ij} \cos \theta)$. The expression for the surface tension becomes

$$\sigma = -\frac{1}{4} \int \rho(z_i) \, dz_i \iiint r_{ij}(1 - 3 \cos^2 \theta) \rho(z_i + r_{ij} \cos \theta)$$
$$\times g^{(2)}(r_{ij}, z_i, r_{ij} \cos \theta) f(r_{ij}) r_{ij}^2 \sin \theta \, dr_{ij} d\theta d\phi. \qquad (8.7)$$

If ρ and $g^{(2)}$ did not depend on $\cos \theta$, the $\cos^2 \theta$ term in the parentheses would give merely an average factor $\frac{1}{3}$ which when multiplied by 3 would cancel the 1, and thus σ would vanish.

Clearly, it will be very difficult to determine ρ and $g^{(2)}$, and even if they could be found, evaluation of the integral would be difficult. A rough approximation may be found for a liquid in contact with its vapor, provided the density of the vapor may be neglected. Assume that the density of the liquid remains constant up to the surface, which we may allow to be determined by $z = 0$, with z positive in the liquid. In this case, for fixed r_{ij} and z_i, $\cos \theta$ goes from 1 to $-z_i/r_{ij}$ if $z_i < r_{ij}$, or from 1 to -1 if $z_i > r_{ij}$. If $z_i < r_{ij}$, then we have

$$\int (1 - 3\cos^2\theta)\sin\theta\,d\theta$$

$$= (-\cos\theta + \cos^3\theta)\Big|_{\cos\theta=1}^{\cos\theta=-z_i/r_{ij}}$$

$$= \frac{z_i}{r_{ij}} - \frac{z_i^3}{r_{ij}^3}$$

$$= \frac{z_i}{r_{ij}^3}(r_{ij}^2 - z_i^2),$$

whereas if $z_i > r_{ij}$, the integral vanishes. Inserting this last expression into Eq. (8.7), we find (after integrating with respect to ϕ and noting that ρ will be constant if $z_i > 0$ and 0 otherwise, while $g^{(2)}$ becomes a function of r_{ij} only)

$$\sigma = -\frac{\pi\rho^2}{2} \int_0^\infty dr_{ij} \int_0^{r_{ij}} dz_i\,(r_{ij}^2 - z_i^2)z_i g^{(2)}(r_{ij})f(r_{ij}). \tag{8.8}$$

Integrating with respect to z_i first, we get

$$\sigma = -\frac{\pi\rho^2}{8} \int_0^\infty r_{ij}^4 g^{(2)}(r_{ij})f(r_{ij})\,dr_{ij}, \tag{8.9}$$

an equation which was originally derived in another manner by Fowler [30, 31]. Calculations of σ were made by Kirkwood and Buff [32], by using an empirical, slightly modified Lennard-Jones potential-energy function for argon:

$$\epsilon_p(r_{ij}) = \frac{8.62 \times 10^{-8}}{r_{ij}^{11.4}} - \frac{1.11 \times 10^{-10}}{r_{ij}^6},$$

with r_{ij} in angstroms, and ϵ_p in ergs, and an approximation for $g^{(2)}(r_{ij})$:

$$g^{(2)}(r_{ij}) = \begin{cases} \left(\dfrac{4.50}{r_{ij}}\right)^7 \exp\left\{\left(\dfrac{3.55}{4.50}\right)^{14} - \left(\dfrac{3.55}{r_{ij}}\right)^{14}\right\} & r_{ij} \leqq 4.50 \\ 1 & r_{ij} > 4.50 \end{cases}$$

with r_{ij} again in angstroms. This approximation for $g^{(2)}(r_{ij})$ reproduced the first peak reasonably well and gave good values for the equation of state. The value of σ obtained was 14.9 dynes per cm as compared with the experimental value of 11.9.

13-9. *Fluctuations and the Distribution Function*

In this section we derive another relation† between the distribution function and the thermodynamic functions, a relation based on the density fluctuations discussed in Chap. 10. We have noted that Eq. (4.9) of Chap. 10 breaks down if $\overline{N^2} - \overline{N}^2$ becomes of the order of $\overline{N}^2$, that is, when $\beta k T$ is of the order of V. At room temperature, with a liquid well below its critical point, $\beta \approx 10^{-4}$ atm^{-1} and $\beta k T \approx 5 \times 10^{-24}$ cc. Thus the volume in which the fluctuations occur can be taken nearly as small as atomic dimensions before appreciable deviations from the formula can be expected.‡ As the critical point is approached and β increases, the difficulties occur at appreciably larger volumes. We may anticipate that the fluctuations will be less than expected from Eq. (4.9) of Chap. 10, because the fluctuations themselves tend to throw the system locally away from the critical condition; therefore, they tend to be self-limiting.

Of course, in any case in which β^{-1} is not exactly zero, it is possible ultimately to find a volume large enough so that Eq. (4.9) of Chap. 10 holds. Thus the fluctuations in a large volume are as great as ever, but fluctuations in a small volume are suppressed. This means that the fluctuations are more uniform over a large volume. This fact may be expressed by saying that correlations of the fluctuations in different parts of the system become more important near the critical point. The fluctuations have been analyzed from this viewpoint by Ornstein and Zernike [33, 34]. They begin by discussing a very small volume, designated for convenience as dv, smaller than the size of a single molecule. This volume will be considered to be occupied if a molecule has its center of gravity in it. There is, therefore, either one or no molecule in it; the respective probabilities are $\rho\,dv$ and $1 - \rho\,dv$, where ρ is the number density, with $\delta\rho$ in these two cases being $(1/dv) - \rho$ and $-\rho$, respectively. For this volume the average

$$\overline{(\delta\rho)^2} = \left(\frac{1}{dv} - \rho\right)^2 \rho\,dv + \rho^2(1 - \rho\,dv).$$

† This section is largely based on this author's contribution to [10, pp. 467–74]. The second paragraph of Sec. 13–9 and the first few lines of the next are almost verbatim quotations.

‡ It is of course true that in a very small volume there may be effects of the surrounding material on the thermodynamic properties of the substance at any given point, and there may also be effects of a gradient in the density. Thus it is not certain that it will be correct to use the macroscopic value of β in the formula. In our considerations we shall neglect this possible source of error.

Since dv is small,

$$\overline{(\delta\rho)^2} \approx \frac{\rho}{dv}. \tag{9.1}$$

The result is quite independent of the properties of the system, other than its density. The fact that the fluctuation in a larger volume has a different value can arise only because of the interatomic forces, which cause fluctuations in one portion of the system to be correlated with fluctuations in another. This follows because Eq. (9.1) may be shown to hold for a perfect gas for any dv, provided only it is small compared with the total volume of the system (or provided it is the volume of an assembly in a grand canonical ensemble). This may be verified for large dv by inserting the appropriate value of β into Eq. (4.9) of Chap. 10 and dividing both sides by $(dv)^2$.

In general, the average value of $\delta\rho$ for any one of the volumes dv is zero, but if the fluctuations are assumed to be given, at some particular instant, for all the volumes except one of them (which may be taken as being located at the origin of coordinates) then the value of $\overline{\delta\rho}$ for the latter [designated as $\overline{\delta\rho(0)}$] will not be zero, because of the correlations. Ornstein and Zernike made the assumption that the direct effect of the fluctuation at the point x, y, z [which we designate as $\delta\rho(x)$, using only the first coordinate x in the functional indication] upon the origin will be given by

$$\overline{\delta\rho(0)} = c(r)\delta\rho(x)\,dv, \tag{9.2}$$

$c(r)$ depending on the distance r of the point x, y, z, from the origin in an isotropic system, and the volume dv being small, as already explained. Since $\delta\rho(x)$ can take only two values, both rather large, it may seem strange that $\delta\rho(0)$ should be proportional to $\delta\rho(x)\,dv$. This means that (if effects from outside the volume at x, y, z average to zero) $\overline{\delta\rho(0)}$ has either the value

$$[\overline{\delta\rho(0)}]_1 = c(r)(1 - \rho\,dv), \tag{9.3}$$

or the value

$$[\overline{\delta\rho(0)}]_0 = c(r)(-\rho)\,dv. \tag{9.4}$$

If $[\overline{\delta\rho(0)}]_1$ is multiplied by its probability of occurrence, ρdv, and $[\overline{\delta\rho(0)}]_0$ by its probability, $1 - \rho dv$, the sum of these vanishes, as is to be expected. This would not occur unless the same function $c(r)$ were present in both Eqs. (9.3) and (9.4). More important is the assumption that $c(r)$ is independent of fluctuations at other positions.

If we add the contributions over all volumes dv we get, instead of Eq. (9.2),

$$\overline{\delta\rho(0)} = \int' c(r)\delta\rho(x)\,dv, \tag{9.5}$$

where the integral is taken over the whole volume. The integrand is not continuous. The prime indicates that the element at the origin is not to be included in the integral.

In the above discussion we have assumed that the fluctuations in all volume elements except that at the origin are arbitrarily fixed at one or the other of the two possible values. We may also wish to consider the situation in which only the fluctuation in the volume element at x, y, z is fixed. In this case the fluctuations at all points are affected because they are correlated with the fluctuation at x, y, z, and the induced fluctuations also affect each other. Thus the fluctuation at the origin will now be

$$\overline{\delta\rho(0)} = c(r)\delta\rho(x)\,dv + \int'' c(r_1)\overline{\delta\rho(x_1)}\,dv_1, \tag{9.6}$$

where the first term gives the direct effect of the arbitrary fluctuation at x, y, z and the integral gives the average effect of the fluctuations at other points as influenced by the fluctuation at x, y, z. The double prime on the integral indicates that elements at the origin and at $x_1, y_1, z_1 = x, y, z$ are to be omitted. We write

$$\overline{\delta\rho(0)} = h(r)\delta\rho(x)\,dv, \tag{9.7}$$

where $h(r)$ is defined by the equation. Although this is the definition of $h(r)$, it is actually related to the pair distribution function $g^{(2)}(r)$ by the equation

$$h(r) = \rho[g^{(2)}(r) - 1]. \tag{9.8}$$

This relationship is readily seen by considering $\delta\rho(0)$ when it is known that there is a molecule in the volume element at x. In this case $\delta\rho(x) = (1/dv) - \rho$, where ρ is the average number density, and the first term predominates if dv is very small; thus we have

$$\overline{\rho(0)} - \rho = \overline{\delta\rho(0)} = h(r).$$

Since under these circumstances $\overline{\rho(0)} = \rho g^{(2)}(r)$, it is seen that Eq. (9.8) follows.

We can write Eq. (9.7) in the more general form

$$\overline{\delta\rho(x_1)} = h(|\mathbf{r}_1 - \mathbf{r}|)\delta\rho(x)\,dv, \tag{9.7a}$$

where $|\mathbf{r}_1 - \mathbf{r}|$ is the distance between x, y, z and x_1, y_1, z_1. If Eqs. (9.7) and (9.7a) are substituted into Eq. (9.6), and if we divide through by $\delta\rho(x)\,dv$, which now appears as a common factor unaffected by the integration, we find

$$h(r) = c(r) + \int'' c(r_1)h(|\mathbf{r}_1 - \mathbf{r}|)\,dv_1$$

$$= c(r) + \int'' c(|\mathbf{r} + \boldsymbol{\sigma}|)h(\sigma)\,d\xi d\eta d\zeta. \tag{9.9}$$

In the last line we have made a change of variables, setting $\xi, \eta, \zeta = x_1 - x, y_1 - y, z_1 - z$ and letting $\boldsymbol{\sigma}$ be the corresponding vector. The relation between $\mathbf{r}, \mathbf{r}_1,$ and $\boldsymbol{\sigma}$ is shown in Fig. 13-7.

Before attempting to reduce this equation, we define another quantity,

$$C = \int' c(r)\,dxdydz = \int' c(|\mathbf{r} + \boldsymbol{\sigma}|)\,dxdydz. \tag{9.10}$$

Since we integrate over all space it does not matter on which point the function c is centered, but the primes must mean that we leave out the volume element at the origin in the first integral and the volume element at $\mathbf{r} + \boldsymbol{\sigma} = 0$ in the second. We also set

$$H = \int h(r)\,dxdydz = \int h(\sigma)\,d\xi d\eta d\zeta. \tag{9.11}$$

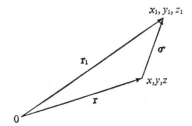

Figure 13-7.

In each case the volume element at the origin is to be omitted; however, this is not important, since the contribution from this element will be negligible.

We now multiply both sides of Eq. (9.9) by $dxdydz$ and integrate with respect to these variables, leaving out volume elements at the origin and at $\mathbf{r} + \boldsymbol{\sigma} = 0$. Leaving out the latter volume element, if it is very small, can make no appreciable difference to the integral of $c(r)$, and likewise the volume element at the origin can make no difference in the integral of $c(|\mathbf{r} + \boldsymbol{\sigma}|)$. Thus we can use Eq. (9.10) as well as Eq. (9.11), and finally integrating over ξ, η, ζ, we again use Eq. (9.11). So we obtain $H = C + CH$ or

$$1 + H = \frac{1}{1 - C}. \tag{9.12}$$

We can now obtain an expression for $\overline{(\delta\rho)^2}$. The fluctuation of the number of molecules in dv is given by $\delta\rho(x)dv$. Over a large volume V the net total fluctuation will be

$$\delta\rho = \frac{1}{V} \int \delta\rho(x) \, dv,$$

and therefore

$$(\delta\rho)^2 = \frac{1}{V^2} \int \delta\rho(x) \, dv \int \delta\rho(x_1) \, dv_1,$$

where both integrals are taken over the volume V, dv being equivalent to $dxdydz$ and dv_1 to $dx_1dy_1dz_1$.

The two integrals can be combined:

$$(\delta\rho)^2 = \frac{1}{V^2} \iint \delta\rho(x)\delta\rho(x_1) \, dvdv_1. \tag{9.13}$$

The variable x_1, y_1, z_1 is only formally different from x, y, z, but they are independent of each other. To get $\overline{(\delta\rho)^2}$ we must average the integrand. We can consider separately that part of the integrand contributed by those volume elements for which $x_1, y_1, z_1 = x, y, z$. These elements contribute an amount $V^{-2}\{\overline{[\delta\rho(x)]^2} \, dv\} V$, which by Eq. (9.1) is equal to ρV^{-1}. For the other volume elements we may hold x fixed and average $\delta\rho(x_1)$, using Eq. (9.7a), then average $\delta\rho(x)$. This gives

$$\overline{\delta\rho(x)\delta\rho(x_1)} = \overline{\delta\rho(x)}\overline{\delta\rho(x_1)}$$
$$= h(|\mathbf{r} - \mathbf{r}_1|)\overline{[\delta\rho(x)]^2}\, dv$$
$$= h(|\mathbf{r} - \mathbf{r}_1|)\rho,$$

the last expression by again applying Eq. (9.1). We may now integrate Eq. (9.13) with respect to x, y, z, holding x_1, y_1, z_1 constant, recalling that the volume element at $x, y, z = x_1, y_1, z_1$, or $\mathbf{r} = \mathbf{r}_1$, is to be omitted, then integrate with respect to x_1, y_1, z_1. This gives, by Eqs. (9.11) and (9.12),

$$\overline{(\delta\rho)^2} = \frac{\rho(1 + H)}{V} = \frac{\rho}{V(1 - C)}. \tag{9.14}$$

Unless β is very large or the total volume of the system is very small, we can find a volume V large enough so that Eq. (4.9) of Chap. 10 holds. If we divide the latter equation by V^2 it becomes

$$\overline{(\delta\rho)^2} = \frac{\rho^2 \beta k T}{V}. \tag{9.15}$$

From Eqs. (9.14) and (9.15) it is seen that

$$\rho\beta k T = 1 + H$$
$$= 1 + 4\pi\rho \int_0^\infty [g^{(2)}(r) - 1]r^2\, dr. \tag{9.16}$$

The integral is to be taken over the volume V, but it can be extended to infinity, since $g^{(2)}(r) \longrightarrow 1$ as $r \longrightarrow \infty$. This result may be compared with Eq. (5.10), remembering that $\beta = \rho^{-1}(\partial\rho/\partial P)_T$.

Near the critical point, β may become very large. We see, then, from Eq. (9.16) that $4\pi \int_0^\infty [g^{(2)}(r) - 1]r^2\, dr$ may become very large. This may, at first sight, seem quite remarkable, because $4\pi\rho \int g^{(2)}(r)r^2\, dr$ taken over V should give one the number N of molecules in volume V, and it might therefore be expected to be equal to $4\pi\rho \int r^2\, dr$, which is equal to $V\rho$. The reason that the two parts of the integral in Eq. (9.16) do not cancel is that the average density in volume V, being defined as that average about some particular molecule, is not equal to the average density in the whole ensemble, whose size is effectively infinite. A particular volume in a grand canonical ensemble has essentially an infinite amount of material to draw upon to determine the fluctuations within it. When there are large fluctuations the average density about a given molecule may differ appreciably from the overall density simply because there are more molecules in regions of high density than in regions of low density.

An essentially similar statement may also be made about $g^{(2)}(r)$, as defined in Sec. 13-4, even though it is thought of as the pair distribution function in a fixed V (an assembly of a canonical ensemble), since it is normalized to be equal to 1 at very great r. Thus $\rho g^{(2)}(r)$ gives the density at r if ρ is defined as the density at very large r rather than strictly as the average density in the volume, because if there is appreciable clustering about the molecule at $r = 0$, there can be some slight difference between the density at large r and the average density.

Not only can the integral H of $h(r)$ attain a large value near the critical point, but the range of $h(r)$ in r may become quite extended under these circumstances. This may be demonstrated by obtaining an asymptotic expression for $h(r)$ at large r. From Eq. (9.12) it will be observed that when H becomes large, C must approach 1. The integrand $c(r)$ of C measures the *direct* effect of a molecule on the surrounding distribution and so should have a range close to that of the intermolecular forces. If we now look at Eq. (9.9) and consider a point $\mathbf{r}$ such that r is fairly large, then the first term on the right-hand side, $c(r)$, will be negligible, the contributions to the integral will come from a region where r_1 is small, and we may write

$$h(r) \approx \int'' c(r_1) h(|\mathbf{r}_1 - \mathbf{r}|)\, dv_1. \tag{9.17}$$

We may then expand $h(|\mathbf{r}_1 - \mathbf{r}|)$, treating it as a function of $\mathbf{r}_1$, or of x_1, y_1, z_1, about $\mathbf{r}_1 = 0$, writing

$$h(|\mathbf{r}_1 - \mathbf{r}|) = h(|\mathbf{r} - \mathbf{r}_1|)$$

$$= h(r) + \frac{\partial h(r)}{\partial x} x_1 + \frac{\partial h(r)}{\partial y} y_1 + \frac{\partial h(r)}{\partial z} z_1$$

$$+ \frac{1}{2} \frac{\partial^2 h(r)}{\partial x^2} x_1^2 + \frac{1}{2} \frac{\partial^2 h(r)}{\partial y^2} y_1^2 + \frac{1}{2} \frac{\partial^2 h(r)}{\partial z^2} z_1^2 + \frac{\partial^2 h(r)}{\partial x \partial y} x_1 y_1$$

$$+ \frac{\partial^2 h(r)}{\partial x \partial z} x_1 z_1 + \frac{\partial^2 h(r)}{\partial y \partial z} y_1 z_1 + \cdots. \tag{9.18}$$

the derivatives being evaluated at x, y, z. If this is substituted into the integral, we note that, since $c(r_1)$ is symmetrical about the point $x_1, y_1, z_1 = 0$, most of the terms vanish, and we are left with

$$h(r) = Ch(r) + \tfrac{1}{2}C'\nabla^2 h(r) \tag{9.19}$$

where C is given by Eq. (9.10), where

$$C' = \int' c(r_1)x_1^2 \, dv_1 = \int' c(r_1)y_1^2 \, dv_1 = \int' c(r_1)z_1^2 \, dv_1, \qquad (9.20)$$

and where the Laplacian operator ∇^2 is given by

$$\nabla^2 = \frac{\partial^2}{\partial x^2} + \frac{\partial^2}{\partial y^2} + \frac{\partial^2}{\partial z^2}. \qquad (9.21)$$

If the higher terms of Eq. (9.19) (those not shown) are neglected, the solution is well known; it is given by

$$h(r) = \frac{A}{r} \exp\left\{\frac{-r}{\varkappa}\right\}, \qquad (9.22)$$

where A is a constant and

$$\varkappa^2 = \frac{\frac{1}{2}C'}{1 - C}, \qquad (9.23)$$

$\varkappa$ giving the effective range of r. Since C approaches 1 at the critical point, $\varkappa$ can become very large. Since $C = \int' c(r)dv$, and since $c(r)$ will be different from zero only for a range of r of a few angstroms, it may be seen from Eq. (9.20) that C' is of the order of a few square angstroms, so that, except very close to the critical point, $\varkappa$ is of the order of atomic dimensions.

If Eq. (9.22) is accepted as an approximation, it may be used to evaluate the higher terms in the expansion in Eq. (9.18) or (9.19). With each successive differentiation there will appear terms having an extra factor r or $\varkappa$ in the denominator, and associated with each such term there will be an extra factor x_1, y_1, or z_1 in the numerator. Equation (9.22) is set up to be valid for large r, and near the critical point $\varkappa$ is large. On the other hand, only small values of x_1, y_1, z_1 contribute to the integrals which arise, just as in Eq. (9.20). Thus, near the critical point and at large distances r, the higher terms in Eq. (9.19) become negligible and it is legitimate to break off the series as we have done.

The large range of $h(r)$, and hence of $g^{(2)}(r)$, near the critical point is of considerable importance in the calculation of the scattering of light in the immediate neighborhood of the critical point.† However, it is actually more relevant to think about this as a manifestation

† See O. K. Rice in [10, pp. 474–86] and [35].

of the correlation of fluctuations. When fluctuations become large, the functional form of $h(r)$ or of $g^{(2)}(r)$ actually gives little information about the distribution of molecules about a given molecule, for under these circumstances $h(r)$ becomes an average over such a variety of different situations that little can be learned about any particular one. Reference to any "average" condition of a system always entails some lack of precision, but becomes essentially meaningless when large fluctuations are involved.

With the insight which has now been gained into the character of the distribution function and its behavior near the critical point, we may compare the two forms involving the compressibility, Eqs. (5.10) and (9.16). We can learn something about the distribution function by such a comparison, although the necessity of satisfying the two equations simultaneously is not sufficient actually to determine it. Various approximate forms of the distribution function have been tried, and it has been pointed out that these may be described as arising from certain relations between $c(r)$ and $h(r)$ or $g^{(2)}(r)$, which are then used with Eq. (9.9). In setting up these approximations we use the function

$$F(r) = \exp\left\{\frac{-\epsilon(r)}{kT}\right\} - 1 \tag{9.24}$$

as defined in Chap. 11. In contrast to the usage in Chap. 11, we here capitalize F so that it will not be confused with the force function $f(r)$ used in earlier sections of this chapter. We also define the function

$$y(r) = g^{(2)}(r) \exp\left\{\frac{\epsilon(r)}{kT}\right\}. \tag{9.25}$$

The approximation of Percus and Yevick [24] may be written as

$$c(r) = \rho F(r)y(r), \tag{9.26}$$

and the so-called hypernetted-chain approximation is equivalent to

$$c(r) = h(r) - \rho \ln y(r). \tag{9.27}$$

Rowlinson [36] has suggested the following modification:

$$c(r) = \rho F(r)y(r) + \rho\Phi(\rho, T)[y(r) - 1 - \ln y(r)], \tag{9.28}$$

which could be shown to be equal to Eq. (9.27) were $\Phi(\rho, T)$ equal to 1. The function $\Phi(\rho, T)$ is a function of ρ and T of the form

$$\Phi = \sum_{l=0}^{\infty} \Phi_l \rho^l, \tag{9.29}$$

where the Φ_l are functions of T only, and are to be determined by making Eqs. (5.10) and (9.16) hold simultaneously. It is assumed that $y(r)$ can be written

$$y(r) = \sum_{i=0}^{\infty} \alpha_i \rho^i, \tag{9.30}$$

where the α_i are functions of r and T. From Eq. (9.25) we write

$$h(r) = \rho[g^{(2)}(r) - 1] = \rho \left[y(r) \exp\left\{ \frac{-\epsilon(r)}{kT} \right\} - 1 \right]$$

$$= \rho y(r) F(r) + \rho[y(r) - 1]. \tag{9.31}$$

Equation (9.9) may be written in the form

$$h(r_{12}) = c(r_{12}) + \int c(r_{13}) h(r_{23}) \, dx_3 dy_3 dz_3 \tag{9.32}$$

if r_{12}, r_{13}, and r_{23} are distances between three points 1, 2, and 3, since the relation between r_{12}, r_{13}, and r_{23} is the same as that between r, r_1, and σ of Eq. (9.9). If $c(r_{12})$ and $c(r_{13})$ from Eq. (9.28), $h(r_{12})$ and $h(r_{23})$ from Eq. (9.31) are substituted into Eq. (9.32), and the expansions for Φ and $y(r)$ substituted, we may equate coefficients of any given power of ρ. One easily finds that $\alpha_0 = 1$. This result is then used in starting the series in the integrand, and one finds that $\alpha_1 = \int F(r_{13}) F(r_{23}) \, dx_3 dy_3 dz_3$. Step-by-step iteration in the integrand gives the rest of the α's. They involve various cluster integrals and the Φ_l. One thus obtains a formal expansion for $h(r)$, and the Φ_l can be determined by setting the results of calculating β from Eqs. (5.10) and (9.16) equal to each other. The relation between the Φ_l and the virial coefficients can be found by substituting in Eq. (5.9), and the virial coefficients can thus be obtained. On this basis Rowlinson made some calculations of the third and fourth virial coefficients for a gas of hard spheres. These compare favorably with those known exactly from numerical calculations of the cluster integrals of Chap. 11.

One would not, however, expect to be able to get a good approximation for the equation of state in the neighborhood of the critical point by comparing Eqs. (5.10) and (9.16), because of the very different character of the integrals involved in the critical region. We have shown that near the critical point the contributions to Eq. (9.16) come from a large range of values of r, but this is never the case with Eq. (5.10), because of the presence of the force function $f(r)$. Any determination of $g^{(2)}(r)$ or $h(r)$ in this region, by comparing the two equations, is bound to be highly insensitive.

REFERENCES

1. J. Hirschfelder, D. Stevenson, and H. Eyring, *J. Chem. Phys.*, **5**, 896 (1937).
2. H. S. Frank, *J. Chem. Phys.*, **13**, 478 (1945).
3. L. Tonks, *Phys. Rev.*, **50**, 955 (1936).
4. O. K. Rice, *J. Chem. Phys.*, **12**, 1 (1944).
5. O. K. Rice, *J. Chem. Phys.*, **14**, 348 (1946).
6. O. K. Rice, *J. Chem. Phys.*, **31**, 987 (1959).
7. O. K. Rice, *J. Chem. Phys.*, **14**, 324 (1946).
8. O. K. Rice in R. Smoluchowski, ed., *Phase Transformations in Solids*, New York, Wiley, 1951.
9. J. A. Barker, *Lattice Theories of the Liquid State*, New York, Macmillan, 1963.
10. J. M. Richardson and S. R. Brinkley, Jr., in F. D. Rossini, ed., *Thermodynamics and Physics of Matter*, Princeton, N.J., Princeton Univ. Press, 1955, pp. 507–22.
11. J. O. Hirschfelder, C. F. Curtiss and R. Byron Bird, *Molecular Theory of Gases and Liquids*, New York, Wiley, 1954, Chap. 4.
12. T. L. Hill, *Statistical Mechanics*, New York, McGraw-Hill, 1956, Chap. 8.
13. H. Eyring, D. Henderson, B. J. Stover, and E. M. Eyring, *Statistical Mechanics and Dynamics*, New York, Wiley, 1964, Chap. 12.
14. S. Ono, *Mem. Fac. Eng. Kyushu Imp. Univ.*, **10**, 195 (1947).
15. T. Sato and S. Ono, *J. Phys. Soc. Japan*, **4**, 103 (1948); **6**, 410 (1951).
16. Landolt-Börnstein, *Zahlenwerte und Funktionen*, Aufl. 6, Berlin, Springer, 1960–1961.
17. C. Domb and M. F. Sykes, *Proc. Roy. Soc.*, **A235**, 247 (1956).
18. D. G. Henshaw, *Phys. Rev.*, **105**, 976 (1957).
19. J. Yvon, *La Théorie statistique des fluides et l'équation d'état*, Paris, Hermann, 1935.
20. M. Born and H. S. Green, *Proc. Roy. Soc.*, **A188**, 10 (1946).
21. J. G. Kirkwood, *J. Chem. Phys.*, **3**, 300 (1935).
22. H. S. Green, *The Molecular Theory of Fluids*, New York, Interscience, 1952, Chaps. 2 and 3.
23. A. Münster, *Statistische Thermodynamik*, Berlin, Springer, 1956, Chap. 19.
24. J. K. Percus and G. J. Yevick, *Phys. Rev.*, **110**, 1 (1958).
25. J. K. Percus in H. L. Frisch and J. L. Lebowitz, eds., *The Equilibrium Theory of Classical Fluids*, New York, Benjamin, 1964, p. II-33ff.
26. A. G. McLellan, *Proc. Roy. Soc.*, **A210**, 509 (1952).
27. J. G. Kirkwood, V. A. Lewinson, and B. J. Alder, *J. Chem. Phys.*, **20**, 929 (1952).

28. A. Harasima in *Advances in Chemical Physics*, Vol. 1, New York, Interscience, 1958, p. 203ff.

29. S. Ono, S. Kondo, and F. P. Buff, in *Handbuch der Physik*, Berlin, Springer, 1960, Band 10, pp. 134–304.

30. R. H. Fowler, *Physica*, **5**, 39 (1938).

31. R. H. Fowler, *Proc. Roy. Soc.* (London), **A159**, 229 (1937).

32. J. G. Kirkwood and F. P. Buff, *J. Chem. Phys.*, **17**, 338 (1949).

33. L. S. Ornstein and F. Zernike, *Proc. Roy. Acad. Sci. Amsterdam*, **17**, 793 (1914).

34. L. S. Ornstein and F. Zernike, *Physik Z.*, **27**, 761 (1926).

35. P. Debye, *J. Chem. Phys.*, **31**, 680 (1959).

36. J. S. Rowlinson, in S. Gratch, ed., *Advances in Thermophysical Properties at Extreme Temperatures and Pressures*, New York, American Society of Mechanical Engineers, 1965, p. 1.

PROBLEMS

13.1. Estimate $N_{\alpha\mathfrak{B}}$ and $g(N_A, N_{\alpha\mathfrak{B}})$ for a solid with few holes and from Eq. (3.4) obtain an expression for μ_A (not $\mu_{A,m}$). Show that with the value of ϕ found in the text μ_A for a solid with few holes is virtually the same as that of a solid with no holes.

13.2. Consider an ensemble with assemblies in thermal contact, containing a single solid phase with few holes, in which N_A is fixed but N is variable. This may be thought of as a condition maintained by a piston which exerts a constant pressure on the system. The (P.F.) will be the same as that encountered in Prob. 13.1 except for a factor $\exp\{-PV/kT\}$ or $\exp\{-PNV_0/kT\}$. By maximization of (P.F.) with respect to N, holding P fixed and subsequently setting $P = 0$, show that

$$z\phi = \ln\left[(N - N_A)/N\right] + z\Delta\epsilon/kT.$$

Discuss this in connection with Eq. (3.11).

13.3. Consider an ensemble similar to that in Prob. 13.2, but for the dilute vapor. Show that maximization with respect to N leads to $PNV_0/kT = N_A$.

13.4. In Eq. (5.5), $f(r_{ij}) = -\partial\epsilon(r_{ij})/\partial r_{ij}$, where $\epsilon(r_{ij})$ is the mutual potential energy of the molecules i and j. Also $f_{x_i} = -\partial\left[\sum_j \epsilon(r_{ij})\right]/\partial x_i$. Remembering that $r_{ij} = \sqrt{(x_i - x_j)^2 + (y_i - y_j)^2 + (z_i - z_j)^2}$, show that Eq. (5.5) follows from this expression for f_x.

13.5. Using the virial expression, find an expression for the pressure of a gas of hard spheres involving an integral which contains $\eta(u_r)$, where $\eta(u_r)\,du_r$ is the number of collisions occurring per second with relative velocities between u_r and $u_r + du_r$. Find the second virial coefficient.

   Hint: Start with the pressure expressed in terms of the virial *sum* [see Eq. (5.8)], and note that only molecules in collision contribute to the sum. Assume that a collision lasts a time τ and calculate the force involved.

13.6. The work required to remove a colliding hard sphere from contact with the other sphere to an average position in a dilute gas is the work of compressing the rest of the molecules, the volume which is available to the rest of the molecules being decreased in this process by a volume equal to the overlap of the two exclusion spheres of the molecules when they are in contact. This overlap is equal to $\frac{5}{12}\pi\sigma^3$ or $\frac{5}{8}b$, where σ is the radius of the exclusion spheres (diameter of the hard-sphere molecules), and b is the van der Waals constant. Use Eq. (6.9) to find how much the collision rate is increased on account of this work. How much will the pressure be increased over that calculated in Prob. 13.5? Calculate the third virial coefficient for the gas of hard spheres.

13.7. Suppose that instead of, or in addition to, two-body forces, there are three-body forces, the mutual potential energy of the system being

$$E_p = \tfrac{1}{2} \sum_{i,j} \epsilon^{(2)}(r_{ij}) + \frac{1}{3!} \sum_{i,j,k} \epsilon^{(3)}(r_{ij},\, r_{ik},\, r_{jk}),$$

where $\epsilon^{(3)}$ vanishes if any *one* of r_{ij}, r_{ik}, or r_{jk} is large. Explain the numerical coefficients. Why is there no corresponding numerical coefficient in Eq. (5.5)?

Show that the contribution to f_{x_i} from the second sum in E_p is $-\tfrac{1}{2}\partial \left[\sum_{j,k}\epsilon^{(3)}\right]/\partial x_i$.

Show what additional contribution will be made to Eq. (5.6), and show that the additional contribution to the pressure will be

$$-\tfrac{1}{6} \rho^3 \iint r_{ij} \frac{\partial \epsilon^{(3)}}{\partial r_{ij}} g^{(3)}(r_{ij},\, r_{ik},\, r_{jk})\, d\tau_j d\tau_k,$$

the integration being carried out at fixed x_i, y_i, z_i. You should combine sums which can be seen to be equal by interchange of the running suffixes.

13.8. Integrate Eq. (6.10) or (6.11) for the case in which ρ is negligibly small and substitute the resulting expression for $g^{(2)}(r_{12})$ into Eq. (5.19) to obtain an expression for the second virial coefficient. Show that this expression is equivalent to that obtained in Chap. 8.

13.9. Using the result of Problem 13.8 to evaluate $g^{(2)}$ in the integral in Eq. (6.18), find a second approximation to $g^{(2)}$, and obtain an expression for the third virial coefficient in the form of a definite integral.

13.10. Derive Eq. (8.5) in the alternative manner suggested in the paragraph following the equation.

13.11. Using Eq. (9.22), assuming that it holds even for small values of r, find an expression for H. From this result find a relation for A near the critical point, and show that it has a value of a few angstroms.

Chapter 14

Ideal Gases: Quantum Theory

14-1. *Bose-Einstein and Fermi-Dirac Statistics*

In deriving the formula for the canonical partition function of a perfect gas $(\text{P.F.}) = (\text{p.f.})^N/N!$ we assumed that the number of molecules having their energy in any given range was always small compared with the number of energy levels in that range, so that the chances of multiple occupation of energy levels would be small. This assumption was carried over in setting up the expression for the grand partition function of a perfect gas, when we used the above-mentioned formula for the (P.F.). Actually the assumption is unnecessary, and the grand partition function offers a powerful method for handling the more general case. We start from the formula

$$(\text{G.P.F.}) = \sum_N (\text{P.F.})_N \lambda^N. \tag{1.1}$$

By substituting the general expression for $(\text{P.F.})_N$, we obtain

$$(\text{G.P.F.}) = \sum_N \sum_{L_N} \exp\left\{\frac{-E_{L_N}}{kT}\right\} \lambda^N, \tag{1.2}$$

where L_N denotes a collective quantum number for an assembly containing N molecules in the designated volume V. In an ideal gas the molecules are independent of each other. We may therefore write

$$E_{L_N} = \sum_i^N n_{i,L_N} \epsilon_i, \tag{1.3}$$

where the superscript N on the summation sign indicates that

$$\sum_i^N n_{i,L_N} = N. \tag{1.4}$$

In Eq. (1.3) n_{i,L_N} represents the number of molecules in the ith energy level when the overall quantum state is that indicated by L_N. Substituting Eqs. (1.3) and (1.4) into Eq. (1.2) and converting a quantity with a sum in the exponent to a product, we obtain

$$\text{(G.P.F.)} = \sum_N \sum_{L_N} \prod_i^N \left(\lambda \exp\left\{ \frac{-\epsilon_i}{kT} \right\} \right)^{n_{i,L_N}}$$

$$= \sum_{(n_i)} \prod_i \left(\lambda \exp\left\{ \frac{-\epsilon_i}{kT} \right\} \right)^{n_i}. \tag{1.5}$$

The last expression in (1.5) means that we are going to sum over every product with every possible combination of n_i's. This is the same as the preceding expression, for

$$\sum_{L_N} \prod_i^N \left(\lambda \exp\left\{ \frac{-\epsilon_i}{kT} \right\} \right)^{n_{i,L_N}}$$

means that we are to sum over every product with every possible value of n_i such that for the whole product $\sum_i n_i = N$; only in this way will we get every possible energy level of an assembly of N molecules. The summation over all N removes the restriction implied by $\sum_i n_i = N$. Thus we obtain Eq. (1.5). We may write Eq. (1.5) in the form

$$\text{(G.P.F.)} = \prod_i \left[1 + \lambda \exp\left\{ \frac{-\epsilon_i}{kT} \right\} + \left(\lambda \exp\left\{ \frac{-\epsilon_i}{kT} \right\} \right)^2 + \cdots \right]$$

$$= \prod_i \frac{1}{1 - \lambda \exp\left\{ -\epsilon_i/kT \right\}}, \tag{1.6}$$

because the first product of Eq. (1.6) will be a sum of products of the type of Eq. (1.5), with every possible combination of exponents.

Throughout this discussion we have tacitly assumed that n_i, the number of molecules in the ith energy level, can have any value whatsoever. This is the assumption of the Bose-Einstein statistics. The Fermi-Dirac statistics makes the assumption, based on the Pauli exclusion principle, that there cannot be more than one molecule in a single quantum state. If this is so, then n_i can take the values 0 and 1 only, and in place of Eq. (1.6) we obtain

$$\text{(G.P.F.)} = \prod_i \left(1 + \lambda \exp\left\{ \frac{-\epsilon_i}{kT} \right\} \right). \tag{1.7}$$

Whether a molecule or atom obeys the Bose-Einstein or Fermi-Dirac statistics depends upon the number of elementary particles making up this molecule or atom. If the number of elementary particles is even, the molecule will obey Bose-Einstein statistics; if it is odd the molecule will obey Fermi-Dirac statistics. It does not matter whether the elementary particles are in the nucleus or the electron shells. Thus ^{4}He which has two protons and two neutrons in the nucleus, and two electrons outside the nucleus obeys Bose-Einstein statistics; whereas ^{3}He, differing in that it has only one neutron in the nucleus obeys the Fermi-Dirac statistics. This behavior follows from the discussion, in Sec. 1-7, of the symmetry of the wave functions, since wave functions for systems which have an even number of elementary particles are symmetrical whereas functions for systems with an odd number of elementary particles are antisymmetric. If two molecules are in the same energy level, exchange of these molecules must leave the wave function identical. Thus if it also changes the sign (antisymmetrical case) such a wave function must vanish, so we cannot have states with two molecules in the same energy level. If the two molecules are in different states, the exchange of two particles changes a function of x_1, x_2 (x_1 and x_2 representing the collection of coordinates of the two molecules) into a function of x_2, x_1. Since in this case the functional dependence on the first set of coordinates, x_1, is different from the dependence on the second set x_2, before exchange, the function of x_1, x_2 will differ from that of x_2, x_1.

We may now consider some of the consequences of Eqs. (1.6) and (1.7). Applying Eq. (3.5) of Chap. 10 we find for the Bose-Einstein gas

$$
\begin{aligned}
\bar{N} &= -\lambda \, \frac{\partial \sum_i \ln\left(1 - \lambda \exp\left\{-\epsilon_i/kT\right\}\right)}{\partial \lambda} \\[2mm]
&= \sum_i \frac{\lambda \exp\left\{-\epsilon_i/kT\right\}}{1 - \lambda \exp\left\{-\epsilon_i/kT\right\}} \\[2mm]
&= \sum_i \frac{1}{\lambda^{-1} \exp\left\{\epsilon_i/kT\right\} - 1} \\[2mm]
&= \sum_i \frac{1}{\exp\left\{(\epsilon_i - \mu)/kT\right\} - 1}
\end{aligned}
\tag{1.8}
$$

where we have written $\lambda = \exp\left\{\mu/kT\right\}$ (omitting the subscript on $\mu_{\max}$).

Similarly, for the Fermi-Dirac gas we obtain

$$\bar{N} = \lambda \frac{\partial \sum_i \ln (1 + \lambda \exp \{-\epsilon_i/kT\})}{\partial \lambda}$$

$$= \sum_i \frac{\lambda \exp \{-\epsilon_i/kT\}}{1 + \lambda \exp \{-\epsilon_i/kT\}}$$

$$= \sum_i \frac{1}{\lambda^{-1} \exp \{\epsilon_i/kT\} + 1}$$

$$= \sum_i \frac{1}{\exp \{(\epsilon_i - \mu)/kT\} + 1}. \tag{1.9}$$

From these expressions we naturally infer that a term in the sum represents the average number of molecules in the ith level,† or for the Bose-Einstein gas,

$$\bar{n}_i = \frac{1}{\exp \{(\epsilon_i - \mu)/kT\} - 1}; \tag{1.10}$$

and for the Fermi-Dirac gas,

$$\bar{n}_i = \frac{1}{\exp \{(\epsilon_i - \mu)/kT\} + 1}. \tag{1.11}$$

As further justification of Eqs. (1.10) and (1.11) we may treat the molecules in the various energy levels as tautomers, writing an individual λ_i for each level. Then Eq. (1.5) reduces to

$$(\text{G.P.F.}) = \sum_{(n_i)} \prod_i \left(\lambda_i \exp \left\{\frac{-\epsilon_i}{kT}\right\}\right)^{n_i}$$

and Eqs. (1.6) and (1.7) become, respectively,

$$(\text{G.P.F.}) = \prod_i \frac{1}{1 - \lambda_i \exp \{-\epsilon_i/kT\}}$$

and

$$(\text{G.P.F.}) = \prod_i \left(1 + \lambda_i \exp \left\{\frac{-\epsilon_i}{kT}\right\}\right).$$

† Although Eqs. (1.10) and (1.11) are commonly thought of as giving the numbers present in specific translational states of a monatomic gas, they will also apply to a gas which has internal energy levels, in which case i is a collective quantum number that determines both internal and translational states.

Application of Eqs. (6.5) of Chap. 10 now gives

$$\bar{n}_i = \frac{\lambda_i \exp\{-\epsilon_i/kT\}}{1 - \lambda_i \exp\{-\epsilon_i/kT\}}$$

for the Bose-Einstein case, and

$$\bar{n}_i = \frac{\lambda_i \exp\{-\epsilon_i/kT\}}{1 + \lambda_i \exp\{-\epsilon_i/kT\}}$$

for the Fermi-Dirac case. Since the condition for equilibrium is that all λ_i should be equal, these yield Eqs. (1.10) and (1.11), respectively.

It will be observed that if $\exp\{(\epsilon_i - \mu)/kT\}$ is very large compared with 1, then in either case $\bar{n}_i$ is very small and both Eqs. (1.10) and (1.11) reduce to the Boltzmann expression.

Equations (1.10) and (1.11) can also be obtained by a more elementary calculation based upon the discussion of Chap. 6. We consider the phase space to be divided up into cells, the ith cell containing C_i quantum levels. If we have, say, N_i molecules in the ith cell, the problem in the Bose-Einstein statistics is that of distributing N_i identical objects in C_i boxes. The number of distinguishable arrangements is $(C_i + N_i - 1)!/(C_i - 1)!N_i!$. The total number of arrangements in the entire number of cells, with fixed numbers of molecules in each cell, will be†

$$\mathfrak{Z} = \prod_i \frac{(C_i + N_i - 1)!}{(C_i - 1)!N_i!}. \tag{1.12}$$

The total possible number of arrangements will be the sum of all terms of the form $\mathfrak{Z}$ which satisfy the conditions

$$\sum_i N_i = N \tag{1.13}$$

and

$$\sum_i \epsilon_i N_i = E \tag{1.14}$$

As usual we find the maximum term by differentiating $\ln \mathfrak{Z}$ and setting the result equal to zero, taking account of the conditions (1.13) and (1.14) by the use of Lagrange multipliers. This gives

$$N_i = \frac{C_i}{\exp\{-\alpha - \epsilon_i \beta\} - 1}, \tag{1.15}$$

† See footnote p. 221.

provided that C_i and N_i are large compared with 1, which is clearly equivalent to Eq. (1.10) if $\alpha = \mu/kT$ and $\beta = -1/kT$.

With the Fermi-Dirac statistics we have n_i equal to either 0 or 1. Thus $N_i \leq C_i$. We have the problem of finding the number of different ways in which N_i boxes can be filled and $C_i - N_i$ can be empty, which is the same as the number of ways of arranging N_i objects of one class and $C_i - N_i$ objects of another. This is equal to $C_i!/N_i!(C_i - N_i)!$. In place of Eq. (1.12) we have then

$$3 = \prod_i \frac{C_i!}{N_i!(C_i - N_i)!}, \tag{1.16}$$

and again the total number of arrangements will be the sum of all terms of the form of Eq. (1.16) which satisfy conditions (1.13) and (1.14). The condition that $\ln 3$ shall be a maximum yields in this case

$$N_i = \frac{C_i}{\exp\{-\alpha - \epsilon_i\beta\} + 1}, \tag{1.17}$$

which is equivalent to Eq. (1.11) with the proper identification of α and β.

The original method of deriving Eqs. (1.10) and (1.11), by using the grand partition function, has the advantage that no selection of the largest term is necessary.

14-2. *Partition Functions (p.f.), and Thermodynamic Relations*

The partition function (p.f.) is useful for a gas of independent particles because it can be evaluated as a sum over states, on the one hand, and related to the thermodynamic functions on the other. In Bose-Einstein and Fermi-Dirac gases there is an effective statistical interaction between the particles, even though they have no mutual potential, and the partition function (p.f.) is much less useful. It can be defined through the chemical potential by the equation

$$\mu = -kT \ln \frac{(\text{p.f.})}{N} \tag{2.1}$$

or, what is equivalent:

$$(\text{p.f.}) = N \exp\left\{\frac{-\mu}{kT}\right\} = \frac{N}{\lambda}. \tag{2.2}$$

By combining this with Eq. (1.8) or (1.9) we get

$$(\text{p.f.}) = \sum_i \frac{1}{\exp\{\epsilon_i/kT\} \mp \exp\{\mu/kT\}}, \tag{2.3}$$

the negative sign being correct for the Bose-Einstein gas and the positive sign for the Fermi-Dirac gas. This equation has the sum-over-states form, but is actually an implicit equation for μ or (p.f.). It reverts to the classical expression when $\exp\{\epsilon_i/kT\} \gg \exp\{\mu/kT\}$ or $\exp\{(\epsilon_i - \mu)/kT\} \gg 1$.

These partition functions have the same relation to an equilibrium ratio as in the Boltzmann case. Let (p.f.)$'$ be the sum over one set of energy levels and (p.f.)$''$ that over another set of levels. Then $N''/N' = (\text{p.f.})''/(\text{p.f.})'$, but since (p.f.)$''$ and (p.f.)$'$ depend upon N'' and N', in general the ratio N''/N' itself depends upon the concentration; thus it is *not* an equilibrium constant. Only the Boltzmann case gives rise to an equilibrium constant.

The canonical partition function (P.F.) depends only on the energy levels of an assembly, and bears the usual relations to the thermodynamic properties. Since $\mu = (\partial A/\partial N)_{T,V}$, we can write

$$kT \ln (\text{P.F.}) = -A$$

$$= -\int \mu \, dN + \text{const.}$$

$$= -kT \int \ln \lambda \, dN + \text{const.}$$

$$= kT \int \ln \frac{(\text{p.f.})}{N} \, dN + \text{const.} \tag{2.4}$$

Instead of attempting to evaluate the constant of integration, we can write this expression as a definite integral with variable upper limit:

$$-kT \ln (\text{P.F.}) = A$$

$$= kT \int_0^N \ln \lambda \, dN$$

$$= -kT \int_0^N \ln \frac{(\text{p.f.})}{N} \, dN. \tag{2.5}$$

This is the correct form, because if N is small enough (the volume being fixed) it should revert to the classical form. Under these circumstances (p.f.) approaches the classical form, which does not depend on N, and the integral written reverts to the usual classical expression $N \ln (\text{p.f.}) - N \ln N + N$. For larger values of N, we cannot assume (p.f.) to be independent of N, as is clear from Eq. (2.3), since μ depends on N. Only if the term involving μ is negligible can the dependence on N at constant volume be neglected.

14-3. *The Bose-Einstein Condensation*

It is obvious from the preceding discussion that the behavior of μ will play a central role in the discussion of the Bose-Einstein and Fermi-Dirac gases. In the Bose-Einstein case we can see from Eq. (1.10) that μ cannot be greater than any ϵ_i, for if this were the case n_i would be negative, which is of course impossible. Thus, if ϵ_0 is the energy of the lowest energy level,

$$\mu \leqq \epsilon_0. \tag{3.1}$$

We can also see how μ changes with temperature. We can write†

$$N = \sum_i n_i,$$

where n_i may be thought of as a function of μ and T defined by Eq. (1.10), the volume V being held constant, and we have

$$\left(\frac{\partial \mu}{\partial T}\right)_N = - \frac{(\partial N/\partial T)_\mu}{(\partial N/\partial \mu)_T}.$$

From Eq. (1.10) we obtain

$$\left(\frac{\partial n_i}{\partial T}\right)_\mu = \frac{\exp\{(\epsilon_i - \mu)/kT\}}{[\exp\{(\epsilon_i - \mu)/kT\} - 1]^2} \frac{\epsilon_i - \mu}{kT^2} > 0, \tag{3.2a}$$

and

$$\left(\frac{\partial n_i}{\partial \mu}\right)_T = \frac{\exp\{(\epsilon_i - \mu)/kT\}}{[\exp\{(\epsilon_i - \mu)/kT\} - 1]^2} \frac{1}{kT} > 0. \tag{3.2b}$$

Then from the relation for $(\partial \mu/\partial T)_N$, noting that $(\partial N/\partial T)_\mu = \sum_i (\partial n_i/\partial T)_\mu$ and $(\partial N/\partial \mu)_T = \sum_i (\partial n_i/\partial \mu)_T$, it is seen that

$$\left(\frac{\partial \mu}{\partial T}\right)_{N,V} < 0. \tag{3.3}$$

---

† Although we shall, when convenient, continue to apply the results arising from use of the grand partition function, we shall leave off the averaging sign (overrule) in the remainder of this chapter.

In order to see the results of this behavior of μ we shall examine Eq. (1.8) further. The right-hand side of (1.8) may be converted into an integral, since the energy levels of a gas in a moderately sized box are extremely close together. We first write (exp $\{(\epsilon_i - \mu)/kT\} - 1)^{-1}$ as exp $\{(\mu - \epsilon_i)/kT\}/[1 - \exp\{(\mu - \epsilon_i)/kT\}]$. We recognize the denominator of the last expression as the value of a geometric series since, in view of the inequality (3.1), we see that exp $\{(\mu - \epsilon_i)/kT\}$ is less than 1. Hence we may write

$$\frac{\exp\{(\mu - \epsilon_i)/kT\}}{1 - \exp\{(\mu - \epsilon_i)/kT\}} = \sum_{l=1}^{\infty} \exp\left\{\frac{l(\mu - \epsilon_i)}{kT}\right\}. \tag{3.4}$$

The number of energy levels in the range ϵ to $\epsilon + d\epsilon$ in a box of volume V is given approximately [Eq. (5.19) of Chap. 1] by $2\pi V(2m/h^2)^{3/2}(\epsilon - \epsilon_0)^{1/2} d\epsilon$, since, if we neglect the very small kinetic energy of the lowest level, $\epsilon - \epsilon_0$ *is* the kinetic energy. Thus, converting Eq. (1.8) into an integral, and using Eq. (3.4), we have

$$N = 2\pi V\left(\frac{2m}{h^2}\right)^{3/2} \int_{\epsilon_0}^{\infty} \sum_{l=1}^{\infty} \exp\left\{\frac{l\mu}{kT}\right\} (\epsilon - \epsilon_0)^{1/2} \exp\left\{\frac{-l\epsilon}{kT}\right\} d\epsilon. \tag{3.5}$$

Integrating the series term by term, changing the variable to $\epsilon - \epsilon_0$, yields [1]

$$N = \left(\frac{2\pi mkT}{h^2}\right)^{3/2} V \sum_{l=1}^{\infty} \frac{1}{l^{3/2}} \exp\left\{\frac{l(\mu - \epsilon_0)}{kT}\right\}. \tag{3.6}$$

We note that if $\mu > \epsilon_0$ the series on the right-hand side of Eq. (3.6) does not converge, which is not surprising in view of the inequality (3.1). If $\mu = \epsilon_0$, the series becomes

$$\sum_{l=1}^{\infty} \frac{1}{l^{3/2}} = 2.612, \tag{3.7}$$

and inserting this in Eq. (3.6) we see that this defines a temperature T_0 given by

$$kT_0 = \frac{h^2}{2\pi m}\left(\frac{N}{2.612V}\right)^{2/3}. \tag{3.8}$$

From (3.1) and (3.3) it appears that we can get no solution for $T < T_0$. This unexpected result requires further scrutiny. It arises because the approximate expression for the number of energy levels in the range between ϵ and $\epsilon + d\epsilon$ goes to zero at $\epsilon = \epsilon_0$. Actually, of course, there is one energy level at $\epsilon = \epsilon_0$, and this energy level, as it happens, plays a decisive role. This might have been anticipated from Eq. (1.10), for it is seen that if μ approaches ϵ_0, then n_0 (the n_i corresponding to ϵ_0) becomes very large. This particular energy level should, therefore, have been singled out, and to get a universally valid expression for N we should have written in place of Eq. (3.6),

$$N = \frac{1}{\exp\{(\epsilon_0 - \mu)/kT\} - 1}$$
$$+ \left(\frac{2\pi mkT}{h^2}\right)^{3/2} V \sum_{l=1}^{\infty} \frac{1}{l^{3/2}} \exp\left\{\frac{l(\mu - \epsilon_0)}{kT}\right\}. \qquad (3.9)$$

Of course, for $T < T_0$ Eq. (3.9) will reduce to

$$N = \frac{1}{\exp\{(\epsilon_0 - \mu)/kT\} - 1} + 2.612 \left(\frac{2\pi mkT}{h^2}\right)^{3/2} V$$
$$= n_0 + 2.612 \left(\frac{2\pi mkT}{h^2}\right)^{3/2} V, \qquad (3.10)$$

whereas for $T > T_0$ it reduces to Eq. (3.6). There is essentially no range for which either Eq. (3.6) or Eq. (3.10) is not valid, as will soon become clear.

Since N is not infinite, μ can never really become equal to ϵ_0, but it can approach it very closely, and an appreciable fraction of the molecules can actually accumulate in one energy level, the lowest one. This is a very unusual situation, for under ordinary circumstances there are exceedingly many energy levels and the molecules over a range of energies equal to kT are fairly uniformly distributed over them, giving a practically infinitesimal fraction in any one energy level.

Let us see how closely μ must approach ϵ_0 in order for there to be an appreciable fraction of the molecules in the lowest energy level. If, for example, $n_0 = 10^{15}$, we see that $(\epsilon_0 - \mu)/kT$ must be approximately 10^{-15}, so that $\epsilon_0 - \mu$ is very small compared with kT, in fact, so small that the sum of Eq. (3.6) will reduce to the value given in Eq. (3.7). Yet if n_0 is equal to 10^{15}, this is still only a small fraction of N, assuming the latter to be of the order of Avogadro's number. So T will be very close to T_0, given by Eq. (3.8). As μ approaches ϵ_0 still more closely, however, n_0 can become comparable to N. If we substitute $N - n_0$ for N in Eq. (3.8), this equation will then give the true value of T, which can go below T_0. Thus for $T < T_0$, we have

$$kT = \frac{h^2}{2\pi m} \left(\frac{N - n_0}{2.612 V}\right)^{2/3}.$$ (3.11)

For all T's below T_0 the value of μ will be practically constant and equal to ϵ_0.

We shall now investigate the validity of Eq. (3.9). To justify the use of the integral [see Eq. (3.5)] in place of the summation, we must investigate the number of molecules in the energy levels above the lowest one. To take a simple but typical case, let us consider a gas in a cubic box of length a. The energy levels in such a box are given by the formula [Eqs. (5.16) and (5.17) of Chap. 1]

$$\epsilon_i = \frac{h^2}{8ma^2} (i_x^2 + i_y^2 + i_z^2),$$ (3.12)

where i_x, i_y, and i_z are the quantum numbers for the motions in the x, y, and z directions (the subscript i being a composite quantum number, standing for the group i_x, i_y, and i_z). For the lowest energy level $i_x = i_y = i_z = 1$. The next lowest energy level will be threefold, with either i_x or i_y or i_z equal to 2. Calling the energy of this level ϵ_1, we see that

$$\epsilon_1 - \epsilon_0 = \frac{3h^2}{8ma^2} = \frac{3h^2}{8mV^{2/3}}$$ (3.13)

where $V = a^3$ is the volume of the system. At T_0 the number n_1 in one of these three states will be

$$n_1 = \frac{1}{\exp\{(\epsilon_1 - \mu)/kT_0\} - 1}$$

$$\approx \frac{1}{\exp\{(\epsilon_1 - \epsilon_0)/kT_0\} - 1}$$

$$\approx \frac{1}{\exp\{3\pi \cdot 2.612^{2/3}/4N^{2/3}\} - 1},$$

using Eqs. (3.8) and (3.13). Since the exponent is a very small number, this may be written

$$n_1 = \frac{4N^{2/3}}{3\pi \cdot 2.612^{2/3}}.$$ (3.14)

Although n_1 is a very large number, it is very small compared with N if N is also large. As T goes below T_0, we replace N in Eq. (3.14) by

$N - n_0$, and, until T is virtually equal to zero, so that $N - n_0$ itself is small, n_1 will be only a small part of $N - n_0$. A considerable number of the low-lying energy levels must therefore contribute to $N - n_0$, none of them contributing an excessive amount, so the integration will be a valid approximation, and the larger N is, the better the approximation.

It is now clear that μ behaves as follows. If we assume V/N to be fixed, μ increases with decreasing T until it virtually reaches the value ϵ_0 when T_0 is reached. As T is further decreased, μ remains essentially constant, and simultaneously the lowest energy level fills up. On the other hand, if T and N are held constant, μ will (as always) increase with decreasing V until a volume is reached that is given by

$$V_0 = \frac{N}{2.612} \left(\frac{h^2}{2\pi m k T} \right)^{3/2}, \tag{3.15}$$

which is simply Eq. (3.8) solved for V instead of T. For $V < V_0$ then, μ remains virtually constant and equal to ϵ_0, while the lowest energy level fills up. This process in which μ remains constant [and, by Eq. (3.15) of Chap. 10, the pressure also remains constant] resembles a condensation. It has been described as a condensation in momentum space, since the energy levels extend throughout the box, and there is no physical separation of the "condensed" phase and the "vapor" phase.

This latter statement must be somewhat modified for a system in a gravitational field [2–4], where the potential energy is not constant in the box. Let x be the coordinate which measures the distance up from the bottom of the box. The potential energy as a function of x is shown schematically with some exaggeration in Fig. 14-1. Some energy levels are shown schematically in the diagram. It is clear that the wave func-

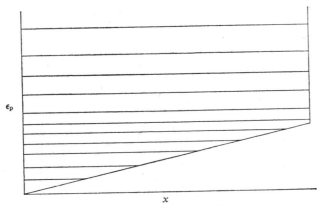

Figure 14-1. Energy diagram for a gas in a field of force.

tion for the lowest energy level will not extend clear up the box from $x = 0$ to $x = a$, but will give an appreciable probability for finding a molecule only in the bottom part of the box. Indeed, for helium in a gravitational field the lowest energy level will extend up a distance of only about 10^{-3} cm. This energy level will fairly quickly fill up, not because of any statistical limitations, but simply because of the space-filling properties of any real molecules. This will leave the volume of the system effectively slightly smaller, and the number of molecules appreciably less. The assembly will then be ready to start condensing into the next energy level. The general process of condensation will not be greatly altered but it should be clear, although the above description is somewhat schematic, that even a weak field will cause the condensation to take place in ordinary space as well as momentum space.

Furthermore, if there is an appreciable attractive potential between the molecules, there will be a state, the liquid state, in which the energy of the system is lower than it would be if all the molecules were in the lowest energy level of the vapor. In this case, the condensation to the liquid will clearly take place before the Bose-Einstein condensation, as was pointed out by Band [5], because the liquid will always have a lower chemical potential than would the same molecules in the lowest vapor level (where their entropy would vanish). Thus in a real substance the Bose-Einstein condensation probably cannot occur in the vapor phase, but something analogous to it may take place in a liquid phase.

It is thought that the general ideas of the Bose-Einstein condensation find a qualitative application in the case of liquid helium, which undergoes a transition at $2.17°$K, whereas for a Bose-Einstein ideal gas having the same density as liquid helium, T_0 would be about $3.14°$. This is very good agreement, considering that in the ideal gas the liquid forces are neglected completely. (The properties of liquid helium will be described in the following chapter.)

14-4. *Thermodynamic Functions of the Bose-Einstein Gas*

Although we now have a qualitative idea of the behavior of an ideal Bose-Einstein gas, we still do not have explicit expressions for the thermodynamic functions. Let us write

$$\lambda_0 = \exp\left\{\frac{\mu - \epsilon_0}{kT}\right\}, \tag{4.1}$$

where λ_0 is a function which may, at least for some applications, be used in place of λ, provided we are willing to use ϵ_0 as our zero of energy. Indeed, λ_0 is scarcely different from λ if the lowest potential energy in the box containing the gas is taken as zero, since in all practical cases ϵ_0 will then be essentially indistinguishable from zero. Eq. (3.6) then takes the form

$$\frac{N}{V\eta} = \frac{1}{v\eta}$$

$$= \sum_{l=1}^{\infty} \frac{\lambda_0^l}{l^{3/2}}, \tag{4.2}$$

where $v = V/N$ and

$$\eta = \left(\frac{2\pi mkT}{h^2}\right)^{3/2}. \tag{4.3}$$

We now set, for $T > T_0$, since λ_0 must clearly be a function of T and v in the combination $v\eta$ only,

$$\lambda_0 = \frac{a}{v\eta} + \frac{b}{(v\eta)^2} + \frac{c}{(v\eta)^3} + \cdots, \tag{4.4}$$

where $a, b, c, \cdots$ are undetermined constants. On substituting this expression for λ_0 into Eq. (4.2), the constants may be determined by making the coefficients of the powers of $1/v\eta$ equal on the two sides of the equation. Thus we find

$$a = 1,$$

$$b = -\frac{1}{2^{3/2}} = -0.3536,$$

$$c = \frac{1}{4} - \frac{1}{3^{3/2}} = 0.0576 \tag{4.5}$$

$$\cdot \quad \cdot \quad \cdot \quad \cdot \quad \cdot \quad \cdot.$$

Thus λ_0 is completely determined; above T_0 it is given by Eq. (4.4) with the coefficients given in Eq. (4.5), while below T_0 it is equal to 1. This puts us in a position to obtain expressions for the thermodynamic functions of a Bose-Einstein gas. †

There are several ways in which we might proceed. Perhaps the

† The thermodynamic functions are given in slightly greater detail by Mayer and Mayer [6].

easiest is to use Eq. (3.9) of Chap. 10. Combining this with Eq. (1.6) of the present chapter we write

$$P = -\frac{kT}{V} \sum_i \ln\left(1 - \lambda \exp\left\{\frac{-\epsilon_i}{kT}\right\}\right). \tag{4.6}$$

Neglecting for the present the special effects of the lowest energy level,[†] i.e., assuming $T > T_0$, we may expand the logarithm

$$\ln\left(1 - \lambda \exp\left\{\frac{-\epsilon_i}{kT}\right\}\right) = -\sum_{l=1}^{\infty} \frac{1}{l}\left(\lambda \exp\left\{\frac{-\epsilon_i}{kT}\right\}\right)^l. \tag{4.7}$$

At the same time, the sum in Eq. (4.6) may be converted into an integration, just as was the sum of Eq. (1.8) in Eq. (3.5). We obtain [1]

$$\begin{aligned} P &= 2\pi V \left(\frac{2m}{h^2}\right)^{3/2} \frac{kT}{V} \int_{\epsilon_0}^{\infty} \sum_{l=1}^{\infty} \frac{\lambda^l}{l} (\epsilon - \epsilon_0)^{1/2} \exp\left\{\frac{-l\epsilon}{kT}\right\} d\epsilon \\ &= \left(\frac{2\pi mkT}{h^2}\right)^{3/2} kT \sum_{l=1}^{\infty} \frac{\lambda_0^l}{l^{5/2}} \exp\left\{\frac{-l\epsilon_0}{kT}\right\} \\ &= \eta kT \sum_{l=1}^{\infty} \frac{\lambda_0^l}{l^{5/2}}, \end{aligned} \tag{4.8}$$

or

$$\frac{Pv}{kT} = \eta v \sum_{l=1}^{\infty} \frac{\lambda_0^l}{l^{5/2}}. \tag{4.9}$$

We substitute Eq. (4.4) into this, obtaining

$$\frac{Pv}{kT} = a + \left(b + \frac{a^2}{2^{5/2}}\right)\frac{1}{\eta v} + \left(c + \frac{ab}{2^{3/2}} + \frac{a^3}{3^{5/2}}\right)\frac{1}{(\eta v)^2} + \cdots. \tag{4.10}$$

Making use of Eqs. (4.5), we find

$$\begin{aligned} \frac{Pv}{kT} = \frac{PV}{NkT} &= 1 + \left(\frac{1}{2^{5/2}} - \frac{1}{2^{3/2}}\right)\frac{1}{\eta v} + \left(\frac{1}{4} - \frac{1}{3^{3/2}} - \frac{1}{2^3} + \frac{1}{3^{5/2}}\right)\frac{1}{(\eta v)^2} \\ &= 1 - \frac{0.1768}{\eta v} - \frac{0.0033}{(\eta v)^2} + \cdots, \end{aligned} \tag{4.11}$$

giving the pressure in the form of a virial equation.

[†] Equation (4.6) may be used even in the region of condensation. The term in the sum arising from the lowest energy level is $\ln (1 - \lambda \exp \{-\epsilon_0/kT\}) = \ln (1 - \lambda_0)$, and since λ_0 approaches 1 at T_0, it might be thought that the contribution from this term would approach infinity. As we have seen, however, the value of $(\epsilon_0 - \mu)/kT$ for a mole of gas may be of the order of 10^{-15} at T_0, and in most of the condensation range it cannot go much lower than 10^{-23}. Thus $1 - \lambda_0$ will be itself of the order of 10^{-23}, which means that $\ln (1 - \lambda_0)$ will be about -50. The resulting contribution to the pressure, approximately $50\, kT/V$, will be entirely negligible. Theoretically it eventually approaches infinity, but this occurs in a range of V or T which may be regarded, for practical purposes, as infinitesimal, and only if N is infinite.

From this the energy can be obtained at once, for we can derive a general theorem for P, which holds for any ideal gas whatever. To get this we make use of Eq. (6.3) of Chap. 5, which states that

$$P = -\frac{\sum_L (dE_L/dV) \exp\{-E_L/kT\}}{\sum_L \exp\{-E_L/kT\}}, \tag{4.12}$$

where the summation is over energy states of the complete assembly. Any E_L is a sum of energies of individual molecules, each molecule being in a definite quantum state. If the gas is in a rectangular box with edges a, b, and c, the kinetic energy of each individual quantum state is given by an expression like $(h^2/8m)(i_x^2/a^2 + i_y^2/b^2 + i_z^2/c^2)$, the quantum numbers i_x, i_y, i_z remaining fixed in the differentiation with respect to V. If the volume is increased in such a way that a, b, and c remain in constant ratio it is seen that each individual energy level and hence $E_L - N\epsilon_0$ varies as $V^{-2/3}$. Hence $dE_L/dV = -\frac{2}{3}(E_L - N\epsilon_0)/V$ and we see from Eq. (4.12) that

$$PV = \tfrac{2}{3}(E - N\epsilon_0), \tag{4.13}$$

where E is the average energy of the assembly.

The entropy is most expeditiously obtained from the equation

$$\begin{aligned}
S &= \frac{E + PV - N\mu}{T} \\[4pt]
&= \frac{E + PV}{T} - Nk \ln \lambda \\[4pt]
&= \frac{E - N\epsilon_0 + PV}{T} - Nk \ln \lambda_0 \\[4pt]
&= \frac{5}{2}\frac{PV}{T} - Nk \ln \lambda_0. \tag{4.14}
\end{aligned}$$

The specific heat C_v can be obtained by direct differentiation of the expression for $E - N\epsilon_0$.

The above results all hold for $T > T_0$ at fixed V or for $V > V_0$ at any given T. For $T < T_0$ or $V < V_0$ we note that λ_0 is equal to 1. In the region in which the Bose-Einstein condensation is taking place, it is somewhat easier to consider an isotherm, since at constant temperature P must remain constant for $V < V_0$, since λ_0 is constant (at least until the volume becomes so small that the lowest energy ϵ_0 begins to rise appreciably, but this will not occur at a normal macroscopic vol-

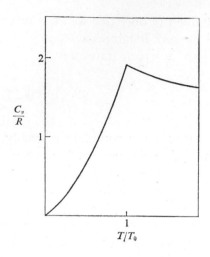

Figure 14-2. Specific heat of the ideal Bose-Einstein gas. (From London [11 of Chap. 15].)

ume). The value of the pressure in the condensation region is found by setting $\lambda_0 = 1$ in Eq. (4.8), which gives

$$P = \eta k T \sum_{l=1}^{\infty} \frac{1}{l^{5/2}} = 1.341\ \eta k T. \tag{4.15}$$

This can also be written in the form

$$PV = 1.341\ Nv\eta k T$$
$$= \frac{1.341\ NkT}{\sum_{l=1}^{\infty} (1/l^{3/2})} \left(\frac{T}{T_0}\right)^{3/2}. \tag{4.16}$$

In the last part of this equation we have taken explicit account of the variation of $v\eta$ with T, setting $v\eta = v\eta_0(T/T_0)^{3/2}$, where η_0 is η at $T = T_0$, for a given V, and using Eq. (4.2) with λ_0 set equal to 1 for $v\eta_0$. We find

$$PV = \frac{1.341}{2.612}\ NkT \left(\frac{T}{T_0}\right)^{3/2}$$
$$= 0.5134\ NkT \left(\frac{T}{T_0}\right)^{3/2}, \tag{4.17}$$

which gives

$$(E - N\epsilon_0) = 0.5134 \cdot \frac{3}{2}\ NkT \left(\frac{T}{T_0}\right)^{3/2}, \tag{4.18}$$

$$S = 0.5134 \cdot \frac{5}{2}\ Nk \left(\frac{T}{T_0}\right)^{3/2}, \tag{4.19}$$

and

$$C_v = 0.5134 \cdot \frac{15}{4} Nk \left(\frac{|T|}{T_0}\right)^{3/2}. \tag{4.20}$$

In Fig. 14-2 we show C_v as a function of T, and in Fig. 14-3 we show several isotherms. The behavior of the pressure at the critical volume V_0 is of interest. It will be noticed that $(\partial P/\partial V)_T$ is equal to zero at this point, so that the two parts of an isotherm run smoothly into each other. If we differentiate Eq. (4.8) we obtain

$$\left(\frac{\partial P}{\partial V}\right)_T = \frac{\eta k T}{\lambda_0} \sum_{l=1}^{\infty} \frac{\lambda_0^l}{l^{3/2}} \left(\frac{\partial \lambda_0}{\partial V}\right)_T. \tag{4.21}$$

It can be shown that $(\partial \lambda_0/\partial V)_T$ approaches zero as $\lambda_0 \longrightarrow 1$ by differentiating Eq. (4.2), which gives

$$-\frac{1}{v^2 \eta} = \frac{1}{\lambda_0} \sum_{l=1}^{\infty} \frac{\lambda_0^l}{l^{1/2}} \left(\frac{\partial \lambda_0}{\partial v}\right)_T$$

$$\underset{\lambda_0 \to 1}{=} \sum_{l=1}^{\infty} \frac{1}{l^{1/2}} \left(\frac{\partial \lambda_0}{\partial v}\right)_T.$$

The equation holds if $\lambda_0 < 1$, and the left-hand side clearly remains finite and nonzero. However $\sum_{l=1}^{\infty} (1/l^{1/2})$ is infinite, therefore $(\partial \lambda_0/\partial v)_T$ must approach zero.

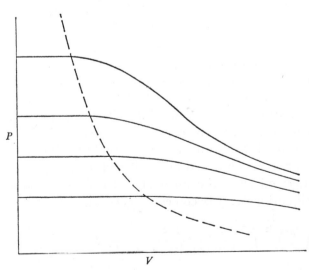

Figure 14-3. Isotherms of the ideal Bose-Einstein gas. [From Rice, *Phys. Rev.*, **93**, 1161 (1954).]

14-5. *The Fermi-Dirac Gas*

We now consider the properties of a Fermi-Dirac gas. In this case we know that n_i can never become greater than 1 for any i, and Eq. (1.11) is, indeed, consistent with this condition. At very low temperatures there will, of course, be a tendency for the molecules to go into the low energy levels, but in no case can there be more than one molecule in a given level. Let us suppose that at $T = 0$ the value of μ is μ_0. Then for $\epsilon_i > \mu_0$ we see that $\exp\{(\epsilon_i - \mu)/kT\}$ is infinite and for $\epsilon_i < \mu_0$ it is zero. Thus for $\epsilon_i > \mu_0$, from Eq. (1.11), $n_i = 0$; for $\epsilon_i < \mu_0$ the value of n_i is 1 at 0°K. Therefore, there must be just N energy levels with $\epsilon_i < \mu_0$. If the number of energy levels in a given energy range is given by [Eq. (5.19) of Chap. 1]

$$n_\epsilon \, d\epsilon = 2\pi g V \left(\frac{2m}{h^2}\right)^{3/2} \epsilon^{1/2} \, d\epsilon, \tag{5.1}$$

where g is the degeneracy factor,† and where we have set $\epsilon_0 = 0$, then

$$N = 2\pi g V \left(\frac{2m}{h^2}\right)^{3/2} \int_0^{\mu_0} \epsilon^{1/2} \, d\epsilon$$
$$= \frac{4}{3} \pi g V \left(\frac{2m\mu_0}{h^2}\right)^{3/2}. \tag{5.2}$$

It is seen that μ_0 is a function of the density.

The distribution of molecules with varying energy at 0°K will be as shown in Fig. 14-4 by the solid curve; in this figure n_ϵ is the number of molecules per unit energy range, and for $\epsilon < \mu_0$ this is given by the factor multiplying $d\epsilon$ in Eq. (5.1). Equation (5.2) gives μ_0.

At a slightly higher temperature the curve will be somewhat rounded at the corners, as indicated by the broken lines; μ will also be slightly changed. Just as for the Bose-Einstein gas, μ must decrease with increasing temperature, and in general μ is determined by Eq. (1.9), which may be converted into an integral as before, but this time without the difficulty which was encountered in the Bose-Einstein gas, although the power series derived from the integral will diverge at sufficiently low values of T. Equation (1.9) becomes, in general,

$$N = 2\pi g V \left(\frac{2m}{h^2}\right)^{3/2} \int_0^\infty \frac{\epsilon^{1/2}}{1 + \exp\{(\epsilon - \mu)/kT\}} \, d\epsilon \tag{5.3}$$

---

† We have not considered this factor in previous applications of this particular equation, but it is, of course, necessary if there is spin degeneracy. For example, if the particles we are considering are electrons, $g = 2$.

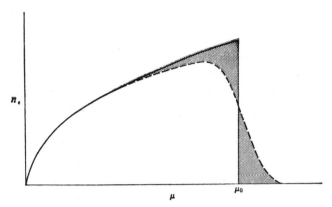

Figure 14-4. Energy distribution of molecules in the ideal Fermi-Dirac gas.

Since

$$\frac{1}{1 + \exp\{(\epsilon_i - \mu)/kT\}} = \frac{\exp\{(\mu - \epsilon_i)/kT\}}{1 + \exp\{(\mu - \epsilon_i)/kT\}}$$

$$= \exp\left\{\frac{\mu - \epsilon_i}{kT}\right\} - \exp\left\{\frac{2(\mu - \epsilon_i)}{kT}\right\} + \cdots,$$

term-by-term integration gives [compare Eq. (3.6)]

$$N = -g\eta V \sum_{l=1}^{\infty} (-1)^l \frac{\lambda^l}{l^{3/2}}. \tag{5.4}$$

where $\eta = (2\pi mkT/h^2)^{3/2}$ and $\lambda = \exp\{\mu/kT\}$. We write

$$\lambda = \frac{a}{g\eta v} + \frac{b}{(g\eta v)^2} + \frac{c}{(g\eta v)^3} + \cdots, \tag{5.5}$$

insert it into Eq. (5.4), and compare coefficients as in the Bose-Einstein case. The results are as follows:

$$a = 1$$

$$b = \frac{1}{2^{3/2}} = 0.3536 \tag{5.6}$$

$$c = \frac{1}{4} - \frac{1}{3^{3/2}} = 0.0576.$$

Proceeding, then, in the same way as in the Bose-Einstein case we find

$$PV = NkT\left(1 + \frac{0.1768}{g\eta v} - \frac{0.0033}{(g\eta v)^2} + \cdots\right), \tag{5.7}$$

from which the other thermodynamic functions can be found by use of Eqs. (4.13) and (4.14), which are equally valid in this case.

The equation for N diverges if λ is greater than 1, which happens at low temperatures, since $\lambda \longrightarrow \exp \{\mu_0/kT\}$ and μ_0 is positive as is seen in Fig. 14-4. It is difficult to apply the standard criteria of convergence to Eq. (5.7), but, in any case it becomes desirable at low temperatures to use another method, based on the properties illustrated in Fig. 14-4, involving expansions around the energy μ_0. Equation (5.2) is simply the specialization of Eq. (5.3) for $T = 0$, and since N is independent of T, the right-hand sides of these equations may be set equal to each other, which gives

$$1 = \frac{3}{2\mu_0^{3/2}} \int_0^\infty \frac{1}{1 + \exp \{(\epsilon - \mu)/kT\}} \epsilon^{1/2} \, d\epsilon. \tag{5.8}$$

It will be convenient to set

$$\frac{\epsilon - \mu}{kT} = x \tag{5.9}$$

and to write

$$\epsilon = \mu + (\epsilon - \mu) = \mu \left(1 + \frac{\epsilon - \mu}{\mu}\right) = \mu \left(1 + \frac{xkT}{\mu}\right). \tag{5.10}$$

We may express $\epsilon^{1/2}$ in terms of a binomial expansion of Eq. (5.10):

$$\epsilon^{1/2} = \mu^{1/2} \left[1 + \frac{1}{2}x\frac{kT}{\mu} - \frac{1}{8}x^2\left(\frac{kT}{\mu}\right)^2 + \frac{1}{16}x^3\left(\frac{kT}{\mu}\right)^3 - \cdots \right]. \tag{5.11}$$

We further remark that

$$\frac{1}{1 + \exp \{x\}} = 1 - \frac{\exp \{x\}}{1 + \exp \{x\}}$$

$$= \frac{\exp \{-x\}}{1 + \exp \{-x\}}. \tag{5.12}$$

Since $1/(1 + \exp \{x\})$ is nearly equal to 1 if $x \ll 0$ and nearly equal to 0 if $x \gg 0$, we substitute the first expression from Eq. (5.12) into Eq. (5.8) for $x < 0$ and the second expression for $x > 0$. The factor which arises from the 1 in the first expression of Eq. (5.12) can be immediately integrated over the region $x < 0$, and for the other parts we substitute for $\epsilon^{1/2}$ from Eq. (5.11). We thus obtain

$$1 = \left(\frac{\mu}{\mu_0}\right)^{3/2} - \frac{3\mu^{1/2}kT}{2\mu_0^{3/2}} \int_{-\infty}^{0} \frac{\exp\{x\}}{1 + \exp\{x\}} \left(1 + \frac{1}{2} x \frac{kT}{\mu} - \cdots\right) dx$$

$$+ \frac{3\mu^{1/2}kT}{2\mu_0^{3/2}} \int_{0}^{\infty} \frac{\exp\{-x\}}{1 + \exp\{-x\}} \left(1 + \frac{1}{2} x \frac{kT}{\mu} - \cdots\right) dx. \quad (5.13)$$

In the first integral we have taken the lower limit as $x = -\infty$ (or $\epsilon = -\infty$) instead of $\epsilon = 0$, since if T is small $|x|$ will become large while $|\epsilon - \mu|$ is still small, and the integrand will have become virtually zero long before ϵ has approached zero. Now it may be readily seen that

$$\int_{-\infty}^{0} \frac{\exp\{x\}}{1 + \exp\{x\}} dx = \int_{0}^{\infty} \frac{\exp\{-x\}}{1 + \exp\{-x\}} dx,$$

and, in general, where n is an integer,

$$\int_{-\infty}^{0} x^n \frac{\exp\{x\}}{1 + \exp\{x\}} dx = (-1)^n \int_{0}^{\infty} x^n \frac{\exp\{-x\}}{1 + \exp\{-x\}} dx. \quad (5.14)$$

Therefore Eq. (5.13) reduces to

$$1 = \left(\frac{\mu}{\mu_0}\right)^{3/2} + \frac{3\mu^{1/2}kT}{2\mu_0^{3/2}} \int_{0}^{\infty} \frac{\exp\{-x\}}{1 + \exp\{-x\}} \left[x \frac{kT}{\mu} + \frac{1}{8} x^3 \left(\frac{kT}{\mu}\right)^3 + \cdots\right] dx. \quad (5.15)$$

The integral may be evaluated by expanding the first factor in a series:

$$\frac{\exp\{-x\}}{1 + \exp\{-x\}}$$
$$= \exp\{-x\} - \exp\{-2x\} + \exp\{-3x\} - \cdots. \quad (5.16)$$

The resulting expression may be integrated term by term. We have [1]

$$\int_{0}^{\infty} x^m \exp\{-nx\} dx = \frac{1}{n^{m+1}} \int_{0}^{\infty} y^m \exp\{-y\} dy = \frac{m!}{n^{m+1}}, \quad (5.17)$$

from which it may be seen that the integral in Eq. (5.15) reduces to

$$-\frac{kT}{\mu} \sum_{n=1}^{\infty} \frac{(-1)^n}{n^2} - \frac{3}{4} \left(\frac{kT}{\mu}\right)^3 \sum_{n=1}^{\infty} \frac{(-1)^n}{n^4} + \cdots. \quad (5.18)$$

The sums in this expression can be evaluated [7]:

$$-\sum_{n=1}^{\infty} \frac{(-1)^n}{n^2} = \frac{\pi^2}{12}; \qquad -\sum_{n=1}^{\infty} \frac{(-1)^n}{n^4} = \frac{7\pi^4}{720}; \quad \cdots. \quad (5.19)$$

therefore

$$1 = \left(\frac{\mu}{\mu_0}\right)^{3/2}\left[1 + \frac{\pi^2}{8}\left(\frac{kT}{\mu}\right)^2 + \frac{7\pi^4}{640}\left(\frac{kT}{\mu}\right)^4 + \cdots\right]. \qquad (5.20)$$

Expanding the bracketed term by the binomial theorem, to obtain its $-\frac{2}{3}$ power, we find

$$\mu = \mu_0\left[1 - \frac{\pi^2}{12}\left(\frac{kT}{\mu}\right)^2 + \frac{\pi^4}{720}\left(\frac{kT}{\mu}\right)^4 + \cdots\right].$$

We wish, of course, to express the bracket on the right-hand side in terms of μ_0. If we were interested in an expression correct only to the second power, we could simply substitute the first approximation $\mu = \mu_0$ in the second term in the last equation, obtaining

$$\mu \approx \mu_0\left[1 - \frac{\pi^2}{12}\left(\frac{kT}{\mu_0}\right)^2\right].$$

If we wish to carry the approximation further, we may substitute this value of μ in the second term and $\mu = \mu_0$ in the third term; thus we obtain

$$\mu = \mu_0\left[1 - \frac{\pi^2}{12}\left(\frac{kT}{\mu_0}\right)^2 - \frac{\pi^4}{80}\left(\frac{kT}{\mu_0}\right)^4 + \cdots\right]. \qquad (5.21)$$

An expression for the total energy $E = N\bar{\epsilon}$ of the Fermi gas may be found by multiplying the integrand of Eq. (5.3) by ϵ, that is, by substituting $\epsilon^{3/2}$ for $\epsilon^{1/2}$, and by use of Eq. (5.2). This yields

$$E = \frac{3N}{2\mu_0^{3/2}}\int_0^\infty \frac{\epsilon^{3/2}}{1 + \exp\{(\epsilon - \mu)/kT\}}\,d\epsilon. \qquad (5.22)$$

The evaluation of this integral may be carried out in a manner entirely analogous to that used in the evaluation of the integral in Eq. (5.8) to obtain Eq. (5.20). It is necessary only to expand $\epsilon^{3/2}$, instead of $\epsilon^{1/2}$ as in Eq. (5.11), making the necessary changes in the subsequent equations. Having obtained an expression for E in terms of μ, it may be converted to μ_0 by use of Eq. (5.21). In this way one obtains

$$E = \frac{3}{5}N\mu_0\left[1 + \frac{5\pi^2}{12}\left(\frac{kT}{\mu_0}\right)^2 - \frac{\pi^4}{16}\left(\frac{kT}{\mu_0}\right)^4 + \cdots\right]. \qquad (5.23)$$

From this expression and from Eq. (5.21), all the thermodynamic functions may be obtained. The pressure may be obtained from

Eq. (4.13), which is a general relation, remembering that in treating the Fermi-Dirac gas we have set $\epsilon_0 = 0$. In using Eq. (5.23) we note that μ_0 depends on the density according to Eq. (5.2).

A few remarks about Eq. (5.23) will be in order. At $T = 0$ it will be noted that $E = \frac{3}{5}N\mu_0$, with μ_0 given, of course, by Eq. (5.2). This appreciable zero-point energy arises because of the fact that not more than one particle can occupy a given energy level. The energy then, is equal to N times the average of the N lowest energy levels, the situation being as illustrated in Fig. 14-4. When T increases, the shaded areas in Fig. 14-4 will increase as T. (These shaded areas are proportional, respectively, to the second and third terms on the right-hand side of Eq. (5.13), which, it will be observed, start off proportional to T.) Also the difference in the average energies of the two shaded areas will increase proportionally to T. Since the particles represented by the low energy area are transferred to the high energy area, the energy of the system will increase as the product of the areas and the difference in average energy, or as T^2, as appears in Eq. (5.23).

One can, of course, immediately obtain C_v by differentiating Eq. (5.23) with respect to T, which gives

$$C_v = \frac{\pi^2 N k^2 T}{2\mu_0}\left[1 - \frac{3\pi^2}{10}\left(\frac{kT}{\mu_0}\right)^2 + \cdots\right].\tag{5.24}$$

The specific heat at constant density thus starts out being proportional to T.

The expression for the entropy is in this case obtained as easily as any way by integration of C_v/T. Thus

$$S = \frac{\pi^2 N k^2 T}{2\mu_0}\left[1 - \frac{\pi^2}{10}\left(\frac{kT}{\mu_0}\right)^2 + \cdots\right].\tag{5.25}$$

There is no possibility of a transition, corresponding to condensation into a lowest energy level, in the case of the Fermi-Dirac gas and in this respect it differs qualitatively from the Bose-Einstein gas. The isotopic form of helium, ³He, is a substance which should obey the Fermi-Dirac statistics. It is thus of interest that pure liquid ³He shows no sign of a λ-point transition, such as occurs in liquid ⁴He, down to the lowest temperature at which it has been investigated, about 0.003°K. Although the interatomic forces in the liquid prevent the direct application of the laws of the ideal gas, the qualitative difference in the properties of ³He and ⁴He is certainly significant.

A more direct application of the Fermi-Dirac statistics may be made to electrons in metals. It has long been supposed that the electrons in metals, particularly in the highly "metallic" metals, such as the alkali metals, are free to move about. They may be treated approximately as an ideal gas of free electrons held in a "box" by the attractive forces of the positive ions. This model was suggested before the discovery of the quantum theory, and was quite successful in explaining the high conductivity of metals for electricity and for heat, and the ratio of these two conductivities. It was very puzzling, however, that the electrons did not appear to contribute to the specific heat. As we have seen in Chap. 9 the high-temperature value of C_v for a monatomic metal containing N atoms is very close to $3Nk$. This is just the value expected from the $3N$ lattice vibrations which describe the motions of the atoms, with no allowance for any contribution from the electrons. This, however, may be well understood from Eq. (5.24). From Eq. (5.2) it may be readily found that μ_0 for the electrons in an ordinary metal is of the order of several electron volts, which is much greater than the values of kT usually attained (at room temperature kT is about 0.025 ev). Thus it is seen from Eq. (5.24) that, at room temperature, C_v for the electrons is much less than $3Nk$, and hence is generally negligible.

However, it will be recalled that at very low temperatures the specific heat due to the lattice vibrations goes to zero as T^3, whereas the specific heat of the electrons goes to zero as T. Therefore, if the temperature is low enough, the latter should predominate, and the residual specific heat of a metal very close to absolute zero should fall off as T. This is actually found to be so [8].

Since the specific heat due to the electrons is very small in actual magnitude, even at room temperature, for many purposes the expression for E in Eq. (5.23) may be approximated by its first term. If we insert the value of μ_0 found from Eq. (5.2), Eq. (5.23) becomes

$$E = \frac{3}{10} \frac{Nh^2}{m} \left(\frac{3N}{4\pi gV} \right)^{2/3}. \tag{5.26}$$

It is seen that E increases as V decreases; thus E acts as a repulsive potential for the metal. Indeed, although its dependence on V is rather weak, it actually appears that in such metals as the alkali metals this is the principal repulsive potential [9, 10]. Before exploring this further, we must take account of the specific interactions between the electrons and the ions which form the lattice. In the first place, there will be an attractive potential between the electrons and the ions surrounding them, and, in the second place, there will be specific effects due to the inner electrons which are not free but are attached to individual ions.

These populate the lowest energy levels of the ions, and so may be said to occupy certain regions of the phase space in the immediate neighborhood of the positive nuclei. A free electron can penetrate close to the nucleus, but when it does so it will have a relatively high velocity compared with the bound electrons. Thus it will not stay in such a region long, and the region will act like an excluded volume. To take care of the attractive forces, it has been suggested that the potential energy of an electron be approximated by $-e^2 A/(V/N)^{1/3}$. Here $(V/N)^{1/3}$ is, of course, proportional to the average electron–positive-ion distance, so that this is the proper form for an electrostatic potential. The constant A (a form of the Madelung constant) takes into account the electrostatic effects of all the neighboring charged particles, some attractive and some repulsive, with the attractive forces predominating, since the electrons are closest to the positive ions. We might expect A to have a value fairly near that of a uniunivalent crystal. This suggests that we write for the energy of the electrons, using the first term of Eq. (5.23) and Eq. (5.2), setting $g = 2$ and adding the potential-energy term:

$$E = N^{5/3} \frac{3h^2}{10m} \left(\frac{3}{8\pi(V - V_i)} \right)^{2/3} - N^{4/3} A \frac{e^2}{V^{1/3}}, \tag{5.27}$$

where V_i is the excluded volume. An expression for the equilibrium value of V may be obtained by setting $dE/dV = 0$. Since the equilibrium value of V may be observed experimentally, this equation may be used to determine V_i empirically. This value of V_i can be substituted back into Eq. (5.27) to obtain a value of E.

Equation (5.27) states in essence that the kinetic energy of an electron in the lowest energy level for a "free" electron vanishes when the electron is in the space between the ions, its total energy being given by the last term, the potential-energy term, in Eq. (5.27). The other electrons in the higher states, of course, have a higher kinetic energy, the total excess energy of all the electrons being given by the first term on the right-hand side of Eq. (5.27). If the metal is expanded to an infinite volume, so that the ions and electrons are effectively separated from each other, the energy will be zero on the same energy scale. Thus $-E$, given by Eq. (5.27) when V has its equilibrium value, should be equal to the sum of the energy of sublimation of the metal plus its ionization potential, since sublimation and ionization together separate the electrons and positive ions.

The model of a metal described in the above paragraphs will be an approximation at best, and might be expected to be most successful in the case of the alkali metals, since it is in these metals that the con-

TABLE 14-1

The Cohesive Energy of the Alkali Metals

(V_e in angstroms³, energies in electron volts)

Metal	V_e	V_i/V_e	$-E_e$ (calc)	$-E_e$ (expt)
Li	20.71	0.32	7.13	6.98
Na	37.60	.39	6.18	6.27
K	71.6	.46	5.25	5.28
Rb	87.6	.49	4.98	5.08
Cs	108.7	.51	4.70	4.72

Note: Subscript e signifies equilibrium value. Calculations are from [9]. (These were made with the old values of the fundamental constants. With the present values, A would have to be lowered about 1%.) The experimental energies E_e (expt) are from [11], with values at, or corrected to, 0°K.

duction electrons appear to be most nearly free. Assignment of the value 2.08 for A (values of A for simple uniunivalent crystals range from 2.0 to 2.4) gives the results shown in Table 14-1. These are compared with the observed values of the sum of the ionization potential and the energy of sublimation, and it is seen that the agreement is very reasonable.

Theoretically the compressibility could be found by twofold differentiation of Eq. (5.27), but the twofold differentiation is too sensitive to slight changes in the form of the expression for this to give accurate results.

REFERENCES

1. B. O. Peirce, *A Short Table of Integrals*, 3d ed., Boston, Ginn, 1929, Nos. 481, 493.
2. W. E. Lamb, Jr., and A. Nordsieck, *Phys. Rev.*, **59**, 677 (1941).
3. O. Halpern, *Phys. Rev.*, **86**, 126 (1952).
4. O. Halpern, *Phys. Rev.*, **87**, 520 (1952).
5. W. Band, *Phys. Rev.*, **79**, 871 (1950).
6. J. E. Mayer and M. G. Mayer, *Statistical Mechanics*, New York, Wiley, 1940, Chap. 16.
7. L. B. W. Jolley, *Summation of Series*, 2d ed., New York, Dover, 1961, No. 306.
8. F. Seitz, *The Modern Theory of Solids*, New York, McGraw-Hill, 1940, Chap. 4.

9. O. K. Rice, *J. Chem. Phys.*, **1**, 649 (1933).

10. O. K. Rice, *Electronic Structure and Chemical Binding*, New York, McGraw-Hill, 1940, pp. 370–76. [Obtainable from University Microfilms, Ann Arbor.]

11. U.S. Bureau of Standards, "Selected Values of Chemical Thermodynamic Properties," Circular 500, Washington, D.C., Supt. of Doc., 1952.

PROBLEMS

14.1. Derive Eq. (1.15) from Eq. (1.12).

14.2. Derive Eq. (1.17) from Eq. (1.16).

14.3. Show that Eqs. (1.12) and (1.16) reduce to the Boltzmann form (Chap. 6) when $C_i \gg N_i$.

14.4. The kinetic energy levels of an ideal gas in a rectangular box with edges of length a, b, and c, are given by

$$\epsilon_i = \frac{h^2}{8m}\left(\frac{i_x^2}{a^2} + \frac{i_y^2}{b^2} + \frac{i_z^2}{c^2}\right) = \epsilon_{i,x} + \epsilon_{i,y} + \epsilon_{i,z}$$

From Eq. (1.10) or (1.11) show that if i_y and i_z are fixed, the average value of $\epsilon_{i,x}$ is not independent of i_y and i_z. Show that the average value of $\epsilon_{i,x}$ over *all* states is equal to the similar averages of $\epsilon_{i,y}$ and $\epsilon_{i,z}$, regardless of the relative values of a, b, and c, provided that the sum over states contributing appreciable amounts of kinetic energy can be replaced by an integral.

14.5. If the wave function for the lowest energy level in a box in a gravitational field extends a distance $z = 10^{-3}$ cm from the bottom of the box, make a rough estimate of the average kinetic energy of a particle in this level from the uncertainty principle. Show that this is, indeed, the same order of magnitude as the gravitational potential energy 10^{-3} cm from the bottom, assuming the latter to be zero at the bottom of the box.

14.6. An atom has two electronic states, which differ by energy ϵ_0. In the lower state it is designated as A; in the upper state by A^*. Set up an equation for the ratio N_{A*}/N_A if the atoms obey Bose-Einstein statistics. State what will happen when the Bose condensation begins. Will Bose condensation of A^* occur?

14.7. Verify Eq. (4.5).

14.8. What is the (P.F.) for an assembly in a fixed overall quantum level (i.e., having a fixed number of molecules in every molecular energy level)? Using this result, show that the unnumbered equation immediately following Eq. (1.11) follows directly from the definition of (G.P.F.).

14.9. Using the result of Prob. 14.4, show that Eq. (4.13) can be derived by assuming that the change is effected by a change in a only, b and c remaining fixed.

14.10. Find μ_0 in electron volts if the density of electrons is one per 30 A³.

14.11. Show that the series expansions for the Fermi-Dirac case satisfy

$$N\mu = E - TS + PV.$$

14.12. A gas consists of atoms with spin $\frac{1}{2}$, so that all translational energy levels are doubly degenerate. If the gas is placed in a magnetic field H the atoms will have components of magnetic moment μ_z or $-\mu_z$ in the magnetic field, depending on orientation, and the energy levels will be lowered or raised, respectively, by $\mu_z H$. Assume that the gas obeys Fermi-Dirac statistics.

   a. Write out an expression for the number n_{i+} in the energy level i with component of magnetic moment $+\mu_z$ in field H.

   b. Assuming an ideal gas using the expression for the number of energy levels in a given energy range, and assuming that the energy levels would be filled at 0°K to $\epsilon = \mu_0$ if there were no field, find an expression for the average value μ_z at 0°K in field H.

14.13. Assuming that the temperature is low enough so that the electronic specific heat is given by the first term in Eq. (5.24) and the lattice specific heat is given by the T^3 law, find an expression for the temperature at which the two specific heats are equal. Evaluate this temperature for the case where μ_0 has the value of Prob. 14.11 and the Debye Θ is equal to 100°.

14.14. Verify V_i/V_e and $-E_e(\text{calc})$ for sodium in Table 14-1.

Chapter 15

Quantum Liquids

15-1. *Properties of Liquid Helium*

At about 2.17°K, liquid helium (^{4}He) undergoes a transition believed to be connected with the Bose-Einstein condensation. The Bose-Einstein condensation is a manifestation of quantum phenomena on a macroscopic scale, and any phenomenon of such a nature in a real physical system holds great interest. It will therefore, repay us to examine the properties of liquid helium (for general references, see [1–6]).

First, we note that there is an anomaly in the specific heat at the transition, but no latent heat. Thus it is not an ordinary first-order transition. The course of the specific-heat curve is shown in Fig. 15-1. The curve has some resemblance, but not a very close one, to that for a Bose-Einstein gas (see Fig. 14-2). Because of the shape of the curve shown in Fig. 15-1, the transition point is known as the λ point.

At ordinary pressures the λ point is the only transition observed in condensed helium. At low pressures, helium remains liquid to 0°K, and it requires an elevated pressure of about 25 atm to cause solidification.

More remarkable than the thermodynamic properties of liquid helium are its flow properties. The phase which exists above the λ point, which is known as helium I, is a rather ordinary liquid. The remarkable properties appear in the phase known as helium II, which exists below the λ point. This phase has an exceedingly low resistance to flow; the viscosity virtually disappears under small pressure heads, and the liquid no longer obeys the ordinary laws of viscous flow. Helium II is also an exceedingly good conductor of heat, especially in the temperature range just below the λ point. Helium forms a film on glass or other surfaces,

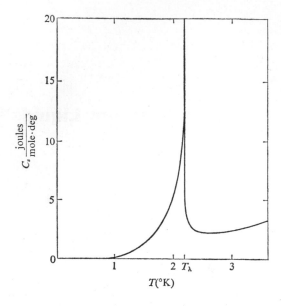

Figure 15-1. Specific heat of liquid ^{4}He at its vapor pressure.

because of the van der Waals forces between the helium atoms and the surface. Although such a film is not unique with helium, some of its properties are, particularly its mobility below the λ point. It is difficult to get the film to come to equilibrium above the λ point, but because of the extreme mobility of helium II, the film forms almost instantly below the λ point. Indeed, if helium II is held in a beaker suspended in a system which is evacuated except for the helium vapor, the liquid will drip off the bottom of the beaker.

Some further light on these properties of helium is thrown by a remarkable experiment first performed by Andronikashvili. In this experiment a very closely spaced pile of disks is suspended on a fiber (Fig. 15-2). Such a set of disks can perform rotational oscillations about the fiber as an axis. The period of the oscillations is determined by the mass of the disks and the characteristics of the fiber. If the disks are immersed in helium I, the helium trapped between the disks is carried around with them and effectively adds to their mass. When the λ point is reached and the temperature is further lowered, it is found that the mass of helium carried with the disks, as measured by the period of oscillation, rapidly diminishes until, around 1°K, virtually none moves with the disks. It is as if the helium consisted of two fluids. One, the normal fluid, behaves like an ordinary liquid, whereas the other, called the superfluid, moves freely through the normal fluid and around other objects. The fraction of superfluid increases as the temperature decreases, and it can be measured by noting the decrease of effective mass in the oscillating-disk experiment. The two-fluid theory offers a phenomenological description of many of the properties of liquid helium. For example, the appearance of the superfluid below the λ point causes the sudden loss of viscosity. The high heat conductivity is connected with the relative motion of the superfluid, the low-energy form, and the normal fluid, which has higher energy. At lower temperatures, where there is little normal fluid, the heat conductivity decreases again.

Because of the extreme mobility of the superfluid, it can pass freely through fine capillaries which block the motion of the normal fluid. In this way it is possible, in a certain sense, to separate superfluid and normal fluid. For example, an equilibrium as far as concerns superfluid can be set up between two portions of helium II at different temperatures, connected by a fine capillary, by applying an excess pressure to the portion at the higher temperature. The excess pressure increases the escaping tendency of the superfluid at the higher pressure until it matches that at the lower temperature where the concentration of superfluid is higher.

Another characteristic phenomenon, which was predicted by the two-fluid theory, is the so-called second sound. Normal fluid and superfluid move past each other without friction, and if an excess of normal fluid is periodically introduced into some region of the liquid (by heating it), this excess will be transmitted through the liquid by a kind of wave motion involving periodic displacement of the two fluids with respect to each other. The velocity of this wave motion depends, among other things, upon the ratio of the amounts of normal fluid and superfluid, and it can be used as a means of measuring this ratio. Early experiments indicated that the results thus obtained agreed with the Andronikashvili oscillating disk experiment. With more recent work on the latter, however, discrepancies have appeared.

Lately much work has been done on the formation of vortices in superfluid helium and on the properties of rotating helium. These properties involve quantization of momentum on a macroscopic scale.

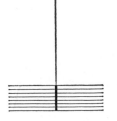

Figure 15-2. Pile of disks for rotating-disk experiment.

A great deal of work has been done in recent years on the theoretical explanation of these and other properties. It has involved various aspects of quantum mechanics, including the theory of many-body processes, most of which are outside the scope of this book (for example, see Pines and Sessler in [5], and [7, 8]). However, some aspects of these phenomena can be at least roughly understood by some relatively simple applications of statistical mechanics.

15-2. *Liquid ⁴He: The Phonon Spectrum*

The thermal properties of any condensed phase can be handled by means of a canonical ensemble, provided that the energy levels of the assemblies can be found. Finding these is primarily a problem in quantum mechanics rather than statistical mechanics; nevertheless, it is a problem which, if we wish to understand the system, cannot be entirely neglected, even though some of its aspects may be beyond the scope of this book. We shall, therefore, make some efforts at least to understand the general nature of the distribution of energy levels.

In many ways, as we have already seen, a liquid resembles a solid, and so we might expect to obtain some information concerning the energy levels by analogy. In particular, sound waves may pass through a liquid and, at least if the wavelength is long compared with the intermolecular spacing, they should exhibit a frequency distribution much like that in a solid. One important difference is to be noted, however; a liquid can sustain compressional vibrations, but cannot sustain transverse oscillations, since it has essentially no resistance to shear. If it were supposed that all the excitations could be represented as compressional vibrations, application of the Debye approximation would lead to an equation

$$\frac{4\pi V}{u_1^3} = \frac{9N}{\nu_m^3}, \tag{2.1}$$

replacing Eq. (2.9) of Chap. 9. The corresponding wavelength will be

$$\lambda_m = \frac{u_1}{\nu_m} = \left(\frac{4\pi V}{9N}\right)^{1/3}. \tag{2.2}$$

This is only slightly greater than the cube root of the atomic volume; that is, only slightly greater than the average distance between atoms. This is too small a wavelength (and hence too high a frequency) properly to represent the atomic displacements.

The correctness of the last statement can be understood by considering a one-dimensional array. Suppose that the equilibrium position of an atom in the array is given by some coordinate x, the equilibrium distance between adjacent atoms by a, and the displacement of the ith atom by

$$\delta_i = A \sin \frac{2\pi x_i}{\lambda},$$

where, of course, $x_i = ia$. This displacement has a wave-like dependence on the position of the atom, λ being the wavelength. If $\lambda = 2a$, then it is seen that the displacements of atom i and atom $i + 1$, whose coordinate is $x_i + a$, are just out of phase. If, however, λ is less than $2a$, then the displacements of the adjacent atoms start to come back into phase, and when $\lambda = a$, they are exactly in phase, and the situation is just the same as if the wavelength were infinite. In general, the physical situation will repeat itself in intervals of λ from ∞ to $2a$, $2a$ to a, a to $2a/3$, etc., and the intervals subsequent to the first do not represent a new situation. This is of course consistent with the fact that the number of degrees of freedom is finite and is related to the existence of a maximum frequency.

For solid argon the maximum frequency calculated from Eq. (2.9) of Chap. 9 does not obviously indicate too short a wavelength. In this case the wavelength for the transverse waves corresponding to the maximum frequency is given by

$$\lambda_{t,m}^3 = \frac{4\pi V}{9N} \left(\frac{u_t^3}{u_l^3} + 2 \right).$$

From Eqs. (4.11) and (4.14) of Chap. 9 (considering only the contribution of $d^2\epsilon_p/dr^2$ to the first term in the sum), $u_t/u_l \approx \sqrt{\frac{1}{3}}$. In a face-centered cubic crystal, $V/N = a^3/2^{1/2}$, where a is the distance between lattice points. However, it is not clear that $\lambda_{t,m}$ should be compared with a directly; in a close-packed structure the distance between adjacent close-packed planes is less than this, so we shall compare $\lambda_{t,m}$ with $a' = (V/N)^{1/3}$. We find

$$\lambda_{t,m} = 1.45 \, a';$$

thus $\lambda_{t,m}$ is, indeed, less than $2a'$, but on a similar basis

$$\lambda_{l,m} = 2.51 \, a',$$

This result suggests that in setting up the approximate distribution of frequencies we should extend the longitudinal waves to higher frequencies and cut out some of the transverse waves. When this correction is considered, along with the inherent limitations of the Debye frequency distribution, the relation to a' seems satisfactory. But, as we have seen, with a liquid, lacking the transverse waves, it will not be possible to have as many as $3N$ vibrations with frequencies less than a reasonable maximum frequency. Thus other types of excitation must occur, and these are related to the transverse vibrations of the solid. At sufficiently low temperatures, however, the specific heat varies as T^3 and is given well by the Debye limiting law, omitting the contribution from the transverse vibrations. This means that we can leave out the term $2/u_t^3$ in Eq. (2.19) of Chap. 9, writing

$$C_v = \frac{16\pi^5 k^4 T^3 V}{15 h^3 u_l^3},\tag{2.3}$$

a relation which is confirmed by measurements at low temperatures [9, 10].

This part of the excitation spectrum of liquid helium is called the phonon spectrum, since the excitations can be described as moving particles, the phonons, which bear a relation to the sound waves similar to that of photons to light waves.

15-3. *Liquid ⁴He: The Roton Excitations*

Since not all the modes of excitation of helium are included in the phonon spectrum, it is necessary to ascertain the nature of the other excitations (the so-called rotons). If the liquid is considered as a quasi-solid, it is natural to start with an Einstein model in which each atom moves in the field of its neighbors independently of the motion of the other atoms. Of course, this approximation is even cruder for the liquid than for the solid because of the ease with which the atoms can exchange places, and the motions will be far from harmonic. The lack of harmonicity will be especially pronounced in liquid helium because of its extremely low density and large amount of empty space. Nevertheless, this picture may be used as a starting point to get a qualitative idea of the situation.

The motions of the separate atoms are, of course, not actually independent, and their interaction has the effect of spreading the energy of the elementary excitations (more or less equivalent or similar to singly excited normal modes of vibration in the solid) over a range. Thus the compressional waves give a range of energies from zero to a fairly high value. However, as we have noted, these do not include all the excitations. The excitations of low frequency or low energy involve cooperation of many atoms. But cooperation of many atoms cannot occur in the form of transverse waves in a liquid because of its lack of resistance to shear. It would therefore appear that the excitations not included in the photon spectrum would remain localized, involving perhaps the motion of a single atom or the rotation of a few atoms about each other. It will be shown later (next to last paragraph of Sec. 15-8) that this limited type of cooperative motion will not result in appreciably lower energy levels. One might infer, therefore, that there would be a lowest possible energy for localized excitations, that their range of energies would not on the whole be very great, and that it might be roughly given by the Einstein approximation.

Because of the light mass of the atoms, helium has a high zero-point energy. The higher the density of the helium, the less the freedom of motion of any atom, and the higher the zero-point energy would be. Thus the zero-point energy acts like a repulsive force and tends to expand the liquid against the attractive forces until a balance is reached. It is this effect which causes the density of liquid helium to be as low as it is. The zero-point energy was estimated by London in a semi-empirical manner [2, Chap. B; 11]. He first made an estimate of the potential energy of the helium atoms at their average mutual distances in the liquid from the more-or-less well-known potential-energy curve of a pair of helium atoms (taking well-separated atoms as having zero potential energy). This estimate was then compared with the energy of vaporization at $0°K$, which is the energy required to separate the atoms. It is very difficult to make a quantitative calculation in this way, but at least the order of magnitude may be obtained. The energy of vaporization at absolute zero is 14.3 cal per mole, and the potential energy may be estimated to lie somewhere in or near the range -45 to -55 cal per mole. This means that the zero-point energy will be about $50 - 14.3 \approx 36$ cal per mole, or around 12 cal per mole-degree-of-freedom. If the atom acts somewhat like a harmonic oscillator, which is of course a very rough approximation, we could expect the energy of the first excited state to be in the neighborhood of 24 cal per mole-degree-of-freedom, or about $12°K$, if we express the energy in the form ϵ/k, as is customary in this case. This value actually turns out to be not too far from the "observed" energy of the roton.

The "observation" of the roton energy depends on interpretation of specific-heat data. We have noted that at very low temperatures the specific heat varies as T^3. Starting at 0.8° to 1.0°K it begins to increase very much more rapidly than this. If we extrapolate the T^3 contribution of the phonons and subtract it from the total specific heat, the remainder, which we denote as C_r, can be attributed to the rotons.

If $\bar{\epsilon}_r$ is the average energy of the rotons (which depends slightly on temperature), and if we are in a temperature range where there are only a few rotons, the total number of rotons in N atoms will be given by †

$$ n = Nm \exp\left\{\frac{-\bar{\epsilon}_r}{kT}\right\}. \tag{3.1} $$

Here $k \ln m$ will be an entropy factor, and m may be interpreted as the multiplicity of roton states. The term n/N is a sort of equilibrium constant between rotons and unexcited atoms, provided that the number of the latter is not appreciably diminished from N. Since the temperature coefficient of the equilibrium constant is given by

$$ \frac{d \ln (n/N)}{dT} = \frac{d \ln n}{dT} = \frac{\bar{\epsilon}_r}{kT^2}, \tag{3.2} $$

we see by differentiating Eq. (3.1) that

$$ kT \frac{d \ln m}{dT} = \frac{d\bar{\epsilon}_r}{dT}, \tag{3.3} $$

which is the usual relation between the temperature coefficients of the energy and entropy terms. The roton specific heat will clearly be given by

$$ C_r = \frac{d(n\bar{\epsilon}_r)}{dT} $$

$$ = \bar{\epsilon}_r \frac{dn}{dT} + n \frac{d\bar{\epsilon}_r}{dT} $$

$$ = n \left(\frac{\bar{\epsilon}_r^2}{kT^2} + \frac{d\bar{\epsilon}_r}{dT}\right). \tag{3.4} $$

The various relations embodied in Eqs. (3.1), (3.2), (3.3) and (3.4) enable one to obtain the best values of $\bar{\epsilon}_r$, n, and m, given a series of values of C_r over a range of temperatures. The results of such a calculation [16], based on specific heat data of Kramers, Wasscher, and

† This follows the procedure of Rice [12] and differs somewhat from the theory of Landau [13, 14, 15]. In general the account given here of the excitations in both ⁴He and ³He differs from that current in the literature.

TABLE 15-1

Roton Densities from Specific-Heat Data

(T and ϵ_r/k in °K; C and C_r in joules g^{-1} deg^{-1})

T	C	C_r	$\bar{\epsilon}_r/k$	$d(\bar{\epsilon}_r/k)/dT$	$100n/N$	m	$\bar{\epsilon}_r/k$
0.8	0.0222	0.01175	9.39	0.6	0.0041	5.11	
							9.46
1.1	0.191	0.1638	9.57	0.8	0.1030	6.19	
							9.71
1.4	0.780	0.724	9.88	1.2	0.683	7.94	
							10.10
1.7	2.11	2.01	10.4	2.3	2.44	11.1	

Gorter [17], as modified [9], are given in Table 15-1. In the last column, as a check, $\bar{\epsilon}_r$ is calculated by integrating Eq. (3.2) over an interval of 0.3°K, taking $\bar{\epsilon}_r$ as constant, in order to find an average value of $\bar{\epsilon}_r$ appropriate to the interval.

This table shows that the density of rotons remains very small up to 1.7°K, and it seems reasonable to suppose that they are independent of each other, and that Eq. (3.1) holds up to 1.4°K.

The values of m seem rather high. This implies that there is a number of energy levels considerably greater than can be accounted for by excitation of $2N$ modes of vibration of the N atoms, N modes having already been taken up in the phonon spectrum. There are reasons, which will shortly be discussed, for believing that both $\bar{\epsilon}$ and m should be somewhat smaller.

15-4. *Momentum and Energy Relations*

The distribution of energy levels in liquid helium depends upon the relation between energy and momentum. Let us first consider the situation in the phonon or sound-wave region. Suppose that a sample of liquid helium is confined in a rectangular container, one end of which is a piston (perpendicular to the x axis). This piston is assumed to be permeable to liquid helium but to reflect sound waves. Let there be a standing sound wave of wavelength λ in front of the piston. We define components λ_x, λ_y, and λ_z of the wavelength, such that

$$\lambda_x = \frac{\lambda}{\cos \alpha}, \tag{4.1}$$

and so on, where $\cos \alpha$ is the direction cosine of the wave's propagation vector with respect to the x axis (cf. Sec. 9-2). In view of Eq. (4.1), we have

$$\frac{1}{\lambda^2} = \frac{1}{\lambda_x^2} + \frac{1}{\lambda_y^2} + \frac{1}{\lambda_z^2}, \tag{4.2}$$

or, since

$$\lambda \nu = u_1, \tag{4.3}$$

we can write Eq. (4.2) in terms of the frequency and quantities defined by $\nu_x = u_1/\lambda_x$, and so on (these are *not* components of the frequency, which does not have a directional character), as follows:

$$\nu^2 = \nu_x^2 + \nu_y^2 + \nu_z^2. \tag{4.4}$$

If this frequency is singly excited, the energy (above the zero-point energy) is

$$\epsilon = h\nu. \tag{4.5}$$

If the piston moves, since it moves along the x axis, ν_y and ν_z remain constant, and by Eq. (4.4)

$$\nu \, d\nu = \nu_x \, d\nu_x, \tag{4.6}$$

provided the change is carried out adiabatically. Thus

$$d\epsilon = h d\nu = h \frac{\nu_x}{\nu} d\nu_x = h \cos \alpha \, d\nu_x. \tag{4.7}$$

The excitation, then, may be considered to exert a pressure on the piston (above that due to zero-point energy) given by

$$d\epsilon = -P \, dV, \tag{4.8}$$

where dV is the change of volume when the piston moves. The standing wave can be taken as the superposition of two traveling waves with total absolute momentum p; let the x component be p_x. The momentum reaching the piston per unit time per unit area will be $\frac{1}{2}(p_x/V)u_1 \cos \alpha$, with p_x/V the momentum per unit volume, and $u_1 \cos \alpha$ the component of the velocity in the x direction. The factor $\frac{1}{2}$ arises because only one of the two traveling waves is moving in the right direction; however, since the momentum changes in sign on reflection, the *change* in momentum per unit time will be twice the above expression, and we may write

$$P = \frac{p_x}{V} u_1 \cos \alpha, \tag{4.9}$$

and from Eqs. (4.7) and (4.8)

$$h dv_x = -\frac{p_x}{V} u_1 \, dV. \tag{4.10}$$

From the definition of v_x, we have

$$\lambda_x v_x = u_1. \tag{4.11}$$

Therefore, we obtain

$$dv_x = -\frac{u_1}{\lambda_x^2} d\lambda_x = -\frac{u_1}{\lambda_x} \frac{dV}{V}, \tag{4.12}$$

since λ_x will be proportional to V. Thus from Eq. (4.10) we obtain for the part of the momentum associated with the excitation

$$p_x = \frac{h}{\lambda_x}, \tag{4.13}$$

from which we easily get the familiar form [see Sec. 1-6]

$$p = \frac{h}{\lambda}, \tag{4.14}$$

showing that this holds for sound waves as well as for light or for the waves associated with particles. From Eqs. (4.5), (4.3) and (4.14), we have

$$\epsilon = p u_1. \tag{4.15}$$

The energy is therefore proportional to the absolute value of the momentum.

There will be one possible value of the energy for every possible combination of values of p_x, p_y, p_z. Since $\lambda_x = 2a/n_x$, where n_x is an integer, etc., [Eq. (2.4) of Chap. 9] we will have, in view of Eq. (4.13), $p_x = n_x h/2a$, etc. In any element of momentum space $dp_x dp_y dp_z$ (confined now to regions where p_x, p_y, and p_z are all positive, since λ_x, λ_y, λ_z are always positive), the number of elementary excitations will be

$$\frac{2^3 abc}{h^3} dp_x dp_y dp_z = \frac{8V}{h^3} dp_x dp_y dp_z.$$

The volume of momentum space between p and $p + dp$ will be $4\pi p^2 dp/8$ (divided by 8 since only the positive octant is included). Thus the number of energy levels with momentum between p and $p + dp$ will be

$$dn_p = \frac{4\pi V p^2}{h^3} dp. \tag{4.16}$$

This is the same relation as that for the number of energy levels of a single particle.† This is, indeed, the basis of the phonon picture of the low-frequency excitations. If a given excitation corresponds to a higher quantum level than the first, this is represented by the assumption that there is more than one phonon in this particular energy level (i.e., the energy level having the particular values of p_x, p_y, p_z). Since there is no limit to the number of phonons per energy level, they obey Bose-Einstein statistics, but the total number of phonons is not fixed.‡ This model gives the same average energy for the compressional waves as the Debye theory of the solid.

Can we also describe the roton excitations in terms of a relation between energy and momentum? The outstanding characteristic of the superfluid is its inability to accept small amounts of localized energy. The energy of a roton is not readily broken up into smaller bits of energy, presumably because the states of small energy involve cooperation of large numbers of atoms. It is not possible to split up a roton into two or three parts having appreciable fractions of the total energy in a localized situation, because such excitations do not exist. Thus it can also be expected that small changes in energy of a single roton will not occur, since this would involve the balancing of this energy change by the rest of the system, and this would mean that the other parts of the system would have to change in energy by a small amount. Even changes only in the direction of the momentum of a roton would not

---

† Equation (4.16) depends only on the relation between p and λ, and will hold even if the relation between energy and momentum is not linear, as will happen if u_1 is not constant. The relation between p and λ, or Eq. (4.16) itself, is generally considered the fundamental relationship on quantum mechanical grounds.

‡ In this respect the distribution is like that of the Bose-Einstein gas in the condensation region, since the particles in the lowest energy level are, in effect, an infinite reservoir of phonons in the lowest level. Since phonons act just like photons, the same calculation will give the energy density in black-body (equilibrium) radiation.

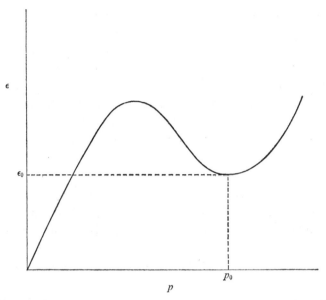

Figure 15-3. Schematic diagram of excitation energy as a function of momentum for liquid ^{4}He.

occur, unless somehow this could be balanced by a change in the translational motion of the whole system. Since each excitation can be represented by a specific wave function, which determines momentum and energy, it is natural to suppose that there is a relation between them. In fact, some of the characteristics of these wave functions have been worked out by Feynman and Cohen [18, 19]. It was conjectured by Landau [20] and verified by Feynman, and by others,† that the energy of the excitations depends on the momentum, as shown schematically in Fig. 15-3.

In this figure the low-momentum excitations are the phonons, and the excitations in the neighborhood of the minimum are the rotons. The existence of the minimum is in accord with the existence of a lower bound for the energy of local excitations. The portion of the curve lying between $2\pi p/h = 0.5$ and $2\pi p/h = 2.5$ has been determined experimentally by Yarnell, Arnold, Bendt, and Kerr [21]. They used neutrons of known energy to produce rotons, and measured the energy (and hence the momentum) and the direction of motion of the scattered neutrons after they caused the excitations to occur. From conservation of momentum and energy, the momentum and energy of the rotons

† See contribution by D. Pines in [5], which gives further references.

produced were determined. It was found that ϵ_0/k (i.e., ϵ/k at the minimum) is 8.68° at the lowest temperatures.† This value is somewhat less than the values of ϵ_r used in Table 15-1 to fit the specific-heat data. However, $\bar\epsilon_r$ is an average energy which, as will be shown immediately, exceeds the minimum by about $\frac{1}{2}kT$. When allowance is made for this thermal energy, the values of $\bar\epsilon_r/k$ of Yarnell, Arnold, Bendt, and Kerr are only about 0.3° less than those of Table 15-1. If the values of m are somewhat reduced (e.g., to 3.5 at 0.8°K), the values of C_r calculated on the basis of the lower $\bar\epsilon_r$ values will again agree with the experimental values. However, since there is a slightly different temperature coefficient, the agreement cannot be made quite as good at all temperatures, but it is probably within experimental error. These conclusions are quite in accord with those of Bendt, Cowan, and Yarnell [22], based directly on the experimentally determined curve for energy vs. momentum.

The relation between the curve, Fig. 15-3, and the parameters of Eq. (3.1) may be seen in the following way. The energy near the minimum in Fig. 15-3 may be expressed in terms of the momentum by the relation

$$\epsilon_r - \epsilon_0 = \frac{(p - p_0)^2}{2\mu_0}, \tag{4.17}$$

where p_0 is the momentum at the minimum and μ_0 is a constant which is often called the effective mass. If the density of rotons is low, the probability that one with energy ϵ_r will be excited is‡ $\exp\{-\epsilon_r/kT\}$. Thus the total number of rotons with momentum between p and $p + dp$ is given with sufficient approximation, using Eq. (4.16), by

$$\frac{4\pi Vp^2}{h^3} \exp\left\{\frac{-\epsilon_r}{kT}\right\} dp = \frac{4\pi Vp^2}{h^3} \exp\left\{\frac{-\epsilon_0}{kT}\right\} \exp\left\{-\frac{(p - p_0)^2}{2\mu_0\,kT}\right\} dp.$$

This relation permits us to write for the total number of rotons

$$n = Nm \exp\left\{\frac{-\bar\epsilon_r}{kT}\right\} = \frac{4\pi V}{h^3} \exp\left\{\frac{-\epsilon_0}{kT}\right\} \int p^2 \exp\left\{-\frac{(p - p_0)^2}{2\mu_0\,kT}\right\} dp. \tag{4.18}$$

† It was found that the curve depended slightly on temperature, and that ϵ_0 tended to decrease with increasing temperature. This is undoubtedly due to interaction between the rotons. We confine ourselves to temperatures low enough so that the density of the rotons is so small that any effects of interaction are negligible.

‡ It is commonly assumed that the rotons obey Bose-Einstein statistics. However, if the density is small, Boltzmann statistics is sufficient, and if the density is large, interactions between the rotons are likely to be a larger source of error than that caused by use of Boltzmann statistics.

Since because of the exponential the probability falls off rapidly with $|p - p_0|$, we may replace p^2 before the exponential by p_0^2 and carry the integration with respect to $p - p_0$ from $-\infty$ to ∞. This gives

$$m = \frac{4\pi V p_0^2}{N h^3} (2\pi\mu_0 k T)^{1/2} \exp\left\{\frac{\bar{\epsilon}_r - \epsilon_0}{kT}\right\}. \tag{4.19}$$

Since $\bar{\epsilon}_r - \epsilon_0$ is the average excess of energy over ϵ_0, it is given by [Sec. 2-6]

$$\bar{\epsilon}_r - \epsilon_0 \approx \frac{\int_{-\infty}^{\infty} [(p - p_0)^2/2\mu_0] \exp\{-(p - p_0)^2/2\mu_0 kT\} \, dp}{\int_{-\infty}^{\infty} \exp\{-(p - p_0)^2/2\mu_0 kT\} \, dp}$$

$$= \frac{kT}{2} \tag{4.20}$$

(again replacing p^2 by p_0^2 before the exponential in the expression for the number of rotons in a given momentum range). Equation (4.20), incidentally, is reasonably concordant with the value of $d(\bar{\epsilon}_r/k)/dT = 0.6$, as given in Table 15-1 for the temperature 0.8°K. If Eq. (4.20) is inserted into Eq. (4.19), we have

$$m = \frac{4\pi V p_0^2}{N h^3} (2\pi\mu_0 e k T)^{1/2}. \tag{4.21}$$

Yarnell, Arnold, Bendt, and Kerr give μ_0 as 0.16 times the mass of a helium atom, and $2\pi p_0/h$ as 1.92 Å^{-1}, while N/V can be obtained from the known density of helium, 0.1455 g/cc. From these values we find $m = 3.6$ at 0.8°K, which agrees well with the corrected value of m mentioned on page 404. Thus we see the consistency of the neutron scattering data with the specific-heat data.

If we assume that the rotons resemble vibrations of single atoms in the fields of their neighbors, we must conclude that we have reached the end of the spectrum of elementary vibrations at a momentum slightly greater than p_0. Far enough beyond this point, greater momentum and energy must correspond more closely to double excitation of the vibrating atoms, or even to "dissociation" of the atoms from their equilibrium positions.† If we assume that $2\pi p/h = 2.2$ Å^{-1} is a rough

---

† The concepts become somewhat hazy when we consider excitations of very short wavelength, which can be treated as localized excitations. In the long-wavelength range, excitation of higher vibrational states was described by saying that there were several phonons of a particular energy. We cannot, however, describe multiple excitation of a mode in the roton range by saying that there are several localized excitations. Of course, even if the excitations are localized, a stationary-wave function will not give information about their position.

cutoff point for elementary excitations then from Eq. (4.16), setting V equal to N times the atomic volume, and integrating from $p = 0$ to $p = 2.2 \times 10^{-8} h/2\pi$ c.g.s. units, we find that the total number of elementary excitations per atom is about 8.2. This is considerably higher than the three normal modes of vibration per atom assumed in the Debye solid. Even in a solid, however, we would expect extra modes, owing to the possible occurrence of interstitial atoms and vacancies, but they would correspond to quite high energies, and so would not be easily excited. In a liquid, and especially one in which the space is as loosely filled, as in helium, similar excitations would be much more easily excited, although they should not occur close to the minimum of the curve of Fig. 15-3. Thus the large number of excitations may be looked upon as contributing to the disorder characteristic of the liquid state.

15-5. *Pressure in the Superfluid*

Second sound, mentioned in Sec. 15-1, results from the tendency of the liquid to come to a uniform temperature. The mechanism by which this occurs depends upon the tendency of the superfluid to flow from a region where the concentration of superfluid is high (i.e., where the normal-fluid density is low) to a region where it is low (where the normal-fluid density is high). Since this flow is frictionless, it overshoots the mark, and then starts back in the opposite direction. This is the reason that a temperature inhomogeneity can be transmitted as a wave motion.

The superfluid behaves as if it were under a pressure, a gradient in which causes it to flow [23]. Considering only the effect of rotons (in this section we confine our attention to temperatures high enough so that rotons predominate over phonons, but low enough so that there are still not many rotons), it appears that the rotons exert a pressure on adjacent portions of the superfluid, so that a region of superfluid in which there are fewer rotons tends to be squeezed at its boundary by the rotons in the region containing more rotons. Thus the superfluid in a region of low roton density is under a higher pressure than the surrounding regions, and tends to flow into them.

An expression for the pressure P_s in the superfluid can be obtained from an elementary calculation [24]. We assume that this is a real pressure and that the total pressure P is given by

$$P = x_sP_s + x_nP_n \tag{5.1}$$

where x_s and x_n are the mole fractions of superfluid and of normal fluid, respectively. We assume that there are two portions of helium II, one in contact with a thermostat at $0°K$, and one at T. They are separated by a porous plug with very fine capillaries which allow only superfluid to pass, but which can support a difference in pressure. Each portion is under pressure from a separate piston, and the pressures are adjusted so that there is no tendency of superfluid to flow in either direction. Now suppose that, by movement of the pistons, one gram of helium is caused to flow from $0°K$ to T. The work done on the helium is $P_0/\rho_0 - P_T/\rho_T$, where the P's and the ρ's are the pressures and densities at the two temperatures. The increase in energy of the entire system, helium and thermostats, is equal to $\epsilon_T - \epsilon_0 - Ts_T$ where ϵ_T and ϵ_0 are the respective energies per gram and s_T is the entropy per gram at T, the specific entropy at $0°K$ being of course zero. Thus

$$\frac{P_0}{\rho_0} - \frac{P_T}{\rho_T} = \epsilon_T - \epsilon_0 - Ts_T. \tag{5.2}$$

It will be sufficiently accurate to set $\rho_0 = \rho_T = \rho$, and we may as well take $\epsilon_0 = 0$. Now if we suppose that at equilibrium the pressure is the same throughout the superfluid (and at $0°K$ there is *only* superfluid) we see that P_s for the portion at T is also equal to P_0, so that from Eq. (5.2)

$$P_s = P + \rho(\epsilon - Ts) = \rho g, \tag{5.3}$$

where we have dropped the subscript T on the quantities on the right-hand side of the equation, and where g is the Gibbs free energy per gram.

This deduction rests on the assumption that the heat absorbed from the thermostat is equal to Ts_T, since the heat is absorbed in an essentially isothermal region, despite the fact that complete equilibrium is not established throughout the whole system.

It is postulated [23] that actual acceleration of superfluid with respect to normal fluid is caused by gradients of P_s. The effective force per unit volume of the entire volume is, since the force is exerted only in the superfluid, $-(\rho_s/\rho)\,\mathrm{grad}\,P_s$, where ρ_s is the mass of superfluid per unit volume. The equation of motion to the first order (small velocities and pressure gradients) in a fluid which is at constant *total* pressure is

$$-\frac{\rho_s}{\rho}\,\mathrm{grad}\,P_s = \frac{\rho_s\rho_n}{\rho}\left(\frac{\partial \mathbf{v}_s}{\partial t} - \frac{\partial \mathbf{v}_n}{\partial t}\right). \tag{5.4}$$

The term in parentheses is the relative acceleration of superfluid with respect to normal fluid, and $\rho_s \rho_n / \rho$ is the reduced mass per unit volume. From Eq. (5.3), we have

$$\text{grad } P_s = \rho \left(\frac{\partial \epsilon}{\partial T} - T \frac{\partial s}{\partial T} - s \right) \text{grad } T$$

$$= - \rho s \text{ grad } T, \tag{5.5}$$

whence Eq. (5.4) becomes

$$\frac{\partial \mathbf{v}_s}{\partial t} - \frac{\partial \mathbf{v}_n}{\partial t} = \frac{\rho}{\rho_n} s \text{ grad } T \tag{5.6}$$

which is the equation upon which discussion of the second sound is based [2, p. 83]. It can be applied in the phonon as well as the roton region.

15-6. *Fluctuations in Energy*

The usual fluctuations in energy will occur in liquid helium. In the temperature range of interest, these can be considered to be fluctuations in the density of the rotons, and from them something can be learned about the nature of the rotons [24]. We start with the standard formula [Eq. (3.2) of Chap. 4], applying it to the fluctuation in energy δE_{N_0} occurring in a volume containing N_0 atoms:

$$\overline{(\delta E_{N_0})^2} = k T^2 C_{v,N_0}. \tag{6.1}$$

Where the rotons predominate over the phonons, we may write, of course,

$$E_{n_0} = n_0 \bar{\epsilon}_r \tag{6.2}$$

where n_0 is the number of rotons associated with N_0 atoms. From Eq. (3.4), neglecting the small term $d\bar{\epsilon}_r / dT$, we may write

$$C_{v,N_0} \approx \frac{n_0 \bar{\epsilon}_r^2}{k T^2}. \tag{6.3}$$

Assuming that δE_{n_0} is controlled by δn_0 (rather than by $\delta \epsilon_r$) we obtain from Eqs. (6.1), (6.2) and (6.3)

$$\overline{(\delta n_0)^2} \approx n_0, \tag{6.4}$$

showing that the fluctuations in the density of rotons behave like the density fluctuations of an ideal gas [Eq. (4.9) of Chap. 10 with $\beta = V/\bar{N}kT$, the ideal-gas value]. We also require an expression for the entropy S_{N_0}. This can be evaluated from the integral $\int_0^T (C_{v,N_0}/T)\,dT$, substituting Eq. (6.3) and then using Eq. (3.1) to obtain an explicit expression for the integrand. Carrying out the integration, assuming $\bar{\epsilon}_r$ is constant, gives

$$S_{N_0} \approx N_0 mk \exp\left\{-\frac{\bar{\epsilon}_r}{kT}\right\}\left(1 + \frac{\bar{\epsilon}_r}{kT}\right)$$

$$\approx \frac{n_0 \bar{\epsilon}_r}{T}. \tag{6.5}$$

The fluctuations will involve fluxes of superfluid whose rates will be controlled by Eq. (5.6). The fluctuation δE_{N_0} may be considered equivalent to a fluctuation δT in temperature with

$$\delta E_{N_0} = C_{v,N_0}\delta T. \tag{6.6}$$

If the liquid is divided into cubic cells of volume V_0 containing N_0 atoms each, one can assume that temperature differences between centers of adjacent cells will be about δT on the average, δT being given by Eqs. (6.6) and (6.1). The temperature gradient then will on the average be about $\delta T/V_0^{1/3}$. The superfluid and normal fluid will suffer a relative acceleration owing to the force arising from this temperature gradient. Thus the system will have a kinetic energy arising from the relative motion of superfluid and normal fluid associated with the fluctuations. The amount of this energy per unit volume will be roughly that required to bring the system which has undergone fluctuations to a uniform roton density. To restore uniform density between adjacent cells, between which the difference in density of rotons is δn_0, will require a flow of superfluid (with respect to the rotons) through a distance of about $V_0^{1/3}\delta n_0/n_0$. Since the force acting will be of the order of (ρ_s/ρ) grad P_s per unit volume, the kinetic energy per unit volume due to fluctuations among cells of the size chosen will be

$$\rho e_k \approx \left|\frac{\rho_s}{\rho} V_0^{1/3} \text{ grad } P_s \frac{\delta n_0}{n_0}\right|, \tag{6.7}$$

where e_k is the kinetic energy per unit mass. We may now apply Eq. (5.5), noting that ρs is the entropy per unit volume and hence equal to S_{N_0}/V_0, so that

$$- \operatorname{grad} P_{\mathrm{s}} = \frac{S_{N_0}}{V_0} \operatorname{grad} T$$

$$= \frac{n_0 \bar{\epsilon}_{\mathrm{r}}}{V_0 T} \operatorname{grad} T \qquad [\text{by Eq. (6.5)}]$$

$$= \frac{n_0 \bar{\epsilon}_{\mathrm{r}}}{V_0 T C_{v,N_0}} \operatorname{grad} E_{N_0}$$

$$\approx \frac{n_0 \bar{\epsilon}_{\mathrm{r}}}{V_0 T C_{v,N_0}} \frac{\delta E_{N_0}}{V_0^{1/3}}$$

$$\approx \frac{kT}{\bar{\epsilon}_{\mathrm{r}} V_0} \frac{\delta E_{N_0}}{V_0^{1/3}} \qquad [\text{by Eq. (6.3)}]$$

$$\approx \frac{kT}{V_0} \frac{\delta n_0}{V_0^{1/3}}. \tag{6.8}$$

Substituting into Eq. (6.7) and using Eq. (6.4), we have

$$\rho e_{\mathrm{k}} \approx \frac{\rho_{\mathrm{s}}}{\rho} \frac{kT}{V_0}. \tag{6.9}$$

In the temperature range in which the roton density is low, $\rho_{\mathrm{s}}/\rho \approx 1$. Since ρe_{k} is the relative kinetic energy per unit volume, $\rho e_{\mathrm{k}} V_0/n_0$ is equal to $\bar{\epsilon}_{\mathrm{k,r}}$, the average relative kinetic energy per roton. Thus from Eq. (6.9), we get

$$\bar{\epsilon}_{\mathrm{k,r}} \approx \frac{kT}{n_0}. \tag{6.10}$$

Thus we see that the relative kinetic energy associated with the fluctuations has a temperature dependence similar to that of an ideal gas, which is not surprising in view of Eq. (6.4). The actual estimated value for $\bar{\epsilon}_{\mathrm{k,r}}$ will depend on n_0, which in turn depends upon how large we choose the original cells. They should clearly be chosen as small as they can be so that the idea of fluctuations retains a meaning. It would be senseless to choose them so small that n_0 were less than 1; thus the largest possible fluctuation energy is of the order of magnitude of kT per roton. In Sec. 15-4 we saw that the thermal energy of the rotons is equal to $kT/2$, and it seems reasonable to identify this with $\bar{\epsilon}_{\mathrm{k,r}}$. This identification seems capable of giving some idea of the nature of the rotons, which will be developed in the following section.

15-7. *The Nature of the Rotons*

According to the picture just developed, the thermal energy of the rotons is, at least primarily, kinetic energy due to relative motion of the rotons with respect to the superfluid. The momentum is a measure of the transport of mass associated with this relative motion. In view of the narrowness of the energy vs. momentum curve, the momentum can be considered roughly constant at p_0, and the average momentum, since it comes from contributions on both sides of the minimum, is very nearly constant, indeed. Yet because the thermal energy changes with temperature, we infer that the relative velocity of the rotons must change. The obvious conclusion is that the mass also changes.

Rotons consist primarily of localized excitations, and the pressure existing in the superfluid sets up bodily motion of the superfluid with respect to these excitations. However, an excitation can also pass from one atom to another in, we should suppose, more-or-less-random fashion. Thus there are two modes of motion of the roton: one by direct transfer of the excitation, and one by bodily motion of the excited atom; we designate these as exciton transfer and mass transport, respectively. Only the latter contributes to the momentum. The time required for exciton transfer would be expected to be of the order of magnitude of the period of vibration τ of the excitation. This excitation would have a frequency of about $\epsilon_0/h = 8.6k/h$ or 2×10^{11}/sec, with a corresponding τ of 5×10^{-12} sec.

As a roton moves bodily past the superfluid, its structure and identity are continually changing because of exciton transfers.† Ahead of the roton there must be atoms which are just beginning to move with it, while behind it atoms are dropping off. In addition, some atoms are merely pushed around it. Thus a roton consists of atoms with varying velocities, moving in various directions, and it is a little difficult to decide which atoms belong to the normal fluid and which to the superfluid. Let us suppose that the velocity of the roton with respect to the superfluid is u_r; this is the over-all velocity, and perhaps may be taken as the bodily velocity of the atom directly associated with the excitation. Let the magnitude of the velocity of the ith atom at any instant be u_i, and the angle its direction of motion makes with the direction of $\bar{u}_r$ be θ_i.‡ Then the total momentum is

---

† The description of a roton which we present here is probably a little too detailed to be completely consistent with quantum theory, in the light of the uncertainty principle, but it seems probable that this will not cause any gross error.

‡ Much of this section, from this point through the paragraph following Eq. (7.13), is based on [25]. This includes some almost verbatim quotation.

$$p_r = m \sum_i u_i \cos \theta_i$$

$$= m z_p u_r, \tag{7.1}$$

where

$$z_p = \sum_i \frac{u_i}{u_r} \cos \theta_i, \tag{7.2}$$

and where the sum is taken over all atoms associated with the roton. Thus z_p is the effective number of atoms in the roton as far as momentum is concerned, and the contribution of any atom is proportional to the component of its velocity in the direction of u_r. The total thermal energy will be given by

$$\epsilon_{k,r} = \tfrac{1}{2}m \sum_i u_i^2$$

$$= \tfrac{1}{2}m z_\epsilon u_r^2. \tag{7.3}$$

Of course z_ϵ will not have the same value as z_p, but it is reasonable to assume that they have a constant ratio. Since p_r is essentially constant, z_p must be inversely proportional to u_r, from which we infer the average $\bar{z}_p$ to be about inversely proportional to $\bar{u}_r$, and, if z_ϵ is proportional to z_p, it follows from these relations, from Eq. (7.3), and from $\bar{\epsilon}_{k,r} = \tfrac{1}{2}kT$, that $\bar{u}_r$ is proportional to T. If we divide the mass of normal fluid present at any given temperature, as determined by second sound, by the number of rotons present, we find, as shown in Table 15-2,† that the mass of a roton does, indeed, fall off rapidly with the temperature. The agreement with the results of the oscillating-disk experiment is not good at the lower temperatures. The reason for this is not clear, but the oscillating-disk experiment becomes more difficult when the normal-fluid density is low, and it involves a number of corrections. All the various theories of liquid helium have in common the conclusion that the apparent mass of a roton is inversely proportional to the temperature, and we shall accept that conclusion for the present discussion.

Inverse proportionality between the number of atoms involved in the motion of a roton and its velocity may be rationalized in the following way. The excitation moves from atom to atom by exciton motion, and the bodily motion of any atom must change in the course

---

† The calculations of Table 15-2 are taken from the author's papers [23, 24], which see for the original references. Some corrections have been made. The oscillating-disk experiments used were those of Dash and Taylor [26].

The mass associated with a phonon is very small compared with that of a roton, and above 0.8°K the contribution of phonons to normal-fluid density is negligible and was not taken into account in Table 15-2.

TABLE 15-2

Fraction f_n of Normal Fluid, and Apparent Size, $z = f_n/(n/N)$, of the Rotons (T in °K)

T	$100\,f_n$ (*second sound*)	$100\,f_n$ (*oscillating disk*)	z (*second sound*)	z (*oscillating disk*)
0.8	0.089	.....	21.8	....
1.1	1.48	(0.95)*	14.4	(9.2)*
1.4	7.40	6.56	10.8	9.6
1.7	23.8	21.9	9.8	8.9

* Extrapolated.

of excitation and de-excitation. Thus the atoms belonging to a roton must be in a process of acceleration or deceleration. If this process is completed in the period during which the roton moves a certain distance, say a molecular distance, the time available for the process will be inversely proportional to the velocity of the roton, and the longer the time, the more atoms will be involved because of the exciton transfer. Let us consider, in more detail, the deceleration of an atom deserted by an excitation. The loss of relative velocity in a collision with another atom might be supposed to be proportional to the relative velocity u itself, whereas the number of superfluid atoms it will encounter in unit time is also proportional to u. Consequently we might guess that

$$\frac{du}{dt} = -au^2,$$

where a is a constant, or, integrating, that

$$\frac{1}{u} = at + \frac{1}{u_r},$$

where u_r is the atom's velocity at the time $t = 0$ that it was deserted by the roton. The time required to reduce u to any given fraction of u_r will be inversely proportional to u_r; so the time for effective loss of this atom to this particular roton can be assumed proportional to $1/u_r$. Thus the higher the temperature, which is proportional to u_r, the smaller the roton. This is, of course, an exceedingly rough picture, since it is not symmetrical with respect to acceleration and deceleration and does not properly take into account the quantum aspects of the problem.

Also, if one integrated over all lifetimes, and did not cut the integration off at the point where u had gone to a given fraction of u_r, but let u go to zero, one would find an infinite contribution to the momentum. (Each atom would contribute to the roton's momentum for an infinite time.) However, the roton will actually be surrounded by atoms belonging to the superfluid which are moving in the opposite direction. So the relative motion between the decelerating atom and the *immediately* surrounding atoms does not need to go to zero before the former ceases to be part of a roton.

It is possible to make some rough estimates of the orders of magnitude involved. From Table 15-2 we see that at 1.4°K the value of z is around 10. As will be seen later, this is actually an approximate measure of $2z_\epsilon$. If a roton has a kinetic energy of $\frac{1}{2}kT$, then, from Eq. (7.3), $\bar{u}_r$ is about 2.4×10^3 cm sec^{-1}. If $z_\epsilon = 5$, an atom is part of the roton for something like 5τ (defined on p. 411), or 2.5×10^{-11} sec. In this time the roton would move about 6 Å. Thus an atom will be part of the roton for the length of time it takes the roton to move about two interatomic distances, which seems quite reasonable.

We may also check on the magnitude of the momentum. Using the figures in the above calculation we find that $z_\epsilon m\bar{u}_r = 0.8 \times 10^{-19}$ gm cm sec^{-1}, whereas the minimum in Fig. 15.3 occurs at $p = 2.0 \times 10^{-19}$ gm cm sec^{-1}. Thus z_p must be somewhat more than twice z_ϵ. This is not too surprising (although the difference between z_ϵ and z_p may seem somewhat large), since most of the atoms in a roton are moving more slowly than u_r, and a slow atom contributes relatively less to the kinetic energy than to the momentum. However, an atom moving in the wrong direction will contribute to kinetic energy but will contribute momentum to the superfluid rather than to the roton. An analogy may be seen in a sphere moving through an extremely large, but enclosed, mass of perfect fluid of its own density. Such a sphere suffers an apparent increase of mass of 50% because of the kinetic energy of the fluid as it is pushed out of the way [27]. The momentum of the fluid, however, is equal and opposite to that of the sphere, since the fluid has to have an equal net motion in the opposite direction. We can only conclude that in the case of liquid helium there is a relatively great effect of the slowly moving atoms, in holding down the ratio of effective mass for kinetic energy to that for momentum, as opposed to the opposite effect of the back motion surrounding the roton, which contributes to the apparent kinetic energy but not to the momentum of the roton.

We now need to consider more carefully what is meant by relative motion of a roton and the superfluid. The velocity of the roton should be referred to the distant portions of the superfluid, at least when the density of rotons is low. The momentum of the roton is then equal and opposite to the back momentum of the superfluid. When a roton is suddenly accelerated by a neutron, the system acquires a total momentum equal to that lost by the neutron. The system as a whole then receives forward momentum equal to the momentum of the roton; the superfluid (or the superfluid plus its container), therefore, acquires no net momentum in the laboratory coordinates, the back momentum around the roton being cancelled by a very small forward motion of the entire system. The total momentum, then, is equal to the relative momentum of the roton with respect to the superfluid plus the container, the latter being so massive compared with the roton that the motion of the roton depends negligibly on the motion of the system as a whole.

When rotons collide or, as would seem more usual, interact through the superfluid in the manner indicated in the analysis of the energy fluctuations, they can exchange energy, but one need not consider conservation of momentum, since this is automatically taken care of by the back momentum of the superfluid medium. Since the energy is, according to the picture presented here, proportional to the velocity u_r, it acts in a certain sense like a vector. If two rotons act upon each other, conservation of energy requires that the forces act in such a way that the sum of the magnitudes of the velocities remains constant. This requirement, however, is not sufficient to determine the dynamics of the situation. The quasi-vector character of the energy suggests that we make the hypothesis of conservation of the vector sum of the velocities, as well as of the scalar sum, although this hypothesis is difficult to prove rigorously, especially since the details of the process are not known. It takes the place of conservation of momentum in an ordinary collision of isolated hard particles; the conservation of energy results, as noted, in the conservation of the scalar sum. These conservation laws can be illustrated by a simple geometrical construction as shown in Fig. 15-4. Let one velocity vector be AB, the other BC, their vector sum being AC. The point B then on collision can change to some other point on an ellipsoid of revolution passing through B and with foci at A and C, for the characteristic of such an ellipsoid is that the sum of the distances from any point to the two foci is a constant.

Let us now consider a situation in which the rotons have an average drift velocity $\bar{u}_z$ in the z direction, relative to the superfluid.

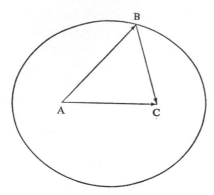

Figure 15-4. Proposed velocity diagram for rotons.

There will, then, according to the preceding paragraph, be two conditions on the roton in this system,† namely

$$\sum_j u_{r,z,j} = \sum_i u_{r,j} \cos \theta_j = n\bar{u}_z = \text{const.} \tag{7.4}$$

and

$$\sum_j \epsilon_{k,r,j} = n\bar{\epsilon}_{k,r} = \text{const.} \tag{7.5}$$

where the sum is over all rotons, θ_j is the angle between the z axis and the velocity of the jth roton, and n is the total number of rotons. If we now attempt to find the number of rotons in any element of the roton phase space as defined in Sec. 15-4, we will have to maximize the number of configurations subject to the conditions embodied in Eqs. (7.4) and (7.5). There will be two Lagrange multipliers, and (assuming Boltzmann statistics, since we deal with the case where the roton density is low) the roton population of a given element of phase space will be proportional to $\exp\{\beta\epsilon_r\} \exp\{\gamma u_r \cos \theta\}$, where $-\beta$ and $-\gamma$ are the Lagrange multipliers. From the discussion preceding Eq. (4.16), the number of energy levels lying in a given range of momenta will be proportional to $p^2 \sin \theta \, dp \, d\theta \, d\phi$, where θ and ϕ are the angles made by the momentum vector with the p_z axis. As in Eq. (4.19), p^2 may be taken as essentially constant, and by Eq. (4.17), noting that $\epsilon_{k,r} = \epsilon_r - \epsilon_0$, it is seen that dp is proportional to $\epsilon_{k,r}^{-1/2} \, d\epsilon_{k,r}$ or to $u_r^{-1/2} \, du_r$, since $\epsilon_{k,r}$ is proportional to u_r.

† It is more usual to place a condition of constant total momentum rather than constant velocity on the rotons. The momentum condition, however, assumes that the rotons have a rather simple structure and apparently some of its consequences have not been worked out. See Prob. 15.2.

We may therefore write

$$\bar{u}_z = \frac{\int_0^\pi \int_0^\infty u_r \cos\theta \exp\{\beta'u_r\} \exp\{\gamma u_r \cos\theta\} u_r^{-1/2}\, du_r \sin\theta\, d\theta}{\int_0^\pi \int_0^\infty \exp\{\beta'u_r\} \exp\{\gamma u_r \cos\theta\} u_r^{-1/2}\, du_r \sin\theta\, d\theta}, \tag{7.6}$$

and

$$\bar{\epsilon}_{k,r} = \frac{\frac{1}{2} m z_e u_r \int_0^\pi \int_0^\infty u_r \exp\{\beta'u_r\} \exp\{\gamma u_r \cos\theta\} u_r^{-1/2}\, du_r \sin\theta\, d\theta}{\int_0^\pi \int_0^\infty \exp\{\beta'u_r\} \exp\{\gamma u_r \cos\theta\} u_r^{-1/2}\, du_r \sin\theta\, d\theta}, \tag{7.7}$$

where $m z_e u_r$ has been taken out of the integral because it is constant, and where β' is a constant related to β. In Eqs. (7.6) and (7.7) the integrations with respect to ϕ cancel between numerator and denominator. If $\bar{u}_z$ is small, we may assume that $\gamma u_r \cos\theta$ will be small for all values of u_r that have any appreciable probability, and so we write

$$\exp\{\gamma u_r \cos\theta\} = 1 + \gamma u_r \cos\theta + \tfrac{1}{2}\gamma^2 u_r^2 \cos^2\theta. \tag{7.8}$$

In the denominator of Eq. (7.6), only the first term, 1, of Eq. (7.8) need be considered, and in the numerator only the term $\gamma u_r \cos\theta$, since $\int_0^\pi \cos\theta \sin\theta\, d\theta = 0$. Carrying out the integrations (β' is a negative quantity) we get (see [1] of Chap. 14),

$$\bar{u}_z = \frac{\gamma}{3\beta'^2} \frac{\Gamma(\tfrac{5}{2})}{\Gamma(\tfrac{1}{2})} = \frac{\gamma}{4\beta'^2},$$

whence

$$\gamma = 4\beta'^2 \bar{u}_z. \tag{7.9}$$

In both the numerator and denominator of Eq. (7.7) we substitute Eq. (7.8), and, since the integrations involving the first power of $\cos\theta$ vanish, we obtain

$$\bar{\epsilon}_{k,r} = -\frac{m z_e u_r}{2\beta'} \frac{[2\Gamma(\tfrac{3}{2}) + \gamma^2\Gamma(\tfrac{7}{2})/3\beta'^2]}{[2\Gamma(\tfrac{1}{2}) + \gamma^2\Gamma(\tfrac{5}{2})/3\beta'^2]}. \tag{7.10}$$

Simplifying (taking into account the relations between the Γ functions), using Eq. (7.9), and expanding to the second power in $\bar{u}_z$, Eq. (7.10) becomes

$$\bar{\epsilon}_{k,r} = -\frac{m z_e u_r}{4\beta'}(1 + 8\bar{u}_z^2\beta'^2). \tag{7.11}$$

The extra kinetic energy due to the drift velocity is proportional to $\bar{u}_z^2$. Without this term $\bar{\epsilon}_{k,r} = \frac{1}{2}kT$, hence

$$\beta' = -\frac{mz_\epsilon u_r}{2kT}, \tag{7.12}$$

which gives $\exp\{\beta' u_r\}$ the expected value of $\exp\{-\epsilon_{k,r}/kT\}$.

The kinetic energy of drift, $\epsilon(\bar{u}_z)$, is given by the last term of Eq. (7.11):

$$\epsilon(\bar{u}_z) = \frac{\bar{u}_z^2(mz_\epsilon u_r)^2}{kT}$$

$$= \frac{\bar{u}_z^2(mz_\epsilon u_r)}{\bar{u}_r} \qquad [\text{since } \tfrac{1}{2}kT = \tfrac{1}{2}mz_\epsilon u_r \bar{u}_r]$$

$$= m\bar{z}_\epsilon \bar{u}_z^2, \tag{7.13}$$

where $\bar{z}_\epsilon$ is the value of z_ϵ for a roton whose velocity is $\bar{u}_r$.

Thus the total kinetic energy of drift (not just that due to the components of the u_r in the direction of the drift velocity), is associated with an effective roton mass equal to $2m\bar{z}_\epsilon$. Since $2z_\epsilon$ is approximately equal to z_p, it thus appears that the rotons act much like a swarm of ordinary particles of mass $z_p m$.

The above calculation gives the kinetic energy of the drifting rotons in a system in which the center of mass remains fixed. It thus can be said to give the relative kinetic energy for mutual motion of the normal fluid with respect to the superfluid, and it makes it possible to set up a two-fluid theory. In order to have a two-fluid theory we need a definition for the densities of normal and superfluids ρ_n and ρ_s and a relation for the relative kinetic energy and relations for the conservation and motion of mass in terms of ρ_n and ρ_s. In a system with fixed center of mass, we can set for the relative kinetic energy per unit volume, if n is the number of rotons associated with N atoms in volume V,

$$\frac{1}{2}\frac{\rho_s \rho_n}{\rho}(\bar{u}_z - v_s)^2 = \frac{n\bar{z}_\epsilon m\bar{u}_z^2}{V}, \tag{7.14}$$

where $\bar{u}_z$ is taken to be equal to v_n, the velocity of normal fluid. We also have

$$\rho_n + \rho_s = \rho, \tag{7.15}$$

and

$$\rho_n \bar{u}_z + \rho_s v_s = 0, \tag{7.16}$$

the latter expressing the fact that the center of mass is fixed. If it is not fixed, $\bar{u}_z$ and v_s can be taken as velocities relative to that of the center of mass. If we solve Eq. (7.16) for v_s and substitute into Eq. (7.14) then $\bar{u}_z$ will cancel out of the equations. The resulting equation and Eq. (7.15) can thus be taken as determining ρ_n and ρ_s in terms of $n\bar{z}_\epsilon/V$. Equation (7.16) then determines v_s in terms of $\bar{u}_z$ when the center of mass is fixed. Phonons are of course neglected in this formulation.

To get the equation of motion, we add Eq. (5.4) to the list of fundamental equations, assuming that it applies to ρ_s, ρ_n, v_s, and $v_n \,(= \bar{u}_z)$ as defined. To this is added the assumption that, in the relative flow of normal fluid and superfluid, entropy is neither created nor destroyed, but flows with the normal fluid. This has been discussed in some detail elsewhere [23].

Strictly speaking, our discussion is limited to temperatures in which the density of rotons is low, since we have assumed that they obey the Boltzmann statistics and do not interact with each other. The two-fluid theory is usually applied, however, up to the λ point.

It should also be borne in mind that a number of assumptions are involved in the discussion. As has been previously noted, a precise formulation of the two-fluid hypothesis in terms of molecular quantities is difficult, because it is not known whether any particular atom is to be considered part of the normal fluid or part of the superfluid [6]. Thus the picture presented must necessarily be an approximate and tentative one. It should also be noted that the discussion given here does not coincide in all respects with presentations found elsewhere in the literature.

15-8. *Thermodynamic Properties of Liquid ³He*

It is of great interest to compare the properties of ³He and ⁴He because of the difference in statistics.† There is a notable contrast in their thermodynamic properties, which is much too marked to be attributed to the difference in mass alone. In particular, the specific heat rises markedly in ³He at a much lower temperature than in ⁴He and, in fact, in ³He it appears to be proportional to T at very low temperatures, as in the Fermi gas (this has been disputed recently: see first footnote, p. 430).

It is, of course, tempting to suppose that this behavior of the specific heat indicates that liquid ³He really is much like a Fermi gas

---

† General references on liquid ³He are [28–30], the last having many references. See also sections in [3–5, 8].

only slightly perturbed by the interaction of the atoms. In my opinion, however, there is much evidence that the situation cannot be described in such simple terms.† If it could be, we might imagine that ^{4}He would act like a slightly perturbed Bose gas, and would therefore have a specific heat proportional to $T^{3/2}$ at low temperatures, whereas we know that the specific heat has a T^3 dependence, characteristic of cooperative wave motions involving many atoms, much as in a solid. It is true, to be sure, that ^{3}He has a somewhat greater molecular volume than ^{4}He, but the difference is hardly sufficient to make one believe that ^{3}He can act like a gas while ^{4}He acts to some degree like a solid, and besides the greater expansion of ^{3}He undoubtedly occurs because at any given density it has a greater zero-point energy than ^{4}He, on account of the lighter mass of the atoms.

One cannot separate the effect of the Fermi statistics in ^{3}He from the effect of the nuclear spin, and, indeed, these factors are causally connected; we could not imagine the one without the other. The low-temperature specific heat of ^{3}He appears to be related to the excitation of different spin states.‡ The nuclear-spin angular momentum of ^{3}He is the same as that of a proton, which means that any atom can be oriented in either one of two ways. In an assembly of N atoms there are thus 2^N distinct spin states. In the absence of a magnetic field, both orientations have the same energy, but there are possible interactions between the spins that may make certain configurations more stable than others. The magnetic moment associated with nuclear spin is so small that any direct interaction is entirely negligible. However, indirect interaction associated with exchange of atoms can occur, just as indirect interaction (Russell-Saunders coupling) arises from exchange of electrons. We have already seen how this works in the case of ortho- and parahydrogen, in which the lowest energy level with symmetrical nuclear-spin functions lies above the state with antisymmetrical nuclear-spin functions, because of the coupling, due to symmetry, of the rotational and spin-wave functions. A similar situation arises in the case of liquid ^{3}He.

In order to take into account the effects of exchange, it is neces-

---

† However, a considerable success, especially in accounting for properties near 0°K, has been obtained by use of theories which treat the liquid as a rather strongly perturbed Fermi gas [31]. Mention should also be made of the theories of Landau [32–34], also in [8]. We will here be content with a less exact, semi-empirical theory, which is, however, much less involved and gives a fairly good physical picture of the factors involved.

‡ The concept of a spin entropy more or less independent of lattice entropy has been developed by L. Goldstein [35–38].

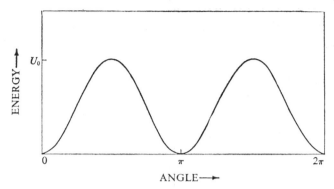

Figure 15-5. Potential-energy function for a hindered plane rotator.

sary to consider at least pairs of atoms, and it seems reasonable, as a first approximation, to think of N atoms of ³He as being composed of $N/2$ pairs ([39–41]; see also [42]). Each of these pairs can rotate in the field of its neighbors; because of the existence of this field it will be a *hindered* rotation. Furthermore, it is most likely that rotation will occur most freely in some one particular plane, so it seems most reasonable to assume that the pairs act as hindered plane rotators, thus describing the effects of the neighboring atoms in a fairly crude but easily visualizable way [43, 44].

In treating this situation, we shall, of course, idealize greatly. We assume that these rotators move in a potential-energy field which is sinusoidal and has two minima and two maxima in the complete circle (Fig. 15-5). The wave functions for a system moving in such a potential-energy field are the so-called Mathieu functions [45], and the energy levels are known as functions of the various parameters involved, such as the hindering potential U_0 (i.e., the difference between the maxima and minima in the potential-energy curve). Figure 15-6 shows the energy levels, expressed in terms of the unit $h^2/4\pi^2 mr_0^2$ (where m is the mass of the ³He atom and r_0 is the effective distance between atomic centers in the pair rotator), as a function of $q = \pi^2 mr_0^2 U_0/8h^2$, which effectively measures the hindering potential. In the limit $q = 0$, which corresponds to free rotation in a plane, the levels above the lowest are doubly degenerate, corresponding to the two possible directions of rotation. In the other limit, $q = \infty$, which corresponds to torsional oscillation, all of the levels are doubly degenerate, corresponding to oscillations about either one of the minima. In the intermediate regions, the levels are nondegenerate, and the connections are as shown.

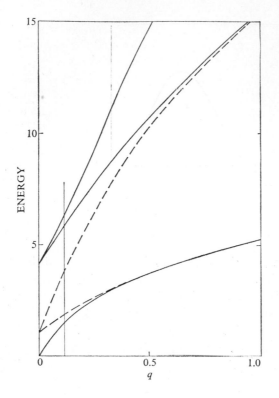

Figure 15-6. Energy levels of a hindered plane rotator. Vertical line shows approximate hindering potential for ^{3}He. (From Rice [**43**].)

The spatial wave functions for the levels shown as solid lines in Fig. 15-6 are symmetrical and must be combined with antisymmetrical spin functions, whereas the levels shown as broken lines are antisymmetrical and combine with symmetrical spin functions. Since there are three possible symmetrical spin combinations, the levels represented by broken lines will be triplets, whereas the others will be singlets.

It can now be seen that the two lowest levels in Fig. 15-6 correspond to the 2^N spin states which occur simply by spin orientation. For with their multiplicities, noted in the last paragraph, these comprise the four lowest levels of each pair, and with $N/2$ pairs there will be altogether $4^{N/2} = 2^N$ possible states. Actually, exchange does not occur too readily in the low-energy levels, and the coupled atoms resemble oscillating pairs more closely than they resemble rotating pairs.

There is some arbitrariness in the representation of the system as $N/2$ particular pairs, because there is no definite criterion for stating with which one of its neighbors a given atom will pair. Thus the assembly can be divided into $N/2$ pairs in a large number of apparently reasonable ways. The analysis given shows, however, that these different possible ways, at least for the low energies, are not independent states of the system. When a pair is in what we shall call a "vibrationally excited state," one which connects with an excited vibrational level in the limit of a high hindering potential, the multiplicity of energy levels may be greater. Such a state ought also to be describable in terms of "lattice" vibrations of a quasi-lattice of atoms. Each atom has three degrees of freedom of vibration, and so could be excited to one of three low vibrational levels. However, as in the case of ⁴He, because of the looseness of the liquid structure, this number could well be doubled. It is again doubled by the possibility of nuclear spin orientation. So we estimate that there will be roughly 12 distinct low vibrational states per atom or 24 per pair. If we assume that the liquid is divided into $N/2$ arbitrary pairs, only three of these levels (constituting a spin triplet) would be accounted for as first vibrationally excited states of hindered plane rotators. However, we could well suppose that there would be more energy levels in this neighborhood, which could perhaps be described as arising from the possibility that different ways of pairing give distinguishable *vibrationally excited* energy levels. There will be a spread in energy, and some of the levels may be found at higher energies.

Empirically, Temperley [41] found that the observed specific heat between about 0.5° and 1.0°K was fairly well reproduced by assuming that the liquid consisted of $N/2$ pairs with pair partition functions as follows:

$$(\text{p.f.})_{\text{pr.}} = 1 + 3 \exp\left\{\frac{-0.4}{T}\right\} + 8 \exp\left\{\frac{-2.7}{T}\right\}. \tag{8.1}$$

Later Rice [44] suggested an effective pair partition function based on the expression

$$1 + 3 \exp\left\{\frac{-0.48}{T}\right\} + 11 \exp\left\{\frac{-2.8}{T}\right\},$$

but with broadened energy levels, i.e.,

$$(\text{p.f.})_{\text{pr.}} = 1 + \int_0^\infty p_\epsilon \exp\left\{\frac{-\epsilon}{kT}\right\} d\epsilon + \int_0^\infty p'_\epsilon \exp\left\{\frac{-\epsilon}{kT}\right\} d\epsilon, \tag{8.2}$$

where the energy-level densities p_ϵ and p'_ϵ fit the equations

$$\int_0^\infty p_\epsilon \, d\epsilon = 3, \tag{8.3}$$

and

$$\int_0^\infty p'_\epsilon \, d\epsilon = 11.$$

(8.4)

The densities are given by error functions broken off at $\epsilon = 0$, thus:

$$p_\epsilon = b \exp\left\{-\frac{(\epsilon - \epsilon_0)^2}{a^2 k^2}\right\}, \qquad \epsilon \geq 0,$$

$$p'_\epsilon = b' \exp\left\{-\frac{(\epsilon - \epsilon_0)^2}{a'^2 k^2}\right\}, \qquad \epsilon \geq 0,$$

(8.5)

and

$$p_\epsilon = p'_\epsilon = 0, \qquad\qquad\qquad \epsilon < 0,$$

(8.6)

with

$$\frac{\epsilon_0}{k} = 0.48°, \qquad \frac{\epsilon'_0}{k} = 2.8°,$$

$$a = 0.40°, \qquad a' = 1.333°.$$

(8.7)

The form (8.2) is an approximation which attempts to put the effects of the broadening of the energy levels into the partition function of *each* of the $N/2$ pairs. [We really should consider (P.F.).] The form for the density of levels, p_ϵ, as given in Eq. (8.5), means that this density has a finite, nonzero value p_0 at $\epsilon = 0$, so that at very low temperatures we will be able to write (do not confuse p_0 with p_0 of Fig. 15-3)

$$(\text{p.f.}) \approx 1 + p_0 \int_0^\infty \exp\left\{\frac{-\epsilon}{kT}\right\} d\epsilon$$

$$= 1 + p_0 kT,$$

(8.8)

whence the energy of $N/2$ pairs is readily seen to be

$$E = \frac{NkT^2}{2} \frac{d \ln (\text{p.f.})}{dT} \approx \frac{1}{2} NkT^2 p_0 k.$$

(8.9)

The specific heat at constant volume (which at low temperature is always practically the same as C_p, and, indeed remains so for the whole temperature range for ³He) is given by

$$C_v \approx Nk^2 p_0 T,$$

(8.10)

which makes it proportional to T at very low temperatures.

The values of the parameters in Eqs. (8.7) give values of the specific heat shown in Table 15-3 and compared there with the exper-

TABLE 15-3

(T in °K, C in cal deg^{-1} mole^{-1})

T	C (expt)	C (calc)
0.05	0.25	0.21
0.1	0.42	0.50
0.2	0.64	0.71
0.333	0.73	0.69
0.5	0.79	0.78
1.0	1.03	0.81

Source: Experimental values averaged from several sources [46–48]; those at 1.0°K from Roberts and Sydoriak [49].

imental data. The calculated value is slightly low at 1°K, where higher excitations may be becoming of importance, and do not agree exactly at lower temperatures, which may mean that some adjustment of the parameters is required. However, further calculation does not seem worth while, in view of the approximate character of the model. It is interesting that the values of ϵ_0/k and ϵ_0'/k agree well with those of the first two excited states of a plane rotator with a hindering potential of 9.2 cal per pair mole. Such a plane rotator, with some broadening of the energy levels and with some allowance for increasing multiplicity of the higher levels, gives a reasonable, though semi-empirical, description of the thermal behavior of ³He.

In view of the results which may be obtained for ³He on the basis of the pair-rotator model, one may inquire why the model is not applicable to ⁴He, in particular, why one does not find a relatively low excitation level corresponding to the tumbling of a pair of atoms about each other in the field of their neighbors. In answering this question, we must remember that ⁴He has no spin, and the over-all wave function is symmetrical. Since only symmetrical spin functions are possible, only symmetrical orbital functions are allowed. The broken lines in Fig. 15-6, then, refer to energy levels that are not present in ⁴He. Thus the lowest excited states are at once eliminated. However, if the hindering potential were the same as for ³He, the value of ϵ_0''/k (the next excited state) for a hindered plane rotator in ⁴He would still be only 5°. The density of ⁴He is greater than that of ³He, and so it should have a larger hindering potential, which would raise the excitation energy to the next level present in ⁴He. Indeed, considering the rapidity with which the repulsive part of the mutual potential-energy curve of two atoms rises as the interatomic distance decreases, it seems probable that this excitation energy would be raised sufficiently in ^{4}He so that this type of excitation would make a relatively small contribution, and the difference between ^{4}He and ^{3}He can be well understood. (A crude calculation [44] gave an estimate of $\epsilon_0''/k = 12.8°$ for this excitation in ^{4}He. This may be an overestimate, but a value of ϵ_0''/k around 8° would be large enough to prevent these excitations from having any distinguishable effect.)

At pressures up to 25 atm, the specific heat of ^{3}He increases with pressure below about 0.15°K and decreases with pressure above this [46]. This behavior appears reasonable from the model used. If the second integral on the right of Eq. (8.2) is neglected, the specific heat has a maximum near 0.2°K. At a higher pressure, the atoms are pushed closer together and we expect the hindering potential to be increased. It is then seen from Fig. 15.6 that ϵ_0/k is *decreased*. This means that the maximum in the specific heat will be shifted to lower temperatures; thus the specific heat will be increased below 0.2°K and decreased above 0.2°K. The decrease above 0.2°K will be made more marked, and its beginning perhaps pushed below 0.2°K by the behavior of the next set of energy levels, represented by the second integral in Eq. (8.2), for ϵ_0'/k will *increase* as ϵ_0/k decreases. No calculations have been made that would enable one to estimate the reasonableness of the actual size of the changes, but the impression is that the observed changes with pressure are somewhat less than might have been expected. At 25 atm the molecular volume of ^{3}He is reduced about to that of ^{4}He at normal pressures. If ϵ_0''/k is raised to about the value it has for ^{4}He, if ϵ_0'/k is not much lower than this, and if ϵ_0/k is much lower than 0.48° because the two lowest levels approach each other, then we would expect the temperature range of the specific-heat contribution associated with ϵ_0 to be separated from those associated with ϵ_0' and ϵ_0''; this does not seem to occur to any great extent.† Thus the hindering potential does not increase as rapidly with decreasing molecular volume as we might expect. This may have some connection with the large zero-point energy of ^{3}He.

15-9. *Magnetic Properties of* ^{3}He

Since the nuclear spin is associated with a magnetic moment, liquid ^{3}He may be expected to have a magnetic susceptibility; indeed, this property

† There may be some indication of the beginning of such a separation at the higher pressures, as indicated by a maximum in the specific heat curve around 0.2°K [48].

was one of the first to be measured, in an effort to discover whether the spins line up, as expected, in a magnetic field [50, 51]. If we use the pair-rotator model, we expect only the triplet spin states to be affected by a magnetic field, since in the singlet state the spins are paired in opposite directions [39–42]. If we let μ be the component of magnetic moment in the direction of the field if a free nucleus is lined up with the field, the three states of the triplet will have effective (component) moments of 2μ, 0, and -2μ, with magnetic energies $-2\mu H$, 0, and $2\mu H$, respectively, where H is the field strength. If ϵ_0 is the energy for excitation of the triplet state [neglecting the broadening of this state described in Eq. (8.2)], then, if we assume that only the lowest singlet and triplet states are involved (which is sufficient to account for the magnetic phenomena in rough outline), the partition function will be

$$(\text{p.f.})_{\text{pr.}} = 1 + \exp\left\{\frac{-\epsilon_0}{kT}\right\}\left(\exp\left\{\frac{2\mu H}{kT}\right\} + 1 + \exp\left\{-\frac{2\mu H}{kT}\right\}\right). \quad (9.1)$$

The net magnetic moment induced in N atoms, which is equal to $\chi_N H$, where χ_N is the susceptibility of the N atoms, is given by

$$\chi_N H = \frac{N}{2}\frac{2\mu \exp\left\{-\epsilon_0/kT\right\}(\exp\left\{2\mu H/kT\right\} - \exp\left\{-2\mu H/kT\right\})}{(\text{p.f.})_{\text{pr.}}}$$

$$\approx \frac{4N\mu^2 H}{kT}\frac{\exp\left\{-\epsilon_0/kT\right\}}{1 + 3\exp\left\{-\epsilon_0/kT\right\}}. \quad (9.2)$$

In the second line of Eq. (9.2), the exponentials have been expanded in terms of $2\mu H/kT$, retaining only the leading terms which are left after cancellations occur. At high temperatures the levels of the singlet and the triplet become equally probable, and this is true, even if higher levels are included. So the second line of Eq. (9.2) gives the correct result at high temperatures even though the higher levels are neglected— it gives an expression which follows Curie's law with the susceptibility inversely proportional to the temperature, i.e.,

$$\chi_N = \frac{N\mu^2}{kT} = \frac{C}{T}, \quad (9.3)$$

where C is the Curie constant. The second line of Eq. (9.2) also gives the correct result if the temperature is low enough;† only at intermediate temperatures can it be slightly in error. It does depend, however, upon

---

† That is, low enough to neglect the higher levels. We must still have $T \gg \mu H/k$, which holds in the experimentally accessible range.

the assumption that the excitation has a definite value ϵ_0, whereas we have seen that these levels must be broadened. We can attempt to allow for this in approximate fashion as before, writing,

$$(\text{p.f.})_{\text{pr.}} = 1 + \frac{1}{3} \int_0^\infty p_\epsilon \exp\left\{-\frac{\epsilon}{kT}\right\} d\epsilon$$

$$\times \left(\exp\left\{\frac{2\mu H}{kT}\right\} + 1 + \exp\left\{-\frac{2\mu H}{kT}\right\}\right), \qquad (9.4)$$

with p_ϵ satisfying Eq. (8.3). This gives

$$\chi_N H \approx \frac{4 N \mu^2 H}{3kT} \frac{\int_0^\infty p_\epsilon \exp\left\{-\epsilon/kT\right\} d\epsilon}{1 + \int_0^\infty p_\epsilon \exp\left\{-\epsilon/kT\right\} d\epsilon}. \qquad (9.5)$$

In the limit of high temperatures, this will reduce to Eq. (9.2), but in the low-temperature limit it becomes

$$\chi_N H = \tfrac{4}{3} N \mu^2 H p_0, \qquad (9.6)$$

where p_0 is the value of p_ϵ at $\epsilon = 0$. This result gives a susceptibility which is independent of temperature at low enough temperatures. A similar result was shown by Pauli [52] to hold for an ideal Fermi gas.

It is convenient to express the results as the ratio $\chi_N/\chi_{N,\infty}$ in which $\chi_{N,\infty}$ is the susceptibility which would be obtained if the limiting high-temperature law held at the temperature under consideration. This ratio is

$$\frac{\chi_N}{\chi_{N,\infty}} = \frac{\tfrac{4}{3} \int_0^\infty p_\epsilon \exp\left\{-\epsilon/kT\right\} d\epsilon}{1 + \int_0^\infty p_\epsilon \exp\left\{-\epsilon/kT\right\} d\epsilon}. \qquad (9.7)$$

Since Eq. (9.3) actually gives $\chi_{N,\infty}$, obviously $\chi_N/\chi_{N,\infty} = (\chi_N/C)T$. In Table 15-4 we have compared theoretical and experimental values of χ_N/C

TABLE 15-4

T (°K)	χ_N/C (expt)	χ_N/C (calc)
0.06	3.41	1.84
0.1	3.18	2.05
0.2	2.69	2.14
0.4	1.99	1.68
1.2	0.83	0.74
2.0	0.50	0.47

(extrapolated to zero pressure) [53] using the parameters of Eq. (8.7). In the higher temperature range the agreement is reasonably good, although the falloff in χ_N/C below the classical value of $1/T$ occurs at somewhat too high a temperature and the susceptibilities are a little low. This may be due in part to neglect of the higher levels. Although it is not certain that both the specific-heat data and the magnetic susceptibilities can be completely accounted for on the basis of the pair-rotator model by a proper choice of parameters, a fairly reasonable description of the properties appears possible. The decrease in the calculated value of χ_N/C in the low-temperature range indicates that the parameters chosen do not give a large enough density of energy levels in the very-low-energy range. The same effect shows up in the rather sharp drop in the specific heat at 0.05°K. It is less marked with the specific heat because in the latter (which, it will be recalled, is proportional to $\overline{E^2} - \overline{E}^2$) the influence of the higher energy levels is more strongly weighted. The density of levels at low energies seems to be given reasonably well by the theory of Brueckner and Gammel [31].

A higher pressure lowers the temperature at which the limiting value of χ is reached [53, 54]. As with the specific heat, this effect is related qualitatively to the increase in the hindering potential for the pair-rotator, and the consequent lowering of the excitation of the lowest triplet state.

Although the character of the approach to the limit at 0°K may be different for the specific heat and the magnetic susceptibility, Eqs. (8.10) and (9.6) show that the limiting values of both quantities are measures of p_0, the density of energy levels at 0°K. Both χ and dC_v/dT increase with pressure.

The relation between χ_N and dC_v/dT may be tested in the following way. Comparing Eqs. (9.3) and (9.6), we see that Eq. (9.6) may be written (recall that C is the Curie constant, C_v the specific heat)

$$\frac{\chi_{N,0}}{C} = \frac{4}{3} k p_0 \tag{9.8}$$

where the subscript zero indicates the value at 0°K. Solving this and Eq. (8.10) each for p_0 and comparing, we find

$$1 = \frac{3(\chi_{N,0}/C)R}{4(dC_v/dT)_0}. \tag{9.9}$$

Both χ_N/C and dC_v/dT have been tabulated as functions of pressure [48, 53] (actually the specific heat given appears to be C_p, but $C_p - C_v$

TABLE 15-5

Test of Eq. (9.9)

(P in atm; $x_{N.0}/C$ and $(dC_v/dT)_0/R$ in $\deg^{-1}$)

P	$x_{N.0}/C$	$(dC_v/dT)_0/R$	R.h.s. of (9.9)
0.1	3.45	2.89	0.895
14.6	4.72	3.84	0.923
28.8	5.71	4.44	0.965

is small), so that we can check the values of the right-hand side of Eq. (9.9); see Table 15-5. The agreement is reasonably good; the slight error may be a measure of the error in the assumptions of the pair-rotator model.†

15-10. *Solutions of ^3He in ^4He*

Dilute solutions of ^3He in liquid ^4He are of special interest because they offer an example of a foreign atom with the same force field as the solvent atoms and because of the superfluid properties of ^4He. In discussing the effect of the introduction of such an impurity atom one may consider two extreme situations, namely, a dilute gas and a solid.‡ In a gas the impurity atom introduces a new set of energy levels, entirely independent of the energy levels of the atoms of the other species. Many more energy levels are introduced than if one more identical atom were added, because of the exchange effects in the latter case. An impurity atom introduced into a solid lattice, if it were restricted to a fixed position, would merely add three new normal modes of vibration, an essentially negligible change. It might also change all the frequencies to some degree, if the solid solution is not ideal. If it is ideal, i.e., if the new atom has almost the same mass and exerts almost the same forces as the other atoms, the effect on frequency will also be negligible. If the impurity atom is not restricted to a particular location, the number of

---

† According to very recent data of W. R. Abel, A. C. Anderson, W. C. Black, and J. C. Wheatly [*Phys. Rev.*, 147, 111 (1966)], the values of $(dC_v/dT)_0/R$ may be 5% higher, which would correspondingly lower the last column of Table 15-5. See this publication for references to some recent theoretical speculations.

‡ This section is based, with some changes, on Rice in [**28**, p. 173].

independent normal modes of vibration is multiplied by the number of possible independent positions. At high temperatures, the average thermal energy of an impurity atom is nearly the same as that of the other atoms in either gas or solid. Also, the entropy of mixing at constant pressure is the same in the ideal case in gas or solid.

The difference in these two states of aggregation begins to show up at low temperatures. If a foreign atom is introduced into a degenerate Bose or Fermi gas, it will have an average energy equal to $\frac{3}{2}kT$, in contrast to that of the "host" gas, which is close to zero in the Bose gas and has a large but nearly constant value with varying (low) temperature in the Fermi gas. On the other hand, the average thermal energy of an impurity atom introduced into a solid will still be that of its neighbors, which at low temperatures is very low, aside from zero-point energy.

In the case of ³He atoms considered as foreign atoms in ⁴He, we have a situation which is intermediate to the two extremes considered above. Although liquid helium, because of the large zero-point motion, is far from being close-packed, the atoms are close enough together so that a pure gaslike picture does not seem appropriate. One might prefer to think of the ³He as occupying any one of the positions in a lattice (and in view of the low density of the liquid there may be more positions than atoms). An ³He atom is presumed to be unexcited at sufficiently low temperatures, so, in what may be called the unperturbed state, the various levels corresponding to different positions have the same energy. However, the ³He atom is bounced around from place to place, owing to the zero-point motion. This results in a broadening of the level into a band with a range of energies. If one starts with this point of view and considers the effect of fluctuations in composition, one arrives eventually at results very similar to those of the gas theory, although differing in some details.

If we have a solution of ³He in ⁴He with a concentration gradient, the concentration will tend to become uniform, just as in any solution. However, if the solution is below the λ point, this particular solution has a unique feature, namely the possibility that superfluid ⁴He will actually flow from a region low in ³He to one high in ³He. If we think of the superfluid as a free-flowing viscosity-free liquid, this feature implies a gradient in pressure, grad P_s, in the superfluid. By a hypothetical experiment very similar to that described at the beginning of Sec. 15-5, in this case having a portion of pure ⁴He at 0°K and a solution of ³He in ⁴He at T, with a semipermeable porous plug which will not pass either normal fluid ^{4}He or ^{3}He, it is possible to show, in analogy to Eq. (5.3), that

$$P_s = P + \rho(\bar{\epsilon}_4 - T\bar{s}_4) = \rho\mu_4, \tag{10.1}$$

where the bars indicate partial quantities per gram of ^{4}He, and where μ_4 is its chemical potential per gram.

Because of this pressure, the ^{3}He atoms will act much like rotons and will undergo similar fluctuations in density.

Let us now divide our system into cubic cells, each containing on the average N_0 atoms of ^{4}He and n_0 atoms of ^{3}He. Further, let us suppose that $n_0 \ll N_0$, and that the temperature is low enough so that the ^{4}He can be considered a superfluid. Under these conditions the average of the square of the fluctuations δn_0 will be given by the same formula as for an ideal gas:

$$\overline{(\delta n_0)^2} = n_0. \tag{10.2}$$

Regression (and hence formation) of the fluctuations will occur through flow of the superfluid. A certain amount of kinetic energy is connected with these fluctuations, and it may be estimated similarly to the way in which we estimated the energy associated with fluctuations in roton density in pure ^{4}He. Again the kinetic energy turns out to be of the order of kT/n_0. If the suitable value of n_0 is about 1, the particles will be almost completely gaslike, but if n_0 is greater than this, but not too much greater, it is still clear that the ^{3}He particles will have many gaslike properties.

The calculation is at best an approximate estimate of the average energy involved in the fluctuations of position of a group of impurity atoms. An exact calculation would have to be based on a knowledge of the distribution of energy levels in the broadened band of levels due to the introduction of an impurity atom. If these energies were all known, the system could be treated exactly by means of a canonical ensemble. Clearly the average energy of ^{3}He atoms which are at a low enough temperature so that they are not involved in individual rotonlike excitations could not exceed the energy breadth of the band. They could be expected to have energies like the energies of gas atoms only at temperatures such that kT is considerably less than the breadth of the band.

If the atoms of ^{3}He in ^{4}He are indeed gaslike, they might be expected [55] to contribute $\frac{3}{2}k$ per atom to the specific heat, and this would be the specific heat of a sufficiently dilute solution of ^{3}He in the low-temperature range where the specific heat of pure ⁴He is negligible. Actually it appears experimentally that the specific heat in the low-temperature region may be a little less than $\frac{3}{2}k$ (perhaps 14% for a solution of about 0.045 mole fraction of ³He, with a slightly greater discrepancy for more concentrated solutions) [56]; possibly the discrepancy would disappear at extremely low concentrations. At temperatures around 1°K, the apparent contribution of ³He atoms to the specific heat increases. This is probably because the presence of ³He introduces the possibility of rotonlike excitations of lower energy. In other words, the ³He atoms induce the formation of normal ⁴He. It is found that ³He lowers the λ point. At very low temperatures the fall-off in specific heat expected for a Fermi-Dirac gas has been observed [57].

Since the ³He atoms are able to move through the superfluid much as the rotons do, they should contribute to the normal fluid in such experiments as the measurement of the velocity of second sound. However, there are some differences. In the first place, a roton can disappear completely, but an ³He atom cannot. In the second place, a roton consists of an excitation which can move from atom to atom by exciton transfer, and therefore the number of atoms which move together in a roton varies with its velocity. Nothing analogous can take place with an ³He atom, which should thus have a nearly constant effective mass. At a low enough temperature, second sound takes on a somewhat different character in a dilute solution of ³He in ⁴He [55]. If heat is introduced into such a system, some of it may form phonons, and some will excite translational motion of the ³He atoms. The latter will move away from the heat source, thus there results a decrease in the concentration of ³He immediately adjacent to the heat source and an increase slightly beyond. These concentration disturbances will be transmitted like a sound wave with the velocity characteristic of a gas of ³He atoms having a certain effective mass. From the velocity the effective mass can be determined. It appears to approach a value of about 2.8 times the mass of an ³He atom at low temperatures and low pressures (see D. J. Sandiford and H. A. Fairbank in [29, p. 154]). At higher pressures the effective mass is slightly greater.

If the ³He atom acted like a sphere moving through a perfect fluid, it would have an excess apparent mass equal to half the mass of the fluid displaced [27]. Even taking into account the greater atomic mass of ⁴He, it is clear that the effective mass of 2.8 times that of an ³He atom would mean that the ³He atoms would have an effective volume more than twice that of an ⁴He atom, which is clearly too large. The molecular structure of the solvent ⁴He must, therefore, play a role in the phenomenon. Feynman [Appendix of **18**] has presented a wave-mechanical picture which gives a slightly higher effective mass for ^{3}He, but still not high enough.

15-11. *Some Observations on Effective Mass*

The similarity between an ^{3}He atom moving in superfluid ^{4}He and a sphere moving in a very large body of perfect fluid (a fluid which is incompressible and has no viscosity) lends new interest to this classical problem. The statement that we have made concerning the effective mass of the sphere means that the total kinetic energy of the sphere and of the surrounding fluid, which is set in motion by the sphere, is given by the equation

$$\epsilon_k = \tfrac{1}{2}(m_s + \tfrac{1}{2}m_f)u^2 \tag{11.1}$$

where m_s is the true mass of the sphere, m_f is the mass of the fluid displaced by it, and u is the velocity of the sphere. The effective mass m_e then is given by

$$m_e = m_s + \tfrac{1}{2}m_f. \tag{11.2}$$

The effective mass is determined by the kinetic energy.

If the fluid is contained in a large, closed vessel, a volume of fluid equal to that of the sphere must move with the same velocity in the opposite direction. Such a motion must in effect be the resultant of the motions of the various portions of the fluid. The question then arises, how much of the momentum of the fluid should be associated with the motion of the sphere?

One is concerned with this question if he wishes to write the wave equation for the system. A general procedure is to get the classical equation in terms of the coordinates and momenta (Hamiltonian form: Sec. 1-9), then replace any momentum by the operator $(h/2\pi i)\partial/\partial q$, where q is the corresponding coordinate. In order to carry out this procedure, the relation of the momentum to the velocity must be known.

The problem of quantization can, however, be approached in another way, using Eq. (4.5) of Chap. 1. When the sphere moving through the ideal fluid approaches a wall, forces will be set up which will slow it down and eventually cause it to move in the opposite direction. If the container is large enough, the details of this process will be unimportant, and during most of the time the velocity will be that given by Eq. (11.1). The period of motion for the sphere moving back and forth in the vessel is therefore virtually the same function of the energy as it would be for a particle of mass $m_s + \frac{1}{2}m_f$, and the distribution of energy levels is the same. The wave functions of the successive energy levels will also be the same as for a particle of mass $m_s + \frac{1}{2}m_f$, and since the wavelength is directly related to the momentum by the de Broglie relation, the momenta of the levels will also be those of a particle of mass $m_s + \frac{1}{2}m_f$. Therefore, in this sense, the same effective mass can be said to apply to energy and to momentum.

This result is consistent with the classical equations of motion, if we use a consistent definition of effective momentum. If a small change in kinetic energy is produced by application of a force to the sphere, this force must operate through a certain distance. It will also operate for a certain time, related to the distance through the velocity u. If we define the change in effective momentum as the force multiplied by the time during which it acts, it may be readily verified that the change is simply that which would be experienced by a body of mass $m_s + \frac{1}{2}m_f$ moving with the velocity u.

The analogy between the sphere moving in a perfect fluid and a particle moving in superfluid helium breaks down if the "particle" is a roton, because of the complicated structure of the roton and the fact that its mass changes with its velocity. The problem of the roton is a many-particle problem, and this cannot be evaded. In discussing the roton we tried to take these complications into account in a classical description. Our description may not be completely successful in every detail, and in particular the difficulty of identifying the particular contributions to the momentum of the roton is not completely resolved. In this connection, the initial difficulty in identifying the contribution of the surrounding medium to the momentum of the sphere in an ideal fluid is instructive.

The analogy between a foreign particle moving in superfluid and the sphere in an ideal fluid (whose motion is described by only three degrees of freedom) is, on the other hand, probably reasonably valid. The same effective mass can be associated with kinetic energy and with momentum, and, as with a freely moving particle, the larger the effective mass, the more densely will the energy levels be spaced. As we have seen at the beginning of Sec. 15-10, the more nearly the system resembles a solid, the less spread out will the energy levels be; thus, the more like a solid the system is, the higher will be the effective mass of a foreign particle, and the more the system resembles a gas, the more nearly will the effective mass be equal to the mass of the impurity atom itself.

REFERENCES

1. W. H. Keesom, Helium, Amsterdam, Elsvier, 1942.
2. F. London, *Superfluids*, New York, Wiley, 1954, Vol. II.
3. K. R. Atkins, *Liquid Helium*, Cambridge, Eng., Cambridge Univ. Press, 1959.
4. C. T. Lane, *Superfluid Physics*, New York, McGraw-Hill, 1962.
5. G. Careri, ed., *Liquid Helium*, New York, Academic, 1963.
6. K. Huang, *Statistical Mechanics*, New York, Wiley, 1963, Chaps. 18 and 19.
7. D. J. Thouless, *The Quantum Mechanics of Many-Body Systems*, New York, Academic, 1961.
8. D. Pines, ed., *The Many-Body Problem* (Lecture Notes and Reprints), New York, W. A. Benjamin, Inc., New York, 1961.
9. J. Wiebes, C. C. Niels-Hakkenberg, and H. C. Kramers, *Physics*, **23,** 625 (1957).
10. A. H. Markham, D. C. Pearce, R. G. Netzel, and J. R. Dillinger, in J. R. Dillinger, ed., *Proceedings of the Fifth International Conference on Low Temperature Physics and Chemistry*, Madison, Univ. Wisconsin Press, 1958, p. 45.
11. F. London, *J. Phys. Chem.*, **43,** 49 (1939).
12. O. K. Rice, *Phys. Rev.*, **96,** 1460 (1954).
13. L. D. Landau, *J. Phys.*, U.S.S.R., **5,** 71 (1941).
14. L. D. Landau, *J. Phys.*, U.S.S.R., **8,** 1 (1944).
15. R. B. Dingle, *Adv. in Phys.*, **1,** 111 (1952).
16. O. K. Rice, *Phys. Rev.*, **108,** 551 (1957).
17. H. C. Kramers, J. D. Wasscher, and C. J. Gorter, *Physica*, **18,** 329 (1952).
18. R. P. Feynman, *Phys. Rev.*, **94,** 262 (1954).
19. R. P. Feynman and M. Cohen, *Phys. Rev.*, **102,** 1189 (1956).
20. L. D. Landau, *J. Phys.*, U.S.S.R., **11,** 91 (1947).
21. J. L. Yarnell, G. P. Arnold, P. J. Bendt, and E. C. Kerr, *Phys. Rev.*, **113,** 1379 (1959).
22. P. J. Bendt, R. D. Cowan, and J. L. Yarnell, *Phys. Rev.*, **113,** 1386 (1959).
23. O. K. Rice, *Phys. Rev.*, **103,** 267 (1956).
24. O. K. Rice, *Nuovo cimento* **9** (suppl.), 267 (1958).
25. O. K. Rice in J. G. Daunt, D. O. Edwards, F. J. Milford, and M. Yaqub, eds., *Low Temperature Physics LT*9 (Ninth International Conference), New York, Plenum Press, 1965, pp. 88–90.
26. J. G. Dash and R. D. Taylor, *Phys. Rev.*, **105,** 7 (1957).
27. R. A. Houstoun, *An Introduction to Mathematical Physics*, Longmans, Green, and Co., London and New York, 1920, pp. 54–58.
28. J. G. Daunt, ed., *Symposia on Solid and Liquid Helium Three* (1st Sym-

posium Proceedings and Supplement), Columbus, Ohio State Univ. Press, 1957.

29. J. G. Daunt, ed., *Symposium on Solid and Liquid Helium Three* (2d Symposium Proceedings), Columbus, Ohio State Univ. Press, 1960.

30. N. Bernardes and D. F. Brewer, *Rev. Mod. Phys.*, **34,** 190 (1962).

31. K. A. Brueckner and J. Gammel, *Phys. Rev.*, **109,** 1040 (1958).

32. L. D. Landau, *Soviet Physics JETP*, **3,** 920 (1957).

33. L. D. Landau, *Soviet Physics JETP*, **5,** 101 (1957).

34. L. D. Landau, *Soviet Physics JETP*, **8,** 70 (1959).

35. L. Goldstein, *Phys. Rev.*, **96,** 1455 (1954).

36. L. Goldstein, *Phys. Rev.*, **102,** 1205 (1956).

37. L. Goldstein, *Phys. Rev.*, **112,** 1463, 1483 (1958).

38. L. Goldstein, *Phys. Rev.*, **117,** 375 (1960).

39. P. J. Price, *Phys. Rev.*, **97,** 359 (1955).

40. O. K. Rice, *Phys. Rev.*, **97,** 263 (1955).

41. H. N. V. Temperley, *Phys. Rev.*, **97,** 835 (1955).

42. J. de Boer, in C. J. Gorter, ed., *Progress in Low Temperature Physics*, Vol. II, New York, Interscience, 1957, p.1.

43. O. K. Rice, *Phys. Rev.*, **98,** 847 (1955).

44. O. K. Rice, *Phys. Rev.*, **108,** 551 (1957).

45. S. Goldstein, *Trans. Cambridge Phil. Soc.*, **23,** 303 (1927).

46. D. F. Brewer, J. G. Daunt, and A. K. Sreedhar, *Phys. Rev.*, **115,** 836 (1959).

47. M. Strongin, G. O. Zimmerman, and H. A. Fairbank, *Phys. Rev.*, **128,** 1983 (1962).

48. A. C. Anderson, W. Reese, and J. C. Wheatley, *Phys. Rev.*, **130,** 495 (1963).

49. T. R. Roberts and S. G. Sydoriak, *Phys. Rev.*, **98,** 1672 (1955).

50. W. M. Fairbank, W. B. Ard, H. G. Dehmelt, W. Gordy, and S. R. Williams, *Phys. Rev.*, **92,** 208 (1953).

51. W. M. Fairbank, W. B. Ard, and G. K. Walters, **95,** 566 (1954).

52. W. Pauli, Jr., *Z. Physik.*, **41,** 81 (1927).

53. A. L. Thomson, H. Meyer, and E. D. Adams, *Phys. Rev.*, **128,** 509 (1962).

54. A. C. Anderson, W. Reese, and J. C. Wheatley, *Phys. Rev.*, **127,** 671 (1962).

55. I. J. Pomeranchuk, *Zhur. Eksp. i Teoret. Fiz.*, **19,** 42 (1949).

56. R. De Bruyn Ouboter, K. W. Taconis, C. Le Pair, and J. J. M. Beenakker, *Physica*, **26,** 853 (1960).

57. A. C. Anderson, W. R. Roach, R. E. Sarwinski, and J. C. Wheatley, *Phys. Rev. Letters*, **16,** 263 (1966).

PROBLEMS

15.1. Calculate the average energy of the compressional waves, using the phonon picture and treating the excitations as a Bose-Einstein gas with energies determined by Eq. (4.15) but without a fixed number of particles; thus verify the statement following Eq. (4.16). Why is the specific heat of the phonon gas proportional to T^3, while that of the ideal gas is proportional to $T^{3/2}$?

15.2. Show that if we assume a condition on the momentum, namely $\sum_j p_0 \cos \theta_j = n\bar{p}_z = \text{const.}$, instead of Eq. (7.4), $\bar{\epsilon}_{k,r}$ does not depend on $\bar{p}_z$.

15.3. Verify the statement in Sec. 15-10 that the kinetic energy of fluctuations of ^{3}He in ^{4}He is about kT/n_0.

Chapter 16

Quantum Statistics

16-1. *Imperfect Gases: The Quantum Case*

Handling quantum effects in an imperfect gas offers an opportunity to illustrate some methods and procedures often called "quantum statistics," although this name might more logically be applied whenever quantum states are dealt with. Before we go on to this more specialized subject, we shall give a more elementary treatment of the second virial coefficient. We have shown [Eq. (1.21) of Chap. 8] that the second virial coefficient for spherically symmetrical molecules is given by

$$B = \frac{2}{3}\pi\sigma^3 - \left(\frac{h^2}{\pi m k T}\right)^{3/2} \frac{(\text{p.f.})_{0,A_2}}{(\text{p.f.})_{0,A}^2}, \tag{1.1}$$

where $(\text{p.f.})_{0,A}$ is the internal partition function for a single molecule, and $(\text{p.f.})_{0,A_2}$ is that for a pair of molecules within an arbitrary distance σ of each other. Since we are not interested in the internal structure of the molecules, we may as well consider them to be monatomic; then $(\text{p.f.})_{0,A}$ is equal simply to g, where g is the spin degeneracy. If the system is quantized, we may write

$$(\text{p.f.})_{0,A_2} = \sum_{j,t} (2j + 1)g_j \exp\left\{\frac{-\epsilon_{j,t}}{kT}\right\}, \tag{1.2}$$

where j is the rotational quantum number for the pair constrained to be within the distance σ (there are, as always, $2j + 1$ states with given j), t is the quantum number for the radial part of the wave function describing the relative motion of this pair of particles, $\epsilon_{j,t}$ is the energy of the relative motion in the state determined by the quantum numbers j and t, and g_j is the spin weight factor for a given rotational state of the pair (assuming the molecules or atoms to be in a singlet state, this is a nuclear spin). The value of g_j depends upon whether the atoms obey Bose-Einstein or Fermi-Dirac statistics, or, more precisely, on the nuclear spin of the atoms and on whether j is odd or even. For example, a pair of atoms of ^{4}He, which has no spin and which obeys Bose-Einstein statistics, is exactly analogous to an ^{16}O$_2$ molecule, so that $g_j = 1$ if j is even, and $g_j = 0$ if j is odd (as discussed in Sec. 2-3). On the other hand, a pair of ^{3}He atoms is analogous to H$_2$ (see Sec. 2-4), so that $g_j = 1$ if j is even, and $g_j = 3$ if j is odd. In general, the average value of g_j at high temperatures is equal to $g^2/2$.

Before going further we need to recollect the origin of the term $\frac{2}{3}\pi\sigma^3$. This got into the equation as an excluded volume for "uncombined" atoms A, and as such it will not be changed. Although the term $\frac{2}{3}\pi\sigma^3$ came into Eq. (1.1) as a sort of arbitrary excluded volume, it also appeared as a factor in the expression for $(p.f.)_{A_2}$ in the classical case when there were no forces between the atoms, as is seen from Eq. (1.8) of Chap. 8. Although this expression was obtained classically, it will still be the same in the quantum case, provided that σ is not too small. Thus we expect the last term in Eq. (1.1) to cancel the first term in the field-free case of point atoms, even though the system is quantized except for contributions of the type seen in Eqs. (4.11) and (5.7) of Chap. 14. Forces between the atoms will cause further changes in the second term of Eq. (1.1), some of which will be affected by quantization.

If there are attractive forces between the atoms, there will be bound states in which they are stuck together, and these states will, because of the rotational potential $j(j + 1)h^2/8\pi^2\mu r^2$ [see Eq. (5.11) of Chap. 1], have a different set of energies for each value of j. The sum in Eq. (1.2) can be broken up into two parts, a sum over these bound states, and a sum over the other states, whose wave functions extend to the arbitrary boundary σ. If σ is assumed to be fairly large, the energy levels of the latter states will be almost continuous. At large values of r and small values of j, the wave function will have the asymptotic form $(r^{-1}) \sin (2\pi r/\lambda + \pi\zeta_j)$ where λ is the wavelength and ζ_j is a phase factor, determined by the exact form of the potential-energy curve in the region of small r, and depending both on λ and on j. The factor $1/r$ ensures that the density for any range dr of r is proportional to dr, since the volume element between r and $r + dr$ is proportional to r^2. At the boundary $r = \sigma$, the wave function must vanish, since this is like the boundary of a box, though an artificially determined one. Thus we have

$$\frac{2\pi\sigma}{\lambda} + \pi\zeta_j = \pi t, \tag{1.3}$$

where t is the quantum number, from which

$$\lambda = \frac{2\sigma}{t - \zeta_j}. \tag{1.4}$$

Here λ is equal to h/p, with p the relative momentum of the particles at large distances where the mutual potential energy of the pair is zero. Thus the relative energy

$$\epsilon_{j,t} = \frac{p_{j,t}^2}{2\mu} = \frac{h^2}{2\mu\lambda^2} = \frac{h^2(t - \zeta_j)^2}{8\mu\sigma^2}, \tag{1.5}$$

where $\mu = m/2$ is the reduced mass, and we can write

$$(\text{p.f.})_{0,A_2} = \sum_{\substack{j,t' \\ j \le j_0}} (2j + 1)g_j \exp\left\{\frac{-\epsilon_{j,t'}}{kT}\right\}$$

$$+ \sum_{j,t} (2j + 1)g_j \exp\left\{\frac{-h^2(t - \zeta_j)^2}{8\mu\sigma^2 kT}\right\}. \tag{1.6}$$

Here t' goes over the bound states and j_0 is taken large enough so that there are no bound states for $j > j_0$. Energies in the two sums may overlap if $j > 0$.

   The second summation in Eq. (1.6) can be changed in part to an integration. Before doing this, however, we must note that if the angular-momentum quantum number is j, the lowest possible relative energy which a pair of particles can have and be classically within a distance σ of each other is the value of the rotational potential at σ,

$$\epsilon_j = \frac{j(j + 1)h^2}{8\pi^2\mu\sigma^2}. \tag{1.7}$$

This assumes σ to be beyond the range of any interaction between the molecules, where the true potential energy ϵ_p vanishes. Then the second summation in Eq. (1.6) becomes

$$\sum_{j,t} = \sum_j (2j + 1)g_j \int_{\epsilon_j}^{\infty} \exp\left\{\frac{-\epsilon_t}{kT}\right\} \frac{dt}{d\epsilon_t} d\epsilon_t, \tag{1.8}$$

where we use the energy ϵ_t (for a particular j) given by Eq. (1.5) as the independent variable, and where $dt/d\epsilon_t$ is the number of states per unit energy range. If we solve Eq. (1.5) for t, we have

$$t = \zeta_j + \frac{(8\mu\epsilon_t)^{1/2}\sigma}{h}$$

and

$$\frac{dt}{d\epsilon_t} = \frac{d\zeta_j}{d\epsilon_t} + \frac{\frac{1}{2}(8\mu/\epsilon_t)^{1/2}\sigma}{h}. \tag{1.9}$$

Equation (1.8) can thus be written

$$\sum_j (2j+1)g_j \int_{\epsilon_j}^{\infty} \exp\left\{\frac{-\epsilon_t}{kT}\right\} \frac{d\zeta_j}{d\epsilon_t}\, d\epsilon_t$$

$$+ \sum_j (2j+1)g_j \int_{\epsilon_j}^{\infty} \exp\left\{\frac{-\epsilon_t}{kT}\right\} \left(\frac{2\mu}{\epsilon_t}\right)^{1/2} \frac{\sigma}{h}\, d\epsilon_t. \tag{1.10}$$

If the molecules are point particles with no forces between them, the first term in Eq. (1.6) vanishes and (1.10) is equal to $(\text{p.f.})_{0,A_2}$. If this value and $(\text{p.f.})_{0,A} = g$ are substituted into Eq. (1.1), the last term will have to cancel $\frac{2}{3}\pi\sigma^3$, except for the quantum term which appears in Eqs. (4.11) and (5.7) of Chap. 14.

If the molecules do interact with each other, ζ_j will have a different value, but with σ large enough to be well beyond the range of the interactions ϵ_j is unchanged. Thus the effect of the interactions will appear only in the first term of Eq. (1.6) and the first term of (1.10). We now define ζ'_j as the difference between the actual phase factor and that which would exist if the molecules exerted no force on each other. The difference between the first integral in Eq. (1.10) and its value for point particles will be

$$\sum_j (2j+1)g_j \int_0^{\infty} \exp\left\{\frac{-\epsilon_t}{kT}\right\} \frac{d\zeta'_j}{d\epsilon_t}\, d\epsilon_t, \tag{1.10a}$$

the lower limit being replaced by 0. This is justified because we see that if j is small ϵ_j may be made as small as desired by making σ large; on the other hand, if j is large, the closest distance of approach will be large in the important lower range of energies, so that the effects of any interaction between the molecules will be negligible and ζ'_j will vanish. The only part of (1.10) that will contribute to B is (1.10a).

If we take account of the first term in Eq. (1.6) and the contributions discussed in Chap. 14, then

$$-B = \pm\frac{0.1768}{g\eta} + \frac{2^{3/2}}{g^2\eta}\left[\sum_{j,t'} (2j+1)g_j \exp\left\{\frac{-\epsilon_{j,t'}}{kT}\right\}\right.$$

$$\left. + \sum_j (2j+1)g_j \int_0^\infty \exp\left\{\frac{-\epsilon_t}{kT}\right\} \frac{d\zeta_j'}{d\epsilon_t} d\epsilon_t\right], \quad (1.11)$$

where the plus sign refers to Bose-Einstein and the minus sign to Fermi-Dirac statistics, and $\eta = (2\pi mkT/h^2)^{3/2}$.

Roughly speaking, the sum over t' in Eq. (1.11) corresponds to the negative contribution to B in the classical case [see Eq. (2.3) of Chap. 8], which comes from the negative part of the potential-energy curve, whereas the integral corresponds largely to the positive contribution, from the positive, repulsive region of the potential-energy curve. The effect of quantization is to suppress the negative contribution to B, since the zero-point energy prevents the lowering of the actual energy of the pair to the minimum of the potential-energy curve.† Indeed, since the attractive forces are of the weak van der Waals type, there may, with light atoms or molecules, actually be no states in which the two atoms are bound together. This is the case with ^{3}He, but in ^{4}He there may be a single bound state. The potential-energy curves are, of course, essentially identical in these two cases, but the mass of ^{4}He is larger, so the zero-point energy is less. But even with ^{4}He, the existence of a bound state is somewhat doubtful, and it certainly will not exist for $j > 0$, because of the effect of the rotational potential.

The character of the integral may be understood by considering the case where the atoms are hard spheres. The ζ_j' is always negative; the phase factor is less than it would be if no forces existed, because the wave function can only start to have nonzero values when r already is appreciable. If we have hard spheres of radius σ_0, we may say, for $j = 0$, that a phase angle equal to $2\pi\sigma_0/\lambda$ is lost, which means that

$$\zeta_0' \approx -\frac{2\sigma_0}{\lambda} = -\frac{2\sigma_0 p_t}{h} = -\frac{2\sigma_0(2\mu\epsilon_t)^{1/2}}{h} \quad (1.12)$$

(where p_t is the momentum and ϵ_t the energy) and

---

† This is reflected in the observed fact that the value of B in light molecules like He does not fall off as rapidly to negative values at low temperatures as is predicted by the classical formula.

$$\frac{d\zeta_0'}{d\epsilon_t} = -\frac{\sigma_0(2\mu/\epsilon_t)^{1/2}}{h} = -\frac{\sigma_0(m/\epsilon_t)^{1/2}}{h}. \tag{1.13}$$

From this we obtain (neglecting the g factor) for the contribution from $j = 0$ to Eq. (1.11)

$$\frac{2^{3/2}}{\eta} \int_0^\infty \exp\left\{\frac{-\epsilon_t}{kT}\right\} \frac{d\zeta_0'}{d\epsilon_t} d\epsilon_t = -\frac{\sigma_0 h^2}{\pi m k T}. \tag{1.14}$$

See [**1**, No. 481].

For a large enough value of j, (since, as we have noted, the rotational potential $j(j + 1)h^2/8\pi^2\mu r^2$ will exert a sufficient apparent repulsion so that the hard spheres will simply pass by each other without feeling each other's true repulsion) the wave function will be essentially the same as for two noninteracting particles. For this case we may write $d\zeta_j'/d\epsilon = 0$. In general, with increasing j and decreasing ϵ_t, the effect of the hard-sphere core on $d\zeta_j/d\epsilon_t$ will decrease. The approximate cutoff for any given j will occur when the energy ϵ_t is equal to $j(j + 1)h^2/8\pi^2\mu\sigma_0^2$, and the integrand in (1.14) will not be large unless this energy is equal to or greater than kT. To get a rough approximation, let us assume that the integral is given by Eq. (1.14) if $j(j + 1) \leq 8\pi^2\sigma_0^2\mu kT/h^2 = 4\pi^2\sigma_0^2 mkT/h^2$. Since $\sum_{j=0}^{j} (2j + 1) \approx j(j + 1)$, we see then by Eq. (1.14) that

$$\sum_j (2j + 1)g_j \frac{2^{3/2}}{g^2\eta} \int_0^\infty \exp\left\{\frac{-\epsilon_t}{kT}\right\} \frac{d\zeta_j'}{d\epsilon_t} d\epsilon_t$$

$$\approx -\frac{1}{2} \frac{4\pi^2\sigma_0^2 mkT}{h^2} \sigma_0 \frac{h^2}{\pi m k T} = -2\pi\sigma_0^3 \tag{1.15}$$

(the factor $\frac{1}{2}$ coming from the average value of g_j/g^2). This is of course an exceedingly rough estimate, but it does bring out the relation of the last term in Eq. (1.11) to the exclusion-sphere term in the classical calculation of the second virial coefficient.

Much more careful and detailed calculations have been made with the Lennard-Jones potential and other potential-energy curves, but we will not pursue the matter further here. An account, including comparison with experimental data, has been given by Hirschfelder, Curtiss, and Bird [2]. Reasonable agreement has been obtained in the region where quantum effects are important, but the results are fairly sensitive to the potential-energy curve.

16-2. *The Slater Sum and the Ideal Quantum Gas*

In the consideration of systems in which quantum mechanical effects are of importance,† certain transformations of the canonical partition function are often useful. We start with the usual form

$$\text{(P.F.)} = \sum_L \exp\left\{\frac{-E_L}{kT}\right\}. \tag{2.1}$$

We multiply each term of this equation by $\Psi_L^* \Psi_L$, where Ψ_L is the eigenfunction of the whole assembly corresponding to the energy E_L and where Ψ_L^* is the conjugate complex, and integrate over the entire configuration space. Since the integral of $\Psi_L^* \Psi_L$ is equal to 1, assuming Ψ_L to be normalized, this does not actually change the value of the term in the sum. Thus we may write [5]

$$\text{(P.F.)} = \sum_L \int \Psi_L^* \exp\left\{\frac{-E_L}{kT}\right\} \Psi_L \, d\tau, \tag{2.2}$$

where $d\tau \equiv d\tau_1 d\tau_2 \cdots d\tau_N$, and includes the spin coordinates as well as the space coordinates. The integration goes over all possible values of the coordinates.‡ This form of the partition function is known as the Slater sum.

We may rewrite Eq. (2.2) as

$$\text{(P.F.)} = \int \sum_L \Psi_L^* \exp\left\{\frac{-E_L}{kT}\right\} \Psi_L \, d\tau. \tag{2.3}$$

Let us now define an operator $\exp\{-H/kT\}$ [where H is the Hamiltonian operator—see Eq. (2.20), below] by the equation

$$\exp\left\{\frac{-H}{kT}\right\} = 1 - \frac{H}{kT} + \frac{1}{2!}\left(\frac{H}{kT}\right)^2 - \frac{1}{3!}\left(\frac{H}{kT}\right)^3 + \cdots. \tag{2.4}$$

It can be seen that the result of this operation on Ψ_L (since $H\Psi_L = E_L\Psi_L$ and $H^2\Psi_L = HE_L\Psi_L = E_L^2\Psi_L$, etc.) gives

---

† The remaining portions of this chapter assume a knowledge of quantum mechanics such as might be obtained from standard works on this subject on an intermediate level, e.g., [3]. For another account of the material in this chapter, see [4].
‡ In order to simplify the notation we shall use a single integral sign to denote multiple integrals in this chapter.

$$\exp\left\{\frac{-H}{kT}\right\}\Psi_L = \exp\left\{\frac{-E_L}{kT}\right\}\Psi_L. \tag{2.5}$$

Therefore we have

$$(\text{P.F.}) = \int \sum_L \Psi_L^* \exp\left\{\frac{-H}{kT}\right\}\Psi_L \, d\tau. \tag{2.6}$$

It is sometimes convenient to choose some other set of orthogonal functions, say Φ_K, as basis functions. It is possible to show that, regardless of what set is chosen,

$$(\text{P.F.}) = \int \sum_K \Phi_K^* \exp\left\{\frac{-H}{kT}\right\}\Phi_K \, d\tau. \tag{2.7}$$

To prove that this equation is correct, we note that we can expand the Φ_K in terms of the Ψ_L; thus

$$\Phi_K = \sum_L a_{KL}\Psi_L, \tag{2.8}$$

where the a_{KL} are constant coefficients. Multiplying both sides of Eq. (2.8) by some particular Ψ_L^*, integrating, and noting that the Ψ_L's form an orthonormal set, we have

$$a_{KL} = \int \Psi_L^* \Phi_K \, d\tau. \tag{2.9}$$

Similarly (the Φ_K, of course, being normalized)

$$\Psi_L = \sum_K b_{LK}\Phi_K, \tag{2.10}$$

where

$$b_{LK} = \int \Phi_K^* \Psi_L \, d\tau. \tag{2.11}$$

We note that

$$b_{LK}^* = a_{KL}. \tag{2.12}$$

Also we note that

$$\int \Psi_L^* \Psi_L \, d\tau = 1 = \int \sum_K b_{LK}^* \Phi_K^* \sum_M b_{LM}\Phi_M \, d\tau = \int \sum_K b_{LK}^* \Phi_K^* b_{LK}\Phi_K \, d\tau$$

(since $\int \Phi_K^* \Phi_M d\tau = \delta_{KM}$, where δ_{KM} is 0 if $K \neq M$ and 1 if $K = M$)

$$= \sum_K b_{LK}^* b_{LK} = \sum_K a_{KL} a_{KL}^*. \tag{2.13}$$

Introducing Eq. (2.8) into Eq. (2.7), we have

$$\text{(P.F.)} = \int \sum_K \sum_L a_{KL}^* \Psi_L^* \exp\left\{\frac{-H}{kT}\right\} \sum_J a_{KJ} \Psi_J \, d\tau$$

$$= \sum_K \sum_L \sum_J \int a_{KL}^* \Psi_L^* \exp\left\{\frac{-E_J}{kT}\right\} a_{KJ} \Psi_J \, d\tau$$

$$= \sum_K \sum_L \int a_{KL}^* \Psi_L^* \exp\left\{\frac{-E_L}{kT}\right\} a_{KL} \Psi_L \, d\tau$$

(since $\int \Psi_L^* \Psi_J \, d\tau = \delta_{LJ}$)

$$= \sum_L \int \Psi_L^* \exp\left\{\frac{-E_L}{kT}\right\} \Psi_L \, d\tau \tag{2.14}$$

by Eq. (2.13). We thus see that Eq. (2.7) has been reduced to Eq. (2.2), which verifies the correctness of Eq. (2.7).

Suppose now that we have a system of particles in a cubic box with sides of length a. We can use for the Φ_K's the eigenfunctions of a set of N noninteracting particles. An eigenfunction of the first particle will be

$$\phi(1) = \left(\frac{2}{a}\right)^{3/2} \sin\frac{2\pi x_1}{\lambda_{x_1}} \sin\frac{2\pi y_1}{\lambda_{y_1}} \sin\frac{2\pi z_1}{\lambda_{z_1}} \omega_1, \tag{2.15}$$

where λ_{x_1}, λ_{y_1}, and λ_{z_1} are wavelengths in the x, y, and z directions and and ω_1 is the spin function; $(2/a)^{3/2}$ is a normalizing factor. The wave function must vanish at the limits $x_1 = 0$, $x_1 = a$, $y_1 = 0$, $y_1 = a$, $z_1 = 0$, $z_1 = a$, so that $\lambda_{x_1} = 2a/i_{x_1}$, $\lambda_{y_1} = 2a/i_{y_1}$, and $\lambda_{z_1} = 2a/i_{z_1}$, where i_{x_1}, i_{y_1} and i_{z_1} are integers. The eigenfunction for a system of N particles will be† $\prod_\alpha \phi(\alpha)$, where the product is to be taken over all the molecules, α. However, this expression assumes that a particular molecule has a particular quantum number. But, as we know, we must give equal weights to all possible exchanges of molecules. Thus if we start with a certain assignment of molecules to quantum states we must also include

---

† To avoid the proliferation of unwieldy subscripts, we write $\phi(\alpha)$ for $\phi_{i_\alpha}(\alpha)$.

$$P \prod_\alpha \phi(\alpha) = \left(\frac{2}{a}\right)^{3N/2} P \prod_\alpha \sin\frac{\pi i_{x_\alpha} x_\alpha}{a} \sin\frac{\pi i_{y_\alpha} y_\alpha}{a} \sin\frac{\pi i_{z_\alpha} z_\alpha}{a} \, \omega_{i_\alpha}(\alpha)$$

$$= \left(\frac{2}{a}\right)^{3N/2} \prod_\alpha \sin\frac{\pi i_{x_\alpha} x_{\alpha P}}{a} \sin\frac{\pi i_{y_\alpha} y_{\alpha P}}{a} \sin\frac{\pi i_{z_\alpha} z_{\alpha P}}{a} \, \omega_{i_\alpha}(\alpha P),$$

where P stands for a permutation in which the molecule αP takes the place of the molecule α in the quantum state i_{x_α}, i_{y_α}, i_{z_α}, and in the associated spin function ω_{i_α}. The double index αP simply stands for this molecule, which replaces α under the permutation P.

Let there be N_P permutations. Normally we will have $N_P = N!$, but if there is more than one molecule in the ith quantum level (where i is a collective quantum number standing for i_x, i_y, i_z and the spin quantum number) we will have

$$N_P = \frac{N!}{\prod_i n_i!}, \tag{2.16}$$

where n_i is the number in the ith state, for any permutations which involve only those molecules in one state will not affect the state of the system as a whole.

We will let P number the various possible permutations serially, and will see that all permutations are so numbered that, if P is odd, an odd number of molecules have been interchanged with respect to the original arrangement, and if P is even, an even number of exchanges have occurred. The total wave function then is

$$\Phi_K = \frac{1}{N_P^{1/2}} \sum_P (\pm 1)^P \, P \prod_\alpha \phi(\alpha), \tag{2.17}$$

where the summation is over all permutations. The plus sign goes with the Bose-Einstein statistics; the minus sign goes with the Fermi-Dirac statistics, and assures that the wave function is antisymmetrical with respect to exchange of any pair of particles. The factor $1/N_P^{1/2}$ is a normalizing factor; it becomes $1/N_P$ when squared and it divides the expression by the number of separate terms in $\Phi_K^* \Phi_K$. It will be noted that since all the distinct sine functions are mutually orthogonal and all the distinct ω_α are also orthogonal, $\prod_\alpha \phi(\alpha)$ and $P \prod_\alpha \phi(\alpha)$ are mutually orthogonal. So only the N_P terms $P \prod_\alpha \phi(\alpha) \cdot P \prod_\alpha \phi(\alpha)$ [in contradistinction to terms like $P' \prod_\alpha \phi(\alpha) \cdot P \prod_\alpha \phi(\alpha)$ where $P' \neq P$] will contribute to $\int \Phi_K^* \Phi_K \, d\tau$. It must be remembered that the products and their permutations depend on K; to avoid cumbersome notation this is not shown, and likewise the spin parts are not shown explicitly, since they can be treated separately as long as we are dealing with functions of the type shown in Eq. (2.15).

Substituting Eq. (2.17) into Eq. (2.7) we obtain

$$
\text{(P.F.)} =
$$

$$
\int \sum_K \frac{1}{N_P} \left[\sum_P (\pm 1)^P \, P \prod_\alpha \phi(\alpha) \right] \exp \left\{ \frac{-H}{kT} \right\} \left[\sum_{P'} (\pm 1)^{P'} \, P' \prod_\alpha \phi(\alpha) \right] d\tau.
$$

$$(2.18)$$

Now $\int \left[\sum_P (\pm 1)^P P \prod_\alpha \phi(\alpha) \right] \exp \left\{ -H/kT \right\} \prod_\alpha \phi(\alpha) \, d\tau$ with any given value of K will not depend upon which of the N_P permutations we started with in the right-hand factor. We may, therefore, write

$$
\text{(P.F.)} = \int \sum_K \left[\sum_P (\pm 1)^P P \prod_\alpha \phi(\alpha) \right] \exp \left\{ \frac{-H}{kT} \right\} \prod_\alpha \phi(\alpha) \, d\tau.
$$

$$(2.19)$$

In this case, we have

$$
H = -\frac{h^2}{8\pi^2 m} \sum_\alpha \nabla_\alpha^2 + E_p \tag{2.20}
$$

where the sum of the Laplacian operators ∇_α^2 goes over all the molecules as usual, and where the potential energy E_p is a function of the positions of all the molecules. Referring to Eq. (2.15), we see that, with the values of the λ's given,

$$
\nabla_\alpha^2 \phi(\alpha) = -\frac{\pi^2}{a^2} (i_{x_\alpha}^2 + i_{y_\alpha}^2 + i_{z_\alpha}^2) \phi(\alpha). \tag{2.21}
$$

However, repeated application of the Hamiltonian operator H, as implied in $\exp \{ -H/kT \}$, introduces difficulties with this set of basis functions, because ∇_α^2 operates on E_p, which is a function of the coordinates. For the rest of this section we consider the case of noninteracting particles for which $E_p = 0$, and will show that the present formalism leads to the results obtained in Chap. 14 by more elementary methods.

With the use of Eq. (2.21), Eq. (2.19) becomes

$$
\text{(P.F.)} =
$$

$$
\int \sum_K \left[\sum_P (\pm 1)^P P \prod_\alpha \phi(\alpha) \right] \exp \left\{ -\frac{h^2}{8ma^2kT} (i_{x_\alpha}^2 + i_{y_\alpha}^2 + i_{z_\alpha}^2) \right\} \prod_\alpha \phi(\alpha) \, d\tau.
$$

$$(2.22)$$

The coordinates appear in the integrand only in the $\phi(\alpha)$, and $P \prod_\alpha \phi(\alpha)$ is orthogonal to $P' \prod_\alpha \phi(\alpha)(P' \neq P)$, hence to $\prod_\alpha \phi(\alpha)$ itself unless P signifies the "unit" permutation which leaves all molecules unchanged. So, by integrating with respect to all x_α, y_α, and z_α, Eq. (2.22) reduces to

$$(\text{P.F.}) = \sum_K \prod_\alpha \exp\left\{-\frac{h^2}{8ma^2kT}(i_{x_\alpha}^2 + i_{y_\alpha}^2 + i_{z_\alpha}^2)\right\}$$

$$= \sum_K \exp\left\{-\frac{h^2}{8ma^2kT}\sum_\alpha (i_{x_\alpha}^2 + i_{y_\alpha}^2 + i_{z_\alpha}^2)\right\}. \qquad (2.23)$$

This is scarcely surprising, since the exponent is equal to $\sum_\alpha \epsilon_\alpha/kT = E_K/kT$, so that the argument has proved to be circular, and we have come back to where we started.

The advantage of Eq. (2.22) lies in the possibility, since a can be made as large as desired, of converting $\sum_K$ (which really indicates summation over all possible values of i_{x_α}, i_{y_α}, and i_{z_α} for all α and also over all spin states) into an integration, which can be carried out before the integration over the coordinates.

One can, indeed, carry out this conversion and integration in Eq. (2.23). The integration over all the quantum states for each α can be carried out separately but then [compare Eqs. (1.5) and (1.6) of Chap. 3] one obtains simply the classical result, which can be written $(\text{P.F.}) = (\text{p.f.})^N$, but which must be converted to $(\text{p.f.})^N/N!$ to allow for interchange of molecules. This, too, is not surprising, for we are accustomed to the idea that conversion of a sum to an integral results in a classical expression. It may appear strange, however, that the possibility of converting to an integral seems assured *merely* by allowing a to become large. This is always legitimate, and to have a system of fixed density in a range where quantum effects may be important we need only to allow N to increase proportionately with a^3; yet N, itself, has nothing to do with the integration under consideration.

Actually the anomaly already resides in Eq. (2.22). It comes about because a value of K which puts more than one molecule in a given quantum state (i.e., makes some of the n_i different from 0 or 1) can give rise to only $N!/\prod_i n_i!$ distinct permutations, which appear as distinct terms in the sum over K; yet, like all other terms (sums over K) in the final summation over P, this is divided by $N!$. This division clearly underrates its importance in the Bose-Einstein statistics. Such a term should not appear at all in Fermi-Dirac statistics, but, as we shall see, is automatically cancelled by action of the minus signs.

The discrepancies arising from this difficulty can be easily compensated for if the integration over the i_{x_α}, i_{y_α}, and i_{z_α} is performed first in Eq. (2.22), where the sum over the permutations still appears explicitly. It is necessary only to count *all* the permutations, including those in which two molecules in the *same* quantum state are exchanged. There are then always $N!$ permutations, and for any given case where some of the n_i are more than unity, the excess of this value over N_P as given by Eq. (2.16) just compensates for the error introduced by dividing by $N!$ instead of by $N!/\prod_i n_i!$ in the case of Bose-Einstein statistics. On the other hand, the minus signs assure the disappearance of these terms in Fermi-Dirac statistics. For if any one of the n_i is greater than one there will be an equal number of even and odd permutations giving rise to identical terms. The identical terms come from permutations involving only the n_i molecules in a given quantum state. Let us take the whole set of even permutations among these n_i. For each even permutation we can generate an odd permutation among them by exchanging the last two molecules. Each one of these odd permutations will clearly be different from all the others. Furthermore, all the odd permutations will be generated. For suppose we could find an extra one; then we could produce a new even permutation by exchanging the last two molecules. But we have already included all the even permutations.

Let us consider the integration with respect to a single i_{x_α} in Eq. (2.22), in a single permutation P. We will again let $\eta = (2\pi mkT/h^2)^{3/2}$ and note that the permutation changes x_α to $x_{\alpha P}$. We designate this integral as $\eta^{1/3}\gamma_{x_\alpha}^{1/3}$ and find

$$\eta^{1/3}\gamma_{x_\alpha}^{1/3} = \frac{2}{a}\int_0^\infty \sin\frac{\pi i_{x_\alpha}x_{\alpha P}}{a}\exp\left\{-\frac{h^2 i_{x_\alpha}^2}{8ma^2kT}\right\}\sin\frac{\pi i_{x_\alpha}x_\alpha}{a}\,di_{x_\alpha}$$

$$= 2\int_0^\infty \sin(\pi l x_{\alpha P})\sin(\pi l x_\alpha)\exp\left\{-\frac{h^2 l^2}{8mkT}\right\}dl \qquad (2.24)$$

where l has been substituted for i_{x_α}/a. On substituting the trigonometric identity

$$2\sin(\pi l x_{\alpha P})\sin(\pi l x_\alpha) = \cos[\pi l(x_{\alpha P} - x_\alpha)] - \cos[\pi l(x_{\alpha P} + x_\alpha)],$$

a known form is obtained:

$$\eta^{1/3}\gamma_{x_\alpha}^{1/3} = \int_0^\infty \cos[\pi l(x_{\alpha P} - x_\alpha)]\exp\left\{-\frac{h^2 l^2}{8mkT}\right\}dl \qquad (2.25)$$

plus another integral involving $\cos [\pi l(x_{\alpha P} + x_\alpha]$. The expression (2.25) is equal to [**1**, No. 508].

$$\eta^{1/3}\gamma_{x_\alpha}^{1/3} = \eta^{1/3} \exp \left\{ -\frac{2\pi^2(x_{\alpha P} - x_\alpha)^2 mkT}{h^2} \right\}. \tag{2.26}$$

For helium at 1°K, the parameter $h^2/2\pi^2 mkT$ is equal to about 2×10^{-15} cm². Therefore, it appears that in any box of ordinary size the other term, involving $x_{\alpha P} + x_\alpha$ in place of $x_{\alpha P} - x_\alpha$, will be almost everywhere negligible. The value of (2.26) will be appreciable only when $x_{\alpha P} - x_\alpha$ is quite small. Every term like (2.26) which appears in the integration of Eq. (2.22) will be accompanied by (multiplied by) similar expressions in which $x_{\alpha P} - x_\alpha$ is replaced by $y_{\alpha P} - y_\alpha$ and $z_{\alpha P} - z_\alpha$. The product of these terms will be

$$g\eta\gamma_\alpha = g\eta \exp \left\{ -\frac{2\pi^2 r_{\alpha P, \alpha}^2 mkT}{h^2} \right\}$$

where $\gamma_\alpha = (\gamma_{x_\alpha}\gamma_{y_\alpha}\gamma_{z_\alpha})^{1/3}$ and where $r_{\alpha P, \alpha}$ is the distance between the molecule α and the molecule αP. We have also multiplied this term by the spin multiplicity g to allow for summation over the various spin states.

Any permutation can be expressed as a combination of cyclic permutations. Thus if we start with a molecule α which is replaced by β, the original β being replaced by γ, etc., we will eventually come to a molecule which is replaced by α, completing the cycle. If this cycle does not contain all the molecules in the assembly, another cycle can be started. Eventually all the molecules will be included. A cycle containing s molecules will contribute to one of the permutations in the expression for the partition function an integral $\eta^s G_s$ with

$$G_s = g \int \gamma_1\gamma_2 \cdots \gamma_s \, dx_1 dy_1 \cdots dz_s$$

$$= g \int \exp \left\{ \frac{-2\pi^2(r_{1,2}^2 + r_{2,3}^2 + \cdots + r_{s,1}^2)mkT}{h^2} \right\} dx_1 dy_1 \cdots dz_s, \tag{2.27}$$

if it starts with molecule 1 and ends at molecule s. Only one factor g will remain after integration over the spin coordinates, since the integral will vanish unless all the spins are alike, because spin functions are orthogonal. The value of the integral depends only on the number s, of molecules involved, and not on which ones they are, since the variables all have the same limits. If in any given permutation there are m_s cycles of length s we will have

$$\sum_s m_s s = N, \tag{2.28}$$

since all the molecules must be included in the totality of cycles. The contribution of any given permutation to the integral in Eq. (2.22) is $\eta^N \prod_s G_s^{m_s}$. The number of ways in which a given set of values of m_s can occur is found in the following manner. We suppose that we have m_1 boxes to contain 1 molecule, m_2 to contain 2, and so on, laid out in the order given. The total number of ways the N molecules can be placed in order in these ordered boxes is $N!$. The permutation will, however, be identical if any of the m_s boxes containing s molecules are interchanged. The permutation does depend upon the order of the molecules within a box, except that it does not depend on which molecule starts the sequence [thus the set of exchanges indicated by 1, 2, 3, 4 (that is $1 \longrightarrow 2, 2 \longrightarrow 3, 3 \longrightarrow 4, 4 \longrightarrow 1$) is the same as 2, 3, 4, 1]. The last two considerations indicate that the number of ways of placing the molecules in order should be divided by $\prod_s m_s!$ and by $\prod_s s^{m_s}$. Thus the partition function becomes

$$(\text{P.F.}) = \frac{1}{N!} \eta^N N! \sum_{(m_s)} \prod_s (\pm 1)^{(s-1)m_s} \frac{G_s^{m_s}}{m_s! s^{m_s}}. \tag{2.29}$$

The sum $\sum(m_s)$ is over all sets of m_s conforming to Eq. (2.28). After this final summation, all the permutations are included. The factor $1/N!$ has the usual origin [see the discussion of Eq. (2.23)]: when we integrate over all values of the quantum number i_α for all α we automatically interchange all molecules; thus the permutations are actually carried out twice. Since the problem connected with the permutations is discussed in detail in the paragraphs between Eqs. (2.23) and (2.24) we need not consider it further. Since each cyclic permutation with s molecules involves an odd number of exchanges if s is even (e.g., one exchange if $s = 2$), and an even number of exchanges if s is odd, and since the total number of exchanges is the sum of those in the cyclic permutations, the factor $\prod_s (-1)^{(s-1)m_s}$ will give the proper sign for any given permutation in the Fermi-Dirac statistics. The $N!$ factors, of course, cancel, so finally

$$(\text{P.F.}) = \eta^N \sum_{(m_s)} \prod_s (\pm 1)^{(s-1)m_s} \frac{G_s^{m_s}}{m_s! s^{m_s}}. \tag{2.30}$$

It is shown in an appendix to this chapter (Sec. 16-5) that

$$G_s = \frac{gV}{\eta^{s-1}s^{3/2}}.$$
(2.31)

If we take account of Eq. (2.28) and make the possible cancellations, Eq. (2.30) reduces to

$$(\text{P.F.}) = \sum_{(m_s)} \prod_s \frac{[(\pm 1)^{s-1}g\eta V/s^{5/2}]^{m_s}}{m_s!}.$$
(2.32)

We may now reduce this equation, either by finding the maximum
term in the sum under the constraint imposed by Eq. (2.28), or else,
preferably (especially when the negative sign is used), by setting up
the grand partition function

$$(\text{G.P.F.}) = \sum_N (\text{P.F.})_N \lambda_0^N$$

where λ_0 is the activity if the state of zero kinetic energy (or minimum
kinetic energy) is taken as the zero of energy, as in Chap. 14. We may
write the exponent on λ_0 as $\sum_s m_s s$, but the restrictions on m_s disappear,
since all values of N are included. With this understanding

$$(\text{G.P.F.}) = \sum_{(m_s)} \prod_s \frac{[(\pm 1)^{s-1}g\eta V\lambda_0^s/s^{5/2}]^{m_s}}{m_s!}.$$
(2.33)

It is now possible, in the usual manner, to interchange the order of
multiplication and summation; then the sum changes into a straight
sum over all possible values of m_s:

$$(\text{G.P.F.}) = \prod_s \sum_{m_s} \frac{[(\pm 1)^{s-1}g\eta V\lambda_0^s/s^{5/2}]^{m_s}}{m_s!}$$

$$= \prod_s \exp\left\{(\pm 1)^{s-1}\frac{g\eta V\lambda_0^s}{s^{5/2}}\right\}$$
(2.34)

whence

$$P = \frac{kT}{V}\ln(\text{G.P.F.})$$

$$= \eta g kT \sum_s \frac{(\pm 1)^{s-1}\lambda_0^s}{s^{5/2}}.$$
(2.35)

Setting $g = 1$ and taking the plus sign, this coincides with Eq. (4.8) of Chap. 14. Using the minus signs, we get the alternations of signs in Eq. (5.7) as compared with Eq. (4.11) of Chap. 14. It is observed that in the Bose-Einstein case this procedure gives results valid only for $T > T_0$. We run into the same difficulty here with respect to the lowest state that we did in Chap. 14, when we change the sum over quantum states to an integration.

16-3. *The General Imperfect Gas: The Quantum Case*

The formalism developed in the preceding section is certainly unnecessarily involved for the ideal gas. Its advantage lies in the possibility of generalization [6].

Let us return to the cluster expansion for a classical gas, as developed in Sec. 11-2. The integrands of cluster integrals, Eqs. (2.1), (2.2), and (2.3) of Chap. 11, may be given special designations:

$$F_1^{(1)} = 1 \tag{3.1}$$

$$F_{12}^{(2)} = f_{12} \tag{3.2}$$

$$F_{123}^{(3)} = f_{13}f_{12} + f_{23}f_{13} + f_{23}f_{12} + f_{23}f_{13}f_{12}. \tag{3.3}$$

In general we will write $F_{(\alpha)}^{(r)}$, the superscript (r) indicating the number of molecules involved, the subscript (α) being a collective designation for the complete set of subscripts which enumerate the molecules involved. In Chap. 11 we generalized these subscripts by using Latin letters; here, as in the preceding section, we shall use Greek letters to avoid confusion with the letters designating quantum states. With this designation we may write the general configuration integral, Eq. (1.7) of Chap. 11, in the form

$$Q_\tau = \int \cdots \int \sum_{(r,\alpha)} \prod_{(\alpha)} F_{(\alpha)}^{(r)} \, d\tau_1 d\tau_2 \cdots d\tau_N, \tag{3.4}$$

where the product is taken over enough factors to make the subscripts α just cover all the molecules, and where the summation is taken over all possible combinations of (r) and (α), except that the indices in (α) are to be taken in a fixed order.

An integral like $\int \cdots \int F_{123}^{(3)} \, d\tau_1 d\tau_2 d\tau_3$ is characterized by the fact that integration over one volume element gives a factor V, but that the other integrations do not depend on V. Integrals of this general type are factors in the summands of Eq. (3.4) (if the sum is carried out after the integration).

In the quantum case we can also order the factors in the terms according to the number of integrations involved, but by a somewhat different procedure. Let us return to Eq. (2.19). The functions $\prod_\alpha \phi(\alpha)$ are eigenfunctions of the operator $-(h^2/8\pi^2 m) \sum_\alpha \nabla_\alpha^2$, but not of the complete operator H. Thus we have

$$\mathrm{H}\phi(\alpha) = \frac{h^2}{8ma^2} (i_{x_\alpha}^2 + i_{y_\alpha}^2 + i_{z_\alpha}^2)\phi(\alpha) + E_\mathrm{p}\phi(\alpha),$$

and

$$\mathrm{H}\prod_\alpha \phi(\alpha) = \frac{h^2}{8ma^2} \left[\sum_\alpha (i_{x_\alpha}^2 + i_{y_\alpha}^2 + i_{z_\alpha}^2) \right] \prod_\alpha \phi(\alpha) + E_\mathrm{p} \prod_\alpha \phi(\alpha).$$

$$(3.5)$$

In a subsequent operation by H, such as is called for in applying the operator $\exp\{-\mathrm{H}/kT\}$, the operator H operates upon E_p as well as on $\prod_\alpha \phi(\alpha)$, since $\sum_\alpha \nabla_\alpha^2$ involves differentiations of the variables upon which E_p depends. Now we may write

$$E_\mathrm{p} = \sum_{\text{all pairs}} \epsilon_{\alpha\beta}, \qquad (3.6)$$

or, more generally, as in Eq. (2.13) of Chap. 11,

$$E_\mathrm{p} = \sum_{\text{all pairs}} \epsilon_{\alpha\beta} + \sum_{\text{all triples}} \epsilon_{\alpha\beta\gamma} + \cdots. \qquad (3.7)$$

The term $\epsilon_{\alpha\beta}$ depends on the distance between the pair α and β, whereas $\epsilon_{\alpha\beta\gamma}$ depends on the configuration of the triple α, β, and γ, and so on, all of them being essentially zero except when all the molecules involved are close together. In $\mathrm{H}\prod_\alpha \phi(\alpha)$ the factors in the terms can be sorted out into those in which one molecule is involved, those in which two molecules are involved,† those in which three are involved, and so on. This fact will not be changed after repeated operations of H occur. These various types of terms may be multiplied

---

† For example, the term $\epsilon_{12}\Pi_\alpha\phi(\alpha)$ is one of the terms occurring in $E_\mathrm{p}\Pi_\alpha\phi(\alpha)$. This contains a factor, namely $\epsilon_{12}\phi(1)\phi(2)$, which necessarily involves the molecules 1 and 2 and factors $\phi(3)$, $\phi(4)$, etc., that involve only one molecule. On the other hand, the kinetic-energy terms in Eq. (3.5) can be separated into factors involving only one molecule.

together in the various summands which arise owing to the expansion of exp $\{-H/kT\}$. They will still be there after summation over the quantum numbers $(\sum_K)$, and in the subsequent integration these terms will be sorted out in the same way as the cluster integrals in the classical case. If we consider the term $\prod_\alpha \phi(\alpha)$ exp $\{-H/kT\} \prod_\alpha \phi(\alpha)$ in which the molecules are *not* permuted, we will have every conceivable combination, i.e., each molecule in a separate or single cluster, any one pair in a cluster with all others in single clusters, two pair clusters with all other single clusters, triplet and single clusters, etc. If, however, we consider a permutation $\prod_\alpha \phi(\alpha P)$ exp $\{-H/kT\} \prod_\alpha \phi(\alpha)$ in which one particular pair has been permuted but no others, the molecules in this particular pair cannot occur as singles, but they will always be connected with each other in the integration, as we shall shortly see in a specific example. In this case, then, the integral does not contribute at all to any terms in which this pair does not occur in a cluster of two or more together. The extension to other cases is fairly obvious. Since the clusters occur in the same combinations as in the classical case, the results can be similarly expressed in terms of cluster integrals. The difficulty, of course, lies in evaluating the integrals.

Let us now consider all the terms in the final integrand (for integration over the coordinates) arising from a cluster of two particular molecules 1 and 2. These terms will be generated by the operation

$$\exp\left\{-\left[-\frac{h^2}{8\pi^2 mkT}\,(\nabla_1^2 + \nabla_2^2) + \frac{\epsilon_{12}}{kT}\right]\right\} \tag{3.8}$$

upon $\phi_i(1)\phi_l(2)$, where i and l denote the quantum states and 1 and 2 the molecules. They will occur multiplied by all other combinations. However, this operator also produces the terms

$$\exp\left\{\frac{h^2}{8\pi^2 mkT}\,(\nabla_1^2 + \nabla_2^2)\right\}\phi_i(1)\phi_l(2),$$

or

$$\exp\left\{\frac{h^2}{8\pi^2 mkT}\,\nabla_1^2\right\}\phi_i(1)\,\exp\left\{\frac{h^2}{8\pi^2 mkT}\,\nabla_2^2\right\}\phi_l(2),$$

which, when combined with the unpermuted product $\phi_i(1)\phi_l(2)$, gives a product of single terms. The operator which will generate *only* the pair-cluster terms for the *non-permuted* case is

$$\exp\left\{-\left[-\frac{h^2}{8\pi^2 mkT}(\nabla_1^2 + \nabla_2^2) + \frac{\epsilon_{12}}{kT}\right]\right\} - \exp\left\{\frac{h^2}{8\pi^2 mkT}(\nabla_1^2 + \nabla_2^2)\right\}$$

$$= \exp\left\{\frac{-H_{12}}{kT}\right\} - \exp\left\{\frac{h^2}{8\pi^2 mkT}(\nabla_1^2 + \nabla_2^2)\right\}. \tag{3.9}$$

Thus the pair-cluster integral will, by analogy to Eq. (2.2) of Chap. 11, be defined by

$$2!Vg^2\eta^2 b_2 = \int \sum_{i,l} [\phi_i(1)\phi_l(2) \pm \phi_i(2)\phi_l(1)] \exp\left\{\frac{-H_{12}}{kT}\right\}\phi_i(1)\phi_l(2)\,d\tau_1\,d\tau_2$$

$$- \int \sum_{i,l} \phi_i(1)\phi_l(2) \exp\left\{\frac{h^2}{8\pi^2 mkT}(\nabla_1^2 + \nabla_2^2)\right\}\phi_i(1)\phi_l(2)\,d\tau_1\,d\tau_2. \tag{3.10}$$

In Eq. (3.10) we have placed the summation sign inside the integral sign to bring out the analogy with the classical cluster integrals. As already noted, the last term needs to be subtracted only when no permutation is involved, because the permuted term is actually a pair-cluster integral; the ∇^2-part of it is what we have defined as $\eta^2 G_2 = g\eta^2 \int \gamma_1\gamma_2 dx_1 dy_1 \cdots dz_2$ [see Eqs. (2.24) and (2.27), and note the expression for ϕ_1 in Eq. (2.15)]. It will be noted from Eq. (2.27) that the integrand is appreciable only when the two particles are close together. The factor g^2 is included in the defining equation because the integration over the nuclear spin coordinates has to be made and the summation over these states is implied. The factor η^2 is included because the integral being evaluated is a part of the partition function rather than simply the configuration integral.

In much the same way, to get b_3 we must subtract from the results of performing the operation

$$\exp\left\{-\left[-\frac{h^2}{8\pi^2 mkT}(\nabla_1^2 + \nabla_2^2 + \nabla_3^2) + \frac{\epsilon_{12} + \epsilon_{13} + \epsilon_{23} + \epsilon_{123}}{kT}\right]\right\}$$

$$= \exp\left\{\frac{-H_{123}}{kT}\right\},$$

the terms which are products of pairs and a single, and the product of three singles. Thus (see appendix, Sec. 16-6)†

---

† As in Sec. 16-2, the symbol $1P$ stands for the molecule which has taken the place of molecule 1 after the permutation.

$3!Vg^3\eta^3 b_3 =$

$$\int \sum_{i,l,k} \sum_P (\pm 1)^P \phi_i(1P)\phi_l(2P)\phi_k(3P) \exp\left\{\frac{-H_{123}}{kT}\right\} \phi_i(1)\phi_l(2)\phi_k(3) \, d\tau_1 d\tau_2 d\tau_3$$

$$- 3\left[\int \sum_{i,l} \sum_P (\pm 1)^P \phi_i(1P)\phi_l(2P) \exp\left\{\frac{-H_{12}}{kT}\right\} \phi_i(1)\phi_l(2) \, d\tau_1 d\tau_2 \right.$$

$$\left. - \int \sum_{i,l} \phi_i(1)\phi_l(2) \exp\left\{\frac{h^2}{8\pi^2 mkT}(\nabla_1^2 + \nabla_2^2)\right\} \phi_i(1)\phi_l(2) \, d\tau_1 d\tau_2 \right]$$

$$\times \int \sum_k \phi_k(3) \exp\left\{\frac{h^2}{8\pi^2 mkT}\nabla_3^2\right\} \phi_k(3) \, d\tau_3$$

$$- \int \sum_{i,l,k} \phi_i(1)\phi_l(2)\phi_k(3)$$

$$\times \exp\left\{\frac{h^2}{8\pi^2 mkT}(\nabla_1^2 + \nabla_2^2 + \nabla_3^2)\right\} \phi_i(1)\phi_l(2)\phi_k(3) \, d\tau_1 d\tau_2 d\tau_3.$$

The sum $\sum_P$ in the first two integrals is over all permutations of the molecules involved, 1, 2, and 3 in the one case, and 1 and 2 in the other. The factor 3 in the middle term arises because of the three ways of selecting a pair out of three molecules, all of which give the same result. We can collect terms and write

$3!Vg^3\eta^3 b_3 =$

$$\int \sum_{i,l,k} \sum_P (\pm 1)^P \phi_i(1P)\phi_l(2P)\phi_k(3P) \exp\left\{\frac{-H_{123}}{kT}\right\} \phi_i(1)\phi_l(2)\phi_k(3) \, d\tau_1 d\tau_2 d\tau_3$$

$$- 3\int \sum_{i,l} \sum_P (\pm 1)^P \phi_i(1P)\phi_l(2P) \exp\left\{\frac{-H_{12}}{kT}\right\} \phi_i(1)\phi_l(2) \, d\tau_1 d\tau_2$$

$$\times \int \sum_k \phi_k(3) \exp\left\{\frac{h^2}{8\pi^2 mkT}\nabla_3^2\right\} \phi_k(3) \, d\tau_3$$

$$+ 2\int \sum_{i,l,k} \phi_i(1)\phi_l(2)\phi_k(3)$$

$$\times \exp\left\{\frac{h^2}{8\pi^2 mkT}(\nabla_1^2 + \nabla_2^2 + \nabla_3^2)\right\} \phi_i(1)\phi_l(2)\phi_k(3) \, d\tau_1 d\tau_2 d\tau_3.$$

$$(3.11)$$

Since the cluster integrals are involved in the expression for (P.F.) in the same way as in the classical case, the whole classical formalism can be carried through, yielding Eqs. (2.5), (2.7), (2.8), and (2.9) of Chap. 11, except that $g\eta$ is substituted for η. Thus the only difference in the quantum case is in the evaluation of the cluster integrals.

It may be readily seen that if E_p is equal to zero, Eq. (3.10) yields the result previously obtained. If $E_p = 0$, the first term in the first integral cancels the second integral, and now the second term in the *first* integral is what we have defined as $\eta^2 G_2 = g\eta^2 \int \gamma_1\gamma_2 dx_1 dy_1 \cdots dz_2$ [see Eqs. (2.24), (2.27), and (2.15)]. It is seen, by comparing with the left-hand side of Eq. (3.10) that $b_2 = \pm G_2/2g^2V$. Taking over Eq. (2.5) of Chap. 11, substituting $g\eta$ for η (the factor g was not included in Chap. 11, but would come in there in just this way, since it is a factor for the total available levels for every molecule), we write out the first two summands in Eq. (2.5) of Chap. 11 (noting that in the first $m_1 = N$ and all other m's vanish, and in the second summand $m_1 = N - 2$, $m_2 = 1$ and all other m's vanish), and obtain

$$(\text{P.F.}) = \frac{(g\eta V)^N}{N!}\left(1 + \frac{N(N-1)}{V} b_2 + \cdots\right). \tag{3.12}$$

Noting, from Eq. (2.31), that $G_1 = gV$, and using the relation $b_2 = \pm G_2/2g^2V$ obtained from Eq. (3.10) it may be readily verified that Eqs. (2.30) and (3.12) coincide at least as far as the second virial terms are concerned.

If E_p does not vanish, it will be advantageous to use a different set of orthogonal functions in the first integral in Eq. (3.10) by applying the theorem connected with Eq. (2.7). This theorem will apply to the special case of two particles, which occurs in Eq. (3.10), and to wave functions in which permutations are included to effect the proper symmetrization. Because of the permuted term, it will not suffice simply to substitute a different set of functions of the space coordinates for $\phi_i(1)\phi_l(2)$ in Eq. (3.10), where integration over the spin coordinates and summation over the spin states has already been carried out. Rather, we must, in setting up the new functions, include the spin parts and carry out the corresponding integrations and summations explicitly.† A spin coordinate can be included in the $d\tau$'s.

The coordinate part of the new wave functions will be a function of the six coordinates of the two particles involved. We will use the eigenfunctions Φ_n of H_{12}, and will make use of the coordinates X, Y, Z of the center of gravity of the pair of particles and the relative (polar) coordinates r, θ, ϕ. Assuming that ϵ_{12} is a function of r only, we can then write the wave function in the form $\Phi =$

---

† A similar procedure involving three particles can be carried out for b_3, and it can be extended to the higher b's.

$W(X, Y, Z)\Theta(\theta)\Phi(\phi)R(r)$ where W is the translational part of the wave function, $\Theta(\theta)\Phi(\phi)$ is a spherical harmonic, and $R(r)$ is a function depending on ϵ_{12}. Let us assume that r can extend only between 0 and r_∞. This restriction will not prevent the set of Φ from being a complete orthogonal set, and if r_∞ is large enough, it will not enter the final results. Introduction of r_∞ changes the continuous range of energy levels into a close-spaced discrete set. Interchange of the two molecules involved is equivalent to $\theta \longrightarrow \pi - \theta$ and $\phi \longrightarrow \phi + \pi$. Such interchange changes the sign of $\Theta(\theta)\Phi(\phi)$ if the rotational quantum number j is odd, and leaves the wave function unchanged if j is even. With the function Φ_n there must be associated a spin function ω_k. If ω_k is antisymmetrical and $j = 0, 2, 4, \cdots$, then, in the Bose-Einstein case [plus sign in Eq. (3.10)], the effect of the permutation will be to cancel out the contribution of this particular wave function in Eq. (3.10). If ω_k is symmetrical, the permuted term adds, and a factor 2 and a spin-multiplicity factor g_j equal to the number of symmetrical spin functions, come in (if the permuted term cancels the other, $g_j = 0$). These statements may readily be altered to fit the case $j = 1, 3, 5, \cdots$, or the Fermi-Dirac case.

Since the wave function Φ_n is an eigenfunction of H_{12}, we have

$$\exp\left\{\frac{-H_{12}}{kT}\right\}\Phi_n = \exp\left\{\frac{-\epsilon_n}{kT}\right\}\Phi_n,$$

and with the proper allowance for the spin functions this may be substituted into the first integral in Eq. (3.10). At the same time we note that

$$\exp\left\{\frac{h^2}{8\pi^2 mkT}(\nabla_1^2 + \nabla_2^2)\right\}\phi_i(1)\phi_l(2) = \exp\left\{\frac{-(\epsilon_i' + \epsilon_l')}{kT}\right\}\phi_i(1)\phi_l(2),$$

where the ϵ_i' or ϵ_l' are eigenvalues of the operator $-(h^2/8\pi^2 m)\nabla^2$, since the ϕ_i are the eigenfunctions of this operator. Of course, ϵ_i' and ϵ_l' are known in terms of the quantum numbers; thus, in a cubic box of edge a we have $\epsilon_i' = i^2 h^2/8ma^2$, where $i^2 = i_x^2 + i_y^2 + i_z^2$. Equation (3.10) becomes, after integrating with respect to $d\tau_1$ and $d\tau_2$ (which aside from the exponential now produces only factors of 1) and summing over the quantum levels

$$2!Vg^2\eta^2 b_2 = \left(\frac{4\pi mkT}{h^2}\right)^{3/2}V\sum_{j,t}2(2j+1)g_j\exp\left\{\frac{-\epsilon_{j,t}}{kT}\right\} - g^2\left\{\frac{2\pi mkT}{h^2}\right\}^3 V^2.$$

$$(3.13)$$

The first term on the right-hand side comes from the first term on the right-hand side of Eq. (3.10). We have to sum over all values of the collective quantum number n. Summing over all states for the motion of the center of gravity of the pair with total mass $2m$ gives the factor $(4\pi mkT/h^2)^{3/2}V$. We must sum over all rotational states j, there being $2j + 1$ with quantum number j, and all states t of the relative translational motion. The factor 2 under the summation arises because we have to add the permuted wave function to the original one, and, as we have noted, if the permuted sum cancels, $g_j = 0$. The last term in Eq. (3.13), arising from the last term in Eq. (3.10), is the usual partition function for a pair of free particles.

At high enough temperatures, the sum can be converted to an integration, and if we can neglect the effect of the mutual potential energy on $\epsilon_{j,t}$, then the summation becomes simply the usual partition function† for the relative motion of a pair of particles, constrained to move within a distance r_∞ of each other. This is the same function as that for a particle of mass $\mu = m/2$ moving inside a sphere of radius r_∞. Thus the summation is equal to $(\pi mkT/h^2)^{3/2}(\frac{4}{3}\pi r_\infty^3)$ times the average value of $2g_j$, which is equal to g^2 [thus, for ³He, the average value of $2g_j$ is $2(1 + 3)/2 = 4 = g^2$, where g is the value, 2, for a single atom]. Clearly b_2 must vanish under these circumstances, which means that we must choose r_∞ so that $\frac{4}{3}\pi r_\infty^3 = V$.

The second virial coefficient, as in Chap. 11, is equal to $-b_2$. If Eq. (3.13) is solved for b_2, a factor of V remains in the last term. However, this dependence on V is cancelled by the first term, and b_2 will be independent of V if V is large enough. This amounts to the same thing as saying that B, as given by Eq. (1.1) is independent of σ if σ is large enough, since the partition function $(\text{p.f.})_{0,A_2}$ is calculated for a pair constrained to move within a distance σ of each other, and Eqs. (1.1) and (3.13) coincide precisely after substitution of Eq. (1.2) and $(\text{p.f.})_{0,A} = g$ into (1.1), provided that V is set equal to $\frac{4}{3}\pi\sigma^3$, the first term on the right-hand side of Eq. (1.1) corresponding to the last term of Eq. (3.13).

The analysis of the present section brings out the source of the first term on the right-hand side of Eq. (1.11). We have seen that it comes from the second term of the first integral in Eq. (3.10). Therefore, it must be hidden in the summation of Eq. (3.13) and would appear if this summation could be evaluated precisely. It must, then, already be contained in Eqs. (1.1) and (1.2). It should not surprise us

---

† Without the symmetry number, which never enters a cluster integral, since exchange effects are taken care of by the division by $N!$, as in Eq. (3.12).

that the study of the integrals involving a single pair of molecules suffices to give an exact expression for the second virial coefficient.

16-4. *The Density Matrix*

A matrix whose K, L component is

$$\rho_{KL} = \int \Phi_K^* \exp\left\{\frac{-H}{kT}\right\} \Phi_L \, d\tau, \tag{4.1}$$

where the Φ's are an orthogonal set of functions of the coordinates, and the asterisk indicates the complex conjugate, is called the density matrix† ρ. A diagonal element is ρ_{KK}, and it is seen that the trace of this matrix, $\sum_K \rho_{KK}$, is just the Slater sum. This is of some interest, because it means that the methods of matrix algebra can be used to transform the Slater sum. We will not go into this in detail, but will indicate a few of the properties of this matrix which provide the basis for these transformations, for the benefit of readers who are already familiar with matrix algebra.

The density matrix is a Hermitian matrix, which means that $\rho_{LK}^* = \rho_{KL}$. If such a matrix is transformed by matrix multiplication to another matrix, $S\rho S^{-1}$, where S is an arbitrary matrix and S^{-1} is the inverse matrix ($S^{-1}S$ is equal to the unit matrix 1, which has diagonal elements equal to 1 and all other elements zero), the trace remains unchanged. This is equivalent to a change of basis functions in the Slater sum. In much the same way that it was shown in Eq. (2.13) that

$$\sum_K a_{KL}a_{KL}^* = 1 \tag{4.2}$$

it may be shown, from $\int \Psi_M^* \Psi_L \, d\tau = 0$ with $M \neq L$ that

$$\sum_K a_{KM}a_{KL}^* = 0 \tag{4.3}$$

if $M \neq L$. According to the laws of matrix multiplication, the results of Eqs. (4.2) and (4.3) give the LL and ML components of the product

---

† Actually this is *proportional* to the density matrix as usually defined. The density matrix is particularly useful because changes of its elements with time can readily be calculated in quantum mechanics [4, 7].

of $\mathbf{a}^*$ and a matrix $\mathbf{a}'$ whose components $a'_{MK} = a_{KM}$. It is thus clear that $\mathbf{a}' = \mathbf{a}^{*-1}$. It is also seen that in the transformation from a set of basis functions Φ to Ψ, the density matrix component

$$\rho_{KL} = \int \Phi_K^* \exp\left\{\frac{-H}{kT}\right\} \Phi_L \, d\tau$$

$$= \int \sum_M a_{KM}^* \Psi_M^* \exp\left\{\frac{-H}{kT}\right\} \sum_N a_{LN} \Psi_N \, d\tau$$

$$= \sum_{M,N} a_{KM}^* \rho'_{MN} a'_{NL} = \sum_{M,N} a_{KM}^* \rho'_{MN} a_{NL}^{*-1} \tag{4.4}$$

where

$$\rho'_{ML} = \int \Psi_M^* \exp\left\{\frac{-H}{kT}\right\} \Psi_L \, d\tau.$$

Thus, transforming this into matrix notation, we obtain

$$\rho = \mathbf{a}^* \rho' \mathbf{a}^{*-1}$$

so that the independence of the Slater sum with respect to its basis functions is equivalent to invariance of the trace of the density matrix under the standard type of transformation.

16-5. *Appendix: Evaluation of G_s*

We may write G_s as [see Eq. (2.27)]

$$G_s = g \int \exp\left\{-\pi\eta^{2/3}(r_{1,2}^2 + r_{2,3}^2 + \cdots + r_{s,1}^2)\right\} dx_1 dy_1 \cdots dz_s. \tag{5.1}$$

If we make the substitution $\pi^{1/2}\eta^{1/3}x_1 \longrightarrow x_1'$, $\pi^{1/2}\eta^{1/3}y_1 \longrightarrow y_1'$, etc., Eq. (5.1) may be written in terms of the new variables of integration:

$$G_s = \frac{g}{\pi^{3s/2}\eta^s} \int \exp\left\{-(r_{1,2}'^2 + r_{2,3}'^2 + \cdots + r_{s,1}'^2)\right\} dx_1' dy_1' \cdots dz_s'. \tag{5.2}$$

The limits (of all the variables but one) may be taken as infinite, since the integrand becomes small for large values of the variables, and we will drop the primes hereafter on the new variables. It will be seen that we can separate the integrations with respect to the x, y, and z variables, which will be all equal, writing

$$G_s = \frac{g}{\pi^{3s/2}\eta^s}\left[\int\exp\left\{-(x_{12}^2 + x_{23}^2 + \cdots + x_{s1}^2)\right\}\,dx_1 dx_2 \cdots dx_s\right]^3,$$

(5.3)

where $x_{12} = x_2 - x_1$, etc.

Now there is a relation between x_{12}, x_{23}, $\cdots$, for

$$x_{12} + x_{23} + \cdots + x_{s1}$$
$$= (x_2 - x_1) + (x_3 - x_2) + \cdots + (x_1 - x_s) = 0.$$

(5.4)

Therefore we can write

$$x_{s1}^2 = (x_{12} + a_1)^2,$$

(5.5)

where we have made use of the first of a series of definitions

$$a_1 = x_{23} + x_{34} + x_{45} + \cdots + x_{s-1,s},$$
$$a_2 = x_{34} + x_{45} + \cdots + x_{s-1,s},$$
$$\cdot \quad \cdot \quad \cdot \quad \cdot \quad \cdot \quad \cdot \quad \cdot \quad \cdot \quad \cdot \quad \cdot$$
$$a_{s-1} = 0,$$

(5.6)

and

$$G_s = \frac{g}{\pi^{3s/2}\eta^s}\left[\int\exp\left\{-x_{12}^2 - (x_{12} + a_1)^2\right\}\exp\left\{-(x_{23}^2 + x_{34}^2 + x_{s-1,s}^2)\right\}\right.$$
$$\left. dx_1 dx_2 \cdots dx_s\right]^3.$$

(5.7)

We now change variables, $x_1, x_2, \cdots, x_s \longrightarrow x_{12}, x_2, \cdots, x_s$. The Jacobian of this transformation (absolute value) is 1. Since a_1 does not depend on x_{12}, we may integrate with respect to x_{12} first (Sec. 2-6):

$$\int_{-\infty}^{\infty}\exp\left\{-x_{12}^2 - (x_{12} + a_1)^2\right\}\,dx_{12}$$

$$= \int_{-\infty}^{\infty}\exp\left\{-2\left(x_{12} + \frac{a_1}{2}\right)^2 - \frac{a_1^2}{2}\right\}\,dx_{12}$$

$$= \left(\frac{\pi}{2}\right)^{1/2}\exp\left\{-\frac{a_1^2}{2}\right\}.$$

(5.8)

We introduce this into the expression for G_s, make another change of variables, $x_2, x_3, \cdots, x_s \longrightarrow x_{23}, x_3, \cdots, x_s$ and perform the integration with respect to x_{23}:

$$\int_{-\infty}^{\infty} \exp\left\{-x_{23}^2 - \frac{a_1^2}{2}\right\} dx_{23} = \int_{-\infty}^{\infty} \exp\left\{-x_{23}^2 - \frac{1}{2}(x_{23} + a_2)^2\right\} dx_{23}$$

$$= \int_{-\infty}^{\infty} \exp\left\{-\frac{3}{2}\left(x_{23} + \frac{a_2}{3}\right)^2 - \frac{a_2^2}{3}\right\} dx_{23}$$

$$= \left(\frac{2\pi}{3}\right)^{1/2} \exp\left\{-\frac{a_2^2}{3}\right\}. \tag{5.9}$$

In general we note that

$$\int_{-\infty}^{\infty} \exp\left\{-x^2 - \frac{(x+a)^2}{n}\right\} dx$$

$$= \int_{-\infty}^{\infty} \exp\left\{-\frac{n+1}{n}\left(x + \frac{a}{n+1}\right)^2 - \frac{a^2}{n+1}\right\} dx$$

$$= \left(\frac{n\pi}{n+1}\right)^{1/2} \exp\left\{-\frac{a^2}{n+1}\right\}. \tag{5.10}$$

So the iteration of the integration procedure may continue, the next-to-last integral being (since $a_{s-1} = 0$)

$$\int_{-\infty}^{\infty} \exp\left\{-x_{s-1,s}^2 - \frac{x_{s-1,s}^2}{s-1}\right\} dx_{s-1,s} = \left[\frac{(s-1)\pi}{s}\right]^{1/2}. \tag{5.11}$$

The final integration over x_s (no change of variable here) must be confined to the limits of the box and gives a factor $\pi^{1/2}\eta^{1/3}V^{1/3}$. The factor $\pi^{1/2}\eta^{1/3}$ is necessary because of the original transformation of variables just after Eq. (5.1). We see then that

$$G_s = \frac{gV}{\eta^{s-1}s^{3/2}}. \tag{5.12}$$

16-6. *Appendix: Proof of Eq. (3.11)*

In order to prove Eq. (3.11), we need first to observe certain properties of an operator such as $\exp\{A + B\}$. If A and B are operators which commute with each other, i.e., if $AB = BA$, then it is possible to write

$$\exp\{A + B\} = \exp\{A\} \exp\{B\}. \tag{6.1}$$

If A and B do not commute, these are not equivalent because the order of the factors in the terms obtained from expanding the exponentials will not be the same.

Now let us consider the expression $\exp\{-H_{123}/kT\}$. If we write $H_i^0 = -(h^2/8\pi^2 m)\nabla_i^2$, then

$$\exp\left\{\frac{-H_{123}}{kT}\right\}$$
$$= \exp\left\{-\frac{(H_1^0 + H_2^0 + H_3^0 + \epsilon_{12} + \epsilon_{13} + \epsilon_{23} + \epsilon_{123})}{kT}\right\}. \qquad (6.2)$$

We note that every term in this operator (after expansion of the exponential) which involves 1 and 2 as a pair will occur in†

$$\exp\left\{-\frac{(H_1^0 + H_2^0 + H_3^0 + \epsilon_{12})}{kT}\right\}; \qquad (6.3)$$

every term which involves 1 and 3 will occur in

$$\exp\left\{-\frac{(H_1^0 + H_2^0 + H_3^0 + \epsilon_{13})}{kT}\right\}, \qquad (6.4)$$

and every term which involves 2 and 3 will occur in

$$\exp\left\{-\frac{(H_1^0 + H_2^0 + H_3^0 + \epsilon_{23})}{kT}\right\}. \qquad (6.5)$$

Each of these exponentials involves some terms in which 1, 2, and 3 appear as singles; in each case these terms are included in

$$\exp\left\{-\frac{(H_1^0 + H_2^0 + H_3^0)}{kT}\right\}, \qquad (6.6)$$

and this must be subtracted from each of the expressions, (6.3), (6.4) and (6.5) and the three results must be added together, to give all of the pair terms. Furthermore, since H_3^0 commutes with H_1^0, H_2^0, and ϵ_{12}, the expression (6.3) can be written

$$\exp\left\{-\frac{(H_1^0 + H_2^0 + \epsilon_{12})}{kT}\right\}\exp\left\{\frac{-H_3^0}{kT}\right\}, \qquad (6.7)$$

and a similar factorization can be made with (6.4) and (6.5). If (6.6) is subtracted from (6.7), the result is

$$\left[\exp\left\{-\frac{(H_1^0 + H_2^0 + \epsilon_{12})}{kT}\right\} - \exp\left\{-\frac{H_1^0 + H_2^0}{kT}\right\}\right]\exp\left\{\frac{-H_3^0}{kT}\right\}$$
$$= \left[\exp\left\{\frac{-H_{12}}{kT}\right\} - \exp\left\{-\frac{H_1^0 + H_2^0}{kT}\right\}\right]\exp\left\{\frac{-H_3^0}{kT}\right\}, \qquad (6.8)$$

---

† A term with a factor like $\epsilon_{12}\epsilon_{13}$ involves 1, 2, and 3 as a triplet.

which is equivalent to the operator in the middle term of the first expression for $3!Vg^3\eta^3 b_3$, which occurs in the unnumbered equation just preceding Eq. (3.11). The reason that no permuted term appears in the negative portion of this middle term is given following Eq. (3.10). In the pair-cluster integrals for molecules 1 and 2, no permuted term involving molecule 3 is introduced, for this would cause pair-cluster terms for 1 and 3 and for 2 and 3 to appear.

The need for the last term in the equation preceding Eq. (3.11) is fairly obvious, so we see that Eq. (3.11) is verified. Again no corresponding permuted terms are subtracted.

REFERENCES

1. B. O. Peirce, *A Short Table of Integrals*, 3d ed., Boston, Ginn, 1929.
2. J. O. Hirschfelder, C. F. Curtiss, and R. B. Bird, *Molecular Theory of Gases and Liquids*, New York, Wiley, 1954, Chap. 6.
3. E. Merzbacher, *Quantum Mechanics*, New York, Wiley, 1961.
4. W. Band, *Introduction to Quantum Statistics*, Princeton, N.J., Van Nostrand, 1955, Chap. 11.
5. J. C. Slater, *Phys. Rev.*, **38**, 237 (1931).
6. B. Kahn and G. E. Uhlenbeck, *Physica*, **5**, 399 (1938).
7. D. ter Haar, *The Elements of Statistical Mechanics*, New York, Rinehart, 1954, Chap. 7.

PROBLEMS

16.1. a. Discuss the low-temperature behavior of B, as given by Eq. (1.11), for the Bose-Einstein case, assuming that the contribution of the last sum in Eq. (1.11) can be replaced by the simple excluded volume term, and that there is one possible value of $\epsilon_{j,t'}$ for $j = 0$ and none for $j \geq 1$. Remember that all energies in Eq. (1.11) must be referred to the same zero of energy.

b. Give a similar discussion for the Fermi-Dirac case, and discuss also the Fermi-Dirac case if no value of $\epsilon_{j,t'}$ is possible.

16.2. Discuss qualitatively, for the case $j = 0$, the effect of the attractive part of the potential-energy curve on ζ_j and $d\zeta_j/d\epsilon_j$ and indicate how this will affect B. How may this be understood physically?

16.3. Evaluate Eq. (2.32) in the Bose-Einstein case by finding the maximum term, under the constraint imposed by Eq. (2.28), and show that, by a proper identification of the Lagrange multiplier, Eq. (2.35) follows. Show that when the density and, hence, the activity are very small, the activity is proportional to the density.

16.4. Carry out the expansion of $\exp\{-H_{12}/kT\} = \exp\{-(H^0_{12} + \epsilon_{12})/kT\}$ to the third power, and show that to these terms (3.9) is the correct operator to generate the pair-cluster terms for the non-permuted case. In carrying out the expansion remember that H^0_{12} and ϵ_{12} do not commute; i.e., $H^0_{12}\epsilon_{12} \neq \epsilon_{12}H^0_{12}$, since H^0_{12} is an operator which operates on ϵ_{12}.

16.5. Using Eq. (2.5) of Chap. 11, verify that, if $E_p = 0$, Eq. (3.11) is consistent with Eq. (2.30).

Chapter 17

Microscopic Reversibility, Approach to Equilibrium, and Irreversible Thermodynamics

17-1. *The Law of Microscopic Reversibility*

The law of microscopic reversibility states that at equilibrium a process and its reverse will occur with equal frequency.† Equilibrium is not maintained merely by a series of cyclic processes; for example, if A, B, and C represent three states of a system we do not have equilibrium preserved by a series of processes

$$A \longrightarrow B, \qquad B \longrightarrow C, \qquad C \longrightarrow A,$$

going at equal rates, which would be *sufficient* to maintain equilibrium, but instead we have

$$A \rightleftharpoons B, \qquad B \rightleftharpoons C, \qquad C \rightleftharpoons A$$

so that equilibrium between A and B is maintained without regard to C. This law finds numerous applications in chemical kinetics, usually in conjunction with other principles or surmises, since chemical kinetics in general does not deal with equilibrium.

We now examine the basis and significance of this law, beginning with the assemblies in a canonical ensemble. Let us suppose that the total number of degrees of freedom of all the molecules in the whole assembly is N. The phase space for a whole assembly then has $2N$ dimensions, N coordinates, which we will consider to be the ordinary Cartesian coordinates of the several atoms, and the corresponding N momenta. Let us first treat the system as classical. The state of

---

† For general references on microscopic reversibility, the approach to equilibrium, including Boltzmann's "*H*-Theorem," and transport properties see [1–10].

the assembly will then be described by a single point in the phase space.

Since the density of energy levels is the same in all regions of the phase space, no part will have an inherent probability greater than any other. The probability of finding a system in any particular region will depend only on the energy of that region, so that the density of phase points will depend only on the energy. Let us now consider the phase points in some region A which move in the course of time to another region B. If all the velocities of all the particles were reversed, the system would simply retrace its path. Let us designate as B' that region of the phase space which has coordinates and range of coordinates (i.e., configuration) the same as B, but in which all the velocities and hence the momenta are reversed in sign. There will be just the same number of phase points in B' as in B, and they will arrive at A', bearing the same relation to A as B' does to B, in just the time required to go from A to B. Thus as many transfers occur from the *configuration* and *absolute* velocities represented by B back to those of A at equilibrium as proceed in the forward direction.† It is in this sense that the law of microscopic reversibility holds in the classical case.

It is true that in a canonical ensemble there is some interaction between assemblies, which may cause a sudden and random shift in the motion of a phase point. However, at equilibrium any trajectory which is displaced will, on the average, be replaced by another similar one in a different assembly. If we are dealing with assemblies that do not interact, this problem would not appear to be present; however, even in this case some interaction (as with the piston in Sec. 5-2) is necessary to assure a statistical distribution.

Often we are interested, not in the configuration of the whole assembly, but rather in that of some small part of it, perhaps a single molecule. In this case we wish to find the projection of the motion of the phase point onto a space with a much smaller number of dimensions. A region, say a, in the restricted space may be the projection of a great many states A in the total phase space. Similarly the region b will be the projection of many states B. And the region a' will be the projection of regions A' with reversed velocities, while the region b' will be the projection of regions B'. From this picture it is clear that

---

† If the system is in an external magnetic field and some of the particles are charged, the points in B' will not return to A' unless the field is simultaneously reversed. However, internal magnetic fields will not affect the results because reversal of the motion of all the particles will automatically reverse the fields which arise from motions of charged particles.

the law of microscopic reversibility will also hold for any part of an assembly that can be defined as a coherent entity.

In systems in which quantization is important, we are usually interested in considering transitions from one quantum state to another. If a system has well-defined quantum levels, this implies that it is, to a first approximation, isolated. However, if there are to be transitions between quantum states, the system cannot be completely isolated. In other words, there are neglected interactions, or perturbations, which produce the transitions. With a canonical ensemble, we can think of the interactions between the assemblies as being the perturbations. If one assembly undergoes a transition from one state to another, another assembly must simultaneously undergo a transition in order for energy to be conserved. The new state of the combined assemblies, having the same energy, has the same probability as the old one. Let the mutual potential energy of the two assemblies, the perturbing potential, be represented by V; this is a function of all the coordinates of both assemblies. Let n_1 be the quantum number defining the initial state of one of the assemblies, n_2 that of the other, and let n_1' and n_2' be the final quantum numbers. Then quantum mechanics shows that the probability of a transition from the state n_1, n_2 to the state n_1', n_2' is proportional † to $|V_{n_1 n_2 n_1' n_2'}|^2$, where

$$V_{n_1 n_2 n_1' n_2'} = \int \psi_{n_1}^* \psi_{n_2}^* V \psi_{n_1'} \psi_{n_2'} \, d\tau_1 d\tau_2. \tag{1.1}$$

Here ψ_{n_1} is the wave function of the first assembly in state n_1, and so on. ($\psi_{n_1}^*$ is its conjugate complex), $d\tau_1$ is the volume element for the configuration space of the first assembly, $d\tau_2$ is that of the second, and the integration is carried out over all allowable values of the coordinates. The probability of the transition in the reverse direction has exactly the same value. Since both conditions are equally likely at equilibrium, it is clear that the direct and reverse transitions will occur with equal frequency. The transition n_1 to n_1' may be coupled with various transitions in other assemblies, but they will all occur with equal prob-

---

† This proportionality remains true as long as the perturbation is small enough. That it should be small is, of course, essential to the assumption that we can deal with the approximate states ψ_{n_1}, etc. However, some question can still arise as to whether the perturbation is small enough to apply the theory of small perturbations from which the proportionality arises. For example, if the perturbations occur as a result of interactions at collisions, the perturbation may be small only because collisions are infrequent, whereas the forces might be quite intense at the time of collision. Under such circumstances the calculation can become quite complicated (see [11]). A more general proof of the proposition that the transition probabilities in the two directions are the same is given in Appendix Sec. 17-6.

ability in either direction. Thus we can say that the transition $n_1 \longrightarrow n_1'$ occurs just as often at equilibrium as $n_1' \longrightarrow n_1$. The same conclusion will hold for the (unperturbed) states of an isolated assembly, subject to a perturbation.

Much the same argument will apply to part of an assembly. If we can say that this part is in a certain quantum state, this means that there is only weak interaction with the rest of the assembly, but this weak interaction is the perturbation, and the part of the assembly under consideration can exchange energy with other parts.

Now let ϵ_n be the energy associated with a state n and $\epsilon_{n'}$ be the energy associated with n', whether these quantum numbers refer to an assembly or part of an assembly; further, let $k_{nn'}$ be the probability that a given system in state n transfers to n', and let $k_{n'n}$ be the probability of transfer $n' \longrightarrow n$. The relative probabilities of the two states will be $\exp\{-\epsilon_n/kT\} : \exp\{-\epsilon_{n'}/kT\}$. Since the rates of transfer in the two directions must be equal at equilibrium, we have

$$k_{nn'} \exp\left\{\frac{-\epsilon_n}{kT}\right\} = k_{n'n} \exp\left\{\frac{-\epsilon_{n'}}{kT}\right\}, \tag{1.2}$$

a relation of great importance in many applications.

17-2. *The Approach to Equilibrium*

Because, in what we have called a state of equilibrium, two quantum levels having the same energy are equally populated, and because quantum mechanics shows that the perturbations on these states will cause transitions from one to the other to occur with equal probability in either direction, we see that a system once in equilibrium will have a high probability of remaining in equilibrium. When we speak of two states of equal energy, we may refer to states of a *pair* (or more) of interacting assemblies in a canonical ensemble, or we may speak of states of a pair (or more) of quasi-independent portions of a single assembly, or, indeed, of different states in a single quasi-independent part of a system. Because of the perturbations, the energies (and so the term, the "same" energy) cannot be defined exactly. However, if the perturbations are such that the energy per degree of freedom becomes uncertain to an extent which is comparable to kT, then this part of the system can scarcely be called quasi-independent. If a part of a system changes energy, it is coupled to another part in such a way that the two together do not change in energy in the particular quantum transition, and so the maintenance of equilibrium involving changes of energy is not an essentially different problem. Because we know the relative probabilities of states of different energy we were able to obtain the result given in Eq. (1.2).

Although we see the sense in which a state of equilibrium is a state in which a system will remain, we have thus far said little about how a system attains a state of equilibrium. This question cannot indeed be answered finally, although much work has been done on it, especially in recent years. We will, however, be able to give a general, if perhaps not completely rigorous, demonstration of the fact that a system tends to go toward equilibrium. With the aid of Eq. (1.2), we will be able to find an expression for the rate of approach of a system that is not too far displaced from equilibrium.

To carry out this program, it is convenient to use the formulation of the entropy given in Sec. 4-5. We write

$$S = -k \sum_n W_n \ln W_n \tag{2.1}$$

for the entropy of any quasi-independent part of an assembly. If this is the whole assembly, then this equation becomes identical to Eq. (5.2) of Chap. 4 by substituting L for the quantum number n. If this is not the whole assembly, then the entropy of the whole assembly can be obtained by adding up the entropies of the separate quasi-independent parts. If the separate parts are individual identical molecules which can exchange positions, we must subtract $k \ln N!$, where N is the number of molecules. This expression will, however, be constant, and so not of great importance for the following considerations.

In Chap. 4 the entropy was defined for a system in internal equilibrium, but it was mentioned that Eq. (2.1) could readily be extended to a quasi-independent part of a system in internal equilibrium. We now wish to deal with systems and parts of systems that are not necessarily in internal equilibrium. We shall *define* the entropy of such a system or portion of a system by Eq. (2.1). It was noted in Chap. 4 that $\sum_n W_n \ln W_n$ is the average value of the logarithm of the probability of the quantum states. The thermodynamic probability of a specified thermodynamic state is defined as the number of quantum states which conform to the constraints defining the thermodynamic state. Thus the greater the thermodynamic probability the less will be the mathematical probability of each individual quantum state's being occupied, the smaller then (the more negative) $\sum_n W_n \ln W_n$ will be, and the larger S will be. So, with the extended definition, S may be taken as determining the thermodynamic probability, even if equilibrium is not established, and it will have a maximum at equilibrium. The changes in S may be used to follow the approach to equilibrium.

Equation (2.1), as applied to the energy levels of an entire assembly, was originally obtained for a canonical ensemble. We shall assume that it applies to other types of ensemble, but the discussion in Chap. 4 should make it clear that this is not a drastic assumption.

In general we will wish to follow the changes which occur, on account of small perturbations, in isolated assemblies which have essentially fixed energy. If such a system has been divided into quasi-independent parts, we may enumerate the separate quantum numbers of all the parts in one sequence and in Eq. (2.1) sum over the entire sequence. Thus we add over all states and all parts of the system at the same time. We also may make the assumption that the behavior of any one of the parts is typical, and that averaged over a period of time, with the system in equilibrium, the probability of finding any one part in a given quantum state is the same as the probability of finding any other in the corresponding quantum state at a particular time, assuming that the parts are all similar. Equation (1.2) can be written in the form

$$k_{nn'}W_{n,e} = k_{n'n}W_{n',e}, \tag{2.2}$$

where the subscript e indicates the equilibrium value.

The maximum value of S, for the entire assembly (with the extended definition of S), occurs when the population of the different states is as uniformly distributed as possible under the constraints imposed, including constant total energy. This should be clear from the discussion of Chap. 4, but perhaps it can be made a little more definite. Consider all those states in any quasi-independent part of the assembly having some particular energy. The maximum of S occurs when these are all equally populated. States having different energies have different probabilities only because of the restriction on total energy. Finally, we can consider the energy levels of the entire system. These are restricted to a certain value within the accuracy allowed by the perturbations which bring about the transitions. The system which we thus consider is an assembly in a so-called microcanonical ensemble. Then we consider transitions among the levels E_L of the assembly, there being no exchange of energy between assemblies. Since the E_L's are all essentially equal and the $W_{L,e}$'s are equal, we see, by applying Eq. (2.2) to the entire assembly, that

$$k_{LL'} = k_{L'L}. \tag{2.3}$$

Let us now consider an ensemble of assemblies *not* in equilibrium. We then have

$$\frac{dW_L}{dt} = \sum_{L'} (k_{L'L}W_{L'} - k_{LL'}W_L). \tag{2.4}$$

If we are considering an ensemble of systems of "fixed" energy, the $k_{L'L}$'s will have the same value as for an equilibrium ensemble, inasmuch as the probability of transition depends only on the initial and final state,† but the W_L's will be different. For the rate of change of entropy we find

$$\begin{aligned}
\frac{dS}{dt} &= -\frac{d}{dt}\left(k \sum_L W_L \ln W_L\right) \\
&= -k \sum_L \frac{dW_L}{dt}(1 + \ln W_L) \\
&= -k \sum_L \frac{dW_L}{dt} \ln W_L \quad \left(\text{since } \sum_L \frac{dW_L}{dt} = 0\right) \\
&= -k \sum_{L,L'} (k_{L'L}W_{L'} - k_{LL'}W_L) \ln W_L. \tag{2.5}
\end{aligned}$$

The value of this expression will not be changed by interchanging L and L', and if one then adds one-half of the result to one-half of Eq. (2.5) one obtains

$$\frac{dS}{dt} = -\frac{k}{2} \sum_{L,L'} (k_{L'L}W_{L'} - k_{LL'}W_L)(\ln W_L - \ln W_{L'}). \tag{2.6}$$

Using Eq. (2.3), and transforming the last factor, we have

$$\frac{dS}{dt} = \frac{k}{2} \sum_{L,L'} k_{L'L}(W_{L'} - W_L) \ln\left(1 + \frac{W_{L'} - W_L}{W_L}\right). \tag{2.7}$$

It is now readily seen that every term in the sum is positive, so

$$\frac{dS}{dt} > 0. \tag{2.8}$$

This means that an ensemble of assemblies, if started out with many of the assemblies in some recognizably unusual configuration,

---

† This may be restated as an assumption that the $k_{L'L}$ do not depend on the history of the assembly.

will ultimately be found distributed among the typical states (which contribute to the thermodynamic probability of the final thermodynamic state) in random fashion. From our previous examination of fluctuations, we may expect the thermodynamic properties to be essentially the same for almost all these typical states. As for an individual assembly, we may expect it to tend to go from an atypical condition to a typical one. This will not always happen, but it is highly probable that it will occur. In this sense, the entropy of the system increases.

If we have to deal with a situation in which the wave functions designated by L and L' are not real, then in accordance with Appendix Sec. 17-6, we will have to substitute for Eq. (2.3) a relation like

$$k_{LL'} = k_{L'*L*}, \tag{2.9}$$

where the star indicates a state whose wave function is the conjugate complex of that without the star.

In this case we can give a plausibility argument which at least tends to show that the entropy will increase with time. For any ensemble, Eq. (2.6) will hold as before. We can consider another ensemble in which for every assembly in any state L there is substituted one in state $L*$. This means physically that any known direction of motion in the state L is replaced by motion in the opposite direction. We call the new ensemble the conjugate ensemble. We may infer that the conjugate ensemble will change in entropy at the same rate as the original ensemble, unless there are possible wall effects. Change of motion toward a wall into motion away from a wall might conceivably result in subsequent changes which are not comparable in the two cases. If the walls are not important, one would expect a conjugate ensemble to go over in the course of time to a new ensemble which is, at least in the limit of a very short time, conjugate to the one which would be formed by the original system.

In the conjugate system, W_L is equal to W_{L*} of the original system. Therefore, for the conjugate system Eq. (2.6) becomes, in terms of the W_L's of the original system,

$$\frac{dS^*}{dt} = -\frac{k}{2} \sum_{L,L'} (k_{L'*L*}W_{L'} - k_{L*L'*}W_L)(\ln W_L - \ln W_{L'}). \tag{2.10}$$

If this is added to Eq. (2.6) and Eq. (2.9) is used, we find

$$\frac{d(S + S^*)}{dt} = \frac{k}{2} \sum_{L,L'} (k_{LL'} + k_{L'L})(W_L - W_{L'})(\ln W_L - \ln W_{L'}), \tag{2.11}$$

where again every term is positive. Since our argument indicates that $dS^*/dt = dS/dt$, this result proves the proposition. Indeed, it would only be necessary that dS/dt and dS^*/dt have the same sign.

Since dS/dt is zero at a state of equilibrium and since it is positive under all other circumstances, it is seen that, assuming the ordinary conditions of continuity, dS/dt is a minimum when the assembly is in equilibrium. Since S cannot increase indefinitely, dS/dt cannot indefinitely remain at any fixed nonzero value. Therefore, in general, and certainly when the approach to equilibrium is nearly complete, d^2S/dt^2 should be negative, and at equilibrium it will be zero. This can be demonstrated by differentiating the third expression for dS/dt in Eq. (2.5). This gives

$$\frac{d^2S}{dt^2} = -k \sum_L \frac{d^2W_L}{dt^2} \ln W_L - k \sum_L \frac{1}{W_L} \left(\frac{dW_L}{dt}\right)^2. \tag{2.12}$$

Clearly the last term is always negative. By using Eqs. (2.4) and (2.3), the first term can be written

$$-k \sum_L \frac{d^2W_L}{dt^2} \ln W_L$$

$$= -k \sum_{L,L'} k_{LL'} \left(\frac{dW_{L'}}{dt} - \frac{dW_L}{dt}\right) \ln W_L$$

$$= -\frac{k}{2} \sum_{L,L'} k_{LL'} \left(\frac{dW_{L'}}{dt} - \frac{dW_L}{dt}\right) (\ln W_L - \ln W_{L'}). \tag{2.13}$$

If the assembly is very close to equilibrium, $\ln W_L - \ln W_{L'}$ may be written $(1/W_L)(W_L - W_{L'})$ and the factor $1/W_L$ will be essentially the same for all L. On applying Eq. (2.4) again, then, Eq. (2.13) becomes

$$-k \sum_L \frac{d^2W_L}{dt^2} \ln W_L$$

$$= -\frac{k}{2W_L} \sum_{L,L',L''} k_{L'L}(k_{L''L'}W_{L''} - k_{L'L''}W_{L'}$$

$$\qquad\qquad - k_{L''L}W_{L''} + k_{LL''}W_L)(W_L - W_{L'})$$

$$= -\frac{k}{2W_L} \sum_{L,L',L''} k_{L'L}[k_{L'L''}(W_{L''} - W_{L'})(W_L - W_{L'})$$

$$\qquad\qquad - k_{LL''}(W_{L''} - W_L)(W_L - W_{L'})], \tag{2.14}$$

using Eq. (2.3). By exchanging L and L' in the last term, we can write Eq. (2.14) as

$$-k \sum_L \frac{d^2 W_L}{dt^2} \ln W_L$$

$$= \frac{k}{W_L} \sum_{L,L',L''} k_{L'L} k_{L'L''} (W_{L''} - W_{L'})(W_L - W_{L'})$$

$$= -\frac{k}{W_L} \sum_{L'} \sum_L k_{L'L}(W_L - W_{L'}) \sum_{L''} k_{L'L''}(W_{L''} - W_{L'}). \quad (2.15)$$

Since $\sum_L k_{L'L}(W_L - W_{L'}) = \sum_{L''} k_{L'L''}(W_{L''} - W_{L'})$, every term under the summation over L' is positive, so that d^2S/dt^2 must be negative if the assembly is close to equilibrium.

The positiveness of dS/dt can be illustrated by a more detailed calculation, in which we deal directly with the expression (2.1) in its more general sense, where the quantum numbers n do not need to refer to states of the same energy. To carry out the calculation, however, we must assume that the $k_{nn'}$'s remain constant. This seems reasonable if the deviations from equilibrium, δW_n (where $W_n = W_{n,e} + \delta W_n$), are of a random nature. If they occur in some systematic way, however, the $k_{nn'}$ may not be constant. For example, if there were temperature gradients in the assembly, the system might tend to undergo a change toward local uniformity of temperature. Only later would the system go to the final state of equilibrium. Since n now represents the quantum number of the state of some part of the system, the probability $k_{nn'}$ that it will transfer to state n' may depend upon the exact nature of the deviations from equilibrium, even though these are small.

We shall, however, neglect this possibility and expand the expression (2.1) about the equilibrium values $W_{n,e}$:

$$S_e + \delta S = -k \sum_n (W_{n,e} + \delta W_n) \ln (W_{n,e} + \delta W_n). \quad (2.16)$$

Subtracting out the expression for S_e, noting that $\ln (W_{n,e} + \delta W_n) = \ln W_{n,e} + \ln (1 + \delta W_n/W_{n,e})$, and expanding the last logarithm, we obtain

$$\delta S = -k \sum_n \left\{ \delta W_n \ln W_{n,e} + (W_{n,e} + \delta W_n) \left[\frac{\delta W_n}{W_{n,e}} - \frac{1}{2} \left(\frac{\delta W_n}{W_{n,e}} \right)^2 + \cdots \right] \right\}$$

$$\approx -\frac{k}{2} \sum_n \frac{(\delta W_n)^2}{W_{n,e}}. \quad (2.17)$$

Only second-degree terms in δW_n appear in the last expression because first-degree terms vanish, since S is expanded about a maximum, and terms of higher degree have been neglected. The terms of first degree, which vanish, are

$$-k \sum_n \delta W_n (\ln W_{n,e} + 1).$$

Since $\sum_n W_n = 1$ and hence $\sum_n \delta W_n = 0$, we see that this gives

$$\sum_n \delta W_n \ln W_{n,e} = 0. \tag{2.18}$$

This equation is ultimately the result of another condition on W_n, namely,

$$\sum_n \epsilon_n W_n = E, \tag{2.19}$$

and since Eq. (2.19) and the condition $\sum_n W_n = 1$ are both linear relationships, so that only certain ratios of the δW_n are required, Eq. (2.18) will hold even if the δW_n are large.

We now note that $dS/dt = d\delta S/dt$ and $dW_n/dt = d\delta W_n/dt$. We then see, by differentiating Eq. (2.16), remembering that $W_n = W_{n,e} + \delta W_n$, that

$$\frac{dS}{dt} = -k \sum_n \frac{dW_n}{dt} (\ln W_n + 1) = -k \sum_n \frac{dW_n}{dt} \ln W_n. \tag{2.20}$$

We have, quite in analogy to Eq. (2.4), since W_n is directly proportional to the population of quantum level n

$$\frac{dW_n}{dt} = \sum_{n'} (k_{n'n} W_{n'} - k_{nn'} W_n). \tag{2.21}$$

We also note that it follows from Eq. (2.18) that

$$\sum_n \frac{dW_n}{dt} \ln W_{n,e} = 0. \tag{2.22}$$

Using Eqs. (2.21) and (2.22) in Eq. (2.20) we find

$$\begin{aligned}
\frac{dS}{dt} &= -k \sum_{n,n'} (k_{n'n} W_{n'} - k_{nn'} W_n) \ln \frac{W_n}{W_{n,e}} \\
&= -k \sum_{n,n'} k_{n'n} W_{n',e} \left(\frac{W_{n'}}{W_{n',e}} - \frac{W_n}{W_{n,e}} \right) \ln \frac{W_n}{W_{n,e}} \qquad \text{[by Eq. (2.2)]} \\
&= -\frac{1}{2} k \sum_{n,n'} k_{n'n} W_{n',e} \left(\frac{W_{n'}}{W_{n',e}} - \frac{W_n}{W_{n,e}} \right) \left(\ln \frac{W_n}{W_{n,e}} - \ln \frac{W_{n'}}{W_{n',e}} \right), \tag{2.23}
\end{aligned}$$

by exchanging n and n', adding the two versions and dividing by 2, as in Eq. (2.6), and again applying Eq. (2.2). Each term in the sum is again seen to be positive (or zero, if $W_n = W_{n,e}$) if the negative sign in front is included with the term.

It is of interest to note the difference in the derivation of Eq. (2.6) and (2.23). In the latter case we needed to make the assumption that the $k_{nn'}$ did not change, whereas in the former case we assumed that all the $W_{L,e}$'s admitted by the constraints were equal, or, what is the same thing, that $k_{LL'} = k_{L'L}$. This relation we will now discuss a little further. To clarify the ideas, consider the application to a gas, and suppose that the states L represent ideal gas states, and that the perturbations are provided by collisions. The perturbation energy will surely be small compared with the entire kinetic energy of the gas, but since there are many collisions occurring at any time it will not be small compared with kT. There is, therefore, an appreciable uncertainty in the energy of the states, L, of the gas, and we may wonder whether the probability of all states represented should really have the same $W_{L,e}$, and hence whether, in all cases, $k_{LL'} = k_{L'L}$. However, if the perturbation is a definite part of the Hamiltonian, then by the quantum mechanical reversibility, as discussed in Sec. 17-6, it should be legitimate to set $k_{LL'} = k_{L'L}$ for all the accessible states of the assembly, and we can scarcely define the situation more precisely than this, the imprecision being apparently inherent in the quantum mechanical description and the idea of the transition's being caused by a perturbation.

The trouble in the derivation of Eq. (2.23) due to the possible variation in the $k_{nn'}$ may be evaded, in a certain sense, by supposing that the system goes from a situation of greater constraint to a situation of less constraint, not by removing the constraints all at once but by relaxing them gradually, somewhat as in the case of a reversible process. In each case the system would tend to proceed to the new equilibrium situation with dS/dt positive and decreasing with time until a new change was effected. At each stage it should be possible to use the $k_{nn'}$ appropriate to the neighboring equilibrium situation, which differs essentially infinitesimally from the state actually present.

17-3. *The Steady State in Transfer Processes*

There has been a great deal of recent interest in the statistical mechanics of transfer processes. This is an application which we shall not present,

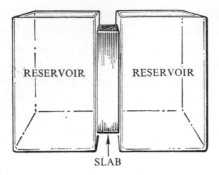

Figure 17-1. Assembly in which there are gradients maintained by reservoirs.

excepting a brief development of the ideas already set forth in this chapter. These offer the possibility of a relatively easy introduction to the discipline of irreversible thermodynamics.†

Let us consider an assembly in which there are two large reservoirs, connected by a system, called the "slab," in which gradients can occur (Fig. 17-1). The reservoirs may be at different temperatures. They may have a different concentration or concentrations of one or more substances that can diffuse through a semipermeable membrane into the system which exhibits gradients. Furthermore, into one of the reservoirs (the one at the higher temperature) heat is introduced at a steady rate while from the other heat is abstracted at the same rate, and/or into one of the reservoirs one or more species of molecules is introduced at a constant rate; these molecules are removed at the same rate from the other. We shall consider only fluid systems in which diffusion occurs readily, and which may be assumed to be isotropic.

If there is to be no accumulation of heat at the boundary between reservoir and slab there must be a heat flow at the boundary just sufficient to supply the heat removed or to take away the heat carried in. A similar remark will apply to the flow of material. The statements of the preceding paragraph thus imply that certain conditions are imposed on the gradients of temperature and chemical potentials at the boundary. However, all substances which pass through the semipermeable membrane are assumed to do so very readily, so that there is, for them, virtually no discontinuity in chemical potential across the boundary, nor is there a discontinuity in temperature.

An assembly like the one described in the preceding paragraphs can be expected to come to a steady state. Suppose that we have an ensemble of such assemblies, each with a certain "fixed" energy and

† For general references on irreversible thermodynamics, see [10, 12–15].

"fixed" amount of the various substances present. Since energy and material are being introduced and withdrawn at the same rate, the energy and composition of every assembly will remain constant.

We can now consider all the energy states L *of such a system* for which the total energy and total amounts of all substances are fixed, and we consider an ensemble composed of systems in these states. For such an ensemble, Eq. (2.6) will hold, if the sum is carried over all the states mentioned. However, since such a system is never truly in equilibrium but is only brought to a steady state determined by outside influences, we cannot apply the law of microscopic reversibility. We can be sure that, in the steady state, the sum in Eq. (2.4) is zero, but we cannot say that the individual terms are zero, just as in a steady state involving chemical reactions. Therefore Eq. (2.3) does not necessarily hold, and we cannot derive Eq. (2.7).

Let us now consider an ensemble in which all the W_L's which are not excluded (i.e., forced to be zero) by the conditions imposed are equal to each other, having a value of W_0. Then we see from Eq. (2.6) that dS/dt will be zero. Furthermore, this is a condition of maximum entropy, so the ensemble will not depart from this state. If this state is once reached it will be a steady state.

That $dS/dt = 0$ does not mean that there is no over-all production of entropy. If, for example, we have a system with a temperature gradient, we are still introducing heat at the higher temperature and taking it out at the lower. Thus there is a constant change of entropy in the *surroundings*. But for the assembly itself, including the reservoirs, the entropy remains constant.

Since the condition $W_L = W_0$ represents a steady state, then, since dW_L/dt must be equal to zero, we see by Eq. (2.4) that

$$\sum_{L'} (k_{L'L} - k_{LL'}) = 0 \tag{3.1}$$

though, as we have remarked, Eq. (2.3) does not necessarily hold.

Now let us suppose we have an ensemble in which W_L is different from the steady state value, W_0. We then write [Eq. (2.5)]

$$\frac{dS}{dt} = -k \sum_{L,L'} (k_{L'L} W_{L'} - k_{LL'} W_L) \ln W_L$$

$$= -k \sum_{L,L'} [k_{L'L}(W_{L'} - W_L) + (k_{L'L} - k_{LL'}) W_L] \ln W_L. \tag{3.2}$$

Since the sum may be taken over L' first, the last term drops out, by Eq. (3.1). Therefore

$$\frac{dS}{dt} = -k \sum_{L,L'} [k_{L'L}(W_{L'} - W_L)] \ln W_L. \tag{3.3}$$

Interchanging L and L', adding the result to Eq. (3.3), and dividing by 2 give

$$\frac{dS}{dt} = -\frac{k}{2} \sum_{L,L'} (W_{L'} - W_L)(k_{L'L} \ln W_L - k_{LL'} \ln W_{L'})$$

$$= -\frac{k}{2} \sum_{L,L'} (W_{L'} - W_L)[k_{L'L}(\ln W_L - \ln W_{L'}) + (k_{L'L} - k_{LL'}) \ln W_{L'}]$$

$$= \frac{k}{2} \sum_{L,L'} k_{L'L}(W_{L'} - W_L)(\ln W_{L'} - \ln W_L)$$

$$+ \frac{k}{2} \sum_{L,L'} (k_{L'L} - k_{LL'})W_L \ln W_{L'}. \tag{3.4}$$

The last relation follows because $\sum_{L,L'} (k_{L'L} - k_{LL'})W_{L'} \ln W_{L'}$ drops out by summing over L first.

In the last form of Eq. (3.4) every term in the first sum is positive or zero. The first sum vanishes only if all the W_L's are equal to W_0; in this case the second sum vanishes also, by Eq. (3.1). Both sums vanish to the second order of $W_L - W_0$. But the second sum is very small, even if the first is not, if the steady state under consideration is very close to an equilibrium state, for then $k_{L'L}$ approaches $k_{LL'}$. Thus, for a steady state near an equilibrium state, dS/dt is not only zero, but it is a minimum, as for the equilibrium state. Since the system at the steady state must have a definite entropy, dS/dt will have to decrease gradually to its minimum value (zero for the assembly without its environment). The approach to a steady state will go much as the approach to equilibrium.

17-4. *Irreversible Thermodynamics*

Irreversible thermodynamics comprises the phenomenological study of the approach to equilibrium and the behavior of, and conditions for, a steady state in a system close to equilibrium. The situation in the part of the assembly between two reservoirs (the slab), considered in the last section, is a typical example.

Let us now consider conditions of the slab in which there are uniform gradients of the various thermodynamic "forces," X_i, which we shall define more precisely shortly. There will be flows or fluxes both of heat and of the various species of molecules present, which will be denoted as J_i. For each X_i there is a corresponding J_i, and the rate of production of entropy of the isolated system slab-plus-reservoirs can be written

$$\frac{dS}{dt} = \sum_i J_i X_i. \tag{4.1}$$

Here S is the entropy of the *assembly* (including the reservoirs) per unit volume of the *slab* (i.e., per unit thickness for a slab of unit cross section). If J_0 is the flow of heat per unit cross section, then the rate of change of entropy due to heat flowing from a temperature T to $T + dT$ is $J_0/(T + dT) - J_0/T \approx -(J_0/T^2)dT$. The entropy change due to internal heat flow per unit thickness of slab is $-(J_0/T^2)dT/dz$, where z is the coordinate in the direction of the thickness. More generally this could be written $-(J_0/T^2)\,\text{grad}\,T$, so $X_0 = -(1/T^2)\,\text{grad}\,T$. If J_l, say, is the flow of some particular species of molecule, then, as we will show immediately, the corresponding $X_l = -(\text{grad}\,\mu_l)_T/T$, where $(\text{grad}\,\mu_l)_T$ is the change of the chemical potential, per unit length, which would occur *at constant temperature* due to the existing gradients in concentration. If there is a change in temperature across the slab, transport of material will cause a change of entropy because of the partial heat capacity of molecular species l, due to absorption of heat from or rejection of heat to the reservoir. However, this entropy change will simply cancel that of the thermostat. In addition, there will be an entropy change due to concentration changes, equal to $J_l(\text{grad}\,\bar{s}_l)_T$, where $\bar{s}_l$ is the partial entropy, and a change of entropy of the reservoir equal to $-J_l(\text{grad}\,\bar{h}_l)_T/T$, where $\bar{h}_l$ is the partial enthalpy. Thus the total change in entropy will be $J_l(\text{grad}\,\bar{s}_l)_T - J_l(\text{grad}\,\bar{h}_l)_T/T = -J_l(\text{grad}\,\mu_l)_T/T$. Since the passage of heat in or out of the reservoir occurs between regions at the same temperature, it will not matter, as far as entropy production is concerned, whether it actually takes place or not. On the same basis, transfer of material from the slab to the reservoir will cause no change in entropy since across the boundary $(\text{grad}\,\mu_l)_T = 0$.

Now we usually consider a situation in which one or more of the substances (including heat) can pass freely between the slab and the reservoirs, which are supposed to be very large. Thus the reservoir acts as a source or sink of the particular substances (or as a thermostat, or both). It is assumed that no other substances can pass between the slab and the reservoirs. Thus the steady state set up is one in which one or more of the X_i, say X_k, is fixed by the reservoir at a predetermined value, and J_k comes to a steady value, while all the other J_i's which are fluxes of substances which cannot pass the boundary, eventually become zero; at the same time their X_i's take on particular values characteristic of the steady state.

The J_i's are themselves functions of the X_i's, and may be taken as linear functions if the X_i's are small enough. Thus we write

$$J_i = \sum_j L_{ij}X_j. \tag{4.2}$$

In order to apply Sec. 17-3 we shall assume that the assemblies in our ensemble consist of the reservoirs and the slab, and that heat or matter or both will be added to one reservoir and an equal amount removed from the other. If the reservoirs are very large, their state over a considerable time will not be appreciably changed by the heat and material added or removed, or by that transferred through the slab, and the latter will come to a steady state that depends only on the state of the reservoirs. It can be arranged that the amount of heat and/or material added to and removed from the reservoirs be such as to exactly balance the transfer through the slab at the steady state. Then the conditions for a steady state, which were developed in Sec. 17-3 may be applied in precisely the same way to the assembly consisting of reservoirs plus slab. However, in making this application we must note that Eq. (4.1) was set up on the basis that no heat or material was transferred to or from the reservoirs, so there was no change of entropy of the surroundings. If it is assumed that the surroundings are in equilibrium with one or the other of the reservoirs (in a sense acting as extensions of the reservoirs), then there is no total change of entropy in the process of transfer from reservoir to surroundings, so that nothing is changed, but this device enables us to isolate in our minds the change of entropy of the surroundings, which we call dS_s/dt, and which under the imposed conditions is constant. At the steady state, dS_0/dt (where S_0 is the entropy of slab and reservoirs only) is zero and a minimum, by the reasoning of Sec. 17-3. At the steady state, dS/dt, which is equal to $dS_0/dt + dS_s/dt$, will itself be a minimum since dS_s/dt is constant, and, by Eq. (4.1), $\sum_i J_i X_i$ will also be a minimum.

Let us now suppose that we have semipermeable membranes which permit heat and all substances, except the substance l to pass between reservoirs and slab. If this is the case, J_l will be zero at the steady state. We may also suppose that the conditions in the reservoirs are such that all X_i's are zero except X_k, which is held at a fixed value, and X_l, which, of course, depends only on conditions in the slab. Thus we suppose that X_l varies because of conditions in the slab, all other

X_i remaining fixed. The steady state will be given by the minimum of $\sum_i J_i X_i$ with respect to variation of X_l. In this case, all other X_i being zero,

$$\sum_i J_i X_i = J_k X_k + J_l X_l,$$

and

$$J_k = L_{kk} X_k + L_{kl} X_l,$$
$$J_l = L_{lk} X_k + L_{ll} X_l.$$

Hence we obtain

$$\sum_i J_i X_i = L_{kk} X_k^2 + (L_{kl} + L_{lk}) X_k X_l + L_{ll} X_l^2.$$

With X_k fixed, the minimum occurs when

$$2 L_{ll} X_l + (L_{kl} + L_{lk}) X_k = 0,$$

and at the same time

$$J_l = L_{lk} X_k + L_{ll} X_l = 0.$$

It is seen that both of these conditions can hold simultaneously only if

$$L_{lk} = L_{kl}. \tag{4.3}$$

The same relation must hold for any pair k, l. This is the reciprocal relation, which Onsager discovered by another method [16, 17].†

17-5. *The Soret Effect*

The science of irreversible thermodynamics is largely a matter of exploiting the reciprocal relations, which is beyond the scope of this book. We shall, however, illustrate the use of Eq. (4.3) by applying it to the Soret effect for a two-component system. The Soret phenomenon occurs when a temperature gradient is established in the system; it is then found that a concentration gradient also develops. Let the flux of heat be designated as J_0 and the corresponding force, related to the temperature gradient, as X_0. Let J_1 and J_2 represent the fluxes

---

† This relation has been derived and examined numerous times in the recent literature. The motivation for the present treatment came from an earlier discussion of mine [18].

of the two components, with forces X_1 and X_2. At the steady state, J_1 and J_2 will have become zero. Thus we have

$$J_1 = L_{10}X_0 + L_{11}X_1 + L_{12}X_2 = 0, \tag{5.1}$$

$$J_2 = L_{20}X_0 + L_{21}X_1 + L_{22}X_2 = 0, \tag{5.2}$$

and furthermore

$$J_0 = L_{00}X_0 + L_{01}X_1 + L_{02}X_2. \tag{5.3}$$

Before applying the condition $J_1 = J_2 = 0$, we note that even if $X_0 = 0$, a nonzero value for J_0 is possible. There will be transport of heat, associated with the currents J_1 and J_2, even though there is no temperature gradient. We write, under conditions of uniform temperature,

$$J_0 = Q_1^* J_1 + Q_2^* J_2. \tag{5.4}$$

Since if $X_0 = 0$

$$J_0 = L_{01}X_1 + L_{02}X_2, \tag{5.5}$$

$$J_1 = L_{11}X_1 + L_{12}X_2, \tag{5.6}$$

$$J_2 = L_{21}X_1 + L_{22}X_2, \tag{5.7}$$

we see that

$$J_0 = (Q_1^* L_{11} + Q_2^* L_{21})X_1 + (Q_1^* L_{12} + Q_2^* L_{22})X_2 \tag{5.8}$$

and, equating coefficients in Eqs. (5.5) and (5.8), and solving the linear system for Q_1^* and Q_2^*, we find

$$Q_1^* = \frac{L_{01}L_{22} - L_{02}L_{21}}{L_{11}L_{22} - L_{21}L_{12}}, \tag{5.9}$$

and

$$Q_2^* = \frac{L_{02}L_{11} - L_{01}L_{12}}{L_{11}L_{22} - L_{21}L_{12}}. \tag{5.10}$$

We have used the condition $X_0 = 0$ to *define* Q_1^* and Q_2^*. Returning now to our steady state, with X_0 having a fixed value and with $J_1 = J_2 = 0$, we can eliminate X_2 between Eqs. (5.1) and (5.2), which gives

$$\frac{X_1}{X_0} = \frac{L_{20}L_{12} - L_{10}L_{22}}{L_{11}L_{22} - L_{21}L_{12}}. \tag{5.11}$$

Comparing (5.9) and (5.11) we see that if the reciprocal relations hold
($L_{12} = L_{21}$, $L_{10} = L_{01}$, $L_{20} = L_{02}$)

$$\frac{X_1}{X_0} = -Q_1^*, \tag{5.12}$$

which, in view of the definitions of X_1 and X_0 (Sec. 17-4), may be written

$$(\text{grad } \mu_1)_T = -\frac{Q_1^*}{T} \text{ grad } T. \tag{5.13}$$

Since $(\text{grad } \mu_1)_T$ depends only on changes in the mole fraction x_1 it
may be written

$$(\text{grad } \mu_1)_T = \left(\frac{\partial \mu_1}{\partial x_1}\right)_T \frac{dx_1}{dz}, \tag{5.14}$$

so that, noting that grad $T = dT/dz$, we can get an expression for the
change of mole fraction with temperature,

$$\frac{dx_1}{dT} = -\frac{Q_1^*/T}{(\partial \mu_1/\partial x_1)_T}, \tag{5.15}$$

which is the usual expression for the Soret effect. A similar equation
could of course be written for dx_2/dT, but we know that $dx_2/dT = -dx_1/dT$.

In the above we have tacitly assumed that the volume of the
slab remains constant. The transport of material may then be accompanied by a change in pressure, and a pressure gradient may be set
up in the slab. If a pressure gradient cannot be supported, then μ_1 and
μ_2 will be connected by the Gibbs-Duhem equation and there will be a
similar relation between Q_1^* and Q_2^*. In any case we must have, if we
neglect the effect of pressure on the chemical potential,

$$\frac{Q_1^*}{(\partial \mu_1/\partial x_1)_T} + \frac{Q_2^*}{(\partial \mu_2/\partial x_2)_T} = 0$$

or

$$\frac{Q_1^*}{(\partial \mu_1/\partial x_1)_T} = \frac{Q_2^*}{(\partial \mu_2/\partial x_1)_T}$$

since $dx_1 = -dx_2$.

17-6. *Appendix: Law of Microscopic Reversibility in Quantum Mechanics*

Suppose that we have an assembly which has certain energy levels with stationary wave functions ψ_I. Now suppose that our observation of this system is carried out in such a way that we effectively ignore certain interactions, and if these interactions are neglected the corresponding wave functions are ϕ_J. We wish to consider a transition between two states, say from ϕ_1 to ϕ_2, and its reverse. Each of these sets of wave functions, the ψ_I's and the ϕ_J's forms a complete orthogonal set, and for the moment, we will assume them to be real. The energy corresponding to ψ_I is called ϵ_I. The complete time-dependent wave function for the Ith state is, therefore, $\psi_I \exp\{-2\pi i \epsilon_I t/h\}$. Only those for which ϵ_I is very close to some fixed value will be represented in an ensemble of systems of "fixed" energy.

Since each of the sets of wave functions ψ_I and ϕ_J is a complete orthogonal set, we can expand one in terms of the other. Thus we write

$$\psi_N = \sum_J a_{NJ}\phi_J, \tag{6.1}$$

and

$$\phi_M = \sum_I b_{MI}\psi_I. \tag{6.2}$$

Multiplying both sides of Eq. (6.1) by ϕ_K and integrating over all space, we find, since the ϕ's are mutually orthogonal and assuming them normalized,

$$a_{NK} = \int \psi_N \phi_K \, d\tau. \tag{6.3}$$

Similarly multiplying both sides of Eq. (6.2) by ψ_L and integrating, we find

$$b_{ML} = \int \psi_L \phi_M \, d\tau. \tag{6.4}$$

Replacing M by K and L by N, we obtain

$$b_{KN} = \int \psi_N \phi_K \, d\tau = a_{NK}, \tag{6.5}$$

a relation which will be of great importance to us.

Let us now consider an assembly at time $t = 0$ which is in the state represented by ϕ_1. The wave function (state function) of this assembly at an arbitrary time may be represented by

$$\Psi = c_1\phi_1 + c_2\phi_2 + c_3\phi_3 + \cdots, \tag{6.6}$$

with

$$c_1 = 1 \qquad c_2 = c_3 = \cdots 0$$

at $t = 0$. At $t = 0$ we may also write [by Eq. (6.2)]

$$\Psi = \phi_1 = b_{11}\psi_1 + b_{12}\psi_2 + \cdots. \tag{6.7}$$

The state function Ψ will change with time, and may always be expressed as a linear function of the true time-dependent wave functions $\psi_I \exp\{-2\pi i\epsilon_I t/h\}$. Thus at an arbitrary time we will have

$$\Psi = b_{11}\psi_1 \exp\left\{-\frac{2\pi i\epsilon_i t}{h}\right\} + b_{12}\psi_2 \exp\left\{-\frac{2\pi i\epsilon_2 t}{h}\right\} + \cdots, \tag{6.8}$$

which reduces to Eq. (6.7) at $t = 0$, but which changes with time in an essential way (i.e., $\Psi^*\Psi$, the probability function, will change) because the energies ϵ_1, ϵ_2, $\cdots$ are not all the same, even though those with appreciable b's are *almost* the same. At time t, the value of c_2 will have become

$$c_2 = \int \left(b_{11}\psi_1 \exp\left\{-\frac{2\pi i\epsilon_1 t}{h}\right\} + b_{12}\psi_2 \exp\left\{-\frac{2\pi i\epsilon_2 t}{h}\right\} + \cdots \right) \phi_2 \, d\tau$$

$$= b_{11}a_{12} \exp\left\{-\frac{2\pi i\epsilon_1 t}{h}\right\} + b_{12}a_{22} \exp\left\{-\frac{2\pi i\epsilon_2 t}{h}\right\} + \cdots, \tag{6.9}$$

by Eq. (6.3).

Similarly, had we started at $t = 0$ with $c_2 = 1$ and $c_1 = c_3 = \cdots = 0$, then at a later time t we would have had

$$c_1 = b_{21}a_{11} \exp\left\{-\frac{2\pi i\epsilon_1 t}{h}\right\} + b_{22}a_{21} \exp\left\{-\frac{2\pi i\epsilon_2 t}{h}\right\} + \cdots. \tag{6.10}$$

Comparing (6.9) and (6.10) and remembering (6.5), we see that these two expressions are equal. In other words, if we start with state ϕ, we generate state ϕ_2 at the same rate as we generate ϕ, starting with ϕ_2.

In the preceding deduction we have assumed the wave functions to be real, except for the time factor. It is sometimes desirable to use complex wave functions. For example, the wave function for a freely moving particle going in one direction (toward greater x) with constant momentum p_x is exp $\{2\pi i p_x x/h\}$, while the wave function for the particle moving in the opposite direction is exp $\{-2\pi i p_x x/h\}$. In general, the complex conjugate of a complex wave function represents a situation in which the average motions are reversed.† It is possible to set up linear combinations which are real, but use of the complex functions may be necessary in some cases. If the functions are complex, we must replace ϕ_K by ϕ_K^* in Eq. (6.3) and ψ_L by ψ_L^* in Eq. (6.4), where the asterisk indicates conjugate complex, and we find, instead of Eq. (6.5),

$$b_{KN}^* = a_{NK}. \tag{6.11}$$

Using ϕ_2^* in Eq. (6.9), we will obtain the same final result. However, in the paragraph following Eq. (6.9) we should start with $c_2^* = 1$ instead of $c_2 = 1$, where c_2^* is the coefficient of ϕ_2^*, which will also be included among the complete orthogonal set of ϕ's. Since ϕ_2^* corresponds to ϕ_2 with some of the motions reversed (and all other motions unspecified as to direction), the reverse of $\phi_1 \longrightarrow \phi_2$ will be $\phi_2^* \longrightarrow \phi_1^*$. Then, instead of Eq. (6.10), we arrive at the result

$$c_1^* = b_{21}^* a_{11}^* \exp\left\{-\frac{2\pi i \epsilon_1 t}{h}\right\} + b_{22}^* a_{21}^* \exp\left\{-\frac{2\pi i \epsilon_2 t}{h}\right\} + \cdots, \tag{6.12}$$

which, on applying Eq. (6.11), will be seen to be identical to Eq. (6.9). So if we start with state ϕ_1, we generate state ϕ_2 at the same rate as we generate ϕ_1^* starting with ϕ_2^*.

It should be noted that if we evaluate the coefficients at infinite time and average over the phases (i.e., average the result over a finite length of time), we still will not have reached a state of equilibrium. What we have presented here is a proof of mechanical reversibility. To get to equilibrium, we still need a process of randomization. This

---

† The current density of probability (essentially proportional to the mean velocity in a wave packet) is given in quantum mechanics by

$$-\frac{ih}{4\pi m} (\psi \operatorname{grad} \psi^* - \psi^* \operatorname{grad} \psi),$$

where ψ is the wave function, m is the mass of the particle, and the asterisk means conjugate complex [19]. If more than one particle is involved, the gradient is applied in the many-dimensional space of all the particles, with the appropriate mass attached to each derivative if there is more than one kind of particle. It is seen that substituting ψ^* for ψ and, hence, ψ for ψ^* reverses the sign.

randomization could be accomplished formally by averaging over the phases and proceeding afresh at intervals as time goes on toward infinity.

REFERENCES

1. R. C. Tolman, *The Principles of Statistical Mechanics*, Oxford, Eng., Clarendon Press, 1938, Chap. 6.
2. J. O. Hirschfelder, C. F. Curtiss, R. Byron Bird, *Molecular Theory of Gases and Liquids*, New York, Wiley, 1954, Pt. 2.
3. I. Prigogine, ed., *Proceedings of the International Symposium on Transport Processes in Statistical Mechanics*, New York, Interscience, 1958.
4. I. Prigogine, *Non-Equilibrium Statistical Mechanics*, New York, Interscience, 1962.
5. R. T. Cox, *Statistical Mechanics of Irreversible Change*, Baltimore, Md., Johns Hopkins Univ. Press, 1955.
6. R. B. Bird, W. E. Stewart, and E. N. Lightfoot, *Transport Phenomena*, New York, Wiley, 1960.
7. H. Mori, I. Oppenheim, and J. Ross, in J. de Boer and G. E. Uhlenbeck, eds., *Studies in Statistical Mechanics*, Amsterdam, North-Holland, Vol. 1, 1962, Part C.
8. C. S. Wang Chang, G. E. Uhlenbeck, and J. de Boer, in J. de Boer and G. E. Uhlenbeck, ed., *Studies in Statistical Mechanics*, Amsterdam, North-Holland, Vol. 2, 1964, Part C.
9. R. D. Present, *The Kinetic Theory of Gases*, New York, McGraw-Hill, 1958.
10. S. R. de Groot and P. Mazur, *Non-Equilibrium Thermodynamics*, New York, Interscience, 1962.
11. O. K. Rice, *Phys. Rev.*, **38,** 1943 (1931).
12. K. G. Denbigh, *The Thermodynamics of the Steady State*, New York, Wiley, 1951.
13. S. R. de Groot, *Thermodynamics of Irreversible Processes*, New York, Interscience, 1951.
14. I. Prigogine, *Introduction to the Thermodynamics of Irreversible Processes*, 2d ed., New York, Interscience, 1961.
15. D. D. Fitts, *Nonequilibrium Thermodynamics*, New York, McGraw-Hill. 1962.
16. L. Onsager, *Phys. Rev.*, **37,** 405 (1931).
17. L. Onsager, *Phys. Rev.*, **38,** 2265 (1931).
18. O. K. Rice, *J. Phys. Chem.*, **64,** 1857 (1960).
19. H. A. Kramers, *Quantum Mechanics*, New York, Interscience, 1957, pp. 31–32.

PROBLEMS

17.1. Find d^2S/dt^2 by differentiation of Eq. (2.23) and show that it is negative.

17.2. Work out the equations for the Soret effect if three components are present.

Chapter 18

Equilibrium Theory of Chemical Reaction Rates

18-1. *Rate of Association and Dissociation of Atoms at Equilibrium*

The discussion of chemical equilibrium given in Chap. 7 lays the foundation for a study of chemical kinetics.† We start with the simple case where A and B are two atoms which form a diatomic molecule, and consider the rate at which the direct and reverse reactions proceed in a state of equilibrium. When an atom A collides with an atom B, the two will inevitably separate again, since the total energy is above the dissociation energy, unless there is a third body in the neighborhood to remove some of the excess energy. However, for the moment we are not interested in whether A and B actually stick together. We shall say there is an association whenever an A and a B come together, and a dissociation whenever they separate. It will not matter that an association is almost always directly followed by a dissociation.

With this definition of dissociation, it is easy to calculate the rate constant for dissociation, that is the number of dissociations per unit time divided by the number of combined pairs, N_{AB}, when equilibrium is established [6]. The equilibrium rate of dissociation will be unchanged by the introduction of certain artificialities which considerably simplify the calculation. We may imagine the atoms A and B to be attached to each other by an inextensible weightless cord, so that the pairs do not separate, but whenever they depart from each other they eventually come to the end of the cord and are pulled back together again. This is equivalent to setting up a special interatomic potential-energy curve for A and B, which goes to infinity at some

† For general references on chemical kinetics, for Chaps. 18–20 see [1–5].

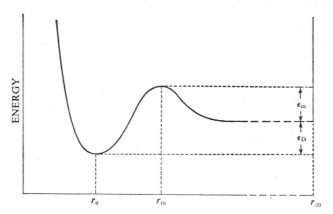

Figure 18-1. Schematic potential-energy curve.

large distance r_∞, as shown in Fig. 18-1. Note that this potential-energy curve is shown with a maximum at r_m. Such a maximum is undoubtedly very rare in the interaction of two atoms, but its presence makes the calculation easier; the effect of removing it is explained later. A maximum does occur in many more complicated cases.

The rate constant for dissociation will equal the rate at which pairs with energy greater than ϵ_m, the energy of the maximum, cross the distance r_m going outward, divided by N_{AB}. The number of such outgoing pairs per unit time is equal to the equilibrium number in the energy levels above ϵ_m times the specific rate at which they move across the top of the "hump." This quantity obviously should not depend on details of the potential-energy curve at great distances, so our device of allowing the potential energy to become infinite at r_∞ should be legitimate.

By letting the potential energy become infinite at r_∞, we make the energy have discrete levels even for the dissociated pairs. The energies of the levels for the region beyond r_m are given approximately by the usual formula for a one-dimensional particle in a box [see, e.g., the equation for ϵ_x, Eq. (5.17) of Chap. 1, replacing M by the reduced mass μ and a by r_∞]:

$$\epsilon = \frac{n^2 h^2}{8 \mu r_\infty^2}, \tag{1.1}$$

where ϵ, the relative energy of the pair, is reckoned from the asymptote of the potential-energy curve as the zero of energy. The irregularity of the potential energy in the small regions of r has no more effect on the levels than a relatively small change in r_∞. Solving for the quantum number n, we find

$$n = \frac{2r_\infty(2\mu\epsilon)^{1/2}}{h}. \tag{1.2}$$

The energy levels are close enough so that we can consider them to be virtually continuously distributed and can differentiate to obtain the number in an energy range $d\epsilon$:

$$dn = \frac{r_\infty}{h}\left(\frac{2\mu}{\epsilon}\right)^{1/2} d\epsilon. \tag{1.3}$$

The equilibrium ratio, of the number of pairs in an energy range, $d\epsilon$, to N_{AB}, is given by

$$\frac{\exp\{-\epsilon/kT\}\, dn}{\sum_v \exp\{-\epsilon'_v/kT\}}, \tag{1.4}$$

where ϵ'_v is the energy of the discrete state with vibrational quantum number v, referred to the asymptote as the zero of energy. The summation is taken over all these discrete levels, since these correspond to the species AB. If ϵ_v is the energy of the state with quantum number v referred to the minimum as the zero of energy, then $\epsilon'_v = \epsilon_v - \epsilon_D$ and we can write $\sum_v \exp\{-\epsilon'_v/kT\} = \exp\{\epsilon_D/kT\}$ (p.f.)$_{\text{vib}}$ where (p.f.)$_{\text{vib}}$ is the vibrational partition function, which can be calculated approximately as in Sec. 2-3. Expression (1.4) therefore becomes,

$$\frac{\exp\{-\epsilon/kT\}\, dn}{\exp\{\epsilon_D/kT\}(\text{p.f.})_{\text{vib}}} = \frac{\exp\{-\epsilon/kT\}(r_\infty/h)(2\mu/\epsilon)^{1/2}\, d\epsilon}{\exp\{\epsilon_D/kT\}(\text{p.f.})_{\text{vib}}}. \tag{1.5}$$

A pair with relative energy $\epsilon > \epsilon_m$ moving toward or back from r_∞ will have a velocity equal to $(2\epsilon/\mu)^{1/2}$ for most of its path, and the time required for r to go to r_∞ and back again will be $2r_\infty/(2\epsilon/\mu)^{1/2}$. In this time the pair will pass the distance r_m, going away from each other, once; the reciprocal of this time gives the number of outward passages per unit time, and is the rate constant k_ϵ for the particular energy level ϵ. The number of outward passages per unit time of pairs in the energy range ϵ to $\epsilon + d\epsilon$, divided by N_{AB}, will be given by multiplying (1.5) by k_ϵ. The total rate constant k_d for dissociation (the number of dissociations per unit time divided by N_{AB}) will then be given by integrating the result from $\epsilon = \epsilon_m$ to $\epsilon = \infty$. We find

$$k_{\mathrm{d}} = \frac{\int_{\epsilon=\epsilon_{\mathrm{m}}}^{\epsilon=\infty} k_{\epsilon} \exp\{-\epsilon/kT\}\, dn}{\exp\{\epsilon_{\mathrm{D}}/kT\}(\mathrm{p.f.})_{\mathrm{vib}}}$$

$$= \frac{(1/h)\int_{\epsilon_{\mathrm{m}}}^{\infty} \exp\{-\epsilon/kT\}\, d\epsilon}{\exp\{\epsilon_{\mathrm{D}}/kT\}(\mathrm{p.f.})_{\mathrm{vib}}}$$

[using the definition of k_{ϵ} and Eq. (1.5)]

$$= \frac{kT}{h(\mathrm{p.f.})_{\mathrm{vib}}} \exp\left\{-\frac{\epsilon_{\mathrm{D}} + \epsilon_{\mathrm{m}}}{kT}\right\}. \tag{1.6}$$

It is seen that all dependence on r_{∞} cancels, as it should. At high temperatures, we may write $(\mathrm{p.f.})_{\mathrm{vib}} = kT/h\nu_0$, where ν_0 is the vibrational frequency, and this constant takes a particularly simple form:

$$k_{\mathrm{d}} = \nu_0 \exp\left\{-\frac{\epsilon_{\mathrm{D}} + \epsilon_{\mathrm{m}}}{kT}\right\}. \tag{1.7}$$

At very low temperatures, $(\mathrm{p.f.})_{\mathrm{vib}} = \exp\{-h\nu_0/2kT\}$, and Eq. (1.6) becomes

$$k_{\mathrm{d}} = \frac{kT}{h} \exp\left\{-\frac{\epsilon_{\mathrm{D}} + \epsilon_{\mathrm{m}} - h\nu_0/2}{kT}\right\}. \tag{1.8}$$

We see from these equations that the expression for k_{d} has an exponential factor and a pre-exponential or frequency factor. The latter is of some interest, because it does not vary much from case to case. Between room temperature and 1000°C the factor kT/h varies from around 6×10^{12} to 3×10^{13}. The frequencies of molecules are also usually around 10^{13} and are thus likely to be of the same order of magnitude as kT/h. Of course, this means that actually neither of the forms (1.7) nor (1.8) will be exactly applicable, but one will have to use the more general Eq. (1.6). In any event, the frequency factor will be of the order of 10^{13}, a value which is often considered to be the "normal" value for dissociations in general.

We will close this section with a remark concerning the nature of the expression we have derived for k_{d}. The numerator of Eq. (1.6) in its first form clearly resembles a partition function, and it seems quite appropriate to write

$$k_{\mathrm{d}} = \frac{(\mathrm{p.f.})'_{\mathrm{react}}}{(\mathrm{p.f.})_{\mathrm{vib}}} \exp\left\{-\frac{\epsilon_{\mathrm{D}}}{kT}\right\}$$

$$= \frac{(\mathrm{p.f.})_{\mathrm{react}}}{(\mathrm{p.f.})_{\mathrm{vib}}} \exp\left\{-\frac{\epsilon_{\mathrm{D}} + \epsilon_{\mathrm{m}}}{kT}\right\}, \tag{1.9}$$

where $(p.f.)'_{react}$ is referred to the asymptote as the zero of energy and $(p.f.)_{react}$ to the top of the maximum. These expressions have many of the properties of ordinary partition functions. For example, since k_ϵ does not depend on T, we see that

$$kT^2 \frac{\partial \ln (p.f.)'_{react}}{\partial T} = \frac{\int_{\epsilon = \epsilon_m}^{\epsilon = \infty} \epsilon k_\epsilon \exp \{-\epsilon/kT\} \, dn}{\int_{\epsilon = \epsilon_m}^{\epsilon = \infty} k_\epsilon \exp \{-\epsilon/kT\} \, dn} = \bar{\epsilon}_{react} \qquad (1.10)$$

where $\bar{\epsilon}_{react}$ is the average energy (reckoned from the asymptote) of all the molecules which react.

It will be noted that Eq. (1.9) looks like an equilibrium equation.

18-2. *Effect of Rotation on the Rate of Dissociation*

In deriving Eq. (1.6) we have tacitly assumed that the molecule is in its lowest rotational state. If this is not so, the effect of the rotation on the dissociation can be taken care of by adding the rotational potential to the potential-energy curve [see Eq. (5.11) of Chap. 1]. For the rotational state with quantum number j, the rotational potential is given by $j(j + 1)h^2/8\pi^2\mu r^2$. The addition of this potential to the potential-energy curve shown in Fig. 18-1 will shift the positions of the minimum and maximum slightly. However, this shift will be relatively negligible, and the principal effect is that the minimum is raised by $j(j + 1)h^2/8\pi^2\mu r_e^2$ and the maximum by $j(j + 1)h^2/8\pi^2\mu r_m^2$. This means that effectively $\epsilon_D + \epsilon_m$ is changed by the difference between these quantities, and we may write in place of Eq. (1.6)

$$k_{d,j} = \frac{kT}{h(p.f.)_{vib}} \exp \left\{ -\frac{\epsilon_D + \epsilon_m + j(j + 1)\kappa^2(r_m^{-2} - r_e^{-2})}{kT} \right\}, \qquad (2.1)$$

where $\kappa^2 = h^2/8\pi^2\mu$. Since the moment of inertia of the diatomic molecule is μr_e^2, the probability that it will be in the rotational state j is equal to

$$\frac{(2j + 1) \exp \{-j(j + 1)\kappa^2/r_e^2 kT\}}{\sum_j (2j + 1) \exp \{-j(j + 1)\kappa^2/r_e^2 kT\}}. \qquad (2.2)$$

(It will be recalled that there are actually $2j + 1$ states† with quantum

---

† This procedure neglects any effects of symmetry, but it is satisfactory, since we are interested only in the classical limit.

number j.) Therefore the average value of k_d for all rotational states is given by

$$k_d = \frac{\sum_j k_{d,j}(2j + 1) \exp\{-j(j + 1)\kappa^2/r_e^2 kT\}}{\sum (2j + 1) \exp\{-j(j + 1)\kappa^2/r_e^2 kT\}}$$

$$= \frac{kT}{h(\text{p.f.})_{\text{vib}}} \exp\left\{-\frac{\epsilon_D + \epsilon_m}{kT}\right\} \frac{\sum_j (2j + 1) \exp\{-j(j + 1)\kappa^2/r_m^2 kT\}}{\sum_j (2j + 1) \exp\{-j(j + 1)\kappa^2/r_e^2 kT\}}.$$

$$(2.3)$$

The sum in the denominator is simply $(\text{p.f.})_{\text{rot}}$, and that in the numerator is $(\text{p.f.})_{\text{rot}}$ with r_m substituted for r_e. In the classical limit, the ratio of these sums becomes r_m^2/r_e^2. Therefore,

$$k_d = \frac{kT}{h(\text{p.f.})_{\text{vib}}} \exp\left\{-\frac{\epsilon_D + \epsilon_m}{kT}\right\} \frac{r_m^2}{r_e^2}. \tag{2.4}$$

Written in the form analogous to Eq. (1.9) this is

$$k_d = \frac{(\text{p.f.})_{\text{react}}}{(\text{p.f.})_{\text{vib}}} \frac{(\text{p.f.})_{\text{rot},r_m}}{(\text{p.f.})_{\text{rot},r_e}} \exp\left\{-\frac{\epsilon_D + \epsilon_m}{kT}\right\}. \tag{2.5}$$

If ϵ_m is equal to zero, as it generally is in the recombination of atoms, then the potential energy has no maximum for $j = 0$. For all j's greater than zero there is a slight maximum due to the rotational potential, but its position will depend on j. Thus r_m becomes somewhat ambiguous, but it may be reasonably well approximated by assuming that it is somewhere near that value of r for which the potential energy curve $(j = 0)$ approaches its asymptotic value within about kT (actually it turns out to be $\frac{1}{3}kT$). This statement can be defended by a calculation which we now present.†

The attractive forces between atoms which probably first become noticeable at great distances are the van der Waals forces, whose potential varies as r^{-6} (see Sec. 8-3). If to these we add the rotational potential, we obtain for the effective potential energy the expression, referred to the asymptote,

$$\epsilon_p = \frac{j(j + 1)\kappa^2}{r^2} - \frac{C}{r^6}. \tag{2.6}$$

The value of r at the maximum of this curve, which depends on j

† For similar calculations on the association (reverse) reaction, see [**3**, pp. 130, 220, 260] and [**7**].

and which we shall call r_j, is found by setting $d\epsilon_\mathrm{p}/dr = 0$, which gives

$$\frac{j(j+1)\kappa^2}{r_j^2} - \frac{3C}{r^6} = 0, \tag{2.7}$$

or

$$r_j = \left[\frac{3C}{j(j+1)\kappa^2}\right]^{1/4}. \tag{2.8}$$

At this value of r

$$\epsilon_\mathrm{p} = \frac{\frac{2}{3}j(j+1)\kappa^2}{r_j^2} = \frac{\frac{2}{3}[j(j+1)\kappa^2]^{3/2}}{(3C)^{1/2}}. \tag{2.9}$$

This is now the effective value of ϵ_m for this particular j and if it is used instead of $\epsilon_\mathrm{m} + j(j+1)\kappa^2/r_\mathrm{m}^2$, we obtain instead of Eq. (2.1),

$$k_{\mathrm{d},j} = \frac{kT}{h(\mathrm{p.f.})_\mathrm{vib}} \exp\left\{-\frac{\epsilon_\mathrm{D} + \frac{2}{3}[j(j+1)\kappa^2]^{3/2}/(3C)^{1/2} - j(j+1)\kappa^2/r_\mathrm{e}^2}{kT}\right\}, \tag{2.10}$$

and instead of Eq. (2.3),

$$k_\mathrm{d} = \frac{kT}{h(\mathrm{p.f.})_\mathrm{vib}} \exp\left\{-\frac{\epsilon_\mathrm{D}}{kT}\right\} \frac{\sum\limits_{j}(2j+1)\exp\left\{-\frac{2}{3}[j(j+1)\kappa^2]^{3/2}/(3C)^{1/2}kT\right\}}{\sum\limits_{j}(2j+1)\exp\left\{-j(j+1)\kappa^2/r_\mathrm{e}^2kT\right\}}. \tag{2.11}$$

The sum in the numerator may be changed into an integral. On writing $x = [j(j+1)]^{3/2}$ it becomes [8]

$$\int_0^\infty \frac{2}{3x^{1/3}} \exp\left\{-\frac{\frac{2}{3}\kappa^3 x}{(3C)^{1/2}kT}\right\} dx = \frac{\frac{2}{3}\Gamma(\frac{2}{3})(3C)^{1/3}(\frac{3}{2}kT)^{2/3}}{\kappa^2}$$

$$= \frac{(\frac{2}{3})^{1/3}\Gamma(\frac{2}{3})8\pi^2\mu(r_\mathrm{m}^2/1.728)kT}{h^2}$$

$$= 0.685 \cdot \frac{8\pi^2\mu r_\mathrm{m}^2 kT}{h^2}, \tag{2.12}$$

where Γ stands for the gamma function, and r_m is defined by

$$r_\mathrm{m}^2 = 1.728\left(\frac{3C}{kT}\right)^{1/3}. \tag{2.13}$$

This definition of r_m comes from averaging r_j^2 according to the number decomposing, i.e.,

$$r_m^2 = \frac{\sum_j r_j^2(2j + 1) \exp \{-j(j + 1)\kappa^2/r_e^2 kT\} k_{d,j}}{\sum_j (2j + 1) \exp \{-j(j + 1)\kappa^2/r_e^2 kT\} k_{d,j}}$$

$$= \frac{\sum_j (2j + 1)r_j^2 \exp \{-\frac{2}{3}[j(j + 1)\kappa^2]^{3/2}/(3C)^{1/2}kT\}}{\sum_j (2j + 1) \exp \{-\frac{2}{3}[j(j + 1)\kappa^2]^{3/2}/(3C)^{1/2}kT\}}. \tag{2.14}$$

One then substitutes for r_j from Eq. (2.8), uses the variable $x = [j(j + 1)]^{3/2}$, and converts to integrals [8]. The result is

$$r_m^2 = \frac{\Gamma(\frac{1}{3})}{(\frac{3}{2})^{1/3}\Gamma(\frac{2}{3})} \left(\frac{3C}{kT}\right)^{1/3}, \tag{2.15}$$

which is worked out numerically as Eq. (2.13). With this definition of r_m, Eq. (2.4) is replaced by

$$k_d = \frac{kT}{h(\text{p.f.})_{\text{vib}}} \exp \left\{-\frac{\epsilon_D}{kT}\right\} \frac{0.685 \, r_m^2}{r_e^2}. \tag{2.16}$$

18-3. *The Rate of Association: The Collision Number*

We may now combine the results of Sec. 18-2 with our previously obtained expression for the equilibrium constant, to obtain the rate of the reverse reaction, the association. Since we are calculating the equilibrium rate of association, and the association is not necessarily to be permanent, we will actually be calculating the rate of collision with sufficient relative kinetic energy to get over the hump at r_m. The number of collisions per unit volume per unit time between A's and B's will be proportional to the number N_A/V of A's in unit volume and the number N_B/V of B's in unit volume. The proportionality constant for collisions of sufficient energy we will call k_a. The rate of association or of collision per unit volume must be equal to the rate of dissociation. This is expressed by

$$k_d \frac{N_{AB}}{V} = k_a \frac{N_A N_B}{V^2}. \tag{3.1}$$

Comparing this with Eq. (1.13) of Chap. 7, clearly we have

$$K = \frac{k_a}{k_d}. \tag{3.2}$$

Combining, then, Eq. (2.4) with Eq. (4.9) of Chap. 7, we obtain

$$k_a = \frac{g_{AB}}{g_A g_B} 4\pi r_m^2 (2\pi a^2 kT)^{1/2} \nu_0 \exp\left\{-\frac{\epsilon_m}{kT}\right\}. \tag{3.3}$$

Since $\nu_0 = 1/(2\pi a\mu^{1/2})$ [Eq. (5.14) of Chap. 1], Eq. (3.3) becomes

$$k_a = \frac{g_{AB}}{g_A g_B} 4\pi r_m^2 \left(\frac{kT}{2\pi\mu}\right)^{1/2} \exp\left\{-\frac{\epsilon_m}{kT}\right\}. \tag{3.4}$$

Aside from the factor $g_{AB}/g_A g_B$ (which limits the collisions counted to those for which the electron spin state coincides with that of the molecule AB), this expression is exactly that derived from the kinetic theory of gases [9] for the rate of collision, per unit volume and at unit concentration, with relative kinetic energy equal to or greater than ϵ_m, of hard spheres of diameter r_m.

Direct substitution of Eq. (2.5) of the present chapter and Eq. (1.13) of Chap. 7 into Eq. (3.2) [remembering that the (p.f.)'s in Eq. (2.5) refer to the molecule AB, so that part of (p.f.)$_{AB}^0$ will be cancelled, and recalling also that the partition functions in Eq. (1.13) of Chap. 7 are referred to the asymptotic value of the potential energy as the zero of energy] gives us Eq. (3.3) or (3.4) in another form:

$$k_a = \frac{g_{AB}(\text{p.f.})_{\text{react}}(\text{p.f.})_{AB,\text{trans}}^0(\text{p.f.})_{\text{rot},r_m}}{g_A g_B (\text{p.f.})_A^0 (\text{p.f.})_B^0} \exp\left\{-\frac{\epsilon_m}{kT}\right\}. \tag{3.5}$$

As in the case of Eqs. (1.9), (1.10), and (2.5), it will be noted that this looks like an equilibrium equation. It would look even more like Eq. (1.13) of Chap. 7 if $(\text{p.f.})'_{\text{react}} = (\text{p.f.})_{\text{react}} \exp\{-\epsilon_m/kT\}$ were substituted; in the latter form all partition functions would be referred to the same zero of energy.

18-4. *The Effect of Spin Multiplicity*

If the deduction which we have just finished is examined carefully, it will be observed that the assignment of the factor $g_{AB}/g_A g_B$ to k_a in Eq. (3.3) is somewhat arbitrary. It comes about because we have arbitrarily assumed that the corresponding factor in k_d is equal to 1. As far as the equilibrium constant is concerned we could have just as well assigned a factor 1 to k_a and a factor $g_A g_B/g_{AB}$ to k_d. It will pay us to re-examine this matter more closely, in the light of some specific examples.

In the case of the reaction $2H \rightleftarrows H_2$ the procedure regarding the multiplicity factor would seem to be correct in a certain sense. For H, the value of g is 2, since the electron spin can be in either direction, whereas for H_2 it is 1. There are four possible spin combinations of 2H, only one of which, in which we describe the electrons as paired, leads to an attractive potential-energy curve, whereas the other three lead to a repulsive curve. What we have done, then, amounts to counting only those collisions in which the pair of atoms is approaching along the attractive potential curve, and correspondingly, only those dissociations which are associated with the attractive curve. That is to say, we count only those collisions which could result in formation of an H_2 molecule if the excess energy were removed and only those dissociations which could have come from an H_2. This is a sensible thing to do if we have in mind the ultimate use of these results to study chemical reactions.

For the reaction $2I \rightleftharpoons I_2$ the situation is much more complicated. For I (spin quantum number $\frac{3}{2}$) the value of g is 4. With two iodine atoms, therefore, there are 16 possible spin combinations, only one of which leads to the ground state of the I_2 molecule. However, not all other combinations lead to repulsive states; there are probably five attractive states, of which one, the ground state, has the lowest minimum. In studying molecule formation it seems reasonable to count all collisions for which the state is attractive. Thus for the reaction $2I \rightleftharpoons I_2$ we do not have a factor of $\frac{1}{16}$ in k_a and a factor of 1 in k_d as one might suppose from Eqs. (3.3) and (2.4), but rather a factor $\frac{5}{16}$ in k_a and 5 in k_d. In general one inserts a factor which we may call $g^*/g_A g_B$ in k_a and g^*/g_{AB} in k_d, so the final forms are

$$k_d = \frac{g^*}{g_{AB}} \frac{kT}{h(\text{p.f.})_{\text{vib}}} \exp\left\{-\frac{\epsilon_D + \epsilon_m}{kT}\right\} \frac{r_m^2}{r_e^2} \tag{4.1}$$

$$k_a = \frac{g^*}{g_A g_B} 4\pi r_m^2 \left(\frac{kT}{2\pi\mu}\right)^{1/2} \exp\left\{-\frac{\epsilon_m}{kT}\right\}. \tag{4.2}$$

If ϵ_m is zero, then [following Eq. (2.16)] these equations are replaced by

$$k_d = 0.685 \frac{g^*}{g_{AB}} \frac{kT}{h(\text{p.f.})_{\text{vib}}} \exp\left\{-\frac{\epsilon_D}{kT}\right\} \frac{r_m^2}{r_e^2}, \tag{4.3}$$

and

$$k_a = 0.685 \frac{g^*}{g_A g_B} 4\pi r_m^2 \left(\frac{kT}{2\pi\mu}\right)^{1/2}, \tag{4.4}$$

where r_m is given by Eq. (2.13).

18-5. *Some Remarks on Reaction Mechanisms*

In the previous discussion it was quite specifically noted that a collision is not usually followed by actual recombination of the atoms, but is usually immediately followed by a "dissociation." In calculating the number of dissociations, we have counted those which followed immediately after a collision. It is clear that these processes are not very closely connected with chemical reactions. If we are interested in chemical reactions, we want to know the number of collisions which are immediately followed by a sticking together of the reacting parts; or we want to know the number of dissociations of reacting parts which were stuck together.

If the particles A and B are atoms, there is only one way in which a collision can be followed by true association. We can have a *three-body collision*, so that there is another particle present to carry away the excess energy. If the mutual energy of the colliding pair is reduced below the dissociation energy, they will stick together. In the reverse reaction, the molecule AB will dissociate only if there has been a collision with a third body to furnish the energy necessary for the dissociation (of course, only a small portion of this energy may need to be furnished at the last collision).

If, on the other hand, the two colliding molecules, A and B, are not monatomic, but have a certain number of internal degrees of freedom, the excess energy may be removed from the bond by the other degrees of freedom. The associated pair of molecules, AB, will then stick together until such time as this energy may, by fluctuation within these degrees of freedom, return to the bond which breaks. If, however, the pressure in the assembly is high enough so that the combined pair will be almost certain to collide with other molecules before this happens, the excess energy will probably be removed, and the combined pair will be stabilized as a single molecule. Every collision of A and B which results in combination may be counted as a chemical reaction to give AB. It is this case which we shall deal with as the first example of a true chemical reaction.

The problem we have just defined is the association of A and B, polyatomic molecules or radicals, to form AB at high pressure. Closely related to this problem, of course, is the dissociation of AB under similar experimental conditions. This, as was first suggested by Lindemann, can only occur after the molecule AB has received sufficient energy by chance accumulation after a series of favorable collisions with other molecules. Once it has received this energy the chances are still in favor, if the pressure is high, of its losing it again before this energy has had an opportunity to become concentrated in the weak bond. Reaction will not occur until and unless this concentration of energy does occur. Nevertheless, at equilibrium the over-all rate of dissociation of AB must be equal to the rate of association of A and B. We can write out a reaction mechanism in which it is assumed that equilibrium is established at every step:

$$A + B \rightleftarrows AB^*, \qquad\qquad (a)$$
$$AB^* + M \rightleftarrows AB + M. \qquad (b)$$

Here AB^* means a molecule with enough energy to decompose, whereas M is some other molecule (it may be another AB) which can remove enough of this energy to stabilize AB.

When we study a chemical reaction, however, we do not have equilibrium conditions, and we generally start with none of the product present. If we have no AB's present at the beginning, we may write the reaction scheme

$$A + B \longrightarrow AB^*, \qquad\qquad (a')$$
$$AB^* + M \longrightarrow AB + M. \qquad (b')$$

If the pressure is high, virtually every AB^* that is formed will collide and be deactivated according to (b'); only rarely will the reverse of (a') occur. Therefore the rate of formation of AB^* will be rate-determining, and we need only to find the rate of reaction (a') to explain what we observe, namely the rate of formation of AB; in other words

$$\frac{d(AB)}{dt} = k_a(A)(B); \qquad\qquad (5.1)$$

here the parentheses denote concentrations, e.g., $(A) = N_A/V$. It is reasonable to assume that reaction (a') goes at the same rate of speed as the formation of AB^* in reaction (a), the only difference being that the reverse reaction does not occur in the second mechanism.

On the other hand, if there are no A's or B's to start with, then the mechanism becomes

$$M + AB \rightleftarrows AB^* + M, \qquad (b'')$$
$$AB^* \longrightarrow A + B, \qquad\qquad (a'')$$

and we may assume that the direct reaction (b″) is just the reverse of reaction (b′), equilibrium being established to a good approximation in each case at high pressures of M, since the usual fate of an AB*, however formed, is to be deactivated by collision. This happens because at high pressures the rate of (b) in either direction is much faster than (a′) or (a″). Since AB* is present in equilibrium numbers, the rate of reaction (a″) can be assumed to be just the same as the rate of dissociation of AB, so that we may write

$$-\frac{d(AB)}{dt} = k_d^*(AB^*) = k_d(AB). \tag{5.2}$$

Again we may assume the rate of (a″) to be just the same as the rate of dissociation of AB* in reaction (a) if AB is present at the same concentration in the two cases, the difference being that in the present instance the reverse reaction does not occur.

If it is true that (a′) and (a″) occur at the same rate as the corresponding reactions at equilibrium, we may write for the equilibrium case

$$k_a(A)(B) = k_d(AB), \tag{5.3}$$

where k_a and k_d are exactly the same constants as appear in Eqs. (5.1) and (5.2). From Eq. (5.3)

$$\frac{k_a}{k_d} = \frac{(AB)}{(A)(B)} = K \tag{5.4}$$

which is the same as Eq. (3.2).

18-6. *Polyatomic Molecules: Calculation of Rate Constants*

The calculation of k_d for a polyatomic molecule may proceed in much the same way as for the dissociation of a diatomic molecule. However, it represents a real reaction rate constant, since it is no longer true that a dissociation has almost invariably been immediately preceded by an association. Our problem is to calculate the equilibrium rate at which dissociation takes place at some particular chemical bond. The breaking of the chemical bond is much like the breaking of the bond in a diatomic molecule. In considering the process in a diatomic molecule, some originally unforeseen factors entered into the calculation of the probability of the pair crossing the point r_m, or, as we may express it, the probability of the "transition state," to use a term introduced by Evans and Polanyi [10], or the probability of the "activated complex," using Eyring's term [11]. In the case of the diatomic molecule we introduced the factor g^*/g_{AB} to allow for the fact that more electronic states might be involved in the transition state than in the normal state of the diatomic molecule. This amounted to a special assumption or decision as to how the factor $g_{AB}/g_A g_B$ in Eq. (4.9) of Chap. 7 is divided between k_a and k_d.

If we look at Eq. (6.1) or Eq. (6.3) of Chap. 7 we see that there is another factor, involving various rotational and vibrational partition functions, in the equilibrium constant of a polyatomic molecule. This we shall in general abbreviate as f_{vib}/f_{rot}, since it has predominately vibrational factors in the numerator and rotational factors in the denominator. We must decide how to divide this factor between k_a and k_d. In general, on going from the state AB to the state A + B, there is a change of vibrational degrees of freedom (bending vibrations) to rotational degrees of freedom, and therefore, as far as this factor is concerned, a change to a condition of greater probability. The question is, how effective is this increase of probability in increasing the rate of dissociation?

Looking at it from the other point of view, we see that transition from the state A + B to the state AB involves a decrease in probability. Parts which previously rotated freely in A + B are held more or less fixed in position when they are combined in AB. The question, then, is how severely restrictive is this necessity of orientation? What fraction of the collisions calculated by Eq. (4.2) will be effective? We may in general expect an orientation factor, but it is difficult to say just what it should be.

It is clear that, barring certain possible complications, there are two extreme possible activated structures, which may be briefly described as the rigid activated complex and the loose activated complex.

For the rigid activated complex, we have

$$k_d = \frac{g^*}{g_{AB}} \frac{kT}{h(\text{p.f.})_{vib}} \exp\left\{-\frac{\epsilon_D + \epsilon_m}{kT}\right\} \frac{\overline{r_m^2}}{r_e^2}, \tag{6.1}$$

and

$$k_a = \frac{g^*}{g_A g_B} 4\pi \overline{r_m^2} \left(\frac{kT}{2\pi\mu}\right)^{1/2} \exp\left\{-\frac{\epsilon_m}{kT}\right\} \frac{f_{vib}}{f_{rot}}. \tag{6.2}$$

In Eq. (6.1) the values $\overline{r_m^2}$ and $\overline{r_e^2}$ are considered to be average values, since the rotational potential and rotational partition functions will contain moments of inertia which involve the positions of all the atoms in the molecule. On this account, $\overline{r_m^2}/\overline{r_e^2}$ for a polyatomic molecule will not usually be as large as r_m^2/r_e^2 for a diatomic molecule.

For the loose activated complex, we have

$$k_d = \frac{g^*}{g_{AB}} \frac{kT}{h(\text{p.f.})_{\text{vib}}} \exp\left\{-\frac{\epsilon_D + \epsilon_m}{kT}\right\} \frac{\overline{r_m^2}}{\overline{r_e^2}} \frac{f_{\text{rot}}}{f_{\text{vib}}}, \tag{6.3}$$

and

$$k_a = \frac{g^*}{g_A g_B} 4\pi\overline{r_m^2} \left(\frac{kT}{2\pi\mu}\right)^{1/2} \exp\left\{-\frac{\epsilon_m}{kT}\right\}. \tag{6.4}$$

If the vibrations have very high frequencies, then (as noted in Chap. 7) $f_{\text{vib}} = \exp\{-\epsilon_0/kT\}$, where ϵ_0 is the sum of the zero-point energies of the vibrations involved, and so may be taken into the exponential factor. It is to be noted that $f_{\text{vib}}/f_{\text{rot}}$ is much less than unity, so the rates given by Eqs. (6.1) and (6.2) are much smaller than those given by Eqs. (6.3) and (6.4).

In attempting actual predictions of reaction rates, various assumptions have been made. Rice and Gershinowitz [6] made an even more restrictive assumption than that represented by Eqs. (6.1) and (6.2), for they first assumed that only one of the quantum states of the degrees of freedom involved in f_{vib} and f_{rot} was available for reaction. This is equivalent to assuming that the vibrations have very high frequencies. However, even in their first paper, Rice and Gershinowitz recognized that if the vibrational frequencies were low this stand would have to be modified. In a later paper [12] they used what they called the "hypothesis of exact orientation," which is equivalent to Eqs. (6.1) and (6.2), as a norm and then considered possible causes of deviations from this state of affairs.

In actual fact one may expect to have something intermediate to the rigid and the loose complexes. Eyring [3, 11] has assumed that one should, in effect, write

$$k_d = \kappa \frac{g^*}{g_{AB}} \frac{kT}{h(\text{p.f.})_{\text{vib}}} \exp\left\{-\frac{\epsilon_D + \epsilon_m}{kT}\right\} \frac{(\text{p.f.})\dagger^*}{(\text{p.f.})_{AB}^\dagger} \frac{\overline{r_m^2}}{\overline{r_e^2}}, \tag{6.5}$$

$$k_a = \kappa \frac{g^*}{g_A g_B} 4\pi\overline{r_m^2} \left(\frac{kT}{2\pi\mu}\right)^{1/2} \exp\left\{-\frac{\epsilon_m}{kT}\right\} \frac{(\text{p.f.})\dagger^*}{(\text{p.f.})_A^\dagger(\text{p.f.})_B^\dagger}. \tag{6.6}$$

Here $(p.f.)\dagger^*$ is the partition function for the activated complex and $(p.f.)^\dagger_{AB}$ or $(p.f.)^\dagger_A(p.f.)^\dagger_B$ is the partition function for the reactant or reactants. The daggers indicate that the "principal" degrees of freedom, given in bold face in the tables in Sec. 7-6 are *not* included, since they are already taken care of in the rest of the expression. The constant κ will be explained shortly. The unique feature of the formulation lies in the method of determining $(p.f.)\dagger^*$. Eyring proposes to calculate $(p.f.)\dagger^*$ as if all the degrees of freedom of an activated complex were in equilibrium as the system crosses the hump in the potential-energy curve of Fig. 18-1 (which is really a saddle point in a complicated potential-energy surface—see the Appendix Sec. 18-9). This means that if the system could be stopped with the "reaction coordinate" (which would be the coordinate r in the cases we have considered) just at the saddle point, the possible energy levels of all the other coordinates could be used in the ordinary manner to form Boltzmann factors and calculate the partition function. It is, however, quite probably incorrect to use the partition functions belonging to the various degrees of freedom when the representative point of the system is exactly at the saddle point of the potential-energy curve, especially if there are drastic changes in the nature of the quantization when the reaction occurs. Another possible reason for inaccuracies in their formulation (or, perhaps, the same reason in a different guise) is the possibility that after the reaction coordinate has crossed the saddle point it may return before the reaction is completed. This is taken care of by the constant κ, which is the probability that the reaction is completed once the crossing of the saddle point is effected.

If one compares Eq. (6.5) with Eqs. (2.4) and (2.5), it will be seen that Eq. (6.5) can be written

$$k_d = \kappa \frac{g^*}{g_{AB}} \frac{(p.f.)_{react}(p.f.)^*}{(p.f.)^0_{AB}} \exp\left\{-\frac{\epsilon_D + \epsilon_m}{kT}\right\}. \tag{6.7}$$

Here $(p.f.)^0_{AB}$ includes all the degrees of freedom of AB except those accounted for in g_{AB}, and $(p.f.)^*$ includes all the degrees of freedom of the activated complex except those in g^* and in $(p.f.)_{react}$. The partition functions in the numerator are referred to the lowest energy (with zero-point energy omitted) of the activated complex as the zero of energy, whereas that in the denominator is referred to the lowest energy of AB. Both $(p.f.)^0_{AB}$ and $(p.f.)^*$ are referred to unit volume. This form coincides more nearly with that used by Eyring.

Similarly, comparing Eq. (6.6) with Eqs. (3.4) and (3.5), we see that Eq. (6.6) can be written

$$k_a = \kappa \frac{g^*}{g_A g_B} \frac{(p.f.)_{react}(p.f.)^*}{(p.f.)_A^0 (p.f.)_B^0} \exp\left\{-\frac{\epsilon_m}{kT}\right\}, \tag{6.8}$$

and, more generally for any type of reaction,

$$k = \kappa \frac{g^*}{g} \frac{(p.f.)_{react}(p.f.)^*}{(p.f.)^0} \exp\left\{-\frac{\epsilon^*}{kT}\right\}, \tag{6.9}$$

where ϵ^* is the energy necessary to go "over the hump," and $(p.f.)_{react}$ is in all cases equal to kT/h. In the most general case, the factor $\overline{r_m^2}/\overline{r_e^2}$, which would in any case be included in $(p.f.)^*/(p.f.)^0$, might not be readily separable from other factors. Equation (6.9) is general enough to take into account unimolecular or bimolecular reactions in which the activated complex goes beyond the categories described as rigid and loose. For example, a reaction might involve not merely the breaking or formation of a single bond, but the breaking of one bond and simultaneous formation of another. This might under some circumstances require the freezing out of more rotational degrees of freedom into vibrational ones than would be required in an ordinary rigid complex. It is not necessary to consider that $(p.f.)^*$ represents an equilibrium partition function in the sense of Eyring's theory, although this is the assumption usually made.

18-7. *The Temperature Coefficient*

In making experimental determinations, the reaction rate constant is usually determined at several temperatures. The temperature coefficient is of great importance, and before discussing the experimental results we should lay the theoretical basis for their interpretation. In the above discussion we have considered certain quantum states from which reaction can occur, and then noted the probability that the system of interest will be in any one of these quantum states, *assuming that this is the same as if equilibrium were established throughout the assembly.* We have also noted the probability that reactions occur from any one of the quantum states, and on this basis we have calculated the average probability of reaction per unit time. The average probability of reaction per unit time will be the number of reactions occurring in unit time divided by the total number of systems (molecules of the reacting species, pairs of molecules in a bimolecular reaction, etc.). Hence it is equal to the rate constant, provided the reaction takes place in unit volume. That the rate constant must be defined with reference to unit volume is clear, when one considers that the rate of a fixed number of pairs, undergoing a bimolecular reaction, depends upon the volume.

We may formulate this procedure in mathematical terms, using superscript zeros to denote unit volume, by writing

$$\bar{k} = \frac{\sum_i^0 k_i \exp\{-\epsilon_i/kT\}}{\sum_i^0 \exp\{-\epsilon_i/kT\}} = \frac{(\text{p.f.})_k^0}{(\text{p.f.})^0}, \tag{7.1}$$

where k_i is the probability of reaction per unit time from the ith quantum state, its average $\bar{k}$ is the rate constant, and $(\text{p.f.})_k^0$ is defined by the equation.

It is quite clear that the above is exactly the method used to obtain Eq. (1.6), although this result was confined to a specific class of diatomic molecules, those with no rotational energy. Indeed, $(\text{p.f.})_{\text{react}} \exp\{-(\epsilon_D + \epsilon_m)/kT\}$ of Eq. (1.9) is exactly equivalent to $(\text{p.f.})_k^0$ of Eq. (7.1), if the proper zero of energy is chosen. Essentially the same process was used in obtaining Eq. (2.4) or Eq. (2.5), except that the averaging was done in steps, and the relation between $(\text{p.f.})_{\text{react}}$ and $(\text{p.f.})_k^0$ is not so direct. The later equations of this chapter, referring to more complicated situations, are also included in Eq. (7.1). The presence of more degrees of freedom means only that there are also more quantum states involved, and, as long as we can assume that equilibrium is maintained in all quantum states up to the point at which reaction occurs, equations like (6.1), (6.2), (6.3), and (6.4) amount only to attempts to evaluate Eq. (7.1) in more detail.

In the case of the bimolecular association, the energies ϵ_i of Eq. (7.1) must refer to a *pair* of molecules, and $(\text{p.f.})^0$ is the partition function for a pair. Then $\bar{k}$ is the average probability of any pair combining.

In considering the temperature coefficient of the reaction rate, it is convenient to write Eq. (7.1) in the logarithmic form

$$\ln \bar{k} = \ln\left(\sum_i^0 k_i \exp\left\{-\frac{\epsilon_i}{kT}\right\}\right) - \ln\left(\sum_i^0 \exp\left\{-\frac{\epsilon_i}{kT}\right\}\right). \tag{7.2}$$

We have then

$$\frac{d \ln \bar{k}}{dT} = \frac{1}{kT^2}\left(\frac{\sum_i^0 k_i \epsilon_i \exp\{-\epsilon_i/kT\}}{\sum_i^0 k_i \exp\{-\epsilon_i/kT\}} - \frac{\sum_i^0 \epsilon_i \exp\{-\epsilon_i/kT\}}{\sum_i^0 \exp\{-\epsilon_i/kT\}}\right). \tag{7.3}$$

The last term in the parentheses in Eq. (7.3) is the average energy $\bar{\epsilon}$ of all the molecules (or, e.g., pairs). Since $k_i \exp\{-\epsilon_i/kT\}$ is proportional to the number of molecules (or, e.g., pairs) which react in unit time, the first term in the parentheses is clearly the average energy of all the molecules which react. We designate this as $\bar{\bar{\epsilon}}$. We have then

$$\frac{d \ln \bar{k}}{dT} = \frac{\bar{\bar{\epsilon}} - \bar{\epsilon}}{kT^2} = \frac{\Delta\epsilon^*}{kT^2} = \frac{\Delta E^*}{RT^2}, \tag{7.4}$$

where ΔE^* is called the energy of activation. Equation (7.4), in the form given, is due to Tolman [13]. This result has been worked out for unit volume, which is appropriate for getting results concerned with $\bar{k}$. However, we may note that neither $\bar{\bar{\epsilon}}$ nor $\bar{\epsilon}$ are volume-dependent when we are dealing with perfect gases. This, of course, is already known for $\bar{\epsilon}$. It follows because the only dependence on volume of the sums in Eq. (7.3) (if the superscript zero is left off) arises from a change in density of energy levels, which is the same for all energies [see Eq. (5.19) of Chap. 1]. The numerator and denominator of each term in Eq. (7.3) will have the same volume dependence.

Since, by Eq. (1.15) of Chap. 7, we may write $G^0 = -RT \ln(\text{p.f.})^0$, it suggests itself that Eq. (7.2) may be put in the form

$$RT \ln \bar{k} = -\Delta G^*. \tag{7.5}$$

This may be written

$$RT \ln \bar{k} = -\Delta E^* + T\Delta S^* - \Delta(P^*V)$$
$$= -\Delta E^* + T\Delta S^* - RT\Delta n^* \tag{7.6}$$

or

$$\bar{k} = \exp\left\{\frac{\Delta S^*}{R}\right\} \exp\left\{-\frac{\Delta E^*}{RT}\right\} \exp\{-\Delta n^*\}, \tag{7.7}$$

where Δn^* is the change in number of moles as between reactants and activated complex (in general, this will be the number of moles involved in the reaction minus one), and where ΔS^* is called the entropy of activation.

We may apply Eq. (7.4) to some of the cases we have already encountered. Applying it to Eq. (2.4) for the high-temperature case where $kT/h(\text{p.f.})_{\text{vib}} = \nu_0$, and assuming that r_m is independent of temperature, we find immediately by logarithmic differentiation of k_d

$$kT^2 \frac{d \ln k_\mathrm{d}}{dT} = \Delta\epsilon^* = \epsilon_\mathrm{D} + \epsilon_\mathrm{m}. \tag{7.8}$$

It is then seen that Δs^*, the entropy of activation per molecule, is given by

$$\Delta s^* = k \ln \frac{\nu_0 r_\mathrm{m}^2}{r_\mathrm{e}^2}. \tag{7.9}$$

In the low-temperature range, for which $kT/h(\text{p.f.})_\mathrm{vib}$ becomes $(kT/h) \exp \{h\nu_0/2kT\}$ [compare Eq. (1.8)], we obtain

$$\Delta\epsilon^* = \epsilon_\mathrm{D} + \epsilon_\mathrm{m} - \frac{h\nu_0}{2} + kT \tag{7.10}$$

and

$$\Delta s^* = k \ln \left(\frac{ekT}{h} \frac{r_\mathrm{m}^2}{r_\mathrm{e}^2} \right). \tag{7.11}$$

In Eq. (7.10) $\epsilon_\mathrm{D} + \epsilon_\mathrm{m} - h\nu_0/2$ is the energy from the lowest vibrational level to the top of the potential-energy hump, and kT is the average additional energy of systems passing over the hump.

At intermediate temperatures, in view of the temperature dependence of $(\text{p.f.})_\mathrm{vib}$ the expressions will be more complicated. In the cases of Eqs. (6.1), (6.3) and (6.5), the expressions will be further complicated by the temperature dependence of $f_\mathrm{rot}/f_\mathrm{vib}$ or $(\text{p.f.})\dagger^*/(\text{p.f.})_\mathrm{AB}^\dagger$. In none of these cases will $\Delta\epsilon^*$ be exactly equal to the quantity in the exponent, although it will not differ greatly from it and $\exp \{\Delta s^*/k\}$ will not be exactly equal to the pre-exponential term, but again will not differ greatly from it. It is of interest to apply Eq. (7.4) to k_a in the simplest case, Eq. (6.4):

$$\Delta\epsilon^* = \epsilon_\mathrm{m} + \tfrac{1}{2}kT. \tag{7.12}$$

If $\epsilon_\mathrm{m} = 0$, Eq. (7.12) reduces to $\Delta\epsilon^* = \tfrac{1}{2}kT$, still neglecting the temperature dependence of r_m. This means that the average energy of all pairs of atoms which collide exceeds the average energy of all pairs by $\tfrac{1}{2}kT$. This result is not unexpected, since we should expect those pairs which have a higher relative velocity to collide more often.

18-8. *Experimental Results and Discussion*

As we have noted, the general procedure in studying reaction rates is to measure the rate over a range of temperatures, and to find the activation energy. The exponential factor is generally taken as $\exp\{-\Delta\epsilon^*/kT\}$ or $\exp\{-\Delta E^*/RT\}$, and the pre-exponential factor is then calculated from the actual rate constant at some particular temperature. The pre-exponential factor calculated in this way, [by use of Eq. (7.7)] will differ, but not significantly, from those of the equations given earlier in this chapter as will be evident from the examples given just above. The energies of activation cover a wide range, and depend upon the particular bonds involved. Methods of calculating activation energies have been developed, especially by Eyring and his coworkers [3, Chap. 3], but are outside the scope of statistical mechanics. It is possible to draw some general conclusions concerning the pre-exponential factor.

A general survey of the known examples of gas-phase unimolecular reactions [4, Chap. 11] indicates that the pre-exponential factor often has a value near 10^{13}. In view of our remarks regarding Eqs. (1.7) and (1.8), this is the result expected for a rigid activated complex. In the reverse bimolecular association, then, it should be necessary to have mutual orientation of the colliding parts before reaction can occur. And, indeed, in many bimolecular associations there is evidence that the reaction occurs at only a small fraction of the collisions which have sufficient energy. This happens, for example, in the case of gaseous Diels-Alder syntheses, which have been investigated by Kistiakowsky and his coworkers. The activated complex in these cases does not appear to be as rigid as the final product molecule; it appears likely, however, that the reacting molecules associate first to an intermediate type of molecule which is really a double free radical and which is not as rigid as the final product, the latter being formed only by a further chemical reaction involving ring closure, which is not rate-determining. See [4, p. 302].

Of recent years a rather large number of unimolecular reactions has been discovered for which the pre-exponential factor ranges† between 10^{15} and 10^{16}. It is possible that this merely indicates that some of the vibrational frequencies are lower in the activated complex than in the normal molecule. The molecules involved in these cases usually have a ring structure, and the lowering of vibrational frequencies is probably associated with opening of the ring structure to form a biradical, which would result in a general loosening of the structure [15].‡

---

† For example, cyclobutane (see [14]). A number of data were assembled by W. D. Walters, A. F. Pataracchia, and P. C. Rotoli for the Symposium on the Kinetics of Pyrolytic Reactions, held at the University of Ottawa, Canada, Sept. 9–11, 1964.

‡ See also paper by S. W. Benson and P. S. Nangia in 1964 Ottawa Symposium.

There are some cases in which the pre-exponential factor is even larger. For example in the decomposition of azomethane [16] the pre-exponential factor is $10^{17.3}$. This is rather large to be accounted for even on the supposition that both radicals are rotating, assuming that the reaction whose rate is being measured is $CH_3NNCH_3 \longrightarrow N_2 + 2CH_3$ occurring in one step. If the methyl radicals are rotating freely about the C—N bond in the azomethane molecule, only two degrees of freedom of each methyl will be loosened. These will presumably be those having moments of inertia of about 3×10^{-40} gm cm^2 (see Sec. 7-6), and they should involve a symmetry number of 2 (out of a total symmetry number for CH_3, assumed flat, of 6). Thus the loosening factor will be

$$\left(\frac{8\pi^2 kTI}{2h^2}\right)^2 = 440$$

at $T = 550°K$, about the temperature of the experiments. If this is multiplied by a frequency of about 3×10^{13}, it gives for the total frequency factor 1.3×10^{16}, which is low by a factor of about 15. If this interpretation is correct, it would appear that rotation of the N_2 portion must also play some role in the high observed frequency factor. However, it is not certain that the CH_3's rotate freely about the C—N bonds in the normal molecule, and there is a possibility of a somewhat different mechanism, as noted at the end of this section.

Another example of a high-frequency factor is the dissociation of C_2H_6 to give $2CH_3$. It is known that two methyl radicals recombine at approximately every collision [17–20], which means that the activated complex for the reaction

$$C_2H_6 \rightleftharpoons 2CH_3$$

must be loose.† The recombinations of ethyl radicals [22, 23] and perfluoromethyl radicals [24] also occur with moderate steric factors of about 0.1, indicating relatively loose activated complexes.

Ree, Ree, Eyring, and Fueno [25] have calculated the rate of recombination of radicals by assuming that they act like a pair of atoms interacting under their mutual van der Waals forces. It is assumed that every pair which crosses the rotational barrier at the r_j appropriate to their particular relative angular momentum will trans-

---

† The recombination reaction in [17] and [18] was actually $2CH_3 \longrightarrow C_2H_6$, although it was interpreted differently at the time. For summaries of data see [4]. The direct reaction has also been reported [21].

fer enough energy to be held near the minimum of the van der Waals potential-energy curve long enough so that eventually they will become properly oriented and recombine. This calculation gives results which fit the experimental results reasonably well; in my opinion, however, it does not properly describe the nature of the loose activated complex.

When the reactive coordinate (or, perhaps less precisely, the bond which breaks in dissociation) is not stretched, even though it may have sufficient energy to break, one must suppose that the loosening of the bending vibrations to rotations has not yet occurred; in other words, the rest of the vibrational frequencies will be approximately as they are in a normal molecule.† On the other hand, when the bond *is* stretched nearly to its breaking point, the vibration-to-rotation change has taken place if the activated complex is loose. Since there are many more available energy levels when the bond is stretched than when it is at its normal length (accounting for the increased rate of reaction of a loose complex), there must be many more molecules, among those having the requisite energy localized in the bond, in which the bond is stretched than in which it is not stretched. In order for this to be true we must suppose that, once the bond is stretched, it is somehow inhibited from readily returning to its equilibrium position. However, if this inhibition held only for those molecules in which sufficient energy is already localized in the reactive bond to break it, this could not result in the high value for the pre-exponential factor characteristic of the loose activated complex. For the reaction then could not proceed without going through a situation in which the reactive bond had sufficient energy and was unstretched. Since the loosening of the bending vibrations would occur only after the bond was stretched, the rate of dissociation would be that characteristic of a rigid complex. We will have to assume that the loosening occurs when the reactive bond is stretched, even though it does not have quite enough energy to break, and that the reaction generally occurs through the attainment of further energy by this bond after it is stretched. In other words, the molecule is loosened first, and breaks up afterward. In the association reaction we must imagine ways by which the associating parts can be held together with the bond stretched, a condition from which the system relaxes only after a lapse of time, but usually before it can dissociate again.

When the reactive bond is stretched, the bending vibrations of

---

† This and the following paragraph have been taken almost verbatim from Rice [26].

the attached groups must become much freer. Such a vibration could change into a wagging motion which is almost as free as rotation. If this were the mechanism in the dissociation of ethane into two methyls, for example, the almost separated methyls could turn their hydrogens toward the bond, in which case the bond could not shorten readily to its normal length. Furthermore, if we assume that equilibrium is established (as we must, if the full increase in rate of reaction is to be attained), the wagging motion would be slower than the vibration in just the ratio that the distance between energy levels would be decreased. The time during which the bond would remain stretched would thus be expected to increase in about the same ratio, whether we look at the situation from a mechanical or statistical point of view.

The van der Waals forces between two methyl radicals do not seem to be strong enough to give a sufficient reservoir of loosened molecules. We may make an estimate of the van der Waals forces by supposing that the methyl radicals resemble methane molecules, which is closely equivalent to what was done by Ree, Ree, Eyring, and Fueno. The heat of sublimation of methane is about 2500 cal/mole; the structure of solid methane is a face-centered-cubic array of methane molecules, each one being surrounded by twelve nearest neighbors and there being, thus, six intermolecular contacts per methane molecule. We may estimate the van der Waals attraction energy, then, to be around 400 cal/pair-mole. This is less than RT even at room temperature, and relatively few molecules will be caught in such a shallow potential minimum. Indeed, there will be fewer molecules in it than exist in a similar range of distances, but having higher energies. We can scarcely conceive that any large fraction of pairs of radicals which collide would be caught in this minimum. But even this would not be sufficient to produce a "loose" activated complex. For such a rapid intake into the potential minimum would be matched at equilibrium by an equally rapid output into the stream of separating pairs. And this in turn would have to be more than matched, if the unimolecular decomposition is to have the pre-exponential factor characteristic of a loose complex, by the rate at which these loosely bound complexes establish equilibrium with the substrate of reactive molecules. Such a process becomes believable only if there is a reservoir of loosely bound complexes in the potential minimum which is somewhat more than comparable to the equilibrium number of actually dissociating pairs within a comparable distance. Furthermore, a potential minimum as small as that which we have estimated for two methyl radicals is easily obliterated completely by the rotational potential if there is only a small amount of angular momentum. Thus a deeper potential-energy minimum, which still allows free rotation of the separate radicals, or its equivalent, appears to be needed. It has been suggested [26] that such an attractive potential might be provided by a three-center bond of the type known in the boranes, viz.:

$$
\begin{array}{cc}
\text{H} & \text{H} \\
\overset{\cdot\cdot}{:\text{C}} \cdot \text{H} \cdot \overset{\cdot\cdot}{\text{C}} : \text{H} \\
\overset{\cdot\cdot}{\text{H}} & \overset{\cdot\cdot}{\text{H}}
\end{array}
$$

Such a bond might be stable enough to provide an intermediate condition with a sufficient lifetime against dissociation to allow equilibrium to be established with the normal stable form. At the same time it would be very loose. Although the wagging motion about the hydrogen bridge would not be able to go over into a complete rotation, if the partial rotation centered about the hydrogen bridge it would involve a moment of inertia considerably greater than that of a methyl radical, which would tend to increase the pre-exponential factor in the reaction-rate expression. Some such mechanism may also be involved in the high pre-exponential factor for the azomethane decomposition, and would perhaps seem more reasonable than a mechanism involving completely free rotation of the various parts of the molecule.

In the recombination of perfluoromethyl radicals the intermediate would have the form

$$
\begin{array}{cc}
\overset{\cdot\cdot}{:\text{F}}: & \overset{\cdot\cdot}{:\text{F}}: \\
\overset{\cdot\cdot}{:\text{C}}:\overset{\cdot\cdot}{\text{F}}:\overset{\cdot\cdot}{\text{C}}:\overset{\cdot\cdot}{\text{F}}: \\
\overset{\cdot\cdot}{:\text{F}}: & \overset{\cdot\cdot}{:\text{F}}:
\end{array}
$$

It must be supposed, however, that the bonds are loose enough to allow considerable freedom of motion about the fluorine in the center.

18-9. *Appendix: Potential-energy Surfaces*

The potential energy of the system AB or A + B is a function of all the coordinates of all the atoms involved. It may therefore be represented as a very complicated surface in a many-dimensional space. If there are n coordinates, there will be $n + 1$ dimensions, the extra one corresponding to the dependent variable, the potential energy. Since there is one relation between the potential energy and the coordinates, the dimensionality of the potential-energy surface will be one less; i.e., it will be a surface of n dimensions.

If the normal state of AB and the normal state of A + B represent relatively stable conditions, they will have relatively low energies; we may say that the system will be in one or another of some depressions or "valleys" in the potential-energy surface. To get from one of these to another the system will have to go over regions of higher energy; it will have to pass over "higher ground." The tendency will be not to go over much higher ground than necessary, on the average, in a statistically governed process. Thus the system will tend to go over the lowest possible saddle point, or "pass," in its journey from one valley to another. The saddle point corresponds to the top of the hump in the potential-energy curve of Fig. 18-1, which shows only the reaction coordinate. We might imagine that if the two parts A and B each consisted of many atoms, the actual height of the hump would depend upon the orientation of A and B with respect to each other. Some particular mutual orientation will give the lowest possible hump in Fig. 18-1, this being then the lowest way over the pass in the many-dimensional diagram. Such a situation would correspond to at least a partial freezing out of rotations into vibrations.

The saddle point is the point of highest energy on the route of lowest energy over the pass, and a system passing over or near it is in the transition state, or may be referred to as an activated complex. More precisely, we use these terms to refer to a sort of statistical mean of all the systems actually passing over the saddle point.

To further illustrate the ideas involved in potential-energy surfaces, we consider an especially simple case, but one involving a reaction which is slightly different from dissociation or association.

Consider the following reaction between three atoms

$$A + BC \longrightarrow AB + C.$$

We shall assume that all three atoms are constrained to move along a straight line. The potential energy, then, will depend upon only two coordinates, which may be taken as the distance r_{AB} between the atoms A and B and the distance r_{BC} between the atoms B and C. The potential energy, ϵ_p, may be plotted on a three-dimensional diagram as function of r_{AB} and r_{BC}; the resulting surface can be displayed as a contour diagram, as in Fig. 18-2. Each line is a line of constant ϵ_p, and the values of ϵ_p, in arbitrary units and from an arbitrary zero of energy are shown at the ends of the lines. In the lower right-hand corner, where r_{AB} is large and r_{BC} is small, we are essentially dealing with the molecule BC. For very small r_{BC} the potential energy rises steeply, and the contour lines are accordingly very close together. There is a minimum of potential energy at the equilibrium value of r_{BC} (along the

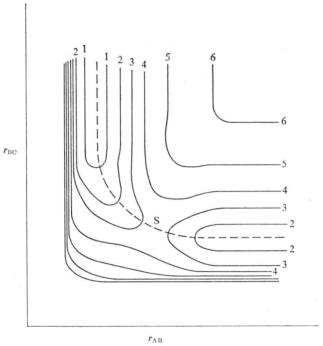

Figure 18-2. Contour diagram for potential energy for reaction $A + BC \longrightarrow AB + C$.

broken curve in Fig. 18-2), and for greater r_{BC} the potential energy rises less rapidly, so the contour lines are not so close together. As we push A closer to BC it is at first repelled, causing a rise in the potential energy, as shown on the diagram. If A is pushed in closer and at the same time the distance r_{BC} is gradually increased, at first we get a rise in potential, but eventually the potential energy will again decrease as the molecule AB is formed. This molecule is represented in the upper left-hand part of the diagram. The broken curve goes from the equilibrium distance for BC to the equilibrium distance for AB over the lowest possible path in the potential-energy surface. The highest point on this lowest path is the saddle point; it occurs at S. The difference between ϵ_p at S and at the equilibrium distance r_{BC} when r_{AB}

is very large, determines the activation energy for the reaction A + BC ⟶ AB + C.

Of course, this is oversimplified, since the atoms are assumed to lie in a straight line, but it will serve to illustrate the nature of the potential-energy surfaces which are so important in reaction kinetics.

REFERENCES

1. L. S. Kassel, *Kinetics of Homogeneous Gas Reactions*, New York, Chemical Catalog Co., 1932.
2. H. J. Schumacher, *Chemische Gasreaktionen*, Dresden, Steinkopff, 1938.
3. S. Glasstone, K. J. Laidler, and H. Eyring, *The Theory of Rate Processes*, New York, McGraw-Hill, 1941.
4. S. W. Benson, *The Foundations of Chemical Kinetics*, New York, McGraw-Hill, 1960.
5. O. K. Rice, in *Transfert d'Energie dans les Gaz* (Proceedings of the Twelfth Solvay Congress on Chemistry), Brussels, Stoops (New York, Interscience) 1964, pp. 17–86.
6. O. K. Rice and H. Gershinowitz, *J. Chem. Phys.*, **2,** 853 (1934).
7. K. Yang and T. Ree, *J. Chem. Phys.*, **35,** 588 (1961).
8. B. O. Peirce, *A Short Table of Integrals*, 3d ed., Boston, Ginn, 1929, Nos. 481 and 493.
9. R. D. Present, *Kinetic Theory of Gases*, New York, McGraw-Hill, 1958, p. 153.
10. M. G. Evans and M. Polanyi, *Trans. Faraday Soc.*, **31,** 875 (1935).
11. H. Eyring, *J. Chem. Phys.*, **3,** 107 (1935).
12. O. K. Rice and H. Gershinowitz, *J. Chem. Phys.*, **3,** 479 (1935).
13. R. C. Tolman, *Statistical Mechanics with Applications to Physics and Chemistry*, New York, Chemical Catalog Co., 1927, Chap. 21.
14. R. W. Carr, Jr. and W. D. Walters, *J. Phys. Chem.*, **67,** 1370 (1963).
15. S. W. Benson, *J. Chem. Phys.*, **34,** 521 (1961).
16. W. Forst and O. K. Rice, *Canadian J. Chem.*, **41,** 562 (1963).
17. W. L. Haden, Jr. and O. K. Rice, *J. Chem. Phys.*, **10,** 445 (1942).
18. V. E. Lucas and O. K. Rice, *J. Chem. Phys.*, **18,** 983 (1950).
19. R. Gomer and G. B. Kistiakowsky, *J. Chem. Phys.*, **19,** 85 (1951).
20. G. B. Kistiakowsky and E. K. Roberts, *J. Chem. Phys.*, **21,** 1637 (1953).
21. C. P. Quinn, *Proc. Roy. Soc.* (London), **A275,** 190 (1963).
22. K. J. Ivin and E. W. R. Steacie, *Proc. Roy. Soc.* (London), **A208,** 25 (1951).
23. K. J. Ivin and M. H. J. Wijnen, *J. Phys. Chem.*, **56,** 967 (1952).
24. P. B. Ascough, *J. Chem. Phys.*, **24,** 944 (1956).
25. T. S. Ree, T. Ree, H. Eyring, and T. Fueno, *J. Chem. Phys.*, **36,** 281 (1962).

26. O. K. Rice, *J. Phys. Chem.*, **65**, 1588 (1961).

27. G. Herzberg, *Infrared and Raman Spectra of Polyatomic Molecules*, Vol. 2 of *Molecular Spectra and Molecular Structure*, 2d. ed., Princeton, N.J., Van Nostrand, 1945.

PROBLEMS

18.1. Write out Eq. (6.3) in more detail for the reaction $C_2H_6 \longrightarrow 2CH_3$, assuming free rotation in the activated complex, including in f_{rot}/f_{vib} only corresponding degrees of freedom in which important changes have occurred. How would this be modified if a three-center bond is involved in the activated complex (see Sec. 18-8)?

18.2. Write out Eq. (6.9) in more detail for the decomposition of

$$
\begin{array}{c}
\text{H} \qquad \text{O--C--R''} \\
\quad \backslash \qquad \qquad \parallel \\
\qquad \quad \text{O} \\
\qquad \text{C} \\
\quad \diagup \quad \diagdown \\
\text{R'} \qquad \text{O--C--R'''} \\
\qquad \qquad \parallel \\
\qquad \qquad \text{O}
\end{array}
$$

which probably goes through the intermediate configuration

$$
\begin{array}{c}
\text{H} \qquad \text{O} \qquad \text{O} \\
\ \backslash \quad \diagup\!\!\diagup \cdots \backslash\!\!\backslash \\
\qquad \text{C} \qquad \ \text{C--R''} \\
\ \diagup \quad \cdots \\
\text{R'} \qquad \text{O} \\
\qquad \quad | \\
\qquad \text{C--R'''} \\
\qquad \quad \parallel \\
\qquad \quad \text{O}
\end{array}
$$

where $\cdots$ indicates a bond which is being formed, and $---$ indicates a bond which is breaking. Cancel out in $(p.f.)^*/(p.f.)^0$ any factors which do not change appreciably in the activated complex.

18.3. Enumerate and classify the degrees of freedom in C_2H_5 and I. Distinguish between rotations with large and small moments of inertia and the different types of vibrational motion. Do the same for C_2H_5I, remembering that the C—C—I skeleton is not a straight line and correlate the degrees of freedom in the two cases. Calculate the collision number (at unit concentration) for C_2H_5 and I, assuming that $r_m = 3\text{Å}$, that $T = 300°\text{K}$, and that there is no hump in the potential-energy curve. Now estimate the orientation factor assuming that the activated complex is like the molecule C_2H_5I (rigid complex), and calculate the number of effective collisions (leading to reaction). The following distances may be taken as given: C—C, 1.54A; C—H, 1.1A; C—I, 2.0Å. The C—C—I angle is about 108 deg. Rough estimates of moments of inertia and vibrational frequencies (see [27]) will be acceptable, and approximately equal factors in the partition functions may be cancelled where appropriate.

18.4. Apply Eq. (7.4) to the reaction $C_2H_6 \longrightarrow 2CH_3$, assuming free rotation in the activated complex (see Prob. 18.1).

18.5. Show from Eq. (7.4) that, if $\bar{k}$ is expressed in the form $A \exp\{-\Delta E^*/RT\}$, then

$$RT d \ln A/dT = d\Delta E^*/dT$$

or, from Eq. (7.6),

$$T d\Delta S^*/dT = d\Delta E^*/dT.$$

Chapter 19

Recombination of Atoms and Dissociation of Diatomic Molecules

19-1. *General Considerations*

In the preceding chapter we considered the rate of recombination of atoms and the rate of dissociation of diatomic molecules, but we derived equations only for what we may call the "provisional rate" at equilibrium, regardless of what may immediately follow or precede. As we have pointed out, an association of a pair of atoms which is immediately followed by a dissociation is not recognized as a chemical reaction. If, however, the association is followed by a collision with a third body, so that energy is lost to the third body, then redissociation does not occur immediately, and we do recognize that a chemical reaction has taken place. Similarly, a dissociation of a diatomic molecule, immediately preceded not by association of the atoms but by a collision which furnished the energy necessary for the dissociation, is recognized as a chemical reaction.

The association and dissociation reactions are, of course, closely related to each other. If we consider the reaction

$$A + B + M \rightleftharpoons AB + M, \qquad (a)$$

where M is the third body, the rate at which the reaction proceeds from left to right is equal to $k_a(A)(B)(M)$, where k_a is the rate constant for (*recognizable*) association, and the rate in the opposite direction is $k_d(AB)(M)$, where k_d is the rate constant for (*recognizable*) dissociation. At equilibrium these two rates must be equal, so we may write for the equilibrium constant

$$K = \frac{(AB)}{(A)(B)} = \frac{k_a}{k_d}.$$ (1.1)

It is often easier to deal with the dissociation rather than with the association, since the former requires only a two-body collision. We can then use Eq. (1.1) to find k_a from k_d.

In attempting to find k_d we can see that the process of collision of AB with M is not one which will keep the pairs AB dissociating at an equilibrium rate [1–5]. It is known that there is considerable difficulty in transferring large amounts of translational energy into vibrational energy; therefore, the process must occur by steps, the molecule AB being excited to higher and higher vibrational states until finally it dissociates. Of course, this will occur only rarely, and essentially never will the process of vibrational excitation be unidirectional. Only occasionally will those collisions which increase the energy of AB predominate sufficiently during a series of collisions to cause the dissociation of some particular molecule.

The higher energy levels of AB will not be maintained in their equilibrium quotas if the atoms A and B are not present at the start of the reaction. For the population of these higher levels will be drained off by dissociation, and there will be no association to balance this. The closer a level is to the dissociation limit, the more its population will depart from the equilibrium expectation. Since the dissociation depends primarily upon the levels close to the dissociation limits, the rate of dissociation will be less than the equilibrium rate; i.e., k_d will be less than the equilibrium calculation would suggest.

For this reason it has been suggested by a number of writers that Eq. (1.1) might lose its validity. However, as will be shown, Eq. (1.1) will remain valid if conditions are such that consistent rate constants can be measured [6, 7]. The main condition is that the rate of relaxation (for attainment of equilibrium among the various energy levels leading to reaction if the reaction did not occur) is rapid compared with the rate of reaction. Under this condition the lifetime of systems in these energy levels is small compared with the mean reaction time, so their populations will come to a steady state. This condition is usually fulfilled, for the energy levels from which dissociation actually takes place are high-energy levels; they are not highly populated even at equilibrium and so cannot cause the reaction to become excessively fast. On the other hand, they can be easily filled to their equilibrium (or steady-state) quota because this quota is low. However, at high enough temperatures the equilibrium population may become large enough so that this condition breaks down, and it is known that the temperature coefficient for the rate of relaxation is less than that for the reaction rate. The dissociation and relaxation of O_2 in shock waves have been studied [8], and it has been found that the dissociation catches up with the relaxation at about 8000°K. At this point it has been found impossible to get consistent measurements of the dissociation rate constant.

Returning now to the discussion of Eq. (1.1), we consider two atoms recombining according to the reaction (a). We may assume that M is different from A or B and is present in considerable excess. In this case the reaction will truly be the one written—if M is not in excess, other reactions (e.g., $2A + B \rightleftarrows AB + A$) might be complicating factors. When A and B react in the presence of M, we may expect that the molecule AB will in general be formed in an excited state, AB*. On subsequent collision with M's, AB* will either redissociate or revert to a state from which redissociation will be very slow. According to the conditions imposed, the period of indecision will be short. The fate of any particular AB* will depend only on the results of its collisions with M, and will be independent of what is happening to any other AB* or AB which may be present.

Similarly, the dissociation reaction, the reverse of (a), will proceed through excited molecules AB*, and the fate of these excited molecules, whether dissociated or deactivated, will not depend appreciably upon whether dissociated atoms are present or not, since in any case M is in great excess. Furthermore, under the conditions we have outlined, they will quickly either be deactivated or will dissociate.

If the reaction is proceeding in both directions, in equilibrium, it is still true that the fate of any individual molecule, or pair of atoms, is independent of the others which are present, if M is in sufficient excess. Thus the actual rate at which atoms go over to molecules or molecules dissociate into atoms is unchanged at equilibrium, and the rate constants which appear in Eq. (1.1), which must hold when A, B and AB are in equilibrium, are the same rate constants which are found when equilibrium is not established. What we call the *equilibrium* rate constant for dissociation, however, includes (as k_d does *not*) the AB*'s which dissociate after being formed from $A + B$, and the *equilibrium* rate constant for association includes the rate of formation of those AB*'s which are going to dissociate again before being deactivated. It is, of course, also true that $K = k_{a,eq}/k_{d,eq}$.

The third body M can, in special cases, be A, B, or AB, but must be in excess in any case. Of course, the effects of various third bodies, present simultaneously, can usually be disentangled by varying the conditions and, in effect, finding by extrapolation what the rate would be if one of them were in great excess. If the effects of different third bodies were additive, the separation of their effects would offer no problem; however, it is by no means certain that this is the case, since a given transition between energy levels will be affected differently by different third bodies, and the effect when the third bodies are acting simultaneously may not be exactly the same as the sum of their separate effects. The argument which we have given for the validity of Eq. (1.1) will of course hold for any mixture of third bodies, provided that the mixture is the same for the forward and the reverse reactions.

The mechanism indicated by reaction (a) is not the only possible mechanism by which association of atoms and dissociation of diatomic molecules can occur. Another possibility involves the intermediate formation of a complex $A \cdot M$ or $B \cdot M$ held loosely together, perhaps by van der Waals forces [9]. We will call this the complex mechanism. As an example, we might have for the association

$$A + M \rightleftharpoons A \cdot M, \qquad \text{(b)}$$
$$A \cdot M + B \longrightarrow AB + M. \qquad \text{(c)}$$

The reaction (b) can be maintained in equilibrium by the frequent encounters with other molecules of the species M, which can serve to remove energy for the direct reaction and furnish energy for the reverse. If M is in excess, reaction (b) will be much faster than reaction (c), and the equilibrium will not be appreciably disturbed. If M is a complex molecule with internal degrees of freedom which can take up or give up energy, the *immediate* intervention of a second M might not be necessary. If the rate constant for reaction (c) is k_a^*, then the rate of association is given by

$$k_a^*(A \cdot M)(B) = k_a^* K_{A \cdot M}(A)(M)(B), \qquad (1.2)$$

where $K_{A \cdot M}$ is the equilibrium constant for reaction (b), and we see then that the over-all rate constant is given by

$$k_a = k_a^* K_{A \cdot M}. \qquad (1.3)$$

The reverse reaction will go through the stages

$$AB + M \longrightarrow A \cdot M + B, \qquad \text{(d)}$$
$$A \cdot M + M \longrightarrow A + 2M. \qquad \text{(e)}$$

Since A is not initially present in the dissociation, the equilibrium of (e) will not be involved. Reaction (e) will be rapid compared to reaction (d) because it will require much less activation energy. Therefore (d) is the rate-determining step, and the rate of dissociation will be $k_d(AB)(M)$. The dissociation (d), although proceeding through a slightly different mechanism than that indicated in (a), will nevertheless involve mostly highly excited molecules AB*, since the energy of formation of A·M can provide only a small fraction of the energy to dissociate the bond in AB. Again, these excited molecules may not be in their equilibrium quota. Complementary to this, some of the AB (really AB*) in reaction (c) may redissociate [reversing (c)]. Again, at equilibrium, in a gas with a large excess of M, the fate of an AB* formed from A and B will not be affected by the presence of other molecules than M, nor will the fate of an AB* formed from an AB be affected by the presence of others. Hence, at equilibrium where direct and reverse reactions must go at the same rate, we must have

$$k_d(AB)(M) = k_a^*(A \cdot M)(B) = k_a(A)(M)(B), \qquad (1.4)$$

by Eqs. (1.2) and (1.3) and, once again, we see that Eq. (1.1) is valid.

19-2. *Rate of Dissociation of Diatomic Molecules by Collision*

In attempting to calculate the rate of dissociation of diatomic molecules most earlier workers ignored the departure from equilibrium in the population of the excited energy levels. Not only because it affords greater accuracy in the calculations, but also because it provides greater clarity in the concepts, it seems desirable at the present time to present calculations which do take the lack of equilibrium into account. However, because very little is known with certainty about the rate of transition from one state to the other, and because in any case it would be an extremely complicated procedure to carry through a steady-state calculation involving all these transition rates in a general case, it is necessary to set up some kind of model before any definite result can be obtained.

In the low-energy range, where the vibrational motion of diatomic molecules is nearly harmonic and where the energy between levels is fairly large, it is known that in most collision processes there is a tendency for vibrational transitions to occur largely between adjacent levels. On this account, it has been suggested that the proper approach to the problem of determining the populations of the excited vibrational levels and ultimately the rate of decomposition of a diatomic molecule reacting according to the reverse of (a) is to consider step-wise transitions from one vibrational level to the next [10]. However, before dissociation occurs, anharmonicity becomes great, and in many cases the energy levels come very close together. Changes of vibrational quantum number considerably greater than ±1 become common, and some aspects of the problem are better treated from the viewpoint of classical mechanics. Therefore I think it is more realistic to assume that constant changes of energy,† closely related to the average energy of the colliding particle M, will occur, rather than constant changes of vibrational quantum number. Actually there is a range of possible energy exchanges, but a qualitative picture should be obtained by assuming that the exchange of energy from vibration to translation always occurs in increments η equal to the average of the true exchanges. It is not proposed to develop a complete theory in this way, but to lay a foundation for discussion of the experimental results.

We may parenthetically remark that these changes in energy level can be assumed to include rotational changes. The potential-energy curve of a diatomic molecule will in general have no maximum (ϵ_m of Chap. 18 equal to zero). However, as soon as the rotational potential $j(j + 1)h^2/8\pi^2\mu r^2$ is added a maximum does appear—the so-called rotational barrier. Some of its consequences were discussed in detail in Sec. 18-2. As was noted there, its position will depend upon the rotational quantum number j. A collision which imparts angular momentum to the molecule will raise the energy more near the minimum of the potential-energy curve than near the rotational barrier. A molecule with a given vibrational quantum number will therefore be raised with respect to the rotational barrier. Thus imparting of rotational energy is equivalent to the imparting of vibrational energy, though perhaps not the same amount. This can be included in the average energy transfer, and we shall suppose that we need to speak only of transfers of vibrational energy.

We can think of the vibrational energy levels of the diatomic molecule as divided into zones of width η designated by a suffix i. Dissociation will always take place from the highest of these zones, for which we set $i = 0$; $i + 1$ refers to a *lower* energy than i. We designate a molecule in state i as AB_i. We have a series of reactions, which can proceed in either direction, with rate constants as indicated:

† The deduction used here follows my 1963 paper [11]. A large part of the present chapter has been taken from, or follows closely, [5] of Chap. 18.

$$AB_i + M \overset{k_i}{\underset{k_{-(i+1)}}{\rightleftarrows}} AB_{i+1} + M \qquad \text{(f)}$$

but for $i = 0$ it can go in only one direction:

$$AB_0 + M \overset{k_{-0}}{\longrightarrow} A + B + M. \qquad \text{(g)}$$

We get a series of steady-state equations by setting $d(AB_i)/dt = 0$. From $d(AB_0)/dt$, we have

$$k_{-1}X_1 - (k_0 + k_{-0})X_0 = 0, \qquad (2.1)$$

and, in general,

$$k_{-(i+1)}X_{i+1} + k_{i-1}X_{i-1} - (k_i + k_{-i})X_i = 0, \qquad (2.2)$$

where X_i is the concentration of AB_i, and so on. The rate constants are, of course, mean values for the different zones. Each zone is characterized by a mean energy ϵ_i and the number g_i of energy levels contained in the zone. We take the zero of energy at the dissociation limit, so that $\epsilon_0 \approx -\eta/2$, and write

$$\frac{\eta}{kT} = a \qquad (2.3)$$

and

$$\frac{\epsilon_i}{kT} = x_i. \qquad (2.4)$$

If all the k_i's were known, we could find all the X_i in terms of X_0 from Eqs. (2.1) and (2.2) by simple iteration. The k_i's are not known but certain relations between them are. From the law of microscopic reversibility we can write

$$\frac{k_i}{k_{-(i+1)}} = \frac{g_{i+1}}{g_i} \exp\{a\}, \qquad (2.5)$$

since this gives the correct ratio X_i/X_{i+1} at equilibrium. For the steady-state concentration, it seems natural to set

$$X_i = c_i g_i \exp\{-x_i\}, \qquad (2.6)$$

since if X_i were the equilibrium concentration all the c_i would be equal. The ratio c_0/c_∞, where c_∞ refers to a low enough energy for its X_i almost to coincide with its equilibrium value, is a measure of the deviation of zone 0 from equilibrium. Substituting Eq. (2.6) in Eqs. (2.1) and (2.2), making use of Eq. (2.5), and setting

$$y_i = \frac{k_i}{k_i + k_{-i}} \tag{2.7}$$

$$y_{-i} = \frac{k_{-i}}{k_i + k_{-i}}, \tag{2.8}$$

we get

$$y_i c_{i+1} + y_{-i} c_{i-1} - c_i = 0, \tag{2.9}$$

which includes the results from both (2.1) and (2.2) if we set $c_{-1} = 0$. We rewrite Eq. (2.9) by replacing $i + 1$ by i to get it in a convenient form for the iteration

$$c_i = \frac{c_{i-1}}{y_{i-1}} - \frac{y_{-(i-1)}}{y_{i-1}} c_{i-2} = (1 + b_i)c_{i-1} - b_i c_{i-2}, \tag{2.10}$$

where

$$b_i = \frac{y_{-(i-1)}}{y_{i-1}} \tag{2.11}$$

is the ratio of a jump upward to a jump downward from the same state. In general we can solve the set of equations (2.10) by iteration if the b_i are known. If b_i is taken as constant $(=b)$, less than 1, then it is readily shown that

$$c_i = (1 + b + b^2 + \cdots b^i)c_0$$
$$= \frac{1 - b^{i+1}}{1 - b} c_0, \tag{2.12}$$

and

$$\frac{c_0}{c_\infty} = 1 - b. \tag{2.13}$$

Now b will be closely related to the energy difference η, and we write

$$b = f \exp \{-a\}, \tag{2.14}$$

where f is presumably not far from unity, which says that the relative probability of up or down transition is nearly equal to the Boltzmann factor.

We can now write down an expression for the dissociation rate constant

$$k_{\mathrm{d}} = \left[4\pi\sigma^2 \left(\frac{kT}{2\pi M} \right)^{1/2} \right] \left[\frac{g^* g_0 \exp\{-\epsilon_{\mathrm{D}}/kT\} \exp\{a/2\}}{g_{\mathrm{AB}}(\mathrm{p.f.})_{\mathrm{vib}}} \right]$$

$$\times \left[1 - f \exp\{-a\} \right] \left[\frac{f \exp\{-a\}}{1 + f \exp\{-a\}} \right] \frac{r_{\mathrm{m}}^2}{r_{\mathrm{e}}^2}. \qquad (2.15)$$

This expression may be understood by analyzing the factors involved. The first bracket is the collision frequency for collisions between AB and M with an effective collision diameter σ; M is the reduced mass of AB + M. In the numerator of the second bracket, g^* is the number of attractive electronic energy levels, having the same asymptote as the ground state, from which dissociation can occur. It is divided by the multiplicity of the ground level g_{AB}. In this bracketed term, g_0 is the average number of states in the zone $i = 0$ in these electronic levels and ϵ_{D} is the dissociation energy so that $\epsilon_{\mathrm{D}} - \eta/2 = \epsilon_{\mathrm{D}} - akT/2$ is close to the average energy in zone $i = 0$. Thus the numerator may be said to represent the partition function for the zone $i = 0$, and $(\mathrm{p.f.})_{\mathrm{vib}}$ is the vibrational partition function for the molecule AB (which, classically, equals $kT/h\nu_{\mathrm{AB}}$); the ratio is equal to the relative number of molecules which are in a position to dissociate at equilibrium. The next factor, which comes directly from Eqs. (2.13) and (2.14) takes into account the deviation from equilibrium, and the fourth gives the relative probability of dissociation (rather than deactivation) at collision. This would complete the expression for a nonrotating molecule. Averaging over rotational levels, taking into account the effect of the centrifugal potential on the dissociation energy, introduces the factor $r_{\mathrm{m}}^2/r_{\mathrm{e}}^2$, where r_{m} is an average value of the internuclear distance at the rotational barrier, much as in Sec. 18-2, and r_{e} is the equilibrium distance for AB.

The quantity g_0 depends on a of Eq. (2.3), and it will be desirable to express g_0 in terms of a. The difference, $\delta\epsilon_v$, between energy levels near dissociation is known empirically to be given roughly by a linear relation in the quantum number v,

$$\delta\epsilon_v = \alpha(v_{\mathrm{D}} - v), \qquad (2.16)$$

where v_{D} is the quantum number at the dissociation limit, where the energy (reckoned from the bottom of the potential energy curve) is ϵ_{D}. There is, of course, a relation between g_0 and $\delta\epsilon_v$, g_0 being just the value of $v_{\mathrm{D}} - v$ when $\epsilon_{\mathrm{D}} - \epsilon_v = akT$. Since the average value of $\delta\epsilon_v$ between quantum numbers $v = v_{\mathrm{D}}$ and $v = v_{\mathrm{D}} - g_0$ is just $\frac{1}{2}\delta\epsilon_v(g_0)$, where $\delta\epsilon_v(g_0)$ is the value of $\delta\epsilon_v$ at $v = v_{\mathrm{D}} - g_0$, we see that

$$\tfrac{1}{2} g_0 \delta\epsilon_v(g_0) = akT. \qquad (2.17)$$

If we let $\delta\epsilon_{v_0}$ be equal to the value of $\delta\epsilon_v$ when $\epsilon_D - \epsilon_v = kT$ and if we let g_0' be the corresponding value of $v_D - v$, then, by the same reasoning

$$\tfrac{1}{2}g_0'\delta\epsilon_{v_0} - kT. \tag{2.18}$$

Use of Eq. (2.16) in Eq. (2.17), setting $v_D - v = g_0$, gives

$$\tfrac{1}{2}\alpha g_0^2 = akT. \tag{2.19}$$

Likewise, use of Eq. (2.16) in (2.18), setting $v_D - v = g_0'$ gives

$$\frac{\tfrac{1}{2}(\delta\epsilon_{v_0})^2}{\alpha} = kT. \tag{2.20}$$

Elimination of α between Eqs. (2.19) and (2.20) gives

$$g_0 = \frac{2a^{1/2}kT}{\delta\epsilon_{v_0}}. \tag{2.21}$$

This gives the desired relation between g_0 and a, since $\delta\epsilon_{v_0}$ will depend only upon the particular molecule and the temperature. In the light of Eq. (2.19), if a is independent of T, then g_0 will be proportional to $T^{1/2}$.

It will be of some interest later to compare the results obtained from Eq. (2.15) with a less exact equation derived earlier [12–14]

$$k_d = \left[4\pi\sigma^2\left(\frac{kT}{2\pi M}\right)^{1/2}\right]\left[\frac{g^*(kT/\delta\epsilon_{v_0})\exp\{-\epsilon_D/kT\}}{g_{AB}(\text{p.f.})_{\text{vib}}}\right]\frac{r_m^2}{r_e^2} \tag{2.22}$$

in which the third and fourth brackets, which take care of the departure from equilibrium, are omitted, and in which the factor $2a^{1/2}\exp\{a/2\}$ is replaced by 1 in the second bracket.

Steiner [15] much earlier derived an equation for the association reaction based on the assumption that reaction would occur if there was a collision with a third body during the time τ_c during which the two atoms were in collision. Steiner's equation, if used with Eq. (1.1), is essentially the same as Eq. (2.22), but with τ_c substituted for $h/\delta\epsilon_{v_0}$. The latter, of course, is equal to τ, the period of vibration of a molecule whose energy is kT below the dissociation limit on the rotational barrier [see Eq. (4.4) of Chap. 1]. An average collision has an energy about kT above the rotational barrier, and τ_c may be considered to be the time that the pair of atoms in such a state remain closer together than the rotational barrier. At $T = 0$ it is clear that $\tau_c = \tau$, and they will both decrease as T increases, τ because the distance of vibration decreases, and τ_c because the average velocity increases. Steiner attempted a direct calculation of τ_c, but use of Eq. (2.22) seems somewhat easier, and application of Eq. (2.15) is preferable.

The evaluation of Eq. (2.15) will depend upon the determination of a. As we have remarked, a collision between M and AB when the latter is in an excited state can probably be well handled classically. Since during a considerable part of their vibration A and B will have a considerable separation, they will exert only small forces on each other, and will be moving slowly relatively to each other. Thus we might expect the transfer of energy from M to occur largely through collision with *one* of the atoms A and B, say B. We can learn something about it by considering a collision between M and B in which B is initially stationary. The maximum amount of kinetic energy which can be transferred from M to B in this way is $4m_M m_B/(m_M + m_B)^2$ times the original kinetic energy of M. We shall make the assumption that

$$a = \frac{4m_M \bar{m}}{(m_M + \bar{m})^2} \tag{2.23}$$

where $\bar{m}$ is the average of m_A and m_B. This is equivalent to assuming that, if the masses were the same, the average energy transferred would be equal to kT, and we hope that it will take care of the mass effects so that we can use the combination of Eq. (2.15) and (2.23) as a working tool in the analysis of experimental data. Equation (2.23) should be applied, however, only when AB is heavier than M, so that AB may be considered, as a first approximation, not to be moving; then it can serve as a reasonable guide. Even in this case, Eq. (2.23) undoubtedly exaggerates the effect of a difference in mass, since it can only be a rough approximation to suppose that the third body M, even if it is only an atom, collides with *one* of the atoms of AB.

19-3. *The Complex Mechanism for Dissociation of a Diatomic Molecule*

In Sec. 19-1 it was noted that the rate of the dissociation of a diatomic molecule may be actually a measure of the rate of a reaction such as

$$AB + M \longrightarrow A \cdot M + B. \qquad \text{(h)}$$

This reaction may itself go through steps [12]

$$AB + M \rightleftharpoons AB \cdot M, \qquad \text{(i)}$$

$$AB \cdot M \longrightarrow A \cdot M + B. \qquad \text{(j)}$$

Of course, the reaction

$$AB \cdot M \longrightarrow B \cdot M + A \qquad \text{(k)}$$

might also occur. The dissociation of the molecule AB may thus be effected, even though there is not quite enough energy to dissociate all three, A, B, and M. A small portion of the dissociation energy is furnished by the binding energy of the complex. This lowers the effective activation energy and allows the reaction to go more rapidly.

If M is a complicated molecule, a complex $AB \cdot M$ can be readily formed, the binding energy being at first absorbed into the internal degrees of freedom of M, and later removed at leisure by a subsequent collision. The rate of decomposition of the complex $AB \cdot M$ according to the reaction (j) can be estimated as the rate of a unimolecular decomposition, using the transition state theory, assuming equilibrium between the various degrees of freedom. A single step process, like reaction (h), will actually involve the same transition state. If the system is supposed to be in equilibrium up to the transition state, the interposition of another equilibrium will make no difference. A one-step reaction would be the only possibility if M were an atom. However, it will be convenient in formulating the problem to suppose that the intermediate equilibrium is established. It is important to note that, even if there is a complex of the type $AB \cdot M$ formed, it is quite essential that the complex $B \cdot M$ or $A \cdot M$ remain at the end of the reaction. Otherwise the effective lowering of the activation energy caused by the formation of the complex would be cancelled by the energy required to break up the complex $B \cdot M$ or $A \cdot M$. These must last until the next collision.

If we assume, as a matter of convenience, that the dissociation reaction goes through the mechanism which involves the complex $AB \cdot M$, we may write

$$k_{\mathrm{d}} = K_{\mathrm{M}} k_{\mathrm{d}}^*, \qquad (3.1)$$

where K_{M} is the equilibrium constant for reaction (i) and k_{d}^* is the rate constant for reaction (j) or (k) or both.

The binding in a complex which is held together by van der Waals forces is so weak that we may assume that the internal degrees of freedom are not affected; so we deal with an equilibrium formally like that of two atoms. We may, therefore, obtain K_M from Eq. (4.9) of Chap. 7, by setting $g_{AB}/g_A g_B = 1$, and setting the quantization factor equal to 1, since to a good approximation this system will be classical. We replace ϵ_D by ϵ_M, which we shall use for the energy of dissociation from minimum to asymptote of the potential-energy curve for this pair, AB and M, and replace r_e by $r_{M,e}$, the equilibrium distance between centers of gravity of AB and M. In doing this we assume ϵ_M to be large enough and kT small enough so that we can deal with a region of the potential-energy curve between AB and M small enough so that we do not need to consider anharmonicity.

To find k_d^*, we may treat the reaction $AB \cdot M \longrightarrow B \cdot M + A$ or $AB \cdot M \longrightarrow A \cdot M + B$ as a unimolecular reaction in which the activated complex differs from the reactant only in the one bond which breaks, i.e., the reaction coordinate, and possibly to a small extent in the bond associated with the complex formation. The latter effect we shall neglect for the moment, except that we note that the energy of the dissociation might be slightly different if M were present than if it were absent, since the binding of M to AB might be slightly different from that to A or B. The dissociation energy $AB \longrightarrow A + B$ in the presence of M we shall call ϵ_D'.

Substituting first Eq. (6.1) of Chap. 18 (setting $\epsilon_m = 0$) into Eq. (3.1) and then applying Eq. (4.9) of Chap. 7 (without the quantization factor) to reactions (i) and (j) yield†

$$k_d = \frac{g^*}{g_{AB}} \frac{kT}{h(\text{p.f.})_{\text{vib}}} \frac{r_m^2}{r_e^2} \exp\left\{-\frac{\epsilon_D'}{kT}\right\} K_M$$

$$= \frac{g^*}{g_{AB}} \frac{kT}{h(\text{p.f.})_{\text{vib}}} \frac{r_m^2}{r_e^2} (4\pi r_{M,e}^2)(2\pi a_M^2 kT)^{1/2} \exp\left\{-\frac{\epsilon_D' - \epsilon_M}{kT}\right\} \qquad (3.2)$$

where $(2\pi a_M^2 kT)^{1/2}$ is a free length characteristic of the vibration of M against AB, and $(\text{p.f.})_{\text{vib}}$ is the vibrational partition function for AB, and r_m and r_e refer to the molecule AB. If we compare this with the corresponding equation for the collision mechanism in the approximate form, Eq. (2.22), we see that σ is replaced by $r_{M,e}$; the factor, having dimensions of distance, $(kT/2\pi M)^{1/2}\tau_c$ (recall that $\delta\epsilon_{v_0} = h/\tau_c$) is replaced by $(2\pi a_M^2 kT)^{1/2}$; ϵ_D is replaced by ϵ_D'; and there is, of course, the extra factor $\exp\{\epsilon_M/kT\}$. Summarizing, we have

---

† One might expect a factor 2 to appear in this equation because of the two possible modes of decomposition to give A·M and B·M. However, each one of these implies a particular orientation of AB with respect to M, and has only half the chance of occurring it would otherwise. The value of ϵ_D' will be some average for the two modes of decomposition.

$$\frac{k_{\rm d}(\text{complex})}{k_{\rm d}(\text{collision})} \approx \frac{r_{\rm M.e}^2}{\sigma^2} \frac{(2\pi a_{\rm M}^2 kT)^{1/2}}{(kT/2\pi M)^{1/2}\tau_{\rm c}} \exp\left\{\frac{\epsilon_{\rm M} + \epsilon_{\rm D} - \epsilon_{\rm D}'}{kT}\right\}. \tag{3.3}$$

It will be recalled that these expressions were derived on the assumption that the mutual vibrations of AB and M in the complex could be treated as those of a harmonic oscillator. This is correct if $\epsilon_{\rm M} \gg kT$. However, it breaks down as kT approaches $\epsilon_{\rm M}$. When kT is greater than $\epsilon_{\rm M}$, each bound state of the complex will contribute a term approaching 1 to the partition function, and the partition function for the complex AB·M will become nearly equal to the number of bound states.† Thus the function will become constant, instead of increasing indefinitely as $kT/h\nu_{\rm M}$ (where $\nu_{\rm M}$ is the frequency of vibration of AB against M), as would be the case if it actually were a harmonic oscillator. A generally valid correction can be made, assuming that $\nu_{\rm M}$ is low enough to treat the complex classically, by multiplying Eq. (3.2) by $(\text{p.f.})_{\rm M} h\nu_{\rm M}/kT$, where $(\text{p.f.})_{\rm M}$ is the correct vibrational partition function for the bound states of the complex. This should be properly averaged over all rotational states, but a good enough approximation can be obtained by considering the case for which $j = 0$.

The problem of evaluating $(\text{p.f.})_{\rm M}$ is the same as that which was considered in Sec. 8-4. With the notation adapted to the usage of the present section, we may take over Eq. (4.8) of Chap. 8. We need to note that here the zero of ϵ is at the bottom of the potential-energy curve, whereas in Chap. 8 it was at the asymptote, and the partition function in each case is referred to the appropriate zero of energy. Then we may write Eq. (4.8) of Chap. 8 as

$$(\text{p.f.})_{\rm M} = \frac{\pi r_{\rm M,e}}{6h}(2M)^{1/2}\int_0^{\epsilon_{\rm M}} \frac{1}{(\epsilon_{\rm M} - \epsilon)^{1/2}} \exp\left\{-\frac{\epsilon}{kT}\right\} d\epsilon. \tag{3.4}$$

Evaluating at the limits, as in Chap. 8, we obtain

$$(\text{p.f.})_{\rm M}_{\substack{\epsilon_{\rm M} \ll kT}} = \frac{\pi r_{\rm M,e}}{3h}(2\epsilon_{\rm M}M)^{1/2}, \tag{3.5}$$

and

$$(\text{p.f.})_{\rm M}_{\substack{\epsilon_{\rm M} \gg kT}} \approx \frac{\pi r_{\rm M,e}kT}{6h}\left(\frac{2M}{\epsilon_{\rm M}}\right)^{1/2}. \tag{3.6}$$

It is interesting that, at $kT = 2\epsilon_{\rm M}$, Eq. (3.6) takes on a value equal to Eq. (3.5). That is, the limiting high-temperature value is the value

† This effect was noted in [14], and a treatment of it was given by Bunker and Davidson [16].

of Eq. (3.6) at $kT = 2\epsilon_M$. Of course, the transition between Eq. (3.6) and (3.5) takes place gradually, probably largely in the region between $T = \frac{1}{2}\epsilon_M/k$ and $T = 2\epsilon_M/k$.

It may be noted that Eq. (3.6) corresponds precisely, as it should, to $(p.f.)_M = kT/h\nu_M$, with ν_M the frequency of a harmonic oscillator whose force constant is given by the curvature of the Lennard-Jones potential, at $r_{M,e}$.

19-4. *Method of Phase-space Trajectories*

Recently there have been several discussions of the problem of atom association and dissociation of diatomic molecules, based upon a consideration of trajectories of representative points in the phase space or on integration of the Liouville equation [17], related to Sec. 1-11. We give here a brief outline of the work of Keck [18], which has been carried to the point where fairly detailed comparison with experiment can be made, and which illustrates the application of the properties of the phase space which were described and developed in Chap. 1.

Keck's theory is a development of an idea, apparently due originally to Marcellin [19], and applied by Wigner [20] to the problem under consideration. Using classical mechanics, one considers the phase space for the system consisting of three atoms, A, B, and M. If the coordinates and momenta of the center of gravity are excluded, only motion relative to the center of gravity being considered, this is a 12-dimensional space. One now seeks a surface, S (11-dimensional), which divides the phase space into two parts, one corresponding to separated atoms A and B, the other to the molecule AB. Such a surface may be so chosen that, when the relative coordinates and momenta of M and AB have any fixed value, and the polar angles made by AB, and the corresponding momenta, are fixed, the projection of the surface in the two-dimensional space r_{AB}, p_{AB} (interatomic distance and relative momentum of A and B) lies at a constant energy just touching the maximum in the potential-energy plus rotational-potential curve for AB (see Fig. 19-1—in the figure the relative energy ϵ_{AB} of the atoms in AB replaces the momentum p_{AB} as a coordinate). This surface was modified by Keck, but for the cases of most interest it was essentially as described.

If the density of phase points at any point on surface S is ρ and if their vector velocity in the phase space is $\mathbf{v}$, then the rate at which they are crossing the surface per unit area at that point is $\rho|\mathbf{v}\cdot\mathbf{n}|$ where

n is a unit vector normal to S. They may be crossing in either direction, depending upon the particular point in the phase space. If we count only those which are crossing in the "positive" direction and integrate over that part, say S_+ of the surface corresponding to that

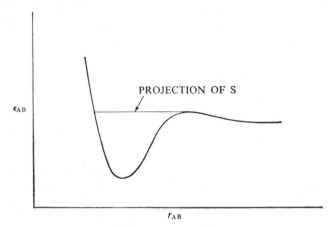

Figure 19-1. (From Rice [**5** of Chap. 18].)

particular direction, we obtain the rate of reaction in that direction, namely

$$R = \int_{S_+} \rho |\mathbf{v} \cdot \mathbf{n}| d\sigma, \tag{4.1}$$

where $d\sigma$ is the element of surface, provided none of the points which thus cross S_+ recross at some other position later, which of course reverses the reaction. This last proviso means that this method of attack can give only an upper bound to the reaction rate. It will still be an upper bound if we substitute ρ_e for ρ, where ρ_e is the density of phase points at the surface in equilibrium with the distribution a great distance from the surface, since ρ could not exceed ρ_e. In general, over any particular area of the surface, if this area is small enough, the value of ρ should be equal either to ρ_e or to 0 (see Sec. 1-11). It is 0 if the phase points at this part of the surface originated on the wrong side, having already crossed once in the wrong direction, for in calculating k_d, for example, we should include in ρ only phase points whose path comes from a region in which AB is not dissociated.

For the dissociation reaction we may write, if the concentrations of AB and M are unity

$$\rho_e = \frac{\exp\{-\epsilon/kT\}}{h^6(\text{p.f.})_{0,AB}(\text{p.f.})_r^0}, \tag{4.2}$$

where $(\text{p.f.})_{0,AB}$ is the internal partition function for the molecule AB and $(\text{p.f.})_r^0$ is the (p.f.) per unit volume of ordinary space for the relative motion of AB and M, and $\exp\{-\epsilon/kT\}/h^6$ is the partition function per unit volume of phase space in the region of the phase space in which ρ_e is located, since $1/h^6$ is the number of energy levels per unit volume of phase space. Therefore we can write

$$k_d \leqq \frac{1}{h^6(\text{p.f.})_{0,AB}(\text{p.f.})_r^0} \int_{S_+} |\mathbf{v}\cdot\mathbf{n}| \exp\left\{-\frac{\epsilon}{kT}\right\} d\sigma. \tag{4.3}$$

Now let us define a function Φ of the six coordinates q_i and six momenta p_i such that at S we have $\Phi = 0$ and such that a unit change of Φ (at least at S) represents a displacement of unit length normal to S in the phase space. We may then write

$$\int_{S_+} |\mathbf{v}\cdot\mathbf{n}| \exp\left\{-\frac{\epsilon}{kT}\right\} d\sigma$$

$$= \int_0^1 \int_{S_+} |\mathbf{v}\cdot\mathbf{n}| \exp\left\{-\frac{\epsilon}{kT}\right\} d\sigma d\Phi$$

$$= \int_{\Phi=0}^{\Phi=1} (\mathbf{v}\cdot\mathbf{n}) \exp\left\{-\frac{\epsilon}{kT}\right\} \prod_i dq_i dp_i, \tag{4.4}$$

assuming $(\mathbf{v}\cdot\mathbf{n}) \exp\{-\epsilon/kT\}$ to be constant between $\Phi = 0$ and $\Phi = 1$. Here $(\mathbf{v}\cdot\mathbf{n}) = |\mathbf{v}\cdot\mathbf{n}|$ if the flow is toward dissociation but 0 otherwise. The components of $\mathbf{v}$ are the time derivatives $\dot{q}_i, \dot{p}_i$, and those of $\mathbf{n}$ are $\partial\Phi/\partial q_i, \partial\Phi/\partial p_i$ (each has 12 components). Thus

$$\mathbf{v}\cdot\mathbf{n} = \sum_i \left(\dot{p}_i \frac{\partial\Phi}{\partial p_i} + \dot{q}_i \frac{\partial\Phi}{\partial q_i}\right)$$

$$= \sum_i \left(-\frac{\partial H}{\partial q_i}\frac{\partial\Phi}{\partial p_i} + \frac{\partial H}{\partial p_i}\frac{\partial\Phi}{\partial q_i}\right), \tag{4.5}$$

where H is the Hamiltonian and we have applied the Hamilton equations [Eqs. (10.1) of Chap. 1]. Since the last quantity in parentheses is the Jacobian J_i of the transformation of $dp_i dq_i$ to $dH d\Phi$, or in other notation $d\epsilon d\Phi$, it is seen that the integral, confined, of course, to regions where the flow is toward dissociation, is transformed to

$$\sum_i \int_{\Phi=0}^{\Phi=1} s_i \exp\left\{-\frac{\epsilon}{kT}\right\} d\epsilon d\Phi \prod_{k \neq i} dq_k dp_k$$

$$= \sum_i \int_{S_+} s_i \exp\left\{-\frac{\epsilon}{kT}\right\} d\epsilon \prod_{k \neq i} dq_k dp_k, \tag{4.6}$$

where $s_i = J_i/|J_i|$ (i.e., $s_i = \pm 1$, depending on the sign of J_i, since each transformed volume element is taken positive). Thus k_d can be calculated, provided we can find the limits of the various variables defined by S_+. The solution is considerably facilitated by the proper choice of variables, and any set of variables chosen must be a canonical set in the sense discussed in the latter part of Chap. 1. Let us designate the coordinates of the reacting atoms, A and B, as x_A, y_A, z_A and x_B, y_B, z_B, respectively. We make a transformation of coordinates to the coordinates of the center of gravity, X_{AB}, Y_{AB}, Z_{AB}, and relative coordinates x_{AB} (equal to $x_B - x_A$), y_{AB}, z_{AB}. Let the original coordinates of the third body M (assumed to be monatomic) be x_M, y_M, z_M. We make a further transformation, replacing X_{AB}, Y_{AB}, Z_{AB}, x_M, y_M, z_M by the coordinates of center of gravity of the whole system X [which is equal to $(m_A + m_B)X_{AB}/(m_A + m_B + m_M) + m_M x_M/(m_A + m_B + m_M)$], Y, Z and relative coordinates x (equal to $x_M - X_{AB}$), y, z. This, of course, is a point transformation, and the transformation of the momenta will follow in the usual way. Since it is a point transformation, the resulting set of coordinates and momenta is a canonical one.

Keck made an additional transformation. In place of x, y, z and the corresponding momenta he introduced coordinates r, ω, ϕ and momenta p_r, p_ω, p_ϕ. Here r is the distance between M and the center of gravity of A and B. Now consider the plane in which the radius vector $\mathbf{r}$ happens to be moving instantaneously. ϕ is the angle made with the original x axis by the intersection of this plane of motion with the x–y plane, and ω is the angle made by $\mathbf{r}$ with this intersection, p_r is the usual radial momentum, p_ω is the total angular momentum of M about the center of gravity of A and B [with reduced mass $(m_A + m_B)m_M/(m_A + m_B + m_M)$], and p_ϕ is the component of this angular momentum about the z axis. The coordinates r_{AB}, ω_{AB}, ϕ_{AB}, and momenta $p_{r_{AB}}$, $p_{\omega_{AB}}$, $p_{\phi_{AB}}$ bear the same relation to x_{AB}, y_{AB}, z_{AB} and their corresponding momenta.

If we consider a special, rather artificial, case in which the force between A and B is directed along the line between them and the force between A and B and M is directed along the line between M and the center of gravity of A and B, then the motion of the point r, ω, ϕ will always remain in a fixed plane and that of r_{AB}, ω_{AB}, ϕ_{AB} will remain in another fixed plane. In this case the Hamiltonian will split into two independent parts, one of which depends only on r, p_r, and p_ω and the other of which depends only on r_{AB}, $p_{r_{AB}}$, and $p_{\omega_{AB}}$. It may be written explicitly,

$$H = H_1 + H_2, \tag{4.7}$$

where

$$H_1 = \frac{p_r^2}{2M} + \frac{p_\omega^2}{2Mr^2} + \epsilon_{p1}, \tag{4.8}$$

and

$$H_2 = \frac{p_{r_{AB}}^2}{2\mu} + \frac{p_{\omega_{AB}}^2}{2\mu r_{AB}^2} + \epsilon_{p2}, \tag{4.9}$$

where the first two terms in each case are the kinetic energy terms, μ being the reduced mass of A and B, and M the reduced mass of M and A + B, with ϵ_{p1} a function of r and ϵ_{p2} a function of r_{AB}. The two motions are quite independent and can be treated separately. In either case, we have the equation for motion in a plane, expressed in cylindrical coordinates, and it is well known that Hamilton's equations (see Secs. 1-9 and 1-10) are obeyed for H_1 and H_2 so far as r, ω, p_r, p_ω, and r_{AB}, ω_{AB}, $p_{r_{AB}}$, $p_{\omega_{AB}}$ are concerned. They are also obeyed for ϕ and p_ϕ, because H_1 does not depend on these quantities, and clearly, since the plane is fixed, and since $p_\omega = 0$, it is true that ϕ and p_ϕ vanish. Similar statements hold for ϕ_{AB} and $p_{\phi_{AB}}$. Therefore the set of coordinates and momenta is a canonical set.

In actuality the potential energy ϵ_{p1} will not depend on r but rather on the distances between M and A and between M and B separately. Then the Hamiltonian will not split into two independent parts, and the motion of r, ω, ϕ, or of r_{AB}, ω_{AB}, ϕ_{AB}, will not remain in a fixed plane. Instantaneously, however, the motion is in some plane, and the equations of transformation to the coordinates x, y, z or x_{AB}, y_{AB}, z_{AB} and their momenta will be the same as if the motion were to remain in the instantaneous plane. [Even if the separation indicated in Eq. (4.7) is correct, the motions can be in *any* pair of planes; the only difference is that formerly the planes remained fixed in time, whereas now they change.] It is clear, however, from Sec. 1-10, that whether a given transformation is canonical does not depend on the actual form of the Hamiltonian, but only on the transformation itself. Thus the variables which Keck has chosen are a canonical set even when all the interactions between the particles are taken into account.

These variables are particularly useful because it can be seen that the positions of the points of the surface S, as shown in Fig. 19-1, are defined by only three of the variables, r_{AB}, $p_{r_{AB}}$, and $p_{\omega_{AB}}$. The other variables may take any value whatsoever; if r_{AB}, $p_{r_{AB}}$, and $p_{\omega_{AB}}$ have the right values, the point will be on the surface. (We may consider an analogy in three dimensions: the surface $x = 0$ is defined by the value of x, whereas y and z can have any values.) This means that Φ depends only on r_{AB}, $p_{r_{AB}}$, and $p_{\omega_{AB}}$. The Jacobians in Eq. (4.5) will be different from zero only if q_i and p_i are r_{AB} and $p_{r_{AB}}$ or ω_{AB} and $p_{\omega_{AB}}$. This shows us that there will be only two terms in the sum in Eq. (4.6). In one of them $dr_{AB}dp_{r_{AB}}$ will be missing from the product of differentials; in the other $d\omega_{AB}dp_{\omega_{AB}}$ will be missing. Since the first of these terms is originally derived from the term which takes into account the components $\dot{r}_{AB}$ and $\dot{p}_{r_{AB}}$ of $\mathbf{v}$ in the phase space, it represents contributions to the rate of reaction which may be described as arising from changes in vibrational energy of AB, whereas the second term represents contributions arising from changes in rotational energy.

We will not attempt to go through the rather complex mathematical procedure by which Keck evaluated the integrals, but we will indicate some of the problems involved. Let us consider first the integral in which $dr_{AB}dp_{r_{AB}}$ is missing. If one attempts to integrate first with respect to $d\epsilon$, then the other variables must be held constant. If, however, r is large, there is no interaction between M and AB. With all the variables of integration, other than ϵ held fixed, with r large, and with our points confined to S (which at fixed $p_{\omega_{AB}}$ corresponds to a fixed ϵ_{AB}), the value of ϵ is itself fixed. Since ϵ thus has no range, the upper and lower limits coincide and the integral vanishes. There will thus be no contributions to the integral if r is large. If r is not large, then, although ϵ_{AB} is fixed on S, a change of r_{AB} will change the total energy through changes in the interaction with M, and limits of ϵ will be assignable in principle for any fixed values of the other variables. (A change in r_{AB} is of course reflected in the integral only as a change in ϵ, since r_{AB} does not appear explicitly in this integral.)

Let us now turn to the other integral, from which $d\omega_{AB}dp_{\omega_{AB}}$ is missing. Here, too, if all the remaining variables except ϵ are held fixed, we can integrate with respect to ϵ first. Again let us consider the case with r large. If r_{AB} and $p_{r_{AB}}$ are both fixed, this automatically fixes $p_{\omega_{AB}}$ if the point is on S, since S is a function of these three variables only. Thus ϵ_{AB}, which is given by

$$\epsilon_{AB} = \frac{p_{r_{AB}}^2}{2\mu} + \frac{p_{\omega_{AB}}^2}{2\mu r_{AB}^2} + \epsilon_{p2}, \tag{4.10}$$

and which is equal on S to the energy of the rotational barrier, is fixed. Since there is no interaction between the motion of AB and the motion of M if r is large, the total energy ϵ will again be fixed, and the upper and lower limits of integration of ϵ will coincide. But when r is small the total energy will obviously depend upon ω_{AB}, which is not one of the explicit variables of integration, and can itself be fixed only by fixing ϵ.

Thus the integrals can certainly be evaluated, at least, in principle, and we know to some extent the nature of the contributions to these integrals. The contributions occur in regions of the phase space where the third body M is close to AB, and in general the contributions will be larger the more sharply the potential energy changes with changes in the configuration of AB. One must, of course, count only those parts of the surface S which are being crossed in one particular direction. However, if the integrals are evaluated over all of S, adding together the absolute values of all contributions, one may then simply divide the result by 2. This follows because at equilibrium the phase points will on the average cross S as often in one direction as the other. We must also remember that the result will yield an upper bound to the reaction rate because of the possibility of the phase point crossing the surface S several times in the course of a single collision of M with AB.

In evaluating these integrals, Keck has represented the potential energy of AB by a Morse function, and he has made an estimate of the mutual potential energies A–M and B–M. The two-body potentials are assumed to be additive. The potentials A–M and B–M include estimates for the van der Waals attraction (e.g., if A or B were an iodine atom, it was assumed for this purpose to be much like xenon, which has about the same number of electrons).

Since this procedure gives only an upper bound, Keck made some calculations on actual trajectories (for a somewhat simplified case) [21]†, so that he could make an estimate as to how great the over-

---

† Further calculations were reported by Kantrowitz [22].

estimate might be.† He randomly selected points in the phase space, all of which lay on the surface S_+ (he investigated association, but the information thus obtained is the same as for dissociation) in such a way that the surface density was proportional to the integrand of Eq. (4.3). The trajectories to which these points belonged were followed by use of a computer, both forward and backward, until M was reasonably far from A and B in both directions. One could then decide whether a given trajectory which crossed S_+ would result in reaction, how many would recross the surface once more and so not react, how many would cross again, etc. Also he could tell how many of those crossing the surface were actually in their second crossing, having originated on the other side of the surface. He investigated 2H + Ar, 2O + Ar, 2I + Ar, 2I + He, and some others. In each case he considered temperatures such that $kT/\epsilon_D = 0.01$ and $kT/\epsilon_D = 0.1$. For 2H + Ar at $kT/\epsilon_D = 0.01$, the ratio of reaction to crossings (counting two of the latter where two crossings occurred in the same direction) was about 0.26, for 2O + Ar it was about 0.40, for 2I + Ar about 0.64, and for 2I + He about 0.80, being a little less at the higher temperature for the first two and a little more for 2I + Ar and 2I + He. It was also possible to find the distribution of energies for the molecule formed when reaction occurred. In all cases, close to half of the combined molecules were within $kT/4$ of the maximum of the potential energy plus rotational potential. Since a pair of colliding particles will have an average relative kinetic energy of kT at the potential-energy maximum this seems fairly reasonable if there is an average transfer of about kT.

19-5. *Some Experimental Material on Atom Recombination*

Early experimental work on the recombination of iodine and of bromine atoms at room temperature was done by Rabinowitch and co-workers using a method which involved a photochemical steady state. More recently use has been made of flash photolysis for measurements up to 250°C, and of shock waves, combined with spectroscopic observations or density measurements back of the shock front, using optical methods, for the dissociation of diatomic gases above

---

† Some direct computer calculations of rates of energy exchange between a diatomic molecule and an atom have been made by Benson and Berend [23]. These results are very interesting, but some of the conclusions, especially as regards temperature coefficients of the reaction, may stand further scrutiny.

1000°C. Since association and dissociation are connected by Eq. (1.1) they can be converted into each other.†

Most work has been done on the recombination of iodine atoms. The recombination rate constants range from around 0.3×10^{-32} cc^2/molecules^{-2} sec^{-1} for He as a third body to 25 to 50×10^{-32} with benzene as a third body, and even higher for some large organic molecules, and 500×10^{-32} or more with I_2 as third body. Even with He, the rate (expressed as a dissociation rate for I_2) is rather large compared with the expected number of collisions having the requisite energy. In large part this is because of the relatively large density of energy levels near the dissociation [the factor g_0 in Eq. (2.15)—g^* and $(r_m/r_e)^2$ also contribute]; in other cases, the very large rates reflect the considerable stability of the complex $I \cdot M$.

In the association of iodine atoms in benzene, a very direct comparison is possible. Atack and Rice (Sec. 8-6) have made equation-of-state measurements of mixtures of I_2 and benzene. Although this has recently been questioned [24] the forces between I_2 and benzene molecules are of the van der Waals type, judging from the magnitude of the deviations from the ideal-mixing law. The value found for the equilibrium constant for the formation of a van der Waals complex $I_2 \cdot C_6H_6$ was used directly in the first line of Eq. (3.2) to calculate k_d, assuming a complex mechanism [14]. In Eq. (3.2) g^* was taken‡ as 5, $\nu_{AB}(=\nu_{I_2})$ was taken from the tabulation of Herzberg [27], $(r_m/r_e)^2$ was estimated as 5, and it was assumed that $\epsilon'_D = \epsilon_D$. In this way, and by use of Eq. (1.1), we found $k_a \approx 30 \times 10^{-32}$ cc^2 molecule^{-2} sec^{-1} which is to be compared with experimental values of about 20 to 50×10^{-32} [28–30], the more reliable ones probably being in the lower part of the range. It is seen that the agreement is very good.

The assumption that $\epsilon'_D = \epsilon_D$ means that the stability of $C_6H_6 \cdot I$ is the same as that of $C_6H_6 \cdot I_2$. We actually have very little to go on in estimating van der Waals constants for I; it may be, how-

---

† For an extensive list of references to experimental work see reference [5] of Chap. 18.
‡ This value is used because there are three attractive states, connecting with unexcited atoms, for I_2, $^1\Sigma_g^+$, $^3\Pi_{1u}$, and $^3\Pi_{2u}$, the last two of which have two-fold degeneracy. The $^3\Pi_{2u}$ has not been observed, but there are theoretical reasons for believing in its existence and its dissociation energy has been estimated (Mulliken [25] and personal communication). Because iodine (and, indeed, also bromine) approaches j–j coupling [26] changes in multiplicity at collision are probable. If such transitions become comparable in rate to energy exchange at an energy below the dissociation limit equal to several times the average energy transferred, the levels of all the electronic states must be considered together. The $^3\Pi_{1u}$ state is, however, so shallow that it is somewhat doubtful if this condition is fulfilled, and it may be that association to this state will be reversed before it can be stabilized by transfer to $^1\Sigma_g^+$ or $^3\Pi_{2u}$ and subsequent loss of energy. If this is true, n should be reduced to 3.

ever, a little surprising that I, with only half as many electrons as I_2, should have the same van der Waals attraction for benzene, and this is not what was assumed by Keck. Porter and Smith [30] have suggested that I forms a charge-transfer complex with benzene. In this connection, however, it should be noted that Atack and Rice found that their van der Waals complex in the gas phase was at least six times as stable as the well-known I_2–benzene charge-transfer complex, which was studied in solution by Benesi and Hildebrand [31]. It is not certain that iodine atoms would be comparable in this respect.

The temperature coefficients of k_d and of k_a may be inferred by scrutiny of Eq. (3.2) and use of Eq. (1.1). If $\epsilon'_D = \epsilon_D$, the factor $\exp\{-\epsilon'_D/kT\}$ cancels the term $\exp\{\epsilon_D/kT\}$, which occurs in Eq. (1.1), when one obtains k_a. Assuming that the attractive forces in I_2 at the distance r_m are chiefly van der Waals forces, having the form $-c/r^6$, where c is a constant, one finds (Sec. 18-2) that r_m is proportional to $1/T^{1/6}$. K_M depends on temperature chiefly through $\exp\{\epsilon_M/kT\}$ and the free length $(2\pi a_M^2 kT)^{1/2}$, which varies as $T^{1/2}$; a similar free length will occur in K. It is seen, then, that we may expect†

$$k_a \propto T^{2/3} \exp\left\{\frac{\epsilon_M}{kT}\right\},$$

which gives an energy of activation equal to $-\epsilon_M + \frac{2}{3}kT$. Atack and Rice found an enthalpy ΔH of reaction for

$$I_2 \cdot C_6H_6 \longrightarrow I_2 + C_6H_6$$

equal to 2.44 kcal per mole, which at the temperature used corresponds to a ΔE of reaction of about 1.55 kcal. Now $\Delta E = -RT^2 d \ln K_M/dT = (R/k)\epsilon_M - \frac{1}{2}RT$. So ϵ_M is equivalent to 2.0 kcal per mole, and the expected activation energy for association of iodine atoms around 400°K will be -1.5 kcal. Probably the most reliable determination is the recent one of Porter and Smith [30], who get -1.7 kcal. All things taken together, we seem to have a reasonably good picture of the effect of benzene on the recombination of iodine atoms.

Porter and Smith have measured the recombination rate and its temperature coefficient for iodine atoms in a number of inert gases. In a general way, large rates go with large negative activation energies, as might be expected if a complex $I \cdot M$ is formed. Russell and Simons

---

† Since $(\text{p.f.})_{\text{vib}} = kT/h\nu_{AB}$, the first kT in Eq. (3.2) cancels out. The quantum corrections in k_d and K also cancel in calculating k_a.

[29] had previously found high rates with third bodies which might be expected to have large van der Waals forces; however, as noted, Porter and Smith suggest that electron-transfer forces are involved.

Although in many cases the iodine recombination almost certainly proceeds through a complex $I \cdot M$, it undoubtedly proceeds according to the collision mechanism with He, Ne, or H_2 as the third body. If iodine atoms exert forces comparable to I_2, then with argon the binding energy for $I \cdot Ar$ should render the contributions of the two mechanisms comparable. It is interesting to apply Eq. (2.15) to the reaction with the rare gases as third bodies. In doing this we take the experimental value [32] of k_d as given and from it calculate σ, the effective collision diameter; we then decide whether the value of σ is reasonable. We again use $g^* = 5$ and $(r_m/r_0)^2 = 5$, and g_0 is taken from Eq. (2.21) using values of $\delta\epsilon_{v0}$ estimated from spectroscopic data and tabulated previously [14]. We evaluate a from Eq. (2.23) and set f equal to 1. The results of this calculation are given in Table 19-1, and

TABLE 19-1

Recombination of Iodine Atoms in Various Gases

Parameter	He	Ne	Ar	Kr	Xe
$k_a \times 10^{32}$ (cc² molec.$^{-2}$ sec^{-1})	0.335	0.45	0.92	1.125	1.495
σ (Å), Eq. (2.22)	1.1	1.9	3.1	3.9	4.9
a	0.119	0.472	0.729	0.957	0.999
$1 - \exp\{-a\}$	0.112	0.376	0.518	0.616	0.632
σ (Å), Eq. (2.15)	5.5	3.7	4.8	5.4	6.6

the values of σ found from Eq. (2.22) are also shown. The effect of the mass of the colliding atom seems to be fairly well taken into account by the factors involving a in Eq. (2.15), but the large value of σ found for He indicates that the effect, as should be expected, is somewhat exaggerated by Eq. (2.23). This conclusion is reinforced by the fact that the values of σ for the heavier gases would be reduced if allowance were made for the part of the reaction going through the complex mechanism.

If we assume that σ and a are temperature independent, take $(p.f.)_{vib} \approx kT/h\nu_{AB}$, allow for the temperature dependence, $r_m^2 \propto 1/T^{1/3}$ use Eq. (2.19) for g_0 (noting that g_0 will probably decrease slightly with

j, the average of which increases with T), we see that the temperature dependence of k_d is very close to $(1/T^{1/2}) \exp \{-\epsilon_D/kT\}$, and (assuming, consistently with setting $(p.f.)_{vib} = kT/h\nu_{AB}$, that K has its classical value) there will then be practically no temperature dependence of k_a. However, even with He as the third body, there is an apparent activation energy† of -0.6 to -0.7 kcal. If one compares the rate at room temperature and the rate determined in a shock tube at 1300°K, the apparent activation energy is about -1.3, but these are consistent with a rate roughly proportional to $1/T$. It has been suggested that the temperature coefficient arises from the lack of equilibrium in the upper vibrational levels. This certainly would happen if η rather than a were constant. The calculations of Keck on the trajectories in $2I + Ar$ seem to indicate that a is nearly constant, but an indefinite increase of η with T might be hindered by a quantum effect, arising from increasingly poorer overlap of the vibrational wave functions as the energy levels get farther apart, especially for those collisions in which the two iodine atoms happen to be close together and hence cannot be treated separately in the collision. It is also true that the effective value of g^* might decrease, since at higher temperatures dissociation could take place more readily from the higher electronic states with relatively shallow minima.‡ Glancing collisions would on the whole last a shorter time and thus be less effective at high temperatures. Finally, with argon or heavier gases, the contribution of the complex mechanism would cause the negative activation energy to be higher. These suggestions, however, do not offer a quantitative solution of the problem.

The theory of Keck (Sec. 19-4) offers a different approach to the cases in which the third body is a rare-gas atom. Calculations were carried out, using potential energies based on the assumption that, as far as concerns van der Waals forces, I is like Xe. In these calculations, in effect, only the ground state, $^1\Sigma_g^+$, was considered. These calculations resulted in good agreement with the experimental rate constants for the recombination of iodine atoms in the presence of rare gas atoms at room temperature, reproducing the observed trend very well. This good agreement actually seems strange, for not only does Keck's calculation give an upper bound, but, since it is an equilibrium theory, it should not be compared directly with the measured rate. It should

---

† There appears to be an error in the activation energy quoted by Porter and Smith [30], since for helium their E_1 and E_2 do not seem to be mutually consistent.

‡ This explanation, however, would seem to be peculiar to I_2, but a similar difficulty with the temperature coefficient arises in other cases. When lighter atoms are involved, quantum effects would be much more important.

be comparable to Eq. (2.15), if the correct value of σ is inserted, and the factor $1 - \exp\{-a\}$ omitted. The latter may well be closer to 1 than shown in Table 19-1, as we have already noted; however, it must be an appreciable factor. Thus Keck's calculated rate would appear actually to be too low. This may be due in part to neglect of the excited attractive electronic states, and in part to an underestimate of the attractive forces between iodine and the rare gases. If Keck's calculation, after correction as suggested, should agree fairly well for He, it would give too large a rate for Xe, since for Xe the correction due to $1 - \exp\{-a\}$ would be negligible. Thus the heavier the molecule, the greater will be the overestimate. This is in qualitative agreement with the trends in the trajectory calculations mentioned at the end of Sec. 19-4, but quantitatively the calculations of 19-4 do not seem to indicate as large a difference as would seem to be required. Whether these apparent discrepancies could arise from errors in the potential-energy curves is difficult to judge.

It is of interest that Keck has stated that for a given potential energy surface, the rate constant is independent of the mass of the third body. This occurs because the density of points in phase space is independent of this mass, and the rate of crossing of S_+ depends only on the masses of the combining atoms. However, the rate of collision decreases with the mass of the third body. On the other hand, the time of a collision increases. This may allow more time for multiple transversal of S_+, thus increasing the upper bound relative to the time rate. The calculations on trajectories which were made by Keck indicate that the number of multiple crossings does increase with mass, but not enough to account for the experimental results. These calculations do not give information concerning the average absolute efficiency of collisions, since a very special type of collision, namely those in which a phase point actually crossed the surface S_+, was selected.

Keck's calculations of the rate by his phase-point method in general give some decrease with temperature, but too small a one. This might be due in part to their giving a higher upper bound at the higher temperatures, but his calculations on trajectories indicate little reason for expecting this. He does not, of course, take nonequilibrium effects into account, and they may be the principal cause of this discrepancy in the cases involving such third bodies as helium, as, indeed, our calculations based on the collision mechanism would suggest.

No other recombination reaction has been investigated as thoroughly as that of iodine atoms, but a number of experiments have been done on bromine atoms [33, 34]. The general features are much the same as with iodine, but the rate constants for bromine recombination are roughly $\frac{2}{3}$ of those for iodine recombination in the same gas, possibly with very slightly higher negative activation energies.

A number of experimental results in the region between 1000° and 2000°K have been obtained in shock tubes, both for bromine and iodine. On the whole, these do not correlate too well with the low temperature results. The shock-tube results tend to be a little higher than expected by extrapolation and to have a somewhat more pronounced temperature coefficient than those obtained by flash photolysis. For example, activation energies in the shock tube have been reported as -4.6 kcal for I in Ar and -8.0 for I in He. In some cases it is possible to draw a smooth curve through all the points, but it has considerable curvature on the usual plot of log k_a vs. $1/T$. Often the data fit reasonably well to a function proportional to $1/T^n$, where n is in the neighborhood of $\frac{3}{2}$ or greater. This has given rise to the suggestion, which keeps recurring in the literature, that the reaction involves a complex of three atoms (or more if the third body is not monatomic) and that the energy can be distributed in any way among the internal degrees of freedom. This, however, cannot be a relevant or instructive way of viewing the situation, for, before the reaction can take place, the energy must be redistributed in the right way. But this redistribution can occur in only a small fraction of the cases and will have a temperature dependence essentially cancelling that which arises from the calculation of the equilibrium fraction of the three-atom complex.

Bunker and Davidson [16] have made a calculation based on the equivalent of Eq. (3.2), but allowing for the fact that the vibrational levels of M against AB in the complex AB·M will become filled, as described in the latter part of Sec. 19-3. This gives a rate constant with about the correct over-all temperature dependence, but still does not correlate the high and low temperature results. This is clearly a problem which needs further consideration.

A rather large number of atom associations or dissociations of diatomic molecules have been measured, but, as noted above, the data are not so complete as in the case of iodine, and we will not consider them here. Some of them have been discussed in another place (see [5] of Chap. 18 and [33, 34]). A warning should perhaps be given that the comparison of experiment and theory with the I_2 molecule may give too optimistic a picture. There are a number of unsolved difficulties, some of which may be resolved by better experimental data or further theoretical work.

REFERENCES

1. R. L. Strong, J. C. W. Chien, P. E. Graf, and J. E. Willard, *J. Chem. Phys.*, **26**, 1287 (1957).
2. B. Widom, *J. Chem. Phys.*, **34**, 2050 (1961).
3. E. E. Nikitin, *Dokl. Akad. Nauk SSSR*, **119**, 526 (1958).
4. E. E. Nikitin, *Dokl. Akad. Nauk SSSR*, **121**, 991 (1958) [trl. *Soviet Phys. Doklady*, **3**, 701 (1958)].
5. E. E. Nikitin and N. D. Sokolov, *J. Chem. Phys.*, **31**, 1371 (1959).
6. O. K. Rice, *J. Phys. Chem.*, **65**, 1972 (1961).
7. N. S. Snider, *J. Chem. Phys.*, **42**, 548 (1965).
8. M. Camac and A. Vaughan, *J. Chem. Phys.*, **34**, 460 (1961).
9. E. Rabinowitch, *Trans. Faraday Soc.*, **33**, 283 (1937).
10. S. W. Benson and T. Fueno, *J. Chem. Phys.*, **36**, 1597 (1962).
11. O. K. Rice, *J. Phys. Chem.*, **67**, 6 (1963).
12. O. K. Rice, *J. Chem. Phys.*, **9**, 258 (1941).
13. O. K. Rice, *J. Chem. Phys.*, **21**, 750 (1953).
14. O. K. Rice, *Monatshefte*, **90**, 330 (1959).
15. W. Steiner, *Z. physik. Chem.*, **B15**, 249 (1932).
16. D. L. Bunker and N. Davidson, *J. Am. Chem. Soc.*, **80**, 5090 (1958).
17. J. C. Light, *J. Chem. Phys.*, **36**, 1016 (1962).
18. J. C. Keck, *J. Chem. Phys.*, **32**, 1035 (1960).
19. R. Marcellin, *Ann. physique*, **3**, 120 (1915) (résumé, p. 226).
20. E. P. Wigner, *J. Chem. Phys.*, **5**, 720 (1937).
21. J. C. Keck, *Disc. Faraday Soc.*, **33**, 173 (1962).
22. A. Kantrowitz, in *Transfert d'Energie dans les Gaz*, (Proceedings Twelfth Solvay Congress on Chemistry) Brussels, Stoops (New York, Interscience), 1962, pp. 517–20.
23. S. W. Benson and G. C. Berend, *J. Chem. Phys.*, **40**, 1289 (1964).
24. F. T. Lang and R. L. Strong, *J. Am. Chem. Soc.*, **87**, 2345 (1965).
25. R. S. Mulliken, *Phys. Rev.*, **57**, 500 (1940).
26. W. Kauzmann, *Quantum Chemistry*, New York, Academic, 1957, Chap. 10.
27. G. Herzberg, *Molecular Spectra and Molecular Structure. I. Spectra of Diatomic Molecules*, 2d ed., Princeton, N.J., Van Nostrand, 1950.
28. E. Rabinowitch and W. C. Wood, *J. Chem. Phys.*, **4**, 497 (1936).
29. K. E. Russell and J. Simons, *Proc. Roy. Soc.* (London), **A217**, 271 (1953).
30. G. Porter and J. A. Smith, *Proc. Roy. Soc.* (London) **A261**, 28 (1961).
31. H. A. Benesi and J. H. Hildebrand, *J. Am. Chem. Soc.*, **71**, 2703 (1949).
32. M. I. Christie, A. J. Harrison, R. G. W. Norrish, and G. Porter, *Proc. Roy. Soc.* (London), **A231**, 446 (1955).
33. T. A. Jacobs and R. R. Giedt, *J. Chem. Phys.*, **39**, 749 (1963).
34. C. D. Johnson and D. Britton, *J. Chem. Phys.*, **38**, 1455 (1963).

PROBLEMS

19.1. Consider the reaction mechanism

$$A \underset{k_a'}{\overset{k_a}{\rightleftharpoons}} A' \underset{k_b^*}{\overset{k_a^*}{\rightleftharpoons}} B' \underset{k_b}{\overset{k_b'}{\rightleftharpoons}} B$$

where A' and B' are high-energy forms, which are consequently present in small concentration. Starting with A present but no B, find the steady-state concentration of A' and the over-all steady-state reaction-rate constant for reaction of A. Work out a similar problem starting with B present and no A. Show that an equation analogous to Eq. (1.1) holds.

19.2. Let us consider the reverse of the process treated in 19-2, and leading to Eq. (2.13), i.e. the bimolecular association, the reverse of reaction (g). Let the actual rate of this association under a given set of circumstances be R_0. If $X_{0,eq}$ would be the value of X_0 were AB_0 in equilibrium with $A + B$, show that $R_0 = k_{-0}X_{0,eq} = k_{-0}c_{0,eq}g_0 \exp\{-x_0\}$. Find the equation which replaces Eq. (2.1) and show that it reduces to $c_1 = (1 + b_1)c_0 - b_1c_{0,eq}$. Combining this with Eq. (2.10) and assuming all the b_1 equal to b, show by induction (start by assuming $c_1 = 0$) that if $c_n = 0$, then

$$c_0 = \frac{b + b^2 + \cdots b^n}{1 + b + \cdots b^n} c_{0,eq} \approx b,$$

if n is large enough, provided $b < 1$. Show then that the *observed* rate of association will be $R_0(1 - b)$ and that this is in accord with Eq. (1.1).

Chapter 20

Unimolecular Reactions

20-1. *Reactions at Low Pressures*

In Chap. 18 we confined our discussion of unimolecular reactions principally to the high-pressure region, where the rate of activation is not rate-determining. At low enough pressures, the time between collisions may become long compared with the average time for an activated molecule to react, and under these circumstances the rate of activation will be the rate-determining step.

As we have seen in Sec. 18-5, at high pressures the activated molecules are maintained at essentially equilibrium concentrations, for the drain on the activated molecules due to the chemical reaction is small. This is no longer true at lower pressures, but the concentration of activated molecules may be calculated by assuming that a steady state is set up in which the rate of activation of the molecules in any energy range is equal to the sum of the rates of deactivation and reaction. It is generally assumed that the rate of activation is the same as it would be if complete equilibrium were established (that is, equal to the equilibrium rate of deactivation). This supposes that sufficient energy is gained or lost on the average on collision so that the activation process in any energy range which contributes appreciably to the reaction is dependent upon collisions of molecules having an energy so much lower that they are present virtually in their equilibrium quota. It is generally conceded (as would be anticipated from Sec. 19-2) that even if this is not true [1, 2], or if departure from equilibrium occurs, which is of a nature similar to that described in Sec. 19-2, the effect is not particularly important if the average energy transferred at collision is not much less than kT.

Let us designate the equilibrium fraction of molecules in the energy range ϵ to $\epsilon + d\epsilon$ (the fraction which would be found if no reaction occurred) as $w_\epsilon \, d\epsilon$, and the actual fraction in the range, taking into account the effect of reaction, as $c_\epsilon w_\epsilon \, d\epsilon$. Then the steady-state hypothesis gives

$$Znc_\epsilon w_\epsilon + k_\epsilon c_\epsilon w_\epsilon = Znw_\epsilon \tag{1.1}$$

(deactivation + reaction = activation)

where Z is the effective collision number per unit volume per unit time at unit concentration (assumed independent of ϵ), n is the number of molecules per unit volume, and k_ϵ is the reaction rate constant for the energy range, but not quite in the same sense as defined for Eq. (1.6) of Chap. 18.† Equation (1.1) gives

$$c_\epsilon = \frac{1}{1 + k_\epsilon/Zn}. \tag{1.2}$$

The high-pressure rate for any energy range then should be reduced by multiplication by c_ϵ. The high-pressure rate constant will have a contribution equal to $k_\epsilon w_\epsilon \, d\epsilon$ from the particular energy range, and will be given by

$$k_\mathrm{d} = \int_{\epsilon_\mathrm{m}}^{\infty} k_\epsilon w_\epsilon \, d\epsilon, \tag{1.3}$$

assuming that no reaction occurs for $\epsilon < \epsilon_\mathrm{m}$, where ϵ_m has the same meaning as in Chap. 18. Thus the general expression for k_d will be

$$k_\mathrm{d} = \int_{\epsilon_\mathrm{m}}^{\infty} \frac{k_\epsilon w_\epsilon \, d\epsilon}{1 + k_\epsilon/Zn}, \tag{1.4}$$

and we now need to evaluate k_ϵ and w_ϵ.

† In Chap. 18, k (which we will now call k_ϵ') was defined as the rate of outward passage referred to all the molecules in the quasi-continuum (the continuum modified by the distance r_∞). Here k_ϵ is the rate of reaction referred to the molecules in the undissociated states. $N_\epsilon \, d\epsilon$ is the number of energy levels which would exist in the range if the molecules did not dissociate, and $w_\epsilon \, d\epsilon$ is the fraction of the molecules in these levels [see Eq. (1.5)]. In Chap. 18 we let n be the quantum number of a quasi-continuum level, and then $k_\epsilon = k_\epsilon' \, dn/d\epsilon$, where $dn/d\epsilon$ is the density of continuum levels. If more than one continuum is involved, $dn/d\epsilon$ must include the levels in all continua. [Note that in Eq. (1.2) n is used in a quite different sense.] It is to be noted that Tolman's derivation of the temperature coefficient (Sec. 18-7) is valid for either formulation, provided only that the quantum states to which k_ϵ is referred, and which contribute to the reaction, are populated in their equilibrium quotas.

An expression for the latter quantity can be obtained by noting that $w_\epsilon \, d\epsilon$ must be the ratio of a partition function for the range ϵ to $\epsilon + d\epsilon$ to the total partition function (p.f.) of the dissociating molecule. Thus we have

$$w_\epsilon \, d\epsilon = \frac{N_\epsilon \exp\{-\epsilon/kT\} \, d\epsilon}{\text{(p.f.)}}, \tag{1.5}$$

where $N_\epsilon \, d\epsilon$ is the number of energy levels in the range, and (p.f.) is based on the same energy zero as ϵ.

We can evaluate k'_ϵ by following the procedure used in Sec. 18-1. If a molecule AB dissociates into two fragments A and B, each of these fragments will appear in some internal energy level. With each pair of such internal energy levels there will be associated a continuum of energy levels representing the relative motion of A and B. Let us first consider the case in which the energy ϵ exceeds ϵ_m so slightly that there is available only one internal energy state of A + B; in this case there is but one continuum.

In Sec. 18-1, we found that k'_ϵ times the number of levels per unit energy range of the continuum† was equal to $1/h$. The contribution to the reaction from an equilibrium outward flow of dissociating pairs in a given energy range $d\epsilon$ was then given by multiplying this factor by $\exp\{-\epsilon/kT\} \, d\epsilon$ and dividing by the partition function of the molecule, or

$$\frac{\exp\{-\epsilon/kT\} \, d\epsilon}{h(\text{p.f.})}. \tag{1.6}$$

Provided we have to consider only one continuum, the same formula should give us the contribution to the equilibrium (high-pressure) rate constant k_d in the present case. However, we wish to evaluate k_ϵ (the rate constant for molecules in the particular energy range) as a rate with respect to the undissociated molecules in the energy range.

In the present case there are intermediate states in which the molecule already has energy in the required range, but in which this energy is not so distributed as to make it possible for the dissociation to occur without some redistribution of energy. By definition there are $N_\epsilon \, d\epsilon$ such states. The equilibrium fraction of undissociated molecules in the energy range will then be $N_\epsilon \exp\{-\epsilon/kT\} \, d\epsilon/(\text{p.f.})$, and the contribution to k_d will be

† See footnote on the preceding page.

$$\frac{k_\epsilon N_\epsilon \exp\{-\epsilon/kT\}\, d\epsilon}{(\text{p.f.})} = \frac{\exp\{-\epsilon/kT\}\, d\epsilon}{h(\text{p.f.})}, \tag{1.7}$$

by expression (1.6), there still being but one continuum. Thus,

$$k_\epsilon = \frac{1}{N_\epsilon h}. \tag{1.8}$$

It is interesting to digress momentarily at this point, and note that $k_\epsilon = 1/\tau_\epsilon$, where τ_ϵ is the average lifetime in the states which are included in $N_\epsilon\, d\epsilon$. We see, then, that

$$\frac{\tau_\epsilon}{N_\epsilon} = h, \tag{1.9}$$

which is a form of the uncertainty relation, since $1/N_\epsilon$ is just equal to the average difference in energy between energy levels. The assumption of equilibrium means that each energy level is contributing outward flowing or dissociating pairs over a range of energies equal to $1/N_\epsilon$, and each energy level is sufficiently broadened to just overlap its neighbors. In the reverse reaction there will be no difficulty in re-combination of the fragments arising from the necessity of matching energy levels [3].

In the more general case, there may be more than one continuum into which the dissociation can occur; i.e., the separated fragments may be in more than one energy level. The number P_ϵ of continua to which connection can be made will depend on the character of the activated complex. For example, if the activated complex is rigid, there will be only one vibrational energy level possible if the energy is only slightly greater than ϵ_m. However, if the energy is increased enough to permit the lowest vibrational degree of freedom to be excited, P_ϵ will be equal to 2. The excess energy above ϵ_m can be divided between the internal vibrational energy and the relative kinetic energy of A and B in such a way as to have either no vibrational energy excited or the one possible excitation. At higher energies, the possibility of more vibrational states will occur, and P_ϵ will increase with ϵ. In a loose activated complex rotations of the fragments may be excited, and since the rotational energies are closer together, P_ϵ will increase much more with energy. For every particular vibrational state, the difference between $\epsilon - \epsilon_m$ and the vibrational energy ϵ_v, or $\epsilon - \epsilon_m - \epsilon_v$, may be distributed in any way between rotational energy of the individual parts A and B and the relative energy of A and B. If an expression is known for the rotational energy as a function of the coordinates and momenta of A and B, it will be a sufficient approximation to find the volume in the phase space of these coordinates for which the rotational energy is less than $\epsilon - \epsilon_m - \epsilon_v$. This volume is then divided by h raised to the appropriate power. The result will be the contribution of the particular vibrational level to P_ϵ. The calculation can be made for each possible vibrational state of the system and all of them added together to get P_ϵ.

In actually calculating P_ϵ, it is customary to leave out the three (or two) degrees of freedom of rotation of the molecule as a whole. [In that event, these degrees are also not included in (p.f.)]. This rotational energy presumably cannot be exchanged with the vibrational degrees of freedom or with rotations of the fragments A or B because of the conservation of angular momentum, and the corresponding degrees of freedom have been called "adiabatic" by Marcus [4]. It is true, if the moment of inertia I_m in the activated complex is greater than that in the equilibrium configuration, I_e, the rotational potential will be less in the activated complex than in the normal situation. Then the extra energy will be available for redistribution, but in complex molecules this will probably be a negligible amount. A partial correction can be made (assuming that the moments of inertia connected with only two degrees of freedom are affected appreciably, and that the molecule behaves like a symmetrical top) by multiplying by I_m/I_e (similar to the factor r_m^2/r_e^2 occurring in other cases). If any of the rotations are believed not to be adiabatic, a correction can be made.

If there is a change in symmetry number for the rotation, this will also have to be taken into account. However, if the number of continua involved in P_ϵ is counted properly, this is taken care of automatically. For example a straight-line molecule ABA has a symmetry number of 2, whereas the activated complex, in which one of the A's is breaking away, has a symmetry number of 1. This corresponds to the fact that there is a continuum associated with the A that happens to be on the left *and* one associated with the A on the right, and both of these must be counted in P_ϵ; whereas with an unsymmetrical molecule ABC, only the A can break off in the particular reaction ABC $\longrightarrow$ A + BC. Since the ratio I_m/I_e enters because of the averaging over all rotational states and is ultimately connected with the change in dissociation energy with rotation, the effect will be at least approximately independent of pressure, and the ratio occurs as a factor in the rate expression. The symmetry number, being connected with the number of continua, is reflected directly in P_ϵ, and we shall see immediately that the effect will depend on pressure.

If there is more than one continuum through which dissociation can occur, the probability of dissociation will be raised accordingly. Thus in the general case we write

$$k_\epsilon = \frac{P_\epsilon}{N_\epsilon h}. \tag{1.10}$$

Insertion of Eqs. (1.5) and (1.10) in Eq. (1.4) and multiplication by I_m/I_e yields

$$k_d = \frac{I_m/I_e}{h(\text{p.f.})} \int_{\epsilon_m}^{\infty} \frac{P_\epsilon \exp\{-\epsilon/kT\}\,d\epsilon}{1 + P_\epsilon/ZnhN_\epsilon}. \tag{1.11}$$

In the limiting case of high pressures, which we have considered before, this becomes

$$k_{d,\infty} = \frac{I_m/I_e}{h(\text{p.f.})} \int_{\epsilon_m}^{\infty} P_\epsilon \exp\left\{-\frac{\epsilon}{kT}\right\} d\epsilon, \tag{1.12}$$

and in the limiting case of low pressures it becomes

$$k_{d,0} = \frac{I_m/I_e}{(\text{p.f.})} Zn \int_{\epsilon_m}^{\infty} N_\epsilon \exp\left\{-\frac{\epsilon}{kT}\right\} d\epsilon. \tag{1.13}$$

It must be borne in mind that $k_{d,0}$, being a rate divided by a concentration, still has the form of a unimolecular rate constant, and it is proportional to the pressure through the factor n.

It will be noted that P_ϵ does not appear in Eq. (1.13); therefore, the change in the symmetry number for the rotation has no effect at low enough pressures. This is readily understandable, for at very low pressures the rate depends only on the rate of activation, not at all on the rate of decomposition once a molecule is activated (they virtually *all* decompose), and hence not on the number of continua involved.

It may be shown that Eq. (1.12) leads to the usual transition state equation. Since P_ϵ is the total number of ways the excess energy, $\epsilon - \epsilon_m$, may be divided among the various degrees of freedom and the reaction coordinate, we have

$$P_\epsilon = \int_0^{\epsilon - \epsilon_m} Q_{\epsilon'} d\epsilon', \tag{1.14}$$

where $Q_{\epsilon'} d\epsilon'$ is the number of energy levels of the degrees of freedom other than the reaction coordinate and the adiabatic rotations lying between ϵ' and $\epsilon' + d\epsilon'$. Inserting this into the integral in Eq. (1.12)

$$\int_{\epsilon_m}^{\infty} P_\epsilon \exp\left\{-\frac{\epsilon}{kT}\right\} d\epsilon = \int_{\epsilon_m}^{\infty} \int_0^{\epsilon-\epsilon_m} Q_{\epsilon'} d\epsilon' \exp\left\{-\frac{\epsilon}{kT}\right\} d\epsilon, \qquad (1.15)$$

and, integrating by parts, we get

$$\int_{\epsilon_m}^{\infty} P_\epsilon \exp\left\{-\frac{\epsilon}{kT}\right\} d\epsilon = -kT \exp\left\{-\frac{\epsilon}{kT}\right\} \int_0^{\epsilon-\epsilon_m} Q_{\epsilon'} d\epsilon' \Big|_{\epsilon_m}^{\infty}$$

$$+ kT \int_{\epsilon_m}^{\infty} Q_{\epsilon-\epsilon_m} \exp\left\{-\frac{\epsilon}{kT}\right\} d\epsilon. \qquad (1.16)$$

The integrated term drops out, since the integral vanishes at the lower limit and $\exp\{-\epsilon/kT\}$ vanishes strongly at $\epsilon = \infty$. Thus we have finally

$$\int_{\epsilon_m}^{\infty} P_\epsilon \exp\left\{-\frac{\epsilon}{kT}\right\} d\epsilon = kT(\text{p.f.})^* \exp\left\{-\frac{\epsilon_m}{kT}\right\}, \qquad (1.17)$$

where

$$(\text{p.f.})^* = \int_0^{\infty} Q_{\epsilon-\epsilon_m} \exp\left\{-\frac{\epsilon-\epsilon_m}{kT}\right\} d(\epsilon - \epsilon_m) \qquad (1.18)$$

is the partition function for the degrees of freedom other than the reaction coordinate, the adiabatic rotations, and the translational degrees of freedom, but reckoned now from ϵ_m as its zero of energy. If we insert Eq. (1.17) in Eq. (1.12) we obtain

$$k_{d,\infty} = \frac{kT}{h} \frac{(\text{p.f.})^*}{(\text{p.f.})} \exp\left\{-\frac{\epsilon_m}{kT}\right\} \frac{I_m}{I_e}. \qquad (1.19)$$

This is equivalent to the transition-state expression, Eq. (6.9) of Chap. 18, except that we have here tacitly assumed κ and g^*/g to be equal to 1, and have exhibited the ratio I_m/I_e explicitly. Note that kT/h is the same as $(\text{p.f.})_{\text{react}}$ and ϵ_m is the same as ϵ^* in Eq. (6.9) of Chap. 18.

In the theory which has just been developed, it is tacitly assumed that there is free exchange of energy among the various degrees of freedom within the molecule, and that the probability of reaction does not depend upon the particular way in which the molecule is activated. Slater has developed a theory of unimolecular reactions which differs somewhat in these respects. He considers the excitation of various normal modes of vibration and the way these will superpose to give the motion occurring about the bond which breaks. When this bond happens to get stretched beyond a certain point, reaction is supposed to occur. In this harmonic model there is no exchange of energy between normal modes of vibration, and certain modes have much more influence on the bond which breaks than do others, so that not all the degrees of freedom are fully effective in promoting dissociation.

In an actual molecule, the vibrations are highly anharmonic, at least if the bonds are sufficiently stretched (and the reaction coordinate is expected to be stretched almost to the breaking point many times before it is actually stretched sufficiently to break). If anharmonicity exists, it is actually no longer possible to analyze the motion of the molecule into normal modes of vibration, but if this is done as an approximation the effect of anharmonicity is to cause exchange of energy between the modes. Some attempts have been made to investigate the effects of anharmonicity and of quantization on Slater's model, but this would complicate the computations greatly and they have been made chiefly for the classical harmonic model. The theory resulting in Eq. (1.11) seems more applicable to the experimental results, so we will not give details of Slater's theory, especially as he has done this himself in a recent book [5]. It is possible that in a few cases there is not completely free exchange of energy within the molecule, and that some of the degrees are not in good communication with the reaction coordinate, so that the molecule acts like a smaller molecule than it really is [6].

In obtaining Eq. (1.11) we assumed that the probability of a molecule's reacting depended only on its energy, and not at all on the length of time since it was activated. However, if there is slow transfer of energy from some degrees of freedom this may not always be the case. This possibility is taken account of in a "new formulation" of rate theory, recently introduced by Slater and somewhat modified by Bunker [5, Chap. 9; 7]. In this formulation the activated molecules which are produced by collision are divided into classes, according to the amount of energy ϵ they contain and the length of time τ which it will require for them to decompose after being formed. Let $f_{\tau, \epsilon} \, d\tau$ be the fraction of all molecules formed in energy range ϵ to $\epsilon + d\epsilon$ which would, if undisturbed, decompose between times τ and $\tau + d\tau$. These will, of course, not decompose if they are deactivated by collision. The probability that such a molecule will not have a collision in time τ and hence will decompose is $\exp \{ -Zn\tau \}$ where Z is the average collision number, and n the total molecular density, so that Zn is the rate of collision suffered by a single molecule. The rate of deactivation of such molecules, at equilibrium, and hence, by the usual assumption, the rate of activation, will be $Zn^2 f_{\tau,\epsilon} \, d\tau \, w_\epsilon \, d\epsilon$. Hence the total number of reactions of such molecules per unit volume per unit time will be $Zn^2 f_{\tau,\epsilon} \, w_\epsilon \exp \{ -Zn\tau \} \, d\epsilon d\tau$, and the corresponding contribution to the rate constant from the range ϵ to $\epsilon + d\epsilon$ will be found by integrating with respect to τ, after dividing by n:

$$c_\epsilon w_\epsilon k_\epsilon \, d\epsilon = \left(\int_0^\infty Zn f_{\tau,\epsilon} w_\epsilon \exp \{ -Zn\tau \} \, d\tau \right) d\epsilon, \tag{1.20}$$

where $w_\epsilon k_\epsilon \, d\epsilon$ is the contribution which would occur at high pressures and c_ϵ is the factor similar to that introduced in Eq. (1.1). If the assumption is made that the probability of decomposition of any molecule at any time depends only on its energy, then of a certain number of molecules activated to a certain energy range the fraction remaining after a time τ (assuming no collisions) would be

$$\int_\tau^\infty f_{\tau,\epsilon} \, d\tau = \exp \{ -k_\epsilon \tau \}, \tag{1.21}$$

where k_ϵ is independent of τ. This is what Slater calls the "random gap" assumption. It can be shown that, with Eq. (1.20) it leads to Eq. (1.2).

20-2. *Calculations on Intramolecular Energy Exchange*

According to the Slater theory, Eq. (1.2) is not expected to hold, for, within any energy range, there will be different groups of molecules having different intrinsic reaction probabilities, depending upon how this energy is distributed; indeed, there will be some which will never decompose. Bunker [7] examined the behavior of classical molecules by setting up a program for a machine calculation which selected molecules within a specific energy range, but otherwise randomly distributed in phase space, and followed them through to dissociation. He did this in his first paper for a linear model, like N_2O, and a triangular model, like O_3. In some cases the potentials were assumed to be harmonic (using Slater's criterion for dissociation); in others anharmonicity was introduced. Bunker was able to follow the process for only a relatively short time, corresponding to collision times which were only long enough to cause a slight decrease of the rate constant from its high pressure value. However, this was long enough to indicate an apparent residual of molecules which were not going to decompose in the harmonic case, and, as far as could be seen, the introduction of anharmonicity caused Eq. (1.2) to be fulfilled. The dependence of k_ϵ on ϵ agreed fairly well with what might be expected, assuming that all the vibrations were exchanging energy, including the bending one in N_2O (only motion in a plane was considered); the power of the dependence on $\epsilon - \epsilon_m$ seemed to decrease slightly going from the harmonic to the anharmonic case, probably because, in the harmonic case, the higher the energy the fewer would be the molecules which never decompose.

In a later paper Bunker [8] extended the calculations to an additional series of models, bringing in one degree of freedom of rotation. He concludes that there may be some cases in which the random-gap assumption is not valid. This can occur at sufficiently high temperatures, where the rate of reaction is very fast and the relaxation rates for energy transfer within the molecule have not increased correspondingly. Only in some bent triatomic molecules do the calculations make it appear likely that the effects could be observed under ordinary laboratory conditions. On the whole, the general conclusion seems to be that the theory developed in Sec. 20-1 should be valid. The effects of quantization cannot, of course, be tested in this way.

In one or two cases the calculations of Bunker seemed to indicate that there was exchange of energy between rotation and vibration. As remarked in one of the paragraphs preceding Eq. (1.10), it is difficult, because of the restricting effects of the conservation of angular momentum, to see how there can be free exchange of energy between rotation and vibration, especially if one considers only one degree of freedom of rotation. However, the release of the rotational energy, for distribution among the vibrations, as suggested in Sec. 20-1, may give the impression that the rotations are not adiabatic.

20-3. *Application of Unimolecular Rate Theory to Experimental Results*

In attempting to apply the equations of Sec. 20-1 to the experimental data, a number of approximations have been made. Rice and Ramsperger assumed that $N_\epsilon \exp\{-\epsilon/kT\}/(\text{p.f.})$ or w_ϵ was to be obtained from the classical formulas for molecules consisting of a given number s of harmonic oscillators with energy in the given range. The energy expression of such a molecule consists of s coordinate terms and s momentum terms, all of which are quadratic. A constant energy surface is therefore a hyperellipsoid in a $2s$-dimensional space [9] and the number of energy levels can be found by dividing the volume of the hyperellipsoidal shell by h^s. It is found that

$$\frac{N_\epsilon}{\text{(p.f.)}} = \frac{(\epsilon/kT)^{s-1}}{\Gamma(s)kT} \tag{3.1}$$

where $\Gamma(s)$ is the gamma function [10], and, here, the zero for ϵ and ϵ_m is the state of no vibration (ϵ_m *includes* the dissociation energy). Then Eq. (1.13) becomes

$$\frac{k_{d,0}}{n} = \frac{I_m}{I_e} \frac{Z}{\Gamma(s)} \exp\left\{-\frac{\epsilon_m}{kT}\right\} \int_0^\infty \left(x + \frac{\epsilon_m}{kT}\right)^{s-1} \exp\{-x\}\, dx,$$

[where x has been used to represent $(\epsilon - \epsilon_m)/kT$] and

$$\frac{k_{d,0}}{n} \approx \frac{I_m}{I_e} \frac{Z}{\Gamma(s)} \left(\frac{\epsilon_m}{kT}\right)^{s-1} \exp\left\{-\frac{\epsilon_m}{kT}\right\} \tag{3.2}$$

provided that ϵ_m/kT is large—generally it is of the order 30 to 40. Other factors being the same, $k_{d,0}$ increases rapidly with increasing s. The more complex a molecule the more energy it can hold, the greater the fraction of molecules with enough energy to react, and the faster the rate of activation so the faster the reaction when activation is the rate-controlling step.

The evaluation of P_ϵ depends upon finding the number of energy levels in a small range when an amount ϵ_m is fixed in the bond that breaks, so that there is only $\epsilon - \epsilon_m$ to be distributed among the oscillators. Classically, then, P_ϵ would depend on $\epsilon - \epsilon_m$ as N_ϵ does on ϵ, and, if the activated complex is rigid and the frequencies are essentially unchanged, we may set

$$\frac{P_\epsilon}{\text{(p.f.)}} = \frac{[(\epsilon - \epsilon_m)/kT]^{s-1}}{\Gamma(s)kT}. \tag{3.3}$$

In the older theories, no distinction was made between loose and rigid activated complexes, but the procedure used was equivalent to assuming that in the case of a loose complex P_ϵ was merely proportional to the right-hand side of Eq. (3.3), the proportionality constant being determined from the experimental value of $k_{d,\infty}$ by use of Eq. (1.12).

Since the functional dependence of P_ϵ on $\epsilon - \epsilon_m$ is about the same as that of N_ϵ on ϵ, the *relative* change of P_ϵ with a given change in ϵ is very much larger than that of N_ϵ. Thus k_ϵ, given by Eq. (1.10), increases strongly with ϵ; that is, the more excited an activated molecule, the more rapidly it decomposes, as is to be expected.

Rice and Ramsperger used the classical approximation about as described above [11, 12]. They believed that the effects of quantization could be allowed for by using a somewhat smaller number of oscillators than were actually to be found in the molecules. Indeed, the hydrogen stretching vibrations in organic molecules are sufficiently high so that they are scarcely excited even in activated molecules. Kassel [13, 14] sought to allow for quantization, and at the same time keep the expression in tractable form, by assuming a certain number of quantized oscillators (somewhat greater in number than in the classical case), all having the same frequency, which was chosen in the range of molecular frequencies.

Marcus and Rice [15] and Marcus [4] attempted to find N_ϵ and P_ϵ by actually counting the vibrational levels, allowing for rotations in P_ϵ as indicated in the paragraph following Eq. (1.9). Sometimes N_ϵ can be evaluated to a better approximation than Eq. (3.1) by a quasi-classical approximation. It can be seen that for a set of s frequencies

$$N_\epsilon \approx N_{\epsilon,\nu_c} \prod_{i=1}^{s} (\nu_c/\nu_i),$$ where N_{ϵ,ν_c} is the value N_ϵ would have if all

the frequencies had some value ν_c low enough so that the partition function $(\text{p.f.})_c$ could be written $(kT/h\nu_c)^s$ and so that $N_{\epsilon,\nu_c}/(\text{p.f.})_c$ could be obtained classically, i.e., from Eq. (3.1). Then

$$\frac{N_\epsilon}{(\text{p.f.})} = \frac{N_{\epsilon,\nu_c}}{(\text{p.f.})_c} \frac{(\text{p.f.})_c}{(\text{p.f.})} \prod_{i=1}^{s} \frac{\nu_c}{\nu_i},$$

$$= \frac{N_{\epsilon,\nu_c}}{(\text{p.f.})_c} \frac{\prod_{i=1}^{s} kT/h\nu_i}{(\text{p.f.})}. \tag{3.4}$$

Thus Eq. (3.2) can be corrected by multiplication by the factor in Eq. (3.4). This may not be adequate to handle the high C—H stretching vibrations, but these may be omitted in the calculation. It would seem that a rough criterion for omitting a frequency would be that Eqs. (3.2) and (3.4) would give a higher rate if it were omitted. From these equations the criterion for omission of a frequency is roughly $h\nu_i > \epsilon_m/s$. Intermediate frequencies can, if necessary, be handled separately.

A number of unimolecular reactions in the second-order region were analyzed by Wieder and Marcus [16] in terms of Eq. (3.2) corrected by the use of Eq. (3.4) but neglecting the factor I_m/I_e. It will be observed that since Eq. (3.4) depends upon the temperature, the value of ϵ_m which is obtained from the temperature coefficient of the experimental data will depend upon whether the quantum correction is made or not. The calculated pre-exponential factor A for the relation

$$k_{d,0} = A \exp\left\{-\frac{E}{RT}\right\}, \tag{3.5}$$

where E is the experimental activation energy, is then also affected. In their calculations Wieder and Marcus used the frequencies of the molecules as far as known (assuming transfer of energy among all the frequencies) and drew on the available reaction data; references may be found in their paper. Table 20-1 summarizes their results, referring to molecules activated by other molecules of the same species.

TABLE 20-1

Unimolecular Reactions in Limiting Low-Pressure Stage

Molecule	σ	A (expt)	A (q)/A (expt)	$\epsilon_m(q) - \epsilon^\circ$	$\epsilon_m(c)$
O_3	3.35	4.6×10^{15}	1.1	23.1	25
F_2O	4.5	2.5×10^{17}	0.12	38.4	40.5
N_2O	3.3	5.2×10^{15}	16.0	59.2	63.5
NO_2Cl	6.7	6.3×10^{16}	11.0	27.6	32
H_2O_2	3.5	4.6×10^{18}	0.07	48.0	54
N_2O_4	5.3	2.0×10^{17}	2.2	11.8	17
C_2H_6	3.5	5.5×10^{23}	2.9	85.0	100
N_2O_5	6.0	3.1×10^{19}	0.19	19.5	26

Note: σ is assumed collision diameter in Å. A(expt) is experimental value of A using Eq. (3.5); units: cc mole^{-1} sec^{-1}. (c) means calculated from Eq. (3.2); (q) means quantum correction used. ϵ° is zero-point energy; energies in kcal mole^{-1}.

In three cases, F_2O, H_2O_2 and N_2O_5 (the latter a fairly large molecule, so the calculations may be subject to some uncertainty) the calculated rate of activating collisions is appreciably less than the observed reaction rate. [The ratio of these two quantities is equal to A(q)/A(expt)]. The difficulty in the case of F_2O had already been pointed out by Koblitz and Schumacher [14], and subsequently was analyzed by Rice [14 of Chap. 19, 5 of Chap. 18]. Two previously neglected factors needed to be considered. The effect of rotation, as represented by the I_m/I_e factor, will not, in as small a molecule as this, be entirely negligible. This ratio was estimated to be about 3. It was also pointed out that anharmonicity would increase the density of energy levels of an excited molecule. If in such a small molecule any of the "normal" modes could lead to dissociation at about the same energy, then in an activated molecule any one of three vibrations would be about one-third excited to dissociation, and the spacing between levels of any one would be about $\frac{2}{3}$ that at the ground level. Thus the density of levels and the number of excited molecules would be increased by another factor of $(\frac{3}{2})^3 \approx 3$. We see that the agreement between observed and calculated rates is rather gratifying if we can indeed assume that deactivation takes place at every collision. Similar considerations will hold for H_2O_2. The effect of anharmonicity will be less, but I_m/I_e may well be greater, since the hydrogens are light and the molecule will act much like a diatomic molecule as regards rotation.

The assumption of deactivation at every collision is often made, but is rather hard to justify on theoretical grounds. There are a number of puzzles in this connection. It is seen from Table 20-1 that, if we are correct in assuming that there is free exchange of energy within the molecule, there is a considerable range of efficiency of activating collisions. On the other hand, it is found, by addition of inert gases, that the efficiency of collisions with respect to activation does not usually vary over an extremely wide range from one gas to another. The cases, such as NO_2Cl, in which the apparent collision efficiency is relatively low, may actually be cases in which there is not entirely free transfer of energy within the molecule. This would mean that, as far as the process of transfer of energy to the bond which breaks and subsequent reaction, the molecule would act like a smaller one than it really is. It might be this effect rather than inefficiency in collision which makes the reaction slow. This supposition has its difficulties, too. This problem is one which has been discussed in more detail elsewhere [5 of Chap. 18].

Wieder and Marcus also made an extensive series of calculations on the pressure dependence of the rate constants of a number of unimolecular reactions (including isomerizations to which the theory should also apply). Basing their calculations on the equivalent of Eq. (1.11), they counted the energy levels, at least approximately, where necessary. The transition region between the limiting cases represented by Eqs. (1.12) and (1.13) sets in at a lower pressure for more complex molecules. The more complex the molecule, the less will be the chance that, in an average reacting molecule, sufficient energy will accumulate in the reaction coordinate, so the lower will be the average value of k_e, or P_e/N_e [see Eq. (1.10)]. From Eq. (1.11) it is seen that this will mean a low value of n (or the pressure) in the transition region.

A loose activated complex tends to cause an increase in P_ϵ, and hence k_ϵ; this will in itself cause the rate constant to fall off at a higher pressure. We may therefore expect to observe the falling off in rate constants most readily in molecules which have a small number of degrees of freedom and in those in which pre-exponential factor is large. [Note, from Eqs. (1.17) and (1.19), the relation between P_ϵ and the pre-exponential factor.]

Wieder and Marcus, since they were principally interested in fitting the pressure dependence of the unimolecular rate constant, assumed a model for the activated complex which would give agreement with the rate at a high pressure. This involved in some cases the assumption of a loose activated complex, or one in which some of the vibrational frequencies had become lowered. The various reactions considered were (a) isomerization of cyclopropane to propylene, (b) decomposition of cyclobutane to ethylene, (c) isomerization of methyl cyclopropane, (d) $N_2O \longrightarrow N_2 + O$, (e) isomerization of *cis*-butene-2 to *trans*-butene-2, (f) $N_2O_5 \longrightarrow NO_2 + NO_3$, (g) decomposition of ethyl chloride (which shows some evidence of complications). The pressure at which the falling off of the rate constant occurs would fit the theory if the following collisional activation efficiencies are assumed: (a) 0.28; (b) 0.17; (c) 0.22; (d) 0.028; (e) 0.042. The shape of the rate–pressure curve for N_2O_5 deviates far enough from the theoretical so that a consistent value is hard to give, but it is about 1. It was assumed that one rotational degree of freedom was nonadiabatic in this case. The experimental curve for N_2O is somewhat flatter than expected, indicating that the rate of reaction depends more strongly on the energy of the activated complex than predicted theoretically for the number of vibrations available.† This could be due to some partial inhibition of intramolecular energy transfer in the lower energy range. There are minor deviations in the shape of the curve in other cases. On the whole, the results give little evidence of any hindrance to the free transfer of energy among all the vibrations. The isomerization of methyl isocyanide and of deuterated methyl isocyanide should also be added to the list of reactions which are well described by the theory. These have been reported in great detail by Schneider and Rabinovitch [18, 19].

Free motion of energy within the molecule is also supported by a number of recent experiments, in which a "hot" molecule or radical

---

† The calculations show that the more P_ϵ depends on the energy, the greater the range of pressures over which the transition from the limiting high-pressure to the limiting low-pressure rate occurs.

is formed by chemical reaction, only to decompose before collision to give different products. Rabinovitch and co-workers [20–22] have, as a matter of fact, successfully used the detailed theory of Marcus and Rice to calculate the relative rates of dissociation of the hot molecule formed, having determined the excess of energy it contains from thermochemical calculations. An example of this is the decomposition of hot *sec*-butyl radicals, $CH_3CH_2CHCH_3$ to give $CH_3 + CH_3CH=CH_2$, the *sec*-butyl radicals having been formed by the addition of H to *cis*-butene-2. Butler and Kistiakowsky [23] formed methylcyclopropane by adding CH_2 radicals with varying amounts of energy either to cyclopropane or to propylene. The methylcyclopropane rearranged to form a mixture of butenes, whose composition was essentially independent of mode of formation or of energy, again showing free intramolecular energy transfer. The decomposition of activated *sec*-butyl radicals from different sources also supports this view [24].

20-4. *Appendix: Evaluation of* P_ϵ

Although conceptually it is easy to visualize the rotational phase space, in practice it is easier to approach the problem of calculating the number of rotational levels (excluding, of course, over-all rotations which produce the factor I_m/I_e) by using the approximate quantum expression for the total rotational energy of the activated complex

$$\epsilon_r = \sum_i \frac{j_i^2 h^2}{8\pi^2 I_i} + \sum_l \frac{j_l^2 h^2}{8\pi^2 I_l},$$ (4.1)

where j_i (or j_l) is the rotational quantum number for the ith or lth rotation and I_i (or I_l) is the corresponding moment of inertia. Since the average value of j_i is large, this holds approximately for space rotations (subscript i), having two degrees of freedom (as a freely rotating diatomic radical in a loose activated complex) †, and it is exact for plane rotations (subscript l) with one degree of freedom (as free rotation about the attaching bond of an attached methyl radical). There are approximately $2j_i$ quantum states for a given j_i for space rotations and 2 quantum states (corresponding to the two directions of rotation) for plane rotators. Thus the total number of quantum states having energies between ϵ_r and $\epsilon_r + d\epsilon_r$ is approximately

† If the radical has three degrees of freedom, we assume that there are two of the type labelled i, and one of the type labelled l.

$$\int \cdots \int \prod_i 2j_i \, dj_i \prod_l 2 \, dj_l, \tag{4.2}$$

where the integration is taken between limits determined by Eq. (4.1) with ϵ_r between ϵ_r and $\epsilon_r + d\epsilon_r$. $\int \cdots \int \prod_i dj_i \prod_l dj_l$ is proportional to the surface of an $(\eta + \lambda)$-dimensional ellipsoidal surface, where η is the number of values of i and λ the number of l. It is, therefore, proportional to $\epsilon_r^{-1+(\eta+\lambda)/2}$. It is then easily seen that

$$\int \cdots \int \prod_i 2j_i \, dj_i \prod_l 2 \, dj_l = A \epsilon_r^{-1+(2\eta+\lambda)/2}$$

$$= A \epsilon_r^{r/2-1} \, d\epsilon_r \tag{4.3}$$

where A is a constant and r is the number of rotational degrees of freedom (excluding over-all rotations) in the activated complex. Each j_i in the integrand introduces an additional factor proportional to the linear dimensions of the ellipsoid.

The partition function of the rotations will be given by

$$(\text{p.f.})_r = \int \cdots \int \exp \left\{ -\frac{\epsilon_r}{kT} \right\} \prod_i 2j_i \, dj_i \prod_l dj_l$$

$$= A \int_0^\infty \exp \left\{ -\frac{\epsilon_r}{kT} \right\} \epsilon_r^{r/2-1} \, d\epsilon_r$$

$$= A(kT)^{r/2} \Gamma \left(\frac{r}{2} \right) \tag{4.4}$$

by the definition of the gamma function [10]. Thus (4.2) becomes

$$\int \cdots \int \prod_i 2j_i \, dj_i \prod_l dj_l = \frac{(\text{p.f.})_r (\epsilon_r/kT)^{r/2-1}}{kT \Gamma(r/2)} \, d\epsilon_r. \tag{4.5}$$

If the total energy of the molecule lies between ϵ and $\epsilon + d\epsilon$ and the vibrational energy is ϵ_v, then the rotational energy lies between $\epsilon - \epsilon_v$ and $\epsilon - \epsilon_v + d\epsilon$. Thus, if N_{ϵ_v} is the number of vibrational energy levels having the energy ϵ_v (usually one), we have

$$N_\epsilon \, d\epsilon = \frac{(\text{p.f.})_r}{kT \Gamma(r/2)} \sum_{\epsilon_v} N_{\epsilon_v} \left(\frac{\epsilon - \epsilon_v}{kT} \right)^{r/2-1} d\epsilon, \tag{4.6}$$

where the sum is taken over all possible values of ϵ_v.

To get P_ϵ, we note that in the activated complex ϵ_r can lie anywhere between zero (all nonvibrational energy in the reaction coordinate) and $\epsilon - \epsilon_m - \epsilon_v$. Hence we integrate between these limits:

$$\int \cdots \int \prod_i 2j_i \, dj_i \prod_l dj_l = \frac{(\text{p.f.})_r^*[(\epsilon - \epsilon_m - \epsilon_v)/kT]^{r/2}}{\Gamma(r/2 + 1)} \tag{4.7}$$

where $(\text{p.f.})_r^*$ refers to the activated complex, and

$$P_\epsilon = \frac{(\text{p.f.})_r^*}{\Gamma(r/2 + 1)} \sum_{\epsilon_v} N_{\epsilon_v}^* \left(\frac{\epsilon - \epsilon_m - \epsilon_v}{kT}\right)^{r/2}; \tag{4.8}$$

r can of course be different for the activated complex and the merely activated molecule.

REFERENCES

1. O. K. Rice and D. V. Sickman, *J. Chem. Phys.*, **4**, 242 (1936).
2. B. J. Zwolinski and H. Eyring, *J. Am. Chem. Soc.*, **69**, 2702 (1947).
3. O. K. Rice, *J. Phys. Chem.*, **65**, 1588 (1961).
4. R. A. Marcus, *J. Chem. Phys.*, **20**, 359 (1952).
5. N. B. Slater, *Theory of Unimolecular Reactions*, Ithaca, N.Y., Cornell Univ. Press, (1959).
6. O. K. Rice, *Z. physik. Chem.*, **B7**, 226 (1930).
7. D. L. Bunker, *J. Chem. Phys.*, **37**, 393 (1962).
8. D. L. Bunker, *J. Chem. Phys.*, **40**, 1946 (1964).
9. R. C. Tolman, *Statistical Mechanics with Applications to Physics and Chemistry*, New York, Chemical Catalog, 1927, pp. 128–30.
10. B. O. Pierce, *A Short Table of Integrals*, 3d ed., Boston, Ginn, 1929, No. 481.
11. O. K. Rice and H. C. Ramsperger, *J. Am. Chem. Soc.*, **49**, 1617 (1927).
12. O. K. Rice, *J. Phys. Chem.*, **50**, 617 (1928).
13. L. S. Kassel, *J. Phys. Chem.*, **32**, 225 (1928).
14. L. S. Kassel, *J. Phys. Chem.*, **32**, 1065 (1928).
15. R. A. Marcus and O. K. Rice, *J. Phys. Coll. Chem.*, **55**, 894 (1951).
16. G. M. Wieder and R. A. Marcus, *J. Chem. Phys.*, **37**, 1835 (1962).
17. W. Koblitz and H. J. Schumacher, *Z. physik. Chem.*, **B25**, 283 (1934).
18. F. W. Schneider and B. S. Rabinovitch, *J. Am. Chem. Soc.*, **84**, 4215 (1962).
19. F. W. Schneider and B. S. Rabinovitch, *J. Am. Chem. Soc.*, **85**, 2365 (1963).
20. B. S. Rabinovitch and R. W. Diesen, *J. Chem. Phys.*, **30**, 735 (1959).
21. R. E. Harrington, B. S. Rabinovitch, and R. W. Diesen, *J. Chem. Phys.*, **32**, 1245 (1960).
22. B. S. Rabinovitch, D. H. Dills, W. H. McLain, and J. H. Currant, *J. Chem. Phys.*, **32**, 493 (1960).

23. J. N. Butler and G. B. Kistiakowsky, *J. Am. Chem. Soc.*, **82,** 759 (1960).
24. R. E. Harrington, B. S. Rabinovitch, and H. M. Frey, *J. Chem. Phys.*, **33,** 1271 (1960).

PROBLEMS

20.1. Show that the random-gap assumption leads to Eq. (1.2).
20.2. Verify Eq. (3.1).

INDEX

[The more important symbols used in the text are included in the index: letters of the English alphabet used as symbols are the first entries under each letter, Greek letters are grouped at the end of the index. The list is not complete, nor are all the meanings of a symbol necessarily given. Only those pages on which a symbol is defined or on which it is used in an important equation are listed for all symbols except those for partition functions, (p.f.) etc., entries for which are more extensive.]